PROCEEDINGS
OF THE
INTERNATIONAL CONFERENCE ON THE
PEACEFUL USES OF ATOMIC ENERGY

———

Volume 16
RECORD OF THE CONFERENCE

Proceedings of the International Conference
on the
Peaceful Uses of Atomic Energy

Held in Geneva
8 August–20 August 1955

Volume 16
Record of the Conference

UNITED NATIONS
New York
1956

UNITED NATIONS PUBLICATION

Sales No. 1956.IX.1.Vol. 16

A/CONF.8/16

Price: U.S. $5.00; 36/- stg.; 21.00 Sw. frs.
(or equivalent in other currencies)

PREFACE

The Proceedings of the International Conference on the Peaceful Uses of Atomic Energy are published in a series of 16 volumes, as follows:

Volume Number	Title	Sessions Included
1	The World's Requirements for Energy; The Role of Nuclear Power	2, 3.2, 4.1, 4.2, 5, 24.2.
2	Physics; Research Reactors	6A, 7A, 8A, 9A, 10A.1.
3	Power Reactors	10A.2, 3.1, 11A, 12A, 13A, 14A.
4	Cross Sections Important to Reactor Design	15A, 16A, 17A, 18A.
5	Physics of Reactor Design	19A, 20A, 21A, 22A, 23A.
6	Geology of Uranium and Thorium	6B, 7B.
7	Nuclear Chemistry and the Effects of Irradiation	8B, 9B, 10B, 11B, 12B, 13B.
8	Production Technology of the Materials Used for Nuclear Energy	14B, 15B, 16B, 17B.
9	Reactor Technology and Chemical Processing	7.3, 18B, 19B, 20B, 21B, 22B, 23B.
10	Radioactive Isotopes and Nuclear Radiations in Medicine	7.2 (Med.), 8C, 9C, 10C.
11	Biological Effects of Radiation	6.1, 11C, 12C, 13C.1.
12	Radioactive Isotopes and Ionizing Radiations in Agriculture, Physiology, and Biochemistry	7.2 (Agric.), 13C.2, 14C, 15C, 16C.
13	Legal, Administrative, Health and Safety Aspects of Large-Scale Use of Nuclear Energy	4.3, 6.2, 17C, 18C
14	General Aspects of the Use of Radioactive Isotopes; Dosimetry	7.1, 19C, 20C.
15	Applications of Radioactive Isotopes and Fission Products in Research and Industry	21C, 22C, 23C.
16	Record of the Conference	1, 24.1, 24.3.

These volumes include all the papers submitted to the Geneva Conference, as edited by the Scientific Secretaries. The efforts of the Scientific Secretaries have been directed primarily towards scientific accuracy. Editing for style has been minimal in the interests of early publication. This may be noted especially in the English translations of certain papers submitted in French, Russian and Spanish. In a few instances the titles of papers have been edited to reflect content.

The editors principally responsible for the preparation of these volumes were: Robert A. Charpie, Donald J. Dewar, André Finkelstein, John Gaunt, Jacob A. Goedkoop, Elwyn O. Hughes, Leonard F. Lamerton, Aleksandar Milojević, Clifford Mosbacher, César A. Sastre, and Brian E. Urquhart.

The verbatim records of the Conference are included in the pertinent volumes. These verbatim records contain the author's corrections and, where necessary for scientific accuracy, the editing changes of the Scientific Secretaries, who have also been responsible for inserting slides, diagrams and sketches at appropriate points. In the record of each session, slides are numbered in numerical order through all presentations. Where the slide duplicates an illustration in the submitted paper, appropriate reference is made, and the illustration does not appear in the record of the session.

TABLE OF CONTENTS

The Palais des Nations, Geneva

The Political Committee of the General Assembly of the United Nations giving unanimous approval to the "Atoms-for-Peace" resolution under which the International Conference was convoked (23 November 1954)

INTRODUCTION

The General Assembly, in resolution 810 (IX) on "International co-operation in developing the peaceful uses of atomic energy" which was adopted by unanimous vote on 4 December 1954, decided "that an international technical conference of Governments should be held, under the auspices of the United Nations, to explore means of developing the peaceful uses of atomic energy through international co-operation, and in particular, to study the development of atomic power and to consider other technical areas—such as biology, medicine, radiation protection, and fundamental science—in which international co-operation might most effectively be accomplished." The General Assembly invited all states members of the United Nations or of the specialized agencies to participate in the Conference. It suggested that the Conference should be held no later than August 1955, at a place to be determined by the Secretary-General, acting upon the advice of an Advisory Committee consisting of representatives of Brazil, Canada, France, India, Union of Soviet Socialist Republics, United Kingdom and the United States of America. The Secretary-General was requested to issue invitations to the Conference and to prepare and circulate a detailed agenda, also in consultation with the Advisory Committee. He appointed a United Nations internal working party to assist him on matters relating to the Conference. The members of this working party were: Dr. Ralph J. Bunche, Dr. Gunnar Randers and Mr. Ilya S. Tchernychev.

The first meeting of the Advisory Committee was held in New York from 17–28 January 1955. Its members were Mr. J. Costa Ribeiro (Brazil), Mr. W. B. Lewis (Canada), Mr. Bertrand Goldschmidt (France), Mr. Homi J. Bhabha (India), Mr. D. V. Skobeltzin (Union of Soviet Socialist Republics), Sir John Cockcroft (United Kingdom) (represented at this meeting by Mr. J. V. Dunworth), and Mr. I. I. Rabi, (United States of America). The Advisory Committee decided that the Secretary-General should act as its Chairman. At this meeting the Rules of Procedure of the Conference and a Topical Agenda were drawn up, and it was decided that the Conference should be held at Geneva, in the Palais des Nations, from 8–20 August 1955.

On 1 February, the Secretary-General issued invitations to the 84 states members of the United Nations and of the specialized agencies to participate in the Conference. Attached to this invitation was the Topical Agenda of the Conference and its Rules of Procedure (q.v.), which also contained rules concerning the submission of abstracts and papers to the Conference by the nations and specialized agencies participating. In this letter of invitation, the Secretary-General also announced the appointment of the President of the Conference, Dr. Homi J. Bhabha of India, and of the Conference Secretary-General, Professor Walter G. Whitman of the Massachusetts Institute of Technology. Dr. Viktor S. Vavilov of the Institute of Physics of the Academy of Sciences of the USSR was appointed Deputy Conference Secretary-General a short time later. The specialized agencies of the United Nations were also invited to participate in the Conference and to co-operate in its preparation to the extent of their competence in the subject matter.

The Conference Secretary-General began the work of organizing the Conference early in February. He recruited a staff of Scientific Secretaries, which ultimately consisted of twenty scientists from fourteen countries, whose initial function was to survey the abstracts of papers submitted by Governments with a view to formulating a workable programme for the Conference. Since, owing to limitations of time, all papers submitted could not be presented orally at the Conference, it had been agreed by the Advisory Committee that a selection of papers, to be presented orally in full or in part, should be made by a panel of qualified scientists designated by the Secretary-General on the advice of the Advisory Committee. The Scientific Secretaries were subsequently appointed as the Review Panel.

The Advisory Committee met for a second time in Paris on 23 May, and made more detailed recommendations as regards the programme of the Conference. Its third meeting was held in Geneva from 3–5 August to review the final arrangements for the Conference.

The number of papers submitted greatly exceeded original expectations. In all, 1132 abstracts were received from thirty-eight Governments, and 1067 full papers were finally submitted for consideration by the Conference. Of the papers submitted, approximately 450 were selected for oral presentation and formed the basis of the programme of the Conference.

A tentative programme, based on the abstracts submitted by Governments, was sent to Advisory Committee members on 22 June. A preliminary programme for the Conference was circulated to Governments on 6 July and a final programme, based on this preliminary programme, was made available to the delegations at Geneva on 6 August.

Seventy-three States and 8 specialized agencies of the United Nations sent delegations to the Conference, the total number of delegates being 1428. In addition, the Conference was attended by approximately 1350 observers, principally from academic institutions and from industrial enterprises in many countries.

The Conference itself was organized on the basis of an initial series of general sessions which surveyed the main aspects of the peaceful uses of atomic energy, followed by three parallel sets of specialized sessions dealing, broadly speaking, with (1) physics and reactors, (2) chemistry, metallurgy and technology, and (3) medicine, biology and radioactive isotopes. The sessions of the Conference were strictly scientific—there were no resolutions and no voting. In view of the extent and variety of the material available to the Conference, the programme was very tightly organized and a rigid timetable was adhered to throughout. The discussions in the formal sessions of the Conference were supplemented by many informal discussions among special groups outside the sessions themselves. All sessions of the Conference were open to the public.

Scientific exhibits were displayed by the following countries: Belgium, Canada, Denmark, France, Norway, Sweden, USSR, UK and the USA. A number of countries also showed films dealing with various aspects of the peaceful uses of atomic energy. All meetings of the Conference and the official exhibits were housed in the European Office of the United Nations at the Palais des Nations.

The Swiss authorities organized the first International Exhibition of the Peaceful Uses of Atomic Energy in the Palais des Expositions in the City of Geneva to run simultaneously with the Conference. This exhibition was devoted to educational and industrial exhibits furnished both by Governments and by private firms.

The Conference was covered by 905 representatives of public information media. Due to the highly technical nature of the sessions, a comprehensive system of press briefing was inaugurated in which both the Scientific Secretaries and the Chairmen and Vice-Chairmen of sessions volunteered to assist. The unprecedented scope and level of information coverage of the Conference all over the world testifies to the effectiveness of this arrangement.

It is appropriate to conclude by quoting the following paragraphs from the report on the Conference submitted to the tenth session of the General Assembly by the Secretary-General of the United Nations, Mr. Dag Hammarskjold:

"For the United Nations this unique undertaking affords lessons and implications which have important significance for its operations and for such future responsibilities in this general field as the Organization may be called upon to assume. The General Assembly resolution called for a conference which would be technical and on an exclusively international basis. The United Nations, in assuming full responsibility for the planning, preparation and conduct of the Conference, sought two basic objectives: (1) to achieve the freest possible discussion, exchange and sharing of general knowledge with a view to harnessing atomic energy to the needs of peace and human wellbeing; and (2) to ensure, notwithstanding the quite obvious and important political, economic and social implications of a conference of this nature, that it would be scientific in the most objective sense and free from all political bias. It may be said without reservation that these objectives were attained. In the light of all circumstances, it is safe to say that the results of the Conference would have been difficult to achieve in a context other than the international framework of the United Nations. This conclusion becomes the more apparent in the light of those practical aspects of the Conference with which the United Nations, uniquely, is equipped to deal...

"The international sharing of scientific knowledge which took place at Geneva in the interests of peace and human progress, under conditions of friendly and balanced co-operation among a large number of States, was an expression in effective action of the purposes and principles of the United Nations. With this Conference the United Nations entered a new field of activity which may properly inspire great hopes and expectations. This encouraging beginning invites projection into the future."

Programme of the Conference

The Conference Secretariat. Front row, left to right: M. Trocheris, I. Rojanski, E. Hughes, L. Lamerton, R. Charpie, C. Sastre, N. Dobrotine, W. G. Whitman, V. Vavilov, A. Salam, A. Milojević, I. Ulehla, D. Littler. Back row, left to right: H. G. Fletcher, F. de Hoffmann, P. Prakash, L. Lopez, J. Goedkoop, D. Dewar, R. Hara, A. Finkelstein, D. G. Sullivan, B. Urquhart, J. Gaunt

Programmes of Sessions 1 - 24

(Note: Papers presented by their authors unless otherwise stated)

Session 1: Monday, 8 August, 10.30 (Vol. XVI)

OPENING SESSION

President: H. J. Bhabha (India)

Opening of the Conference

Welcoming address by Mr. Max PETITPIERRE, President of the Swiss Confederation

Address by Mr. Dag HAMMARSKJOLD, Secretary-General of the United Nations

Messages from Heads of States and Prime Ministers:
Mr. GUILLAUMAT (France) for M. FAURE
Mr. BHABHA (India) for Mr. NEHRU
Mr. SKOBELTZIN (USSR) for Mr. BULGANIN
Sir Edwin PLOWDEN (UK) for Sir Anthony EDEN
Admiral STRAUSS (USA) for Mr. EISENHOWER

Presidential Address by Mr. H. J. BHABHA

Session 2: Monday, 8 August, 14.30 (Vol. I)

WORLD ENERGY NEEDS

Chairman: I. I. Rabi (United States)

2.1 Survey Papers on Estimated Future Power Needs over the Next 50 years: Alternative Power Sources

CHAIRMAN'S REMARKS

P/902 (UN)
World energy requirements in 1975 and 2000
Presented by N. B. Guyol

PANEL DISCUSSION ON:

P/326 (France)
Estimates of energy requirements............P. Ailleret

P/757 (UK)
The world's needs for a new source of energy
E. A. G. Robinson and G. H. Daniel
Presented by E. A. G. Robinson

P/802 (USA)
Energy requirements and economic growth...E. S. Mason

GENERAL DISCUSSION

2.2. Individual Countries' Needs and Possibilities for Power and Heat

CHAIRMAN'S REMARKS

P/1116 (UN)
Contribution of nuclear energy to future world power needs.................*Presented by P. Sevette*

P/125 (Brazil)
The Brazilian plan of electrification and the possibilities of atomic power..........E. Motta Rezende

P/962 (Yugoslavia)
Requirements and possibilities of production of energy in Yugoslavia.....................I. Kovacevic *et al.*
Presented by M. Ristic

P/987 (Australia)
Electric power in Australia — 1955-2004
Presented by D. L. Anderson

P/949 (Belgium)
Probable evolution of energy needs in Belgium and the possible role of nuclear energy.......R. Van Mele

P/799 (Czechoslovakia)
Prospects of power development in Czechoslovakia and the part to be played by nuclear energy for peaceful purposes.........................A. Sevcik

P/1060 (Japan)
Japan's energy utilization, the present and the future
K. Aki

P/998 (Argentina)
Energy needs and resources of the Argentine Republic................................G. Mendivelzua

P/868 (India)
The role of atomic power in India and its immediate possibilities...........................H. J. Bhabha

GENERAL DISCUSSION

Session 3: Tuesday, 9 August, 9.00 (Vol. III)

THE BUILDING OF A NUCLEAR ENERGY ENTERPRISE

Chairman: Sir John Cockcroft (United Kingdom)

3.1 Experience with Nuclear Power Plants

P/615 (USSR)
The first atomic power station in the USSR and the prospects of atomic power development
D. I. Blokhintsev and N. A. Nikolayev
Presented by D. I. Blokhintsev

DISCUSSION

P/851 (USA)
Design and operating experience of a prototype boiling water power reactor...........J. R. Dietrich *et al.*
Presented by W. H. Zinn

DISCUSSION

3.2 Capital Investment Required for Nuclear Energy (Vol. I)

CHAIRMAN'S REMARKS

P/391 (UK)
Capital investment required for nuclear energy
J. M. Hill and S. W. Joslin
Presented by S. W. Joslin

P/477 (USA)
Capital investment required for nuclear energy
W. K. Davis

DISCUSSION

P/395 (UK)
Recent developments of radioisotope uses in industry
H. Seligman

DISCUSSION

7.2 Isotopes in Medicine, Biology and Agriculture

P/309 (USA)
Radioisotopes in medicine.......S. Warren   (Vol. X)

P/618 (USSR)
The utilization of radioactive isotopes in biology and
agriculture in the USSR....A. L. Kursanov (Vol. XII)

P/780 (FAO)
The uses of atomic energy in food and agriculture
Presented by R. A. Silow

DISCUSSION

7.3 Waste Disposal Problems   (Vol. IX)

P/398 (UK)
Long-term aspects of fission product disposal
E. Glueckauf

P/310 (USA)
The management and disposal of radioactive wastes
A. Wolman and A. E. Gorman
Presented by A. Wolman

DISCUSSION

Session 24: Saturday, 20 August, 14.30

CLOSING GENERAL SESSION

Chairman: H. J. Bhabha (India)

**24.1 International Co-operation in the Peaceful
Uses of Atomic Energy**   (Vol. XVI)

P/619 (USSR)
Assistance of the Soviet Union to other countries in
peaceful uses of atomic energy....A. N. Lavrishchev

P/805 (USA)
International co-operation in atomic energy developments............................W. F. Libby

COMMENTS

**24.2 Education and Training of Personnel
in Nuclear Energy**   (Vol. I)

CHAIRMAN'S REMARKS

P/983 (UNESCO)
Training of research staff in the field of peaceful
uses of atomic energy
Presented by P. Auger

DISCUSSION

24.3 Closing Presidential Address   (Vol. XVI)

PHYSICS AND REACTOR SESSIONS
(Sessions 6A - 23A)

Session 6A: Wednesday, 10 August, 14.30 (Vol. II)

SPECIAL TOPICS IN NUCLEAR PHYSICS

Chairman: A. Bohr (Denmark)
Vice-Chairman: M. T. Sigurgiersson (Iceland)

P/714 (Ukr. SSR)
Inelastic scattering of fast neutrons by atomic nuclei
M. V. Pasechnik

P/581 (USA)
Gamma rays from inelastic neutron scattering..R. B. Day
Presented by M. Walt

P/588 (USA)
Angular distributions and non-elastic neutron scat-
tering...............................M. Walt et al.
Presented by M. Walt

DISCUSSION

P/830 (USA)
The theoretical prediction of neutron cross sections
of non-fissionable elements for energies up to 10
Mev................................V. F. Weisskopf

DISCUSSION

P/650 (USSR)
Investigation of the neutron beta-decay
P. E. Spivak et al.
Presented by M. S. Kozodaev

DISCUSSION

P/651 (USSR)
Thermal neutron capture gamma rays...L. V. Groshev et al.
Presented by B. P. Adyassevich

DISCUSSION

P/941 (Poland)
Investigation of the structure of molecules and the
structure of liquids by scattering of thermal neutrons.......................................J. Janik
Presented by H. Niewodniezanski

P/870 (India)
Thermal inelastic scattering of cold neutrons in
polycrystalline solids....K. S. Singwi and L. S. Kothari
Presented by L. S. Kothari

DISCUSSION

Session 7A: Thursday, 11 August, 9.00 (Vol. II)

FISSION PHYSICS

Chairman: V. F. Weisskopf (United States)
Vice-Chairman: N. Ahmad (Pakistan)

P/911 (Denmark)
On the theory of nuclear fission..............A. Bohr

P/593 (USA)
Fission physics and nuclear theory........J. A. Wheeler

P/993 (Yugoslavia)
The time involved in the fission process......D. Popovic

P/1089 (Romania)
Statistics of photographic fission tracks and range
estimate of fragments.....J. S. Ausländer and T. Visky
Presented by J. S. Ausländer

DISCUSSION

P/897 (Brazil)
Studies on the nuclear photoeffect
M. D. de Souza Santos et al.
Presented by M. D. de Souza Santos

P/884 (Norway)
Angular correlation of fission neutrons......K. Skarsvåg
Presented by A. Lundby

P/891 (Norway)
High energy gamma rays from short-lived fission
products..........................A. Lundby et al.
Presented by A. Lundby

DISCUSSION

P/592 (USA)
Determination of fission quantities of importance to
reactors..............................R. B. Leachman

DISCUSSION

Session 12A: Saturday, 13 August, 14.30 (Vol. III)

DESIGN OF REACTORS FOR POWER PRODUCTION
(concluded)

Chairman: D. I. Blokhintsev (USSR)

Vice-Chairman: L. de Heem (Belgium)

P/495 (USA)

Heavy water reactors for industrial power including boiling reactors..............H. P. Iskenderian *et al.*

Presented by W. H. Zinn

P/624 (USSR)

A boiling homogeneous nuclear reactor for power
A. I. Alichanow *et al.*

Presented by L. Y. Suvorov

P/496 (USA)

Aqueous homogeneous power reactors...R. B. Briggs and J. A. Swartout

Presented by J. A. Swartout

DISCUSSION

P/335 (France)

Complete automation of the operation of nuclear reactors....................................J. Weill

DISCUSSION

P/405 (UK)

The Dounreay fast reactor project....J. W. Kendall and T. M. Fry

Presented by T. M. Fry

P/814 (USA)

Review of fast power reactors.............W. H. Zinn

DISCUSSION

Session 13A: Monday, 15 August, 9.00 (Vol. III)

POWER REACTORS, PROTOTYPES

Chairman: E. P. Wigner (United States)

Vice-Chairman: M. S. Vallarta (Mexico)

P/815 (USA)

Description of the pressurized water reactor (PWR) power plant at Shippingport, Pa....J. W. Simpson *et al.*

Presented by J. W. Simpson

DISCUSSION

P/879 (Norway)

Preliminary study of an experimental pressurized heavy water reactor........................O. Dahl

DISCUSSION

P/497 (USA)

The engineering design of a prototype boiling water reactor power plant................J. M. Harrer *et al.*

Presented by J. M. Harrer

DISCUSSION

P/498 (USA)

The homogeneous reactor test...........S. E. Beall and J. A. Swartout

Presented by J. A. Swartout

DISCUSSION

Session 14A: Monday, 15 August, 14.30 (Vol. III)

POWER REACTORS, PROTOTYPES (concluded)

Chairman: G. Randers (UN)

Vice-Chairman: J. V. Dunworth (UK)

P/499 (USA)

The sodium reactor experiment..........W. E. Parkins

DISCUSSION

P/406 (UK)

The graphite-moderated gas-cooled pile and its place in power production.......................C. Hinton

DISCUSSION

P/501 (USA)

The engineering design of ERB II, a prototype fast neutron reactor power plant.........A. H. Barnes *et al.*

Presented by L. J. Koch

P/813 (USA)

Operating experience and experimental results obtained from a NaK cooled fast reactor
H. V. Lichtenberger *et al.*

Presented by H. V. Lichtenberger

DISCUSSION

Session 15A: Tuesday, 16 August, 9.00 (Vol. IV)

EQUIPMENT AND TECHNIQUE USED IN MEASURING CROSS SECTIONS IMPORTANT TO REACTOR DESIGN

Chairman: E. Amaldi (Italy)

Vice-Chairman: C. Simáne (Czechoslovakia)

P/576 (USA)

Neutron velocity selectors used at reactors...D. J. Hughes

P/640 (USSR)

The mechanical neutron velocity selector
V. I. Mostovoi *et al.*

Presented by V. I. Mostovoi

P/641 (USSR)

A neutron selector with the mechanical interrupter
V. V. Vladimirski

DISCUSSION

P/421 (UK)

Neutron spectrometers based on pulsed sources
E. R. Wiblin

P/577 (USA)

Time-of-flight techniques applied to fast neutron measurements..........................L. Cranberg

P/580 (USA)

Recent advances in neutron detection....L. M. Bollinger

P/806 (USA)

Time-of-flight instrumentation for neutron spectrometers..........................W. A. Higinbotham

DISCUSSION

P/573 (USA)

Techniques for measuring elastic, non-elastic, and transport neutron cross sections........R. F. Taschek

DISCUSSION

Session 16A: Tuesday, 16 August, 14.30 (Vol. IV)

EQUIPMENT AND TECHNIQUES (concluded)
CROSS SECTIONS OF NON-FISSIONABLE MATERIALS: DELAYED NEUTRONS

Chairman: L. Janossy (Hungary)
Vice-Chairman: V. M. Pasechnik (Ukraine SSR)

16A.1 Equipment and Techniques (concluded)

P/356 (France)
Testing materials by the pile-oscillation method in the Châtillon reactor......................D. Breton

DISCUSSION

P/642 (USSR)
A neutron spectrometer based on measuring the slowing down time of neutrons in lead..A. A. Bergman *et al.*
Presented by F. L. Shapiro

DISCUSSION

16A.2 Cross Sections of Non-Fissionable Material

P/832 (USA)
The determination and evaluation of fundamental thermal neutron cross sections..........J. A. Harvey

DISCUSSION

P/591 (USA)
Summary of cross-section measurements of the fission product poison Xe-135 as a function of energy
S. Bernstein and E. C. Smith
Presented by S. S. Bernstein

DISCUSSION

16A.3 Delayed Neutrons

P/831 (USA)
Delayed neutrons....................G. R. Keepin *et al.*
Presented by G. R. Keepin

DISCUSSION

Section 17A: Wednesday, 17 August, 9.00 (Vol. IV)

CROSS SECTIONS OF FISSIONABLE MATERIALS

Chairman: D. J. Hughes (United States)
Vice-Chairman: D. Popovic (Yugoslavia)

The session was based on the following papers:

P/354 (France)
Slow neutron cross sections of fissile nuclei
J. M. Auclair *et al.*

P/355 (France)
Energy dependence of U^{233}, U^{235} and Pu^{239}, fast neutron cross sections..........D. Steinsznaider *et al.*

P/422 (UK)
Cross sections of the plutonium isotopes
J. F. Raffle and B. T. Price

P/423 (UK)
The slow neutron cross sections of the uranium isotopes..............J. E. Lynn and N. J. Pattenden

P/586 (USA)
The low energy cross sections of U^{235}..V. L. Sailor *et al.*

P/589 (USA)
The total and fission cross section of plutonium
B. R. Leonard Jr.

P/594 (USA)
Some techniques for measurement of fast neutron flux
B. C. Diven

P/641 (USSR)
A neutron selector with the mechanical interrupter
V. V. Vladimirski

P/644 (USSR)
Determination of the absorption cross section and of the radiation capture cross section of uranium 233 for pile neutrons...............G. H. Kukavadse *et al.*

P/645 (USSR)
Fission and total cross sections of some heavy nuclei for monochromatic neutrons, as measured by a mechanical neutron velocity selector
Y. V. Adamchuk *et al.*

P/646 (USSR)
Time-of-flight measurement of the total neutron cross section of uranium 233, uranium 235 and plutonium 239.........................S. J. Nikitin *et al.*

17A.1 Low energy plutonium cross sections

Presentations by B. T. Price (UK), V. F. Gerasimov (USSR), S. I. Sukhoruchkin (USSR), F. Netter (France), P. F. Gast (USA), V. V. Vladimirski (USSR)

17A.2 Low energy U²³⁵ cross sections

Presentations by V. L. Sailor (USA), V. V. Vladimirski (USSR), V. F. Gerasimov (USSR), S. I. Sukhoruchkin (USSR), G. Vendryes (France), P. A. Egelstaff (UK).

17A.3 Low energy U²³³ cross sections

Presentations by V. V. Vladimirski (USSR), V. F. Gerasimov (USSR), S. I. Sukhoruchkin (USSR), E. R. Wiblin (UK), G. Vendryes (France).

CHAIRMAN'S REMARKS AND DISCUSSION

17A.4 High energy cross sections

Presentations by A. Berthelot (France), B. C. Diven (USA).

DISCUSSION

Session 18A: Wednesday, 17 August, 14.30 (Vol. IV)

PROPERTIES OF FISSIONABLE MATERIALS (ν, η, α): RESONANCE ANALYSIS

Chairman: P. Scherrer (Switzerland)
Vice-Chairman: M. D. de Souza Santos (Brazil)

P/657 (USSR)
Measurement of the neutron multiplication factor for thermal fission of uranium and plutonium
P. E. Spivak and B. G. Yerozolimsky
Presented by M. S. Kozodaev

P/658 (USSR)
Number of fission neutrons per one captured thermal neutron in U^{233} U^{235} and Pu^{239}...A. I. Alichanow *et al.*
Presented by V. V. Vladimirski

P/660 (USSR)
Number of fission neutrons per one captured thermal neutron for natural uranium...........N. A. Burgow
Presented by V. V. Vladimirski

P/425 (UK)
Neutron yields from fissile nuclei....P. A. Egelstaff and J. E. Sanders
Presented by J. E. Sanders

P/587 (USA)

Measurement of capture of fission ratio of U^{235}, U^{233}, and Pu^{239} by a new method.......H. Palevsky

P/595 (USA)

Capture to fission ratio of Pu^{239} and U^{235} for intermediate energy neutrons........W. R. Kanne et al.

Presented by W. R. Kanne

DISCUSSION

P/585 (USA)

Theoretical analysis of neutron resonances in fissile materials..............................H. A. Bethe

P/590 (USA)

Status of information on reactor material cross sections................................H. Hurwitz, Jr.

DISCUSSION

Session 19A: Thursday, 18 August, 9.00 (Vol. V)

INTEGRAL MEASUREMENTS

Chairman: A. de Shalit (Israel)
Vice-Chairman: B. Ferretti

P/661 (USSR)

A study of neutron diffusion in beryllium, graphite and water by the impulse method..A. V. Antonov et al.

Presented by F. L. Shapiro and I. C. Morozov

P/662 (USSR)

A study of Be as a neutron moderator..A. K. Krasin et al.

Presented by F. L. Shapiro and I. C. Morozov

P/359 (France)

Measurements of diffusion length of thermal neutrons in beryllium oxide.................J. C. Koechlin et al.

Presented by J. Martelly

P/872 (India)

On the determination of diffusion and slowing down constants of ordinary water and beryllium oxide using a pulsed neutron source.......R. Ramanna et al.

Presented by R. Ramanna

DISCUSSION

P/360 (France)

Measurement of a complex diffusion length in a solid or liquid to determine the transport mean free path for thermal neutrons.....J. Horowitz and V. Raievski

Presented by V. Raievski

DISCUSSION

P/789 (Sweden)

Measurements on a subcritical reactor with a pulsed neutron source ....N. G. Sjöstrand

P/933 (Netherlands)

Determination of neutron capture to fission ratio in different uranium samples........T. J. Barendregt and M. Bustraan

Presented by T. J. Barendregt

DISCUSSION

P/597 (USA)

Status of experimental and theoretical information on neutron slowing down distribution in hydrogenous media..........................J. E. Wilkins et al.

Presented by J. E. Wilkins

P/357 (France)

Time-of-flight spectrometry equipment for slow neutrons in use at the Saclay reactor. Its applica-

tion to a study of inelastic scattering of cold neutrons............................B. Jacrot et al.

Presented by B. Jacrot

DISCUSSION

Session 20A: Thursday, 18 August, 14.30 (Vol. V)

RESONANCE INTEGRALS; FISSION PRODUCT POISONING; CRITICALITY OF SOLUTIONS

Chairman: G. von Dardel (Sweden)
Vice-Chairman: F. Ba Hli (Burma)

20A.1 Resonance Integrals

P/659 (USSR)

Measurements of resonance absorption integrals for various materials and the multiplication co-efficient (effective number of secondary neutrons) of resonance neutrons for fissionable isotopes

P. E. Spivak et al.

Presented by M. S. Kozodaev

P/833 (USA)

Resonance capture integrals..........R. L. Macklin and H. S. Pomerance

Presented by E. P. Wigner

P/427 (UK)

Studies on the neutron resonance absorption of U^{238}.....................................V. S. Crocker

Presented by F. Fenning

P/883 (Norway)

Measurements of the effective resonance integral of uranium with the pile oscillator....V. O. Eriksen et al.

Presented by V. O. Eriksen

P/948 (Netherlands)

Computation of the effective resonance integral

E. F. M. van der Held

Presented by M. Bogaardt

DISCUSSION

20A.2 Fission Product Poisoning

P/5 (Canada)

Experiments on some characteristics of the N.R.X. Reactor, Part I. Methods and prolonged fuel irradiation..................................D. G. Hurst

P/6 (Canada)

Experiments on some characteristics of the N.R.X. Reactor, Part II. Temperature and transient poison effects..................................A. G. Ward

P/835 (USA)

Reactivity changes and reactivity lifetimes of fixed fuel elements in thermal reactors....B. I. Spinrad et al.

Presented by B. I. Spinrad

P/432 (UK)

Long term reactivity changes in natural uranium reactors..............................D. J. Littler

DISCUSSION

20A3. Criticality in Solutions

P/834 (USA)

Small thermal homogeneous critical assemblies

A. D. Callihan et al.

Presented by A. D. Callihan

P/428 (UK)

Plutonium-water critical assemblies....C. C. Horton and J. D. McCullen

Presented by F. Fenning

DISCUSSION

Session 21A: Friday, 19 August, 9.00 (Vol. V)

ZERO ENERGY AND EXPONENTIAL EXPERIMENTS

Chairman: O. Gamba (Argentina)
Vice-Chairman: A. G. Ward (Canada)

P/600 (USA)
Exponential experiments with slightly enriched uranium rods in ordinary water...........H. Kouts *et al.*
Presented by I. Kaplan

P/601 (USA)
Pressurized water reactor (PWR) critical and exponential experiments....S. Krasik and A. Radkowsky
Presented by S. Krasik

DISCUSSION

P/790 (Sweden)
Some experiences from measurements on an exponential pile of uranium and heavy water
R. Persson *et al.*
Presented by R. Persson

P/791 (Sweden)
Characteristics of the Swedish heavy water reactor
E. Hellstrand *et al.*
Presented by E. Hellstrand

P/361 (France)
Neutron studies on two heavy water piles....J. Horowitz

P/605 (USA)
Exponential experiments on uranium D₂O lattices
E. R. Cohen

P/623 (USSR)
Heavy water research reactor (results of critical experiments)...................A. I. Alichanow *et al.*
Presented by V. V. Vladimirski

DISCUSSION

P/429 (UK)
The experimental basis of lattice calculations
P. W. Mummery

P/607 (USA)
Normal uranium graphite moderated reactors—a comparison of theory and experiment. Water-cooled lattices...........................P. F. Gast

P/606 (USA)
Uranium graphite lattices. Part I. The Brookhaven reactor.....................I. Kaplan and J. Chernik
Presented by I. Kaplan

DISCUSSION

Session 22A: Friday, 19 August, 14.30 (Vol. V)

ZERO ENERGY EXPERIMENTS ON FAST REACTORS AND REACTOR KINETICS

Chairman: S. Eklund (Sweden)
Vice-Chairman: M. Ristic (Yugoslavia)

22A.1 Zero Energy Experiments *(concluded)*

P/404 (UK)
Experimental studies on fast-neutron reactors at A.E.R.E..........................L. R. Shepherd

P/598 (USA)
The fast exponential experiment.......F. C. Beyer *et al.*
Presented by B. J. Spinrad

P/609 (USA)
A survey of the theoretical and experimental aspects of fast reactor physics.................R. Avery *et al.*
Presented by D. Okrent

DISCUSSION

22A.2 Reactor Kinetics

P/775 (Israel)
Stability conditions in the non-linear dynamics of heterogeneous reactors...H. J. Lipkin and R. Thieberger
Presented by H. J. Lipkin

P/934 (Netherlands)
The influence of temperature on the transfer function of a heavy water reactor.............J. Pelser

P/334 (France)
Dynamic problems of power reactors and analogue computers...............................P. Braffort

P/610 (USA)
Kinetics of stationary reactor system......T. A. Welton
DISCUSSION

Session 23A: Saturday, 20 August, 9.00 (Vol. V)

REACTOR THEORY

Chairman: C. Salvetti (Italy)
Vice-Chairman: A. Soltan (Poland)

P/611 (USA)
Survey of neutron thermalization theories....E. R. Cohen

P/433 (UK)
The calculation of the fine structure of the thermal neutron flux in a pile by the spherical harmonics method....................................J. H. Tait

DISCUSSION

P/608 (USA)
Comparison of theory and experiment for intermediate assemblies......H. Hurwitz Jr. and R. Erlich
Presented by H. Hurwitz

P/664 (USSR)
Application of the method of effective boundary conditions for calculating the critical dimensions of reactors...............................A. D. Galanin
Presented by A. Radik

DISCUSSION

P/669 (USSR)
Heterogeneous methods of reactor calculations. Survey of results and comparison with experiments.................................S. M. Feinberg
Presented by T. N. Zubarev

P/649 (USSR)
The theory of resonance absorption in heterogeneous systems........I. I. Gurevich and I. Y. Pomeranchouk
Presented by A. P. Rudik

P/666 USSR)
The thermal co-efficient in a heterogeneous reactor
A. D. Galanin
Presented by A. P. Rudik

P/1003 (Argentina)
Lattice calculations on natural uranium-beryllium oxide and natural uranium-beryllium metal in a cylindrical reactor...................O. Gamba *et al.*
Presented by O. Gamba

DISCUSSION

P/656 (USSR)
Equation for the importance of neutrons, reactor kinetics, and the theory of perturbation. L. N. Ussachoff
Presented by D. I. Blokhintsev

P/796 (Czechoslovakia)
Remarks about the Milne problem with cylindrical symmetry.................................L. Trlifaj

P/667 (USSR)
Effective boundary condition for "grey" bodies
D. F. Zaretsky
Presented by D. I. Blokhintsev

Mr. I. I. Rabi (USA), one of the vice-presidents of the Conference, addressing a session

Mr. J. A. Goedkoop, a scientific secretary, passing a question to the chairman of the session, Mr. Francis Perrin (France)

Discussion of a scientific paper: Mr. G. M. Kruzhilim (USSR), and Mr. Walter H. Zinn (USA). Sir John Cockcroft (UK) presiding

Mr. Victor F. Weisskopf (USA), reading a paper at one of the Physics Sessions

Mr. Otto Hahn (Germany) and Mr. Niels Bohr (Denmark)

The Music Room

CHEMISTRY, METALLURGY AND TECHNOLOGY SESSIONS

(Sessions 6B - 23B)

Session 6B: Wednesday, 10 August, 14.30 (Vol. VI)

OCCURRENCE OF URANIUM AND THORIUM

Chairman: J. da Costa Ribeiro (Brazil)
Vice-Chairman: W. M. Hamilton (New Zealand)

CHAIRMAN'S REMARKS

P/1114 (UN)
  The natural occurrence of uranium and thorium. P. F. Kerr

DISCUSSION

P/470 (USA)
  Nuclear fuel for the world power program. . J. C. Johnson

DISCUSSION

Panel Discussion on Uranium and Thorium Occurrences:

  Moderator: P. F. Kerr (UN)

  Designated members representing:

    Argentina, V. Angelleli
    Australia, J. P. Baxter
    Belgium, J. van der Spek
    Brazil, E. Tavora
    Canada, A. H. Long
    France, M. Roubault
    India, D. N. Wadia
    Italy, F. Ippolito
    Japan, K. Aki
    Portugal, C. P. Lobato
    UK, S. H. V. Bowie
    USA, L. R. Page

GENERAL DISCUSSION

Session 7B: Thursday, 11 August, 9.00 (Vol. VI)

PROSPECTING FOR URANIUM AND THORIUM

Chairman: D. N. Wadia (India)
Vice-Chairman: R. Niini (Finland)

CHAIRMAN'S REMARKS

P/764 (UK)
  Methods of prospecting for uranium and thorium
                          C. F. Davidson and S. H. U. Bowie
                          Presented by S. H. U. Bowie
P/1 (Canada)
  Uranium prospecting in Canada—ground and aerial
    surveys. . . . . .A. H. Lang

DISCUSSION

P/763 (UK)
  Instrumental developments in the prospecting, mining
    and chemical processing of nuclear "materials"
                          H. Bisby *et al.*
                          Presented by H. Bisby
P/994 (Yugoslavia)
  Radiation detectors with halogen counters for use
    in prospecting. . . . . .A. Milojević *et al.*
                          Presented by M. Petrović

DISCUSSION

P/132 (Brazil)
  Air survey applied to the search for radioactive min-
    erals in Brazil. . . .D. A. MacFadyen and S. V. Guedes
                          Presented by S. V. Guedes
P/625 (USSR)
  Aeroradiometric prospecting for uranium and thorium
    deposits and the interpretation of gamma anomalies
                          V. I. Baranov
                          Presented by V. G. Melkov

DISCUSSION

P/503 (USA)
  Techniques for prospecting for uranium and thorium
                          Presented by R. D. Ninninger
P/626 (USSR)
  Radiohydrogeological method in prospecting for ura-
    nium deposits. . . . . .A. A. Saukoff
                          Presented by A. P. Vinogradov
P/869 (India)
  Remote location of uranium and thorium deposits
                          K. G. Vohra

DISCUSSION

Session 8B: Thursday, 11 August, 14.30 (Vol. VII)

THE FISSION PROCESS: FACILITIES FOR HANDLING HIGHLY RADIOACTIVE MATERIALS

Chairman: O. Hahn (Germany)
Vice-Chairman: G. B. Cook (UK)

8B.1   The Fission Process

CHAIRMAN'S REMARKS

P/614 (USA)
  Survey of radiochemical studies of the fission process
                          L. E. Glendenin and E. P. Steinberg
                          Presented by E. P. Steinberg
P/718 (USA)
  Spontaneous fission correlations. . . . . .A. Ghiorso

DISCUSSION

P/881 (Norway)
  The distribution of nuclear charge in low and high
    energy fission. . . . . .A. C. Pappas

DISCUSSION

8B.2   Facilities for Handling Highly Radioactive Materials

CHAIRMAN'S REMARKS

P/438 (UK)
  An atomic energy radiochemical laboratory—design
    and operating experience. . . . . .R. Spence

P/725 (USA)
  Hot laboratory facilities for a wide variety of radio-
    chemical problems. . .P. R. Fields and C. H. Youngquist
                          Presented by W. M. Manning
P/673 (USSR)
  Metal research "hot" laboratory
                          Compiled by N. F. Pravdjuk
                          Presented by G. S. Zhdanov

DISCUSSION

Session 9B: Friday, 12 August, 9.00 (Vol. VII)

CHEMISTRY OF FISSION PRODUCTS

Chairman: A. P. Vinogradov (USSR)
Vice-Chairman: J. W. T. Spinks (Canada)

9B.1 Solution Chemistry of Gross Fission Products

CHAIRMAN'S REMARKS

P/724 (USA)
Chemical processing in intense radiation fields
R. P. Hammond

DISCUSSION

P/719 (USA)
Solvent extraction chemistry of fission products
F. R. Bruce

DISCUSSION

P/837 (USA)
Anion exchange studies of the fission products
K. A. Kraus and F. Nelson
Presented by K. A. Kraus

DISCUSSION

9B.2 Chemistry of Individual Fission Products

CHAIRMAN'S REMARKS

P/437 (UK)
The chemistry of ruthenium..........J. M. Fletcher and
F. S. Martin
Presented by J. M. Fletcher

DISCUSSION

P/671 (USSR)
Some chemical properties of technetium......J. B. Gerlit
Presented by A. P. Vinogradov

P/1023 (Argentina)
Determination of half-life of Tc^{102}

P/1026 (Argentina)
Determination of half-life of Tc^{105}
J. Flegenheimer and W. Seelman-Eggebert
Presented by W. Seelman-Eggebert

P/436 (UK)
The condition of fission product iodine in irradiated
uranium metal....................G. N. Walton *et al.*
Presented by G. N. Walton

DISCUSSION

Session 10B: Friday, 12 August, 14.30 (Vol. VII)

HEAVY ELEMENT CHEMISTRY

Chairman: G. T. Seaborg (USA)
Vice-Chairman: D. I. Ryabchikov (USSR)

10B.1 Surveys of Chemistry of Transuranics

CHAIRMAN'S REMARKS

P/726 (USA)
Thermodynamics of the heavy elements. B. B. Cunningham

DISCUSSION

P/440 (UK)
Electronic configuration of the actinide elements
J. K. Dawson and G. R. Hall
Presented by J. K. Dawson

DISCUSSION

10B.2 Methods of Separating Heavy Elements

P/728 (USA)
Radiochemical separations methods for the actinide
elements................................E. K. Hyde

P/674 (USSR)
Remarks by authors of "On the methods of separation
of neptunium from plutonium"......I. K. Shvetsov and
A. M. Vorobyev
Presented by V. N. Kosiakov
and

P/677 (USSR)
Coprecipitation of Am(V) with double carbonates
of U(VI) or Pu (VI) with potassium
G. N. Yakovlev and D. S. Gorbenko-Germanov
Presented by V. N. Kosiakov

P/929 (Netherlands)
A tracer study of the partition of neptunium between nitric acid solutions and three organic
solvents....................................J. Kooi

DISCUSSION

10B.3 Chemistry of Specific Heavy Elements

P/736 (USA)
Some recent developments in the chemistry of nep-
tunium..........................J. C. Hindman *et al.*
Presented by J. C. Hindman

P/838 (USA)
A review of americium and curium chemistry
R. A. Penneman and L. B. Asprey
Presented by R. A. Penneman

P/676 (USSR)
Spectrophotometric studies of the behaviour of amer-
icium ions in solutions..........G. N. Yakovlev and
V. N. Kosiakov
Presented by V. N. Kosiakov

DISCUSSION

Session 11B: Saturday, 13 August, 9.00 (Vol. VII)

EFFECTS OF RADIATION ON REACTOR MATERIALS

Chairman: J. H. de Boer (Netherlands)
Vice-Chairman: J. P. Howe (United States)

CHAIRMAN'S REMARKS

P/744 (USA)
Radiation damage in reactor materials....D. S. Billington

P/681 (USSR)
Effect of irradiation on structure and properties of
fissionable materials..........S. T. Konobeevsky *et al.*
Presented by G. S. Zhdanov

P/443 (UK)
Damage occurring in uranium during burn-up..S. F. Pugh

DISCUSSION

P/746 (USA)
Irradiation damage to artificial graphite
W. K. Woods *et al.*
Presented by W. K. Woods

P/442 (UK)
The effects of irradiation on graphite.....G. H. Kinchin

DISCUSSION

P/680 (USSR)
The effect of irradiation on the structure and pro-
perties of structural materials..S. T. Konobeevsky *et al.*
Presented by G. S. Zhdanov

DISCUSSION

Session 12B: Saturday, 13 August, 14.30 (Vol. VII)

EFFECTS OF RADIATION ON LIQUIDS

Chairman: I. Dostrovsky (Israel)
Vice-Chairman: G. A. Bazargan (Iran)

CHAIRMAN'S REMARKS

P/738 (USA)
A survey of recent American research in the radiation chemistry of aqueous solutions..........A. O. Allen

P/739 (USA)
The radiation induced reaction of hydrogen and oxygen in water at 25°C to 250°C....C. J. Hochanadel

DISCUSSION

P/363 (France)
Chemical reactions induced by ionizing radiations in various organic substances............L. Bouby *et al.*
Presented by M. Magat

P/683 (USSR)
Radiolytic oxidation of organic compounds...N. A. Bach
Presented by V. N. Kondratyev

DISCUSSION

P/7 (Canada)
Experience with heavy water systems in the NRX reactor..........................R. F. S. Robertson

P/679 (USSR)
Radiolysis of water in the presence of H_2 and O_2 under the action of reactor irradiations, fission fragments and X-rays....P. I. Dolin and B. W. Ershler
Presented by L. V. Suvorov

P/445 (UK)
Effect of radiation on heterogeneous systems of air or nitrogen and water.................J. Wright *et al.*
Presented by J. Wright

DISCUSSION

Session 13B: Monday, 15 August, 9.00 (Vol. VII)

EFFECTS OF RADIATION ON SOLIDS

Chairman: V. N. Kondratyev (USSR)
Vice-Chairman: M. Magat (France)

CHAIRMAN'S REMARKS

P/749 (USA)
The theory of lattice displacements produced during irradiation...............F. Seitz and J. S. Koehler
Presented by F. Seitz

DISCUSSION

P/750 (USA)
Theoretical aspects of radiation damage in metals
G. J. Dienes

P/444 (UK)
Radiation damage in non-fissile materials..J. H. O. Varley
Presented by H. M. Finniston

DISCUSSION

P/362 (France)
Modifications produced in non-metallic materials by radiation and the thermal healing of these effects
G. Mayer *et al.*
Presented by G. Mayer

DISCUSSION

P/753 (USA)
A review of investigations of radiation effects in covalent and ionic crystals....J. H. Crawford Jr. and M. C. Wittels
Presented by J. H. Crawford Jr.

DISCUSSION

P/751 (USA)
Interpretation of radiation damage to graphite
G. R. Hennig and J. E. Hove
Presented by G. R. Hennig

DISCUSSION

Session 14B: Monday, 15 August, 14.30 (Vol. VIII)

TREATMENT OF URANIUM AND THORIUM ORES AND ORE CONCENTRATES

Chairman: B. Goldschmidt (France)
Vice-Chairman: A. H. de Carvalho (Portugal)

CHAIRMAN'S REMARKS

P/519 (USA)
Recovery of uranium from its ores....G. G. Marvin *et al.*
Presented by G. G. Marvin

P/2 (Canada)
Canadian practice in ore dressing and extractive metallurgy of uranium...................A. Thunaes

P/339 (France)
Method for chemical processing of low-grade uranium ores.................P. Mouret and P. Pagny
Presented by P. Mouret

P/521 (USA)
Some unusual problems met in the recovery of uranium from a very low-grade ore
M. D. Hassialis and R. Musa
Presented by M. D. Hassialis

P/524 (USA)
Recovery of uranium from phosphates by solvent extraction.........................R. S. Long *et al.*
Presented by G. G. Marvin

P/784 (Sweden)
Recovery of uranium from uranium bearing alum shale...................................E. Svenke

P/871 (India)
An ion exchange process for the recovery of uranium from carbonate leach solutions.......J. Shankar *et al.*
Presented by J. Shankar

P/977 (Portugal)
Some aspects of the chemical treatment of Portuguese uranium ores.................F. Videira *et al.*
Presented by F. Videira

P/986 (Australia)
Acid pressure leaching of uranium ores....P. M. J. Gray
Presented by R. G. Thomas

P/997 (South Africa)
The South African uranium industry
C. S. McLean and T. K. Prentice
Presented by T. K. Prentice

GENERAL DISCUSSION

Session 15B: Tuesday, 16 August, 9.00 (Vol. VIII)

PRODUCTION OF METALLIC URANIUM AND THORIUM: ANALYTICAL METHODS IN RAW MATERIAL PRODUCTION

Chairman: H. Brynielsson (Sweden)
Vice-Chairman: D. W. Seelman-Eggebert (Argentina)

15B.1   Production of Metallic Uranium and Thorium

CHAIRMAN'S REMARKS

P/407 (UK)
Production of uranium metal...............L. Grainger
Presented by P. V. Danckwerts

P/341 (France)
Preparation of pure uranium metal
B. Goldschmidt and P. Vertes
Presented by B. Goldschmidt

P/636 (USSR)
Metallurgy of thorium.................G. E. Kaplan
Presented by G. A. Meyerson

P/635 (USSR)
Powder metallurgy of thorium........G. A. Meyerson
DISCUSSION

15B.2　Analytical Methods in Raw Material Production

CHAIRMAN'S REMARKS

P/952 (USA)
Analysis of uranium and thorium raw materials
C. J. Rodden

P/627 (USSR)
Physico-chemical methods of uranium production control ....A. P. Vinogradov

Remarks on:

P/942 (Poland)
Contribution to methods of measuring concentrations of uranium and thorium in minerals (nuclear emulsions)..............................A. Soltan

P/964 (Yugoslavia)
Polarography of uranium, polarographic determination of uranium in ores without preliminary chemical separation........................M. W. Susić

P/630 (USSR)
The physical method of determining the content of uranium, radium and thorium in radioactive ores
G. R. Golbek *et al.*
Presented by L. M. Barkov

P/1008 (Argentina)
Determination of U^{235} content in uranium by a radio-chemical method
I. G. de Fraenz and W. Seelman-Eggebert
Presented by I. G. de Fraenz

GENERAL DISCUSSION

Session 16B: Tuesday, 16 August, 14.30 (Vol. VIII)

PRODUCTION TECHNOLOGY OF SPECIAL MATERIALS

Chairman: F. Giordani (Italy)
Vice-Chairman: A. Clemente (Philippines)

16B.1　Heavy Water

CHAIRMAN'S REMARKS

P/819 (USA)
Survey of heavy water production processes..M. Benedict

P/774 (Israel)
Design of isotope separation plants: some basic design equations for the distillation process
I. Dostrovsky and Y. Lehrer
Presented by I. Dostrovsky

P/927 (Switzerland)
Final concentration of heavy water by rectification
P. Baertschi and W. Kuhn
Presented by P. Baertschi

P/958 (Yugoslavia)
Efficiency of some catalysts in the exchange reaction between heavy water and hydrogen....P. Savić *et al.*
Presented by S. Ribnikar

DISCUSSION

P/410 (UK)
Infra-red methods for the analysis of heavy water
J. Gaunt

P/631 (USSR)
On methods of isotopic analysis of heavy water
K. V. Vladimirsky *et al.*
Presented by K. V. Vladimirsky

DISCUSSION

16B.2　Graphite

CHAIRMAN'S REMARKS

P/343 (France)
Production of nuclear graphite in France
P. Legendre *et al.*
Presented by J. Guéron

P/534 (USA)
The production and properties of graphite for reactors
L. M. Currie *et al.*
Presented by L. M. Currie

P/943 (Poland)
Some experiments concerning pile materials....B. Buras

DISCUSSION

Session 17B: Wednesday, 17 August, 9.00 (Vol. VIII)

PRODUCTION TECHNOLOGY OF SPECIAL MATERIALS *(concluded)*

Chairman: C. Eichner (France)
Vice-Chairman: R. Henych (Czechoslovakia)

17B.1　Zirconium

CHAIRMAN'S REMARKS

P/533 (USA)
Zirconium metal production........S. M. Shelton *et al.*
Presented by S. M. Shelton

P/347 (France)
Separation of zirconium from hafnium
J. Hure and R. Saint-James
Presented by J. Hure

P/876 (India)
Separation of hafnium from zirconium by vapour phase de-chlorination..B. Prakash and C. V. Sundaram
Presented by B. Prakash

GENERAL DISCUSSION

17B.2　Beryllium

CHAIRMAN'S REMARKS

P/633 (USSR)
Techniques for manufacturing items of pure beryllium and beryllium oxide for use in nuclear reactors......compiled and presented by G. A. Meyerson

P/820 (USA)
Status of beryllium technology in the USA
A. R. Kaufmann and B. R. F. Kjellgren
Presented by A. R. Kaufmann

P/345 (France)
Sintering of beryllium oxide....R. Caillat and R. Pointud
Presented by R. Caillat

P/1015 (Argentina)
Purification of beryllium oxide
A. E. Cairo and M. B. Crespi
Presented by A. E. Cairo

GENERAL DISCUSSION

Session 21B: Friday, 19 August, 9.00 (Vol. IX)

CHEMICAL PROCESSING OF IRRADIATED FUEL ELEMENTS

Chairman: R. Spence (UK)
Vice-Chairman: H. N. Sethna (India)

CHAIRMAN'S REMARKS

P/414 (UK)
Criteria for the selection of separation processes
C. M. Nicholls

DISCUSSION

P/822 (USA)
Reprocessing of reactor fuel and blanket materials by solvent extraction....................F. L. Culler

P/540 (USA)
Solvent extraction separation of U^{233} and thorium from fission products by means of tributyl phosphate....................................A. T. Gresky
Presented by F. L. Culler

P/349 (France)
Solvent extraction of plutonium from uranium irradiated in atomic piles...........B. Goldschmidt *et al.*
Presented by B. Goldschmidt

P/785 (Sweden)
The extraction of uranium and plutonium with tetrabutylammonium nitrate, cupferron and neocupferron as complexing agents.........E. Haeffner *et al.*
Presented by E. Haeffner

P/824 (USA)
Practical limitations of solvent extraction processes
R. E. Tomlinson

GENERAL DISCUSSION

P/551 (USA)
The chemical processing of aqueous homogeneous reactor fuel...........................D. E. Ferguson

DISCUSSION

Session 22B: Friday, 19 August, 14.30 (Vol. IX)

CHEMICAL PROCESSING OF IRRADIATED FUEL ELEMENTS (concluded) SEPARATION AND STORAGE OF FISSION PRODUCTS

Chairman: J. P. Baxter (Australia)
Vice-Chairman: F. H. Spedding (USA)

22B.1   Chemical Processing of Irradiated Fuel Elements (concluded)

CHAIRMAN'S REMARKS

P/823 (USA)
Survey of separation processes.............S. Lawroski

P/350 (France)
Method for extraction of uranium-233 from thorium irradiated in atomic piles....A. Chesne and P. Regnaut
Presented by P. Regnaut

DISCUSSION

P/544 (USA)
Pyrometallurgical processing of nuclear materials
H. M. Feder

P/545 (USA)
The purification of uranium reactor fuel by liquid metal extraction.........................A. F. Voigt
Presented by F. H. Spedding

DISCUSSION

22B.2.   Separation and Storage of Fission Products

CHAIRMAN'S REMARKS

P/415 (UK)
Chemical processing of fission product solutions
E. Glueckauf and T. V. Healy
Presented by E. Glueckauf

P/552 (USA)
The design and operation of high-level waste storage facilities.........C. R. Anderson and C. A. Rohrmann
Presented by H. M. Parker

P/553 (USA)
Processes for high-level waste disposal..L. P. Hatch *et al.*
Presented by B. Manowitz

DISCUSSION

Session 23B: Saturday, 20 August, 9.00 (Vol. IX)
WASTE TREATMENT AND DISPOSAL

Chairman: A. J. Cipriani (Canada)
Vice-Chairman: A. R. Torky (Egypt)

23B.1   Disposal in the Ground

CHAIRMAN'S REMARKS

P/565 (USA)
Disposal of liquid wastes to the ground
R. E. Brown *et al.*
Presented by H. M. Parker

P/12 (Canada)
Waste disposal into the ground.........C. A. Mawson

DISCUSSION

23B.2   Disposal in the Sea

CHAIRMAN'S REMARKS

P/418 (UK)
The discharge of radioactive waste products in the Irish Sea, Part I......................H. Seligman
Presented by D. R. R. Fair

P/419 (UK)
The discharge of radioactive waste products in the Irish Sea, Part II......................H. J. Dunster
Presented by D. R. R. Fair

P/420 (UK)
The discharge of radioactive waste products in the Irish Sea, Part III....D. R. R. Fair and A. S. McLean
Presented by D. R. R. Fair

DISCUSSION

P/569 (USA)
Disposal of radioactive wastes at sea.........C. E. Renn
Presented by W. D. Claus

DISCUSSION

23B.3   Airborne Problems

CHAIRMAN'S REMARKS

P/571 (USA)
Air and gas cleaning for nuclear energy processes
L. Silverman

DISCUSSION

BIOLOGICAL AND MEDICAL SESSIONS
(Sessions 8C - 18C)

Session 8C: Thursday, 11 August, 14.30 (Vol. X)

RADIOACTIVE ISOTOPES AND NUCLEAR RADIATIONS IN MEDICINE: THERAPY

Chairman: F. Leborgne (Uruguay)
Vice-Chairman: M. Gokmen (Turkey)

CHAIRMAN'S REMARKS

P/685 (USSR)
Medical application of some radioactive isotopes
A. V. Kozlova
Presented by M. N. Fateyeva

P/446 (UK)
Some problems of radiotherapeutics......J. S. Mitchell

DISCUSSION

P/179 (USA)
Teletherapy devices with radioactive isotopes..M. Brucer

DISCUSSION

P/925 (Switzerland)
Internal radioactive isotope therapy of neoplastic diseases by means of radioactive suspensions
J. H. Muller

P/367 (France)
Utilization of colloidal chromium radiophosphate in malignant tumour therapy....A. Chevallier and C. Burg
Presented by A. Chevallier

DISCUSSION

P/183 (USA)
Radioisotopes in hematologic therapy.....J. H. Lawrence

DISCUSSION

P/970 (Portugal)
An accurate method for treatment of hyperthyroidism with I^{131}.........................V. H. Franco et al.
Presented by V. H. Franco

P/177 (USA)
Use of the nuclear reactor for neutron capture therapy of cancer...................L. E. Farr et al.
Presented by L. E. Farr

DISCUSSION

Session 9C: Friday, 12 August, 9.00 (Vol. X)

RADIOACTIVE ISOTOPES AND NUCLEAR RADIATION IN MEDICINE (continued): DIAGNOSIS AND STUDIES OF DISEASE

Chairman: V. R. Khanolkhar (India)
Vice-Chairman: F. Hercik (Czechoslovakia)

CHAIRMAN'S REMARKS

P/768 (UK)
The use of radioactive isotopes in diagnostic procedures...........................W. V. Mayneord

P/684 (USSR)
Experience in clinical and diagnostic application of some radioactive isotopes in the USSR..M. N. Fateyeva

DISCUSSION

P/181 (USA)
Scanning of positron-emitting isotopes in diagnosis of intracranial and other lesions
G. L. Brownell and W. H. Sweet
Presented by W. H. Sweet

P/754 (USA)
The dynamic aspects of erythropoiesis in normal and pathologic states as indicated with the radioactive isotope tracer technique......J. F. Ross and A. Miller
Presented by J. F. Ross

DISCUSSION

P/769 (UK)
The speed of iodine metabolism............E. E. Pochin

P/9 (Canada)
Further clinical studies of thyroid and salivary gland function with radioiodine..........C. H. Jaimet and H. G. Thode
Presented by C. H. Jaimet

P/365 (France)
The role of genetic factors in the development of congenital myxoedema............M. Bernheim et al.
Presented by M. Berger

P/1099 (Romania)
The effect of oestradiol on iodine fixation in the thyroid..............................St. Milcou et al.
Presented by St. Milcou

DISCUSSION

P/199 (USA)
Tissue specific antibodies as carriers of radioactive materials for the treatment of cancer
W. F. Bale and I. L. Spar
Presented by W. F. Bale

DISCUSSION

Session 10C: Friday, 12 August, 14.30 (Vol. X)

RADIOACTIVE ISOTOPES AND NUCLEAR RADIATIONS IN MEDICINE (concluded): DIAGNOSIS AND STUDIES OF DISEASE

Chairman: M. Tsuzuki (Japan)
Vice-Chairman: C. Núñez (Argentina)

CHAIRMAN'S REMARKS

P/178 (USA)
The use of isotopes in biochemical and medical research.........................A. Baird Hastings

P/840 (USA)
The use of isotopes in analysis of metabolic disorders...........................DeWitt Stetton, Jr.
Presented by A. Baird Hastings

P/180 (USA)
The use of radiosodium and radiopotassium tracer studies in man........B. A. Burrows and J. F. Ross
Presented by B. A. Burrows

DISCUSSION

P/447 (UK)
The absorption of vitamin B_{12} and the pathogenesis of vitamin B_{12} deficiency...........D. L. Mollin and E. Lester-Smith
Presented by E. Lester-Smith

P/711 (Ukrainian SSR)
Application of radioactive isotopes to the study of the biochemistry of muscles.........D. L. Ferdman
Presented by R. E. Kavetsky

P/921 (India)
Synthesis of 4:4'-diaminodiphenylsulphone-S^{35}
(DDS) and its uses in leprosy research
P. Saraiya *et al.*
Presented by V. R. Khanolkhar

DISCUSSION

P/224 (USA)
Utilization of nuclear energy in public health prob-
lems on the epidemiology of communicable diseases
D. W. Jenkins

P/140 (Brazil)
A new radioactive method for marking mosquitoes
and its application.................M. B. Aragao *et al.*
Presented by J. Costa-Ribeiro

DISCUSSION

Session 11C: Saturday, 13 August, 9.00 (Vol. XI)

BIOLOGICAL EFFECTS OF RADIATION: MODES OF RADIATION INJURY AND RADIATION HAZARDS

Chairman: R. Latarjet (France)
Vice-Chairman: T. Vlissidis (Greece)

CHAIRMAN'S REMARKS

Modes of Radiation Injury

P/82 (USA)
Commentary on the modes of radiation injury
A. M. Brues

P/150 (UK)
Modes of radiation injury (medical aspects)
E. Rock Carling

P/692 (USSR)
Some aspects of the immunity of the organisms ex-
posed to ionizing radiation.............I. A. Pigalyev
Presented by V. L. Troitsky

DISCUSSION

Carcinogenesis and Metabolism of Bone-Seeking Isotopes

P/847 (USA)
The use of isotopes in study of skeletal physiology
and metabolism.....................W. F. Neuman

P/88 (USA)
The deposition of radioactive substances in bone
F. E. Hoecker

P/242 (USA)
The association of irradiation with cancer of the
thyroid in children and adolescents........D. E. Clark

DISCUSSION

Effects on Reproductive System and on Fetus

P/77 (USA)
Hazards to the embryo and fetus from ionizing
radiation.............L. B. Russell and W. L. Russell
Presented by L. B. Russell

P/257 (USA)
Effects of daily low doses of X-rays on spermato-
genesis in dogs........G. W. Casarett and J. B. Hursh
Presented by G. W. Casarett

P/1070 (Switzerland)
Dominant lethal factors and embryonic mortality after
irradiation at 180 Kev and 31 Mev..H. Fritz-Niggli *et al.*
Presented by H. Staub

DISCUSSION

Session 12C: Saturday, 13 August, 14.30 (Vol. XI)

BIOLOGICAL EFFECTS OF RADIATION *(continued)*: MECHANISMS OF RADIATION INJURY; PROTECTION AND RECOVERY

Chairman: Z. Bacq (Belgium)
Vice-Chairman: A. Smerasuta (Thailand)

CHAIRMAN'S REMARKS

Mechanisms of Radiation Injury

P/899 (UK)
Biological damage resulting from exposure to ionizing radiations............................L. H. Gray

P/898 (UK)
Comparative studies of the biological effects of radiation and of radiomimetic chemical agents....A. Haddow

DISCUSSION

P/904 (India)
Cytological and cytochemical effects of radiation and
radiomimetic substances in actively proliferating
biological systems..............A. R. Gopal-Ayengar

P/690 (USSR)
The biological effect on ionizing radiation on micro-
organisms...........................M. N. Meissel
Presented by N. M. Sisakian

P/371 (France)
The problem of the biological action of low doses of
ionizing radiation.....................H. Marcovich
Presented by R. Latarjet

P/691 (USSR)
On the nature of changes in metabolism under irradiation effects...........................N. M. Sisakian

DISCUSSION

Protection and Recovery

P/78 (USA)
Studies on protection by treatment before and after
exposure to X- and gamma radiation
A. Hollaender and G. E. Stapleton
Presented by A. Hollaender

P/940 (Belgium)
Tissue and cell damage due to radiation; their con-
sequences and their repair..............J. Maisin *et al.*
Presented by J. Maisin

Session 13C: Monday, 15 August, 9.00

BIOLOGICAL EFFECTS OF RADIATION *(concluded)*: GENETIC EFFECTS: HUMAN IMPLICATIONS RADIOACTIVE ISOTOPES AND IONIZING RADIA-TIONS IN AGRICULTURE: RADIATION-INDUCED GENETIC CHANGES AND CROP IMPROVEMENT

Chairman: T. Kemp (Denmark)
Vice-Chairman: A. Gutafsson (Sweden)

13C.1   Genetic Effects: Human Implications   (Vol. XI)

CHAIRMAN'S REMARKS

P/238 (USA)
The genetic structure of Mendelian populations and
its bearing on radiation problems..........B. Wallace

P/235 (USA)
Genetic effects of radiation in mice and their bearing
on the estimation of human hazards.....W. L. Russell

Session 16C: Tuesday, 16 August, 14.30 (Vol. XII)

RADIOACTIVE ISOTOPES IN PHYSIOLOGY AND BIOCHEMISTRY (concluded):

GENERAL BIOCHEMISTRY

Chairman: H. H. Ussing (Denmark)
Vice-Chairman: B. Ahmad (Pakistan)

CHAIRMAN'S REMARKS

P/456 (UK)
Some recent applications of tritium in biological research...............................R. F. Glascock

P/710 (Ukrainian SSR)
The use of radioisotopes in the study of the functional biochemistry of the brain
A. V. Palladin and G. E. Vladimirov
Presented by A. V. Palladin

DISCUSSION

P/262 (USA)
Use of isotopes in the study of enzyme mechanisms
D. E. Koshland, Jr.

P/182 (USA)
Role of radioisotopes in immunologic investigation including recent studies on the rates of antibody synthesis................................F. J. Dixon

DISCUSSION

P/776 (Israel)
Application of C^{14}-labelled substances in the study of adipose tissue metabolism....B. Shapiro and G. Rose
Presented by E. D. Bergman

P/377 (France)
Utilization of sulfites by higher animals
P. Fromageot and F. Chapeville
Presented by P. Fromageot

P/686 (USSR)
Investigation of the incorporation of amino acids into proteins *in vivo* and *in vitro*........V. N. Orekhovich
Presented by A. M. Kuzin

DISCUSSION

P/260 (USA)
Pathways of biosynthesis of nucleic acids....G. B. Brown

P/457 (UK)
Studies on the incorporation of radioactive precursors into the nucleic acids and related compounds of living cells........R. M. S. Smellie and J. N. Davidson
Presented by R. M. S. Smellie

DISCUSSION

Session 17C: Wednesday, 17 August, 9.00 (Vol. XIII)

SAFETY STANDARDS AND HEALTH ASPECTS OF LARGE-SCALE USE OF ATOMIC ENERGY

Chairman: W. V. Mayneord (UK)
Vice-Chairman: J. Coursaget (France)

17C.1 Radiation Safety Recommendations and Control

CHAIRMAN'S REMARKS

P/451 (UK)
Radiation injury and protection—maximum permissible exposure standards...................W. Binks

P/89 (USA)
Maximum permissible exposure standards....R. S. Stone

P/79 (USA)
Maximum permissible concentration of radioisotopes in air and water for short period exposure
K. Z. Morgan *et al.*
Presented by K. Z. Morgan

DISCUSSION

P/689 (USSR)
Health protection of workers exposed to ionizing radiations............................A. A. Letavet
Presented by F. G. Krotkov

P/907 (ILO)
The protection of workers against ionizing radiations
Presented by K. L. Goodall

DISCUSSION

P/792 (Sweden)
Measurements of low-level radioactivity, particularly the gamma radiation from living subjects..R. M. Sievert

DISCUSSION

17C.2. Hazards Related to Uranium Mining

P/370 (France)
The problem of radon in uranium mines
H. P. Jammet and J. Pradel
Presented by H. P. Jammet

P/85 (USA)
Industrial hygiene of uranium processing
M. Eisenbud and J. A. Quigley
Presented by M. Eisenbud

DISCUSSION

Session 18C: Wednesday, 17 August, 14.30 (Vol. XIII)

SAFETY STANDARDS AND HEALTH ASPECTS OF LARGE-SCALE USE OF ATOMIC ENERGY (concluded):

Chairman: J. C. Bugher (United States)
Vice-Chairman: J. C. Jacobsen (Denmark)

18C.1. Hazards Related to Reactor and Chemical Processing

CHAIRMAN'S REMARKS

P/8 (Canada)
Health and safety activities in reactor operations and chemical processing plants.............A. J. Cipriani

P/240 (USA)
Radiation exposure experience in a major atomic energy facility........................H. M. Parker

P/452 (UK)
Control of radiation hazards in the operation of medium powered experimental reactors
W. G. Marley and B. S. Smith
Presented by W. G. Marley

P/845 (USA)
Approaches to treatment of poisoning by both radioactive and non-radioactive elements encountered in atomic energy operations..................J. Schubert

DISCUSSION

18C.2. Ecological Problems Related to Reactor Operation

CHAIRMAN'S REMARKS

P/278 (USA)
The absorption of fission products by plants
J. H. Rediske and F. P. Hungate
Presented by H. M. Parker

P/280 (USA)
The accumulation of radioactive substances in aquatic forms.................... R. F. Foster and J. J. Davis
Presented by R. F. Foster

P/281 (USA)
Radioactivity in terrestrial animals near an atomic energy site............................ W. C. Hanson
Presented by H. M. Parker

P/393 (UK)
The behaviour of I^{131} Sr^{89} and Sr^{90} in certain agricultural food chains........... A. C. Chamberlain *et al.*
Presented by A. C. Chamberlain and R. Scott-Russell

DISCUSSION

RADIOACTIVE ISOTOPES SESSIONS

(Sessions 19C - 23C)

Session 19C: Thursday, 18 August, 9.00 (Vol. XIV)

GENERAL USES, PRODUCTION AND HANDLING OF RADIOACTIVE ISOTOPES

Chairman: **W. E. Libby (United States)**
Vice-Chairman: **Mrs. B. Karlik (Austria)**

CHAIRMAN'S REMARKS

19C.1. General Aspects

P/985 (Australia)
The use of radioisotopes in Australia........ C. E. Eddy

P/801 (Czechoslovakia)
The use of radioisotopes in Czechoslovakia.... C. Shímane

P/146 (USA)
Radioisotopes in industrial research......... S. E. Eaton

19C.2. Production of Radioactive Isotopes

P/314 (USA)
Large-scale production of radioisotopes...... A. F. Rupp

P/461 (UK)
The production of beta-ray sources for industrial and clinical uses..... P. E. Carter and L. C. Myerscough
Presented by P. E. Carter

P/886 (Norway)
Separation of carrier-free isotopes by diffusion methods.................. K. Samsahl and K. Taugböl
Presented by E. Saeland

DISCUSSION

19C.3. Handling of Radioactive Isotopes

P/13 (Canada)
Current techniques of handling and distributing cobalt-60 radiation sources..................... A. B. Lillie

P/69 (USA)
Mechanical arms incorporating a sense of feel for conducting experiments with radioactive materials
J. R. Burnett *et al.*
Presented by R. C. Goertz

DISCUSSION

Session 20C: Thursday, 18 August, 14.30 (Vol. XIV)

DOSIMETRY

Chairman: **E. Saeland (Norway)**
Vice-Chairman: **H. Hulubei (Romania)**

CHAIRMAN'S REMARKS

20C.1. General Aspects

P/150 (USA)
Low-level counting and the future of isotopic tracers
W. H. Johnston

DISCUSSION

20C.2. Dosimetry of Gamma-rays

P/386 (France)
Dosimetry of cobalt-60 gamma-rays and thermal neutrons in heavy water piles......... J. Sutton *et al.*
Presented by J. Guéron

P/70 (USA)
Absolute dosimetry of cobalt-60 gamma-rays
J. S. Laughlin *et al.*
Presented by J. S. Laughlin

DISCUSSION

20C.3. Neutron Dosimetry

P/154 (USA)
Dosimetry of reactor radiations by calorimetric measurement...................... D. M. Richardson *et al.*
Presented by C. J. Hochanadel

P/63 (USA)
Methods of measurement of neutron flux at low levels.................... F. P. Cowan and J. O'Brien
Presented by F. P. Cowan

P/60 (USA)
A gamma insensitive semi-conductor fast neutron dosimeter using single crystal germanium.... B. Cassen

DISCUSSION

20C.4. Counting and Electronics

P/71 (USA)
Dosimetry of ionizing particles................ G. Failla

P/61 (USA)
Recent developments in the scintillation counter field
G. A. Morton

P/66 (USA)
Methods of pulse analysis.................. G. G. Kelley
Presented by A. H. Snell

P/159 (USA)
High resolution radiation detectors in research
H. J. Gomberg *et al.*
Presented by H. J. Gomberg

P/930 (Netherlands)
New Geiger tube design — hollow anode and parallel plate counters......................... J. Hersen *et al.*
Presented by D. van Duuren

DISCUSSION

Session 21C: Friday, 19 August, 9.00 (Vol. XV)

RADIOACTIVE ISOTOPES IN RESEARCH

Chairman: **A. H. W. Aten (Netherlands)**
Vice-Chairman: **J. M. Otero Navascues (Spain)**

CHAIRMAN'S REMARKS

21C.1. Reaction Mechanisms

P/708 (USSR)
Application of tracer atoms in the study of the mechanism of chemical reactions.... V. N. Kondratyev

P/163 (USA)

Stable and unstable isotopes in heterogeneous catalytic reactions..............................J. Turkevich

P/149 (USA)

Tritium as a tool in industrial and chemical research
W. G. Brown *et al.*
Presented by J. J. Katz

DISCUSSION

21C.2. Activation Analysis

P/632 (USSR)

Quantitative determination of impurities in high purity metals through radioactivation analysis..V. V. Jakovlev
Presented by A. P. Vinogradov

P/706 (USSR)

Application of radioactive isotopes in chemical analysis.....................................I. P. Alimarin
Presented by A. P. Vinogradov

P/770 (UK)

Recent advances in radioactivation analysis..A. A. Smales

DISCUSSION

21C.3. Research in Metallurgy

P/702 (USSR)

Investigation of diffusion and atomic interaction in alloys with the aid of radioactive isotopes
G. V. Kurdiumov

DISCUSSION

Session 22C: Friday, 19 August, 14.00 (Vol. XV)

RADIOACTIVE ISOTOPES IN CONTROL AND TECHNOLOGY

Chairman: J. V. Kurdiumov (USSR)
Vice-Chairman: E. Estermann (Switzerland)

CHAIRMAN'S REMARKS

P/463 (UK)

Development in thickness gauges and allied instruments.................................J. L. Putman

P/164 (USA)

Versatility of radiation applications involving penetration or reflection......................C. E. Crompton
Presented by P. C. Aebersold

P/704 (USSR)

Application of radioisotopes to control technological processes...........................G. G. Jordan *et al.*
Presented by S. T. Nazarov

DISCUSSION

P/383 (France)

Studies and industrial applications of bremsstrahlung from the beta rays of yttrium-90......P. Lévêque *et al.*
Presented by P. Lévêque

P/462 (UK)

Application of radioisotopes to leakage and hydraulic problems..............J. L. Putman and S. Jefferson
Presented by J. L. Putman

P/707 (USSR)

The use of artificially radioactive isotopes in the study of the process of steel and pig iron production
A. M. Samarin

P/713 (Ukrainian SSR)

The use of radioactive isotopes in the study of the wear of machine parts....................D. B. Grozin
Presented by A. M. Samarin

DISCUSSION

P/1054 (Japan)

Brief review of applications of isotopes in process and quality control.............................M. Kato

P/882 (Norway)

Some industrial uses of radioisotopes in Norway
U. Been and E. Saeland
Presented by U. Been

DISCUSSION

Session 23C: Saturday, 20 August, 9.00 (Vol. XV)

FISSION PRODUCTS AND THEIR APPLICATIONS

Chairman: J. Guéron (France)
Vice-Chairman: Hsioh-Ren Wei (China)

CHAIRMAN'S REMARKS

23C.1. Polymerisation Induced by Radiation

P/168 (USA)

The effect of gamma radiation on some chemical reactions of possible industrial importance
B. G. Bray *et al.*
Presented by J. J. Martin

P/465 (UK)

Recent developments in the irradiation of long-chain polymers................................A. Charlesby

DISCUSSION

23C.2. Food Sterilization

P/172 (USA)

Progress and problems in the development of cold sterilization of foods..B. E. Proctor and S. A. Goldblith
Presented by B. E. Proctor

P/225 (USA)

Prevention of human helminthic diseases by gamma-radiation of food with particular reference to trichinosis............H. J. Gomberg and S. E. Gould
Presented by H. J. Gomberg

P/175 (USA)

Sterilization of medical supplies with gamma radiation................L. E. Brownell and J. J. Bulmer
Presented by L. E. Brownell

DISCUSSION

23C.3. Conversion of Radiation into Electricity

P/794 (Sweden)

Study on the properties of an electrolytic cell consisting of an electrode system in a chloroform alcohol solution under γ-irradiation
C. G. Osterlundh and E. Haeffner
Presented by E. Haeffner

P/169 (USA)

The direct conversion of radiation into electrical energy..........................E. G. Linder *et al.*
Presented by E. G. Linder

DISCUSSION

Session 1

OPENING SESSION

The Opening Session of the Conference

Record of Proceedings of Session 1

MONDAY MORNING, 8 AUGUST 1955

President: Mr. Homi J. Bhabha (India)

The PRESIDENT: M. le Président de la Confédération, Mr. Secretary-General, ladies and gentlemen: I have the honour to declare open the International Conference on the Peaceful Uses of Atomic Energy and I ask Mr. Max Petitpierre, President of the Swiss Confederation, to take the floor.

Mr. Max PETITPIERRE (President of the Swiss Confederation): Ten years ago, almost to the very day, the first atomic bombs exploded, sowing death and destruction. In this way mankind was rudely awakened to the fact that a new brilliant discovery had been made and that a source of energy of extraordinary power had been uncovered. At the same time it was awakened to the existence of a new threat, which could one day endanger its very existence. For many years nuclear energy was linked in the minds of men with its military uses. Authoritative voices were raised, the voices of scientists who were best able to evaluate the consequences of those fearful developments. Let us recall Einstein's appeal:

"Our world is threatened by a crisis the magnitude of which is apparently not grasped by those who have the power to take great decisions for good or ill. The power unleashed from the atom has changed everything, except our manner of thinking, and as a result we are slipping toward an unprecedented catastrophe. A new way of thinking must be found if mankind is to survive. Averting this threat has become the most urgent task of our time."*

That appeal was heard. On 4 December 1954 the United Nations General Assembly unanimously decided that a conference should be held to explore means of developing the peaceful uses of atomic energy. Events began to take a different course. People everywhere understood the importance of that conference, at which the most eminent scientists of all countries were to meet to serve the cause of peace.

More than seventy Governments accepted the invitation of the United Nations.

You are now assembled here, ready to begin your work, to pool your knowledge and your learning,

* Retranslated from French.

to share your findings, to explore together the many different fields in which atomic energy can become a boon to man and afford him vast new opportunities, both by helping to raise his standard of living and by combating disease.

On behalf of the Federal Council, on behalf of the State Council of the Republic and the Canton of Geneva, on behalf of the Administrative Council of the City of Geneva, and on behalf of the people of Switzerland and Geneva, I welcome you to this country.

When science was still the reserve of the few, the alchemists of the Middle Ages maintained that it was a very serious thing to delve into the secrets of matter and that their study should be undertaken only with a pure heart and a knowledge of the possible implications. This forgotten precept and Einstein's moving appeal have the same underlying thought. Faced with the problems of the use of nuclear energy, we must accustom ourselves to a new way of thinking and a new approach to relations between peoples and nations, so that the knowledge which man has acquired may be a means of progress and help to make life easier for mankind rather than more difficult.

Throughout the centuries peoples and governments paid scant heed to the words of philosophers, scholars and prophets, or at least did not follow their teachings, preferring to be swayed by their passions. Even today politics still lag behind science, and progress in international relations has not kept pace with that made in all the fields of science and technology. This progress has brought about a close inter-dependence between countries and continents and removed all natural geographic barriers. Because of it, international disputes have become dangerous to a degree unknown in the past, and their consequences become more fearsome with each war. The solidarity of mankind has become a fact dictated by reality. We must realize at long last that if we do not go forward as one, we shall all go backward together.

That is why for me your conference has extraordinary importance and significance, transcending the scope of the items on its agenda.

Because of your knowledge you are privileged men and women. The field of nuclear energy, which is familiar ground to you, is full of mystery for most of your fellows. You have already solved or are going to solve problems beyond our ken.

Because of this you have special powers and responsibilities. It is for you to discover new ways of using nuclear energy, to make of it a boon and an asset which can be used to banish hunger, poverty and disease and promote the welfare of peoples whose levels of living are inadequate.

However, over and above your specific task of research and exchanging information, you can also take part in the sincere efforts now being made to overcome the differences and antagonisms which have hitherto been a threat to peace. You have assembled here to take positive action. Thanks to the initiative taken by the United Nations you are going to share your secrets and your findings instead of jealously keeping them to yourselves. For me, this joint effort which is being made in the interests not only of your own countries but of mankind as a whole, to promote the advancement of all without exception, is a source of encouragement and confidence. You can set an example by proving to governments and peoples that co-operation towards a goal transcending their differences is possible.

Switzerland hopes that you will find here an atmosphere favourable for your work and that this work will be profitable and crowned with success. It hopes that this Conference will be a momentous event which will not only enable further progress to be achieved in the sciences you represent, but above all will mark an important stage on the difficult road to peace, understanding between peoples and international co-operation for the common good of mankind.

The PRESIDENT: I now invite Mr. Dag Hammarskjold, the Secretary General of the United Nations, to address the Conference.

The SECRETARY-GENERAL: Mr. President, M. le Président de la Confédération, ladies and gentlemen: This is a conference of master builders of nuclear science and nuclear engineering from more than seventy nations of the world, assembled here under the auspices of the United Nations, to discuss, exchange and share their knowledge with the aim of harnessing atomic energy to the purposes of peace and human welfare.

These are the bare facts, and were I to confine my statement to these, it would yet not fail to bring out the unique quality of this distinguished gathering. When in the history of mankind have men of knowledge, representing so many diverse and distant nations, congregated to offer the best of their minds and goodwill in order to promote knowledge and, through knowledge, peace?

But we would do well to permit ourselves some further contemplation on this occasion in order to place this event in its historical perspective and to try to sense its true significance. Though conceived and arranged as a scientific conference, intercourse amongst specialists on this level would have not only scientific but economic, social and, I believe, political consequences of deep import. Therefore as citizens of this age, it should be our duty to take careful note of its various aspects and to derive inspiration from this event.

Let us not fail to recall on this occasion that it is to the initiative taken by the President of the United States in the General Assembly of the United Nations in December 1953 that we owe the origins of this Conference. He gave expression to the deepest hope of all humanity when he rejected the prospect that "atomic colossi are doomed malevolently to eye each other indefinitely across a trembling world" and urged the development of effective international co-operation in the peaceful uses of atomic energy which would show that "the great Powers of the earth, both of the East and the West, are interested in human aspirations first rather than in building up the armaments of war".

It is to the glory of these human aspirations that the response to his words has been both wide-spread and sincere and the United Nations has had the opportunity of stepping out into another important, though this time utterly novel, field of human activity with limitless possibilities of amelioration through international co-operation. A tribute must therefore be paid to the courage and imagination of those nations which have lent their active co-operation to this Conference as well as to those nations which have lent it their best hopes.

We have left behind us the times when man, exploring what might have then been regarded as inert matter, discovered tremendous energy coiled up at the very heart of the atom. We then entered a phase when, within the lifespan of an individual, this energy assumed destructive shapes and threatened to become our nemesis. The Conference whose inauguration we are celebrating today might well mark the beginning of a phase during which man will have left his bewilderment and his fear behind and will begin to feel the elation of one of the greatest conquests made by his mind.

The exploitation of nuclear energy for social and economic ends will be a considerable relief from the oppressive thought that, in unlocking the atom, we had done no more than unlock the most sinister Pandora's box in nature. This, in itself, will have great psychological value and should free our best creative efforts. But, apart from that, I am sure this Conference will demonstrate the many practical uses to which these discoveries could be put for curing some of our worst physical, social and economic ills, for raising the standards of living, and for lifting mankind to a higher level of well-being.

It will also demonstrate that intellectual co-operation amongst scientists, which was such a feature of our civilization until the last great war and which has since been interrupted by the darker forces of history, is once more recognized as a moral respon-

Presiding over the opening session of the Conference. Left to right: Mr. Max Petitpierre, President of the Swiss Confederation; Mr. Dag Hammarskjold, Secretary-General of the United Nations; Mr. Homi J. Bhabha, President of the Conference; Mr. Walter G. Whitman, Conference Secretary General

sibility which we cannot escape if we are to continue to promote and not to hinder the process of our common civilization.

One is often asked whether this Conference has any political significance. In its conception, its purpose and its approach, this Conference is as non-political as a conference of this nature should be. The personalities that we see around us are not concerned with expediency, with strategy or with tactics of any kind, but with the search for truth and with the idea of brotherhood based on the concept that all knowledge is universal. Nevertheless, since their deliberations are bound to affect human life in all its aspects, it would not be correct to say that they have no political significance. I am sure that their co-operation will ease tensions. I am sure that their exchange of scientific data will turn men's thoughts away from war to peace. We all should render our thanks to the scientists who, by moving in this direction, will expiate on behalf of all of us, that feeling of guilt which has so universally been felt, that man in his folly should have thought of no better use of a great discovery than to manufacture with its help the deadliest instruments of annihilation.

We have a long road ahead of us to traverse before nations can hope to eliminate the threat of atomic destruction. But we cannot hope to travel at all unless we begin to take down the barriers to understanding and friendship and begin to work together in growing confidence. The exchange of scientific

and technical data which will take place here is only a first step, but it is an important and indispensable first step. By the willing help that the participating governments have given in the preparations for this Conference and by the character and quality of the contributions that they are making to its harvest, there is every hope that this first step will prove even more valuable than had been anticipated.

I cannot close these remarks without a word of sincere thanks to Mr. Petitpierre for the generous co-operation of the Federal authorities of Switzerland and of the Canton and City of Geneva in making it possible to hold this Conference here. This summer the demands of the international community on Swiss hospitality have been great, but Switzerland has again given evidence of its international spirit which continues to make this country the centre of many of the world's efforts for peace and progress.

The PRESIDENT: We have had the privilege of receiving messages from the heads of State and Prime Ministers of certain countries which, as Members of the Advisory Committee, have played a prominent role in organizing this Conference. I am sure that the members of this Conference would wish me to call upon the heads of delegations concerned to read these messages to the Conference. I shall first of all invite the head of the French delegation to read the message from Mr. Faure, Chairman of the Council of Ministers of France.

Mr. GUILLAUMAT (France): At the opening of this, the first International Conference on the Peaceful Uses of Atomic Energy under the auspices of the United Nations, I wish, on behalf of France, to express to all participants the hope that they will be successful in the task which they have undertaken for the good of mankind. May the peaceful co-operation now beginning bring to the world the economic advancement and the improved conditions which so many countries, from the most advanced to the most under-developed, expect nuclear energy to provide.

The PRESIDENT: I shall next read a message from Mr. Jawaharlal Nehru, Prime Minister of India:

"I should like to send my greetings to this Conference on the Peaceful Uses of Atomic Energy which has taken shape at the instance of President Eisenhower. Recently, the four-Power conference at Geneva gave a ray of hope to a war-weary world which had suddenly come face to face with the terror of atomic and hydrogen bombs. Now this Conference will, I hope turn people's minds still more from the evil aspect of the misuse of this great force which has come into man's hands and show the way to peaceful progress and co-operation.

"This Conference is of a new type and very different from normal conferences because it leads us to the threshold of the atomic age. We have to adjust ourselves to this new age, to act accordingly, and to think in terms of peace and not of destruction. All my good wishes to the eminent scientists and others who have gathered at Geneva for the purpose."

I received yesterday a telegram from Mr. Bulganin, Chairman of the Council of Ministers of the Union of Soviet Socialist Republics. I now invite Academician D. V. Skobeltzin, head of the USSR delegation, to read out this message to you.

Mr. SKOBELTZIN (USSR): I wish to read out the text of a telegram of greeting from the Chairman of the Council of Ministers of the Union of Soviet Socialist Republics:

"The Soviet Union, attaching great importance to the development of wide international co-operation in the use of the great scientific discoveries of our age, not for purposes of war and destruction but for constructive purposes for the good of mankind, to increase the prosperity and raise the standards of living of peoples, sends greetings to the International Scientific Conference for the exchange of information and knowledge on the peaceful uses of atomic energy.

"The Soviet government expresses the hope that the Conference will be a major step forward toward the development of international co-operation in the peaceful use of atomic energy and wishes the Conference every success in this noble task.

"N. BULGANIN
"Chairman of the Council of Ministers of the Union of Soviet Socialist Republics"

The PRESIDENT: I now invite Sir Edwin Plowden, head of the United Kingdom Atomic Energy Authority, to read out a message from Sir Anthony Eden.

Sir Edwin PLOWDEN: I have great pleasure in conveying the good wishes of Her Majesty's Government of the United Kingdom to the United Nations Conference on the Peaceful Uses of Atomic Energy. They are confident that the Conference will greatly stimulate the development of the peaceful uses of atomic energy. They welcome the Conference as a step towards the raising of standards of living throughout the world and as a splendid example of world-wide co-operation for peaceful purposes.

The PRESIDENT: Finally, I call on Admiral Strauss, head of the United States delegation and Chairman of the US AEC, to read a message from President Eisenhower.

The Secretary-General has already referred to the special part which President Eisenhower has played as the initiator of the General Assembly action which has led to this Conference.

Admiral STRAUSS: Mr. President, Mr. President of the Confederation, Mr. Secretary-General, distinguished delegates and guests, I have the high honor to convey to the Conference the following message from the President of the United States:

"Members of the Conference, please accept my warmest greetings and sincere good wishes on behalf of the people of the United States, for the success of this first International Conference on the Peaceful Uses of Atomic Energy, held under the auspices of the United Nations.

"You, the foremost scientists and engineers in the world, who are penetrating the mysteries of atomic energy, must surely know how the atom stands ready to become man's obedient and tireless servant, if man will only allow it. The knowledge and vision which you possess carries with it a great opportunity and a great challenge. Your lives are dedicated to the search for knowledge and truth. You hold the respect of your peoples because they look to you for words of calm, unadorned scientific fact. You can best unfold to the peoples of the world the bright promise of the benign atom.

"You meet here in Geneva under conditions favourable to this great purpose. No other scientific gathering of such scope and importance or of such wide-spread interest has ever taken place. The peoples of the world are represented. At hand is a rich opportunity to restore all lines of free scientific communication which have been disrupted for so many years. The knowledge and skills which each of you has acquired in his own country to put the atom to work for peaceful purposes will be calculated and shared in the friendly atmosphere of hospitable Switzerland, with its age-old tradition of freedom. This atmosphere is encouraged also by the fact that the United

Nations resolution of 4 December last, which created your Conference, limited its concern to scientific and technical matters. It is expressly non-political. You meet, therefore, as free men of science, interested only in enriching man's store of knowledge about this wonderful discovery. Science speaks in many tongues. The advance of the nuclear arts has been the work of men of many nations. That is so because the atom itself is non-political: it wears no nationality, and recognizes no frontiers. It is neither moral nor immoral. Only man's choice can make it good or evil. The phenomenon of nuclear fission having been revealed to man, it is still left to him to determine the use to which it shall be put.

"On 8 December 1953, I had the privilege of addressing the General Assembly of the United Nations, on the subject which occupies this Conference—world co-operation for the peaceful uses of atomic energy. I stated then, and I reaffirm now, that the United States pledges its determination to help find ways by which the miraculous inventiveness of man shall not be dedicated to his death but consecrated to his life. This pledge, which we gave twenty months ago, has since become the law of our land, written into our statutes by the American Congress in the new Atomic Energy Act of 1954. The new Act states in forthright language that we recognize our responsibilities to share with others in a spirit of co-operation what we know of the peaceful atomic art. To further encourage such co-operation with other nations, the new Act relaxes the previously existing restrictions on independent atomic research and development by private industry, thereby further clearing the way for co-operation with others. Since our new Atomic Energy Act became law just a year ago, we have striven in many ways and ever in a spirit of goodwill to translate its words and its purpose into concrete action.

"That is the way we interpret our responsibility and the responsibility of all nations of goodwill. We appeal not alone to governments to join us in this co-operative endeavour. We are hopeful also that business and professional groups throughout the world will become interested and will provide incentives in finding new ways that this science can be used. All of the enlightened nations of the world are spending large sums every year on programs of health, education and economic development. They do so because they know that disease, ignorance and the lack of economic opportunity are the dark breeding places of disorders and wars. Every scientific tool available has been brought to bear in this effort. Atomic science is the newest and most promising tool of all. In your capable hands I am confident that it can be made to perform greatly for the betterment of human living."

The PRESIDENT: The purpose of this Conference is to discuss the peaceful uses of atomic energy, and to exchange scientific and technical knowledge connected with it. The importance of this exchange of knowledge can hardly be overestimated. Knowledge is perhaps the most important possession of Man. It is the accumulated knowledge of centuries which differentiates modern Man from his ancestor in the dawn of civilization. It is this knowledge, and not any notable change in his physical or mental equipment, which has enabled him to build the civilization of today. One can hardly foresee the far-reaching developments to which this Conference may lead.

In a broad view of human history it is possible to discern three great epochs. The first is marked by the emergence of the early civilizations in the valleys of the Euphrates, the Indus, and the Nile, the second by the industrial revolution, leading to the civilization in which we live, and the third by the discovery of atomic energy and the dawn of the atomic age, which we are just entering. Each epoch marks a change in the energy pattern of society.

In a practical sense, energy is the great prime mover, which makes possible the multitude of actions on which our daily life depends. Indeed, it makes possible life itself.

It may be remarked in passing that by far our greatest source of energy is the sun. It is this solar energy, received as light and heat, which has produced those physical conditions on the surface of the earth, which are necessary for the emergence and continuance of Life. It is well known that atomic energy is the ultimate source of this vast output of radiant energy from the sun. But although life depends on solar energy for its existence, man has made very little progress since time immemorial in the conscious use of this vast source of energy.

Man has existed on this earth for well over 250,000 years. And yet the earliest civilizations of which we have record only date back some 8000 years. It took man several hundred thousand years to acquire those skills and techniques on which the early civilizations were based, and the techniques of agriculture, animal husbandry, weaving, pottery, brick making, and metallurgy. The acquisition of these techniques and the emergence of the early civilizations must be regarded as the first great epoch in human history.

Despite many differences in habit, culture and social patterns, all these early civilizations were built essentially on the same foundation. All the energy for doing mechanical work, for tilling the ground, for drawing water, for carrying loads, and for locomotion was supplied by muscle, whether animal or human. Molecular, or chemical energy, as for example that obtained by burning wood, was only used to a limited extent for cooking and heating, and in a few technical processes, as in metallurgy.

It is important to note the severe limitations that this restricted supply of energy puts on the development of civilization. A man in the course of heavy physical labour in an eight-hour day can hardly turn out more that half a kilowatt-hour of useful work. This is not much more than is necessary to maintain him at a bare subsistence level. It is to be compared with the rough figure of twenty kilowatt-hours or more of energy per person which is daily utilized in the industrially advanced countries today. It followed that a high level of physical comfort and culture could only be enjoyed by a small fraction of the population by making use of the collected surplus labour of the rest. It is sometimes forgotten that all the ancient civilizations were carried on the muscle power of slaves or of a particular class in society. Through the very limitations of the available energy, the fruits of civilization could only be enjoyed by a few.

A departure from this basic pattern only began with the scientific and technical developments of the seventeenth and eighteenth centuries, as a result of which man began to make increasing use of chemical energy for doing and augmenting the mechanical work which had till then been done by muscle. The wide-spread use of chemical energy, especially that obtained by burning the fossil fuels, coal and oil, marks the second great epoch in human history. It led to the industrial revolution, and the industrialized pattern of society and civilization, which is typical of this age. In one highly industrialized country today 25 kilowatt-hours of energy are daily utilized per head, corresponding to the muscular effort of 45 slaves. In another advanced country the figure is about twice this. This shows how radically the energy pattern of a modern industrialized society differs from that of the early civilizations and of a non-industrialized society.

The total consumption of energy in the world has gone up in a staggering manner. It is convenient in dealing with such enormous amounts of energy to use an appropriately large unit, denoted by Q, which is equal to a million-million-million British thermal units of energy, corresponding to the combustion of some thirty-three thousand million tons of coal. It is estimated that in the eighteen and a half centuries after Christ some $9Q$ of energy were consumed, corresponding to an average rate of about half a Q per century. But the actual rate in 1850 was probably about $1Q$ per century. The rate continued to increase, and it appears that by 1950 roughly another $5Q$ may have been consumed, while the rate had risen to $10Q$ per century· How the world demands for energy will continue to increase in the future is one of the important subjects which this Conference will discuss in its sessions.

It is not my intention here to anticipate the work of the Conference, but merely to touch on the many factors which enter into an answer to this question. The population of the world has increased rapidly. It is estimated that it was a few hundred million in 1 A.D. It may have been less than three hundred million. There appears to have been no remarkable increase till about the middle of the seventeenth century. Thereafter, for a reason which we do not understand, the population appears to have increased rapidly. It is estimated to have reached 1500 million in 1900, some 2000 million in 1930, and roughly 2300 million in 1950. We will have to estimate what the world population will be in 1975 and in A.D. 2000. Experts variously place it between 3500 and 5000 million by the end of the century.

Next, we have to determine the future per capita utilization of energy to which I have already alluded. It is estimated that the per capita utilization of energy has been increasing in the world as a whole during the last ninety years at some 2.2 per cent per annum compounded, while the present rate is about 5 per cent. For some highly industrialized countries the rate of increase has been as high as 4 per cent and more. What will the rate be as the under-developed areas of the world, with their large populations, become industrialized, with all the advantages of modern technology at their disposal, and the experience of others to learn from? What is the average per capita utilization of energy which we must anticipate in A.D. 2000?

There is a point which must be remembered in this context. Industrialization has so far proceeded on the basis that most of the materials needed for it are available on demand. This may no longer be so. It is estimated that the known reserves of a number of metals used in industry will not last more than a few decades at their present rate of consumption. The industrialization of large new areas of the

Mr. Homi U. Bhabha (President of the Conference), and Mr. Walter G. Whitman (Conference Secretary-General), examine equipment in the US reactor exhibit. (Photo courtesy of Union Carbide and Carbon Corporation)

world will aggravate the situation still further, and we will be forced to use natural or synthetic substitutes. This will make additional demands for energy beyond those we can anticipate on the present basis.

Of the enormous consumption of energy in the world to-day about 80 per cent is provided by the combustion of coal, oil and gas, while hydro-electric power provides less than about 1.5 per cent. The contribution of muscular energy is estimated to be about 1 per cent. The rest, amounting to something over 15 per cent, is obtained by burning wood and agricultural waste. Hydro-electric power is never likely to contribute more than a small fraction of the total energy consumption of the world, since the total potential capacity is relatively limited. Nor is the contribution from wood and agricultural waste likely to increase substantially. Hence, as the total demand for energy increases, a larger and larger fraction will have to be provided by the fossil fuels, coal and oil, unless some entirely new source of energy is found.

It is, therefore, of importance for us to have fairly accurate estimates of the reserves of coal and oil that remain in the ground. We are not concerned here with the absolute amounts of these substances in the earth's crust, but with the amounts that are recoverable at a cost not substantially different from present costs. This is another problem which will be discussed in the Conference. The consensus of opinion seems to be that the total economically recoverable world reserves of coal, oil, gas and oil shale are equivalent in energy value to under $100Q$. Some have put the figure under $40Q$. It is probable that, at the rate at which the world consumption of energy is increasing, these reserves will be exhausted in under a century.

Let us pause to see what this means. The bulk of our coal, the bituminous coal, comes from the Carboniferous Age, some 250-million years ago. We are exhausting these reserves, which have been built-up by nature over long periods of time, in a few centuries, in a flash of geological time.

It is a matter of regret that there are several areas of the world which are not directly represented at this Conference, and that in these important discussions about the fuel resources and power needs of the world as a whole and of individual countries, the plans of about a quarter of the world's population should not be before us.

Certain important conclusions can be reached without answering in detail the difficult questions which I have just touched on. Of the total world consumption of energy, amounting to $1Q$ per decade in 1950, 37 per cent was in the United States. If the entire population of the world were to consume energy per capita at the same rate as in the United States, the total consumption of energy in the world would be over $5\frac{1}{2}Q$ per decade instead of the present $1Q$. Coupled with a doubling of the world's population within the next hundred years, which is the

least that we can expect, this would exhaust the known reserves of fossil fuels in under a century. In this simple arithmetic no allowance has been made for the fact that the standard of living of the industrially advanced countries is rising and, we hope, will continue to rise.

This conclusion is of great significance. It shows that our presently known reserves of coal and oil are insufficient to enable the under-developed countries of the world, which contain a major part of its population, to attain and maintain for long a standard of living equal to that of the industrially most advanced countries. It shows the absolute necessity of finding some new source of energy, if the light of our civilization is not to be extinguished, because we have burnt out our fuel reserves.

It is in this context that we turn to atomic energy for a solution. The Conference will discuss the known reserves of uranium and thorium in individual countries and in the world as a whole. It has been estimated that the total recoverable world reserves of uranium and thorium contain an amount of energy of the order of $1700Q$. If this is really so, then atomic energy could, first, provide the energy necessary to enable the under-developed countries to reach the standard of living of the industrialized countries, and secondly, enable the entire world to maintain a constantly rising standard of living for very many decades, and possibly for several centuries. For the full industrialization of the under-developed areas, for the continuation of our civilization and its further development, atomic energy is not merely an aid; it is an absolute necessity. The acquisition by man of the knowledge of how to release and use atomic energy must be recognized as the third great epoch in human history.

There is no longer any question that atomic energy can be used for power generation. We know that it has been used for several years to heat houses in winter in a small area in England. We know that a United States submarine has been propelled successfully by atomic energy, and we know that in the Soviet Union an atomic power station of 5000 kilowatts has fed electricity into the grid. An atomic power station of 50,000 kilowatts is expected to be in operation in the United Kingdom next year, and a rapidly accelerating programme of new power stations has been planned. Several atomic power stations of varying designs are under construction in the United States, and others are under construction in the Soviet Union. Further, two atomic power-producing reactors are under construction in France and one is being planned in Canada. There is little doubt that many atomic power stations will be established in different parts of the world during the next ten years. The extent to which atomic energy contributes in future to the total energy production will depend on the capital and running costs involved, and will vary from country to country. Generally, the basic ideas of atomic energy are simple but its technology is sophisticated and difficult. Hundreds of tons of special materials have had to be produced in states of extreme purity surpassing anything hitherto known even in the pharmaceutical industry. Highly radioactive substances have had to be treated chemically in bulk by remote control. All this has required the development of new methods and techniques at great expense and by enormous effort. Many sessions of the Conference are to be devoted to a discussion of the technology of atomic materials. As in all industrial operations, there is always room for technical improvement and alternative processes, and the information which will be interchanged at the Conference is likely to be of value to all.

It is well known that, unlike coal furnaces, which may differ in detail but are basically all of the same design, atomic furnaces can be of at least half a dozen basically different patterns, which differ in the physical and chemical state of the fuel, the moderator used, if any, and the method employed for extracting heat. Perhaps some of the greatest interest will attach to the series of technical sessions which is to be devoted to reactor technology. These sessions will throw important light on the merits and disadvantages of the different types of reactors.

The economics of electricity generation by different types of reactors is a matter of the greatest importance, and it is to be hoped that the information which will be placed before this Conference will allow some preliminary conclusions to be reached. A definite answer will doubtless have to wait until reactors of different types have been tried out on a large scale over a number of years.

A wide-spread atomic power industry will produce vast amounts of radioactive material. There will be papers at the Conference dealing with the use to which some fission products can be put in industry, and perhaps in the preservation of food. The effect of radiation in stimulating and altering the equilibrium of chemical reactions has opened up entirely new possibilities in chemistry, which may have a profound influence on the chemical industry. These new applications in industry may use far more of these fission products than we expect today, but nevertheless the bulk of them may have to be stored in a safe and convenient way. Extreme care will have to be taken with regard to the radioactivity which is allowed to escape into the air.

But there are also purely scientific problems to which answers have yet to be found. The direct biological effects of radiation are fairly well known, and it is possible to prescribe safe tolerance doses, though even here there appears to be some divergence of view among experts. The indirect effects are much more difficult to assess. Above all, not enough is known yet about the genetical effects. We know that irradiation produces artificial mutations, and this method had been used with advantage in improving the strains of plants and crops. But most of the mutations produced are lethal or deleterious. Natural selection perhaps gives an inherent stability to the evolutionary process through the survival of the favourable mutations and the extinction of the carriers of the deleterious ones. Nevertheless, this is too important a matter for any risk to be taken, and it is imperative that the long range genetic effects of a small rise in the general level of radiation should be established beyond doubt. I am sure the many distinguished scientists present will discuss this matter with scientific objectivity and thoroughness. Our first duty as scientists is to establish the truth, and in this matter our responsibility to humanity transcends our allegiance to any state.

Atomic energy also differs from chemical energy in its concentration. The complete combustion of a pound of carbon yields some 14,650 British thermal units of energy, while the complete fission of a pound of uranium would yield some 3.3-thousand-million British thermal units. Consequently, the complete fission of a ton of uranium or thorium would yield as much energy as two and a half to three million tons of coal, depending on its quality. This concentration has typical consequences of its own. For example, it has made possible a submarine whose performance was unachievable through the use of chemical energy, just as the internal combustion engine made aviation possible in the earlier part of this century. We are but at the beginning of these developments, and the coming years will see many new applications and achievements which we can only visualize at present, as for example that of travel into space.

The immense concentration of atomic energy has made possible other developments whose immediate results have been less happy, and which have placed a pall of fear over the peoples of the world. I refer, of course, to the development of atomic and hydrogen bombs. The powerful and technically advanced nations have suffered most from this fear. Atomic weapons lie outside the scope of this Conference, but we cannot entirely separate the applications of peace from the applications of war. The rise of an atomic power industry in many parts of the world, the development of which is necessitated by the growing demands for power, will put into the hands of many nations quantities of fissile material, from which the making of atomic bombs will be but a relatively easy step. A wide-spread atomic power industry in the world will necessitate an international society in which the major States have agreed to maintain peace.

I am sure all will agree with me, if I single out for mention the name of one scientist of our time, who has perhaps done more than anyone else to lay the scientific foundations of the modern age, and who has now taken his place with the giants in the history of science. Some of us had the privilege of knowing him personally; all know of his work. I refer to the late Dr. Albert Einstein. Before he died, Einstein put his signature to a document in which it was pointed out that,

"The best authorities are unanimous in saying that a war with H-bombs might quite possibly put an end to the human race.

"It is feared that if many H-bombs are used, there would be universal death—sudden only for a minority, but for the majority a slow torture of disease and disintegration".

President Eisenhower expressed the same view in a recent speech, when he said:

"There seems to be a growing realization by all that nuclear warfare pursued to the ultimate could be possibly race suicide".

A most important meeting of the Heads of four great States has taken place recently in this very city, which augurs well for the future. Much remains to be done, but one has every reason to hope that the intelligence of man will overcome his fear and his weaknesses. The areas of social organization an orderly peaceful existence have on the average increased continuously with the advance of technology. At no previous period in history have such large and closely integrated States existed. It is, therefore, not surprising that in the atomic age major wars should ultimately become impossible, and that the area of peaceful existence should eventually cover the entire globe.

Last, but not least, I should like to mention the whole series of technical sessions which is devoted to the role of atomic energy in biology and medicine. The importance of tracers in the investigation of biological phenomena is well known. They have already led to an understanding of the pathways followed in the synthesis of biological compounds by living organisms, which might not have been achieved otherwise for many decades. One should also recall in this connexion the discovery and proof of the dynamic state of all parts of the body. Isotopes may also be expected to lead to a better understanding of the infective processes in animal and plant tissues through the migration of micro-organisms. The importance of isotopes in understanding the processes of life cannot be over-estimated, and it may be hoped confidently that with the wider spread of the knowledge and techniques of the handling and use of isotopes, which will result from this Conference, the biological sciences will receive a most important impetus.

The historical period we are just entering in which atomic energy released by the fission process will supply some of the power requirements of the world may well be regarded one day as the primitive period of the atomic age. It is well known that atomic energy can be obtained by a fusion process as in the H-bomb, and there is no basic scientific knowledge in our possession today to show that it is impossible for us to obtain this energy from the fusion process in a controlled manner. The technical problems are formidable, but one should remember that it is not yet fifteen years since atomic energy was released in an atomic pile for the first time by Fermi. I venture to predict that a method will be found for liberating fusion energy in a controlled manner within the next two decades. When that happens, the energy problems of the world will truly have been solved forever for the fuel will be as plentiful as the heavy hydrogen in the oceans.

I am sure you would all like me on this occasion to remember Rutherford who first unravelled the structure of the atom and created the science of nuclear physics upon which atomic energy is based. Few ages in history can claim a scientist of his magnitude. Our generation is fortunate indeed that it has known both Einstein and Rutherford.

All the basic discoveries upon which atomic energy is based were made before the Second World War by scientists of many nations working in free and full collaboration. The war put an end to this free exchange of knowledge, and most of the technical developments concerning atomic energy were made subsequently by a few nations, each working in isolation behind a wall of secrecy. This Conference, arising out of the bold initiative of President Eisenhower, has already broken down many of these barriers and we have come to know of the remarkable advances in atomic energy achieved in several countries of which we were totally ignorant hitherto. It is to be hoped that through the remarkable improvement in the political climate which has taken place recently, and which we hope will continue, the barriers which remain will gradually disappear altogether. If so much has been achieved through the individual and isolated efforts of a few countries how much more could be achieved by the combined effort of all. Those who have the good fortune to participate in this Conference are privileged to be in the vanguard of the march of history. We have the unique opportunity of giving of our knowledge to others for the common good. I hope this Conference will play its part in helping the progress of mankind towards the ever-widening dawn of the atomic age, with the promise of a life, fuller and happier than anything we can visualize today.

Under the mandate given to him by the General Assembly the Secretary-General has appointed Officers of the Conference. According to the rules of procedure I now ask that these appointments be affirmed by acclamation. I take it that these appointments are now affirmed.

I now declare the first session of the Conference closed.

Session 24

CLOSING GENERAL SESSION

LIST OF PAPERS

Co-operation by the United Kingdom in the Use of Atomic Energy for Peaceful Purposes

By Sir John Cockcroft, UK

Co-operation by the United Kingdom has evolved from the personal relationships formed over a period of many years at such traditional centres of nuclear physics research as the Cavendish Laboratory at Cambridge. This process was continued during the war, when United Kingdom scientists worked with many scientists from abroad on defence problems. It was therefore natural that after the war they were consulted on many matters of interest to newly established atomic energy laboratories abroad. Similarly there have been frequent exchanges of results, and discussion of programmes, between individuals and at conferences. At first this was limited to a few aspects of pure physics and chemistry, but as the secrecy restrictions have gradually been lifted the scope of such exchanges has extended.

This pattern of individual inter-communication was greatly developed when the United Kingdom began to send radioisotopes abroad. Visits were made to many countries to describe to scientific and non-scientific audiences the great possibilities inherent in the use of isotopes. It was also necessary in some cases to stress the precautions to be taken in handling radioactive substances, and to give advice and help in the development and supply of the requisite electronic equipment. These visits were no doubt to a considerable extent responsible for the fact that during the year ended 31 March 1955 the United Kingdom made almost 6700 shipments of isotopes to about 40 overseas countries. In addition to these direct supplies, many radiation sources were supplied to British manufacturers of scientific instruments and industrial radiation equipment, and were subsequently sold abroad by them.

In 1951 the Harwell Isotope School was founded to train students in the applications of radioactive materials in research and industry and in the techniques of producing, measuring and handling such materials. Since it began it has had 178 students from 35 countries overseas.

Two major conferences on the applications of radioisotopes have been held under the auspices of the UK atomic energy project and at the second one in July 1954, more than 700 scientists met from 30 countries.

Short specialized courses are also arranged periodically at Harwell in the design and use of electronic instruments used in work with radioisotopes, in nuclear physics and radiochemistry; and on autoradiographic techniques.

Co-operation between the UK and the Canadian and US atomic energy projects began during the war years and has, on the peaceful uses of atomic energy, continued ever since. The UK atomic energy project has for a number of years also increasingly co-operated on an informal basis with the corresponding projects of Commonwealth and other countries on peaceful applications in a wider field, and much assistance on specific subjects has been given to many countries during the course of this co-operation. Recently there has been a movement towards reinforcing the co-operation, which will continue to take place on this informal basis, by making a number of more formal arrangements. These normally provide for the research and development programmes of the two projects to be drawn up with a view to the avoidance of unnecessary duplication of effort, so that the maximum mutual benefit can be obtained as a result of genuinely co-operative effort. In order to ensure this the UK is usually called upon in the first instance to contribute design information and other assistance needed for the building of a research reactor of really high intensity and to provide fuel elements for it.

It is intended that formal agreements of this kind should all follow the same general pattern, but should be made in terms appropriate to each particular set of circumstances. In addition to the recently completed agreement with the United States on the civil aspects of atomic energy and to the continuing arrangements for co-operation with Canada, the UK has now completed formal agreements of varying types with Australia, France and Denmark. Formal and other arrangements for co-operation are under discussion or will shortly be discussed with a number of countries including South Africa, India, Belgium, The Netherlands and Norway.

The United Kingdom was a joint sponsor of the resolution of the United Nations General Assembly to establish an International Atomic Energy Agency; it has subsequently played a prominent part in the negotiations to give effect to that resolution. The United Kingdom has announced that it will contribute 20 kg of fissile material to the Agency when it is formed.

The international Agency, though it will be the most comprehensive of the multilateral organizations of which the UK is a member, for the development of the peaceful uses of atomic energy, was preceded in point of time by the European Council for Nuclear Research (C.E.R.N.) and by the European Atomic Energy Society. C.E.R.N., though not strictly within the terms of this paper, since it is concerned with fundamental nuclear research rather than with the uses of nuclear energy, is nevertheless so closely associated with the development of the basic knowledge of the subject that it is included here. The United Kingdom was one of the countries which signed the Convention setting up C.E.R.N. in July, 1953, and is giving all possible assistance in the design and construction of the apparatus which is to be built; in particular we have seconded key staff for the proton-synchrotron group.

The European Atomic Energy Society was founded with eight member countries in 1954. It is not a formal inter-governmental organization, but consists of senior members of the atomic energy projects in each of the countries. Its aim is to promote co-operation in nuclear research and engineering in the unclassified field. It arranges small technical conferences from time to time, and a recent one, on health physics, was held as Harwell, and another one on heavy water in Italy.

As a further contribution to international co-operation the UK has announced that it will open its Reactor School at Harwell to overseas students for courses in unclassified reactor science and technology. The first of these will open in September, 1955.

CONCLUSION

The magnitude of the effort required to design and construct a nuclear reactor or a modern high-energy particle accelerator, and the unique part played in world affairs by atomic energy, have necessarily led to co-operative effort by groups invested with a formality new in science and technology. The traditional forms of free co-operation between scientists, and the normal diffusion of technological advance through the initiative of industrial firms, must, however, continue and will certainly play an increasingly important part in the development in all countries of atomic energy for peaceful purposes.

The Use of Atomic Energy for Peaceful Purposes in Czechoslovakia

By Frantishek Shorm, Czechoslovakia

As a country which is building Socialism, Czechoslovakia has a great stake in making use of such an important discovery as atomic energy in every conceivable way for the good of mankind.

It is well known that not only our own, but also a number of other countries only have limited energy resources. Atomic energy is the one new source basically capable of solving future power problems. One may come to the conclusion that, even at the present time, the costs of power stations driven by nuclear fuel are comparable to those of thermal plants. Moreover, the growing use of atomic energy will make it possible to utilize coal, which today is the most important energy source, for other purposes, mainly for the chemical industry, in which it is to date one of the most important, and in some cases irreplaceable, raw material.

All the basic prerequisites of the utilization of atomic energy for peaceful purposes are to be found in Czechoslovakia. As is well known, it owns large sources of the raw materials needed for the making of atomic reactors. Together with a highly developed industry and science, Czechoslovakia also has the experienced scientific and technical workers required for research in the field of nuclear physics and its application to industry. However, the problems now facing our specialists require a continuous development of the group working in this field.

After an evaluation of the conditions required for the development of the utilization of sources of atomic energy for peaceful purposes, the Czechoslovakian government has given full support to research in this field.

Soon after the reconstruction of our country following the war, nuclear physics took a prominent place in our scientific life. A nuclear physics laboratory was established, followed by a special science department of the Czechoslovakian Academy of Sciences dealing with nuclear physics and radiochemistry. In the Karl University, a Department of Nuclear Physics was set up and, in addition several students were sent to the Soviet Union to study atomic physics. In the Karl University, as well as in the Soviet Union, graduate students are doing graduate research in this special field. In 1953 a conference of workers in the field of nuclear physics took place, which not only dealt with questions of

utilization of radioisotopes (being received from the Soviet Union) and with the evaluation of our achievements, but also showed that Czechoslovakian scientific workers are prepared for the broadening of research into nuclear power. This has taken place as a result of achievements in nuclear physics, the physics of elementary particles and cosmic radiation, which have led to substantial experience in the design and use of complicated equipment. In addition, the high level of basic research, mainly in the field of the quantum theory and in that of the structure of matter, shows that we have all the prerequisites for work in this field.

In order further to investigate the ways of utilizing nuclear energy, it was first decided to build a thermal neutron experimental reactor operating on natural uranium in which heavy water and a graphite reflector were to be used as moderators. This reactor, compared with other reactors, was to have improved cooling. For operation of this reactor, about 3.3 tons of natural uranium, 7 tons of heavy water, and 38 tons of graphite were to be required. The uranium rods were to be arranged in an hexagonal lattice, 16 cm apart. The reactor was to be cylindrical, with the height equal to the diameter (2.1 m). The positive reactivity was evaluated at 0.035. The centre of the reactor was to be provided with four control rods, four small plates being used on the sides for fine adjustment. There was nothing special about all the other equipment. The reactor design was checked by means of the computations described in the literature for similar reactors. From the chemical and technological standpoints, several methods were investigated for obtaining metallic uranium, heavy water and graphite; analytical methods were worked out for the microanalysis of contaminants in these materials and in the structural materials. Upon completion of preparatory work, the engineering phase of building the reactor commenced.

This reactor was to have served as a means of research to help obtain further necessary knowledge and physical data, and to train specialists. As can well be realized, Czechoslovakian science, engineering and production were facing a large and difficult problem in the solution of which it is impossible to rule out any and all mistakes. The problem entailed extensive work in several branches of industry, and mainly problems which the scientists, the engineers,

Original language: Russian.

and the industrialists of several other countries had already solved. Such a path, when one starts from the very beginning, is a long one, especially if one has to rely strictly on one's own resources; and it often calls for obtaining data already known to science and engineering, but not published as yet.

At this time, the Soviet Union, in its desire to develop international co-operation in research in the field of nuclear physics made an important decision. On January 17, 1955, the Soviet Government offered its assistance to Czechoslovakia and to several other people's democratic governments. This offer, even now, is helping Czechoslovakia to overcome the initial difficulties encountered in developing, within the borders of our republic, a proper basis for reactor research, in order to avoid mistakes, to utilize Soviet experience, and to conduct research at the prevalent world level. This circumstance will undoubtedly also reduce the time needed before we can use atomic energy for power generation. Soviet help is not attended with any political or economic demands, and is a fine example of the noble mutual help among the lands where socialism prevails, for their self-development. The Soviet Union offers, without charge to Czechoslovakia and the other people's democracies, her scientific and technical papers on reactors and particle accelerators; moreover, in the very near future, the USSR will send the equipment needed, as well as scientific and technical workers, to help assemble and start them. In addition, the Soviet Union will give Czechoslovakia the required quantity of pure fissionable material and will extend substantial co-operation in training more Czechoslovakian specialists.

The Czechoslovakian government committee for research and utilization of atomic energy for peaceful purposes has set up an institute in which the present organizations in this field are grouped, and in which a reactor and cyclotron will be built. The research reactor which Czechoslovakia will receive uses slow neutrons, has a power of 2000 kw, and operates on enriched fissionable materials. The reactor will have equipment for the irradiation of test samples, and for all work in neutron physics; in connection with it a laboratory will be built, equipped with mechanical and automatic equipment, for work with highly radioactive materials. The other important device for physical investigation in the field of nuclear physics, which we shall receive from the Soviet Union, is a cyclotron which accelerates particles to an energy of 25 Mev. The institute will serve as research centre whose work will serve as a basis for developing nuclear power in Czechoslovakia.

The substantial acceleration of the development and utilization of nuclear physics, which has been made easier by the Soviet Union's help, bears witness to the importance of international co-operation. Co-operation between scientists the world over is an important moving force in the development of science, and an important factor in the maintenance of the values of human culture and civilization. Naturally, while there is a threat of atomic war, these fields of science which are capable of bringing immeasureable benefits to human society can not develop fully and freely. These conclusions have led Czechoslovakia to give its unstinted support to the international exchange of experience in the field of energy utilization for peaceful purposes, and to strive for the goal wherein science and engineering the world over will fully apply themselves to the utilization of atomic energy for peaceful purposes.

In the present significant times all of humanity enters a new era—the atomic energy era. It now rests on the scientists and engineers of the whole world to determine how soon the people will receive everything that the utilization of atomic energy for peaceful purposes can give them. It is also up to them that this important discovery be not utilized for military purposes and that, instead it give everything for the good of mankind.

With those goals in mind, in the interest of realizing the best traditions of true humanism and science we fully support international co-operation and the exchange of experience which will enable us to reach these goals in the shortest possible time.

Record of Proceedings of Session 24

SATURDAY AFTERNOON, 20 AUGUST 1955

President: Mr. H. J. Bhabha (India)

Scientific Secretaries: Messrs. J. Gaunt, I. Ulehla and A. Salam

PROGRAMME

24.1 International Co-operation in the Peaceful Uses of Atomic Energy

The PRESIDENT: I call upon Mr. Lavrishchev of the Soviet Union to present paper P/619 on "Assistance of the Soviet Union to other countries in the peaceful application of atomic energy."

Mr. A. N. LAVRISHCHEV (USSR) read P/619 as follows:

In order to contribute to the development of international co-operation in the peaceful uses of atomic energy, the Soviet Government has decided to give scientific, technical and operational assistance to the People's Republic of China, the Polish People's Republic, the Czechoslovak Republic, the German Democratic Republic, the Romanian People's Republic, the People's Republic of Bulgaria and the Hungarian People's Republic in the establishment of scientific centres for the development of research in nuclear physics and the peaceful uses of atomic energy.

The Soviet Union regards this aid as a complex of measures designed to ensure that in future each recipient country will be able to develop its own research on the peaceful uses of atomic energy, independently of any other country.

The experience of the Soviet Union shows that if mastery of atomic energy is to be achieved, the first essential is that the specialists should be equipped with modern apparatus for the necessary scientific research and experimentation, i.e., with experimental nuclear reactors and accelerators.

The Soviet Union's offer of assistance in the peaceful uses of atomic energy was accepted by all the countries concerned. Between March and June 1955 delegations of the above countries, including eminent scientists and engineers, visited the Soviet Union.

In discussions with these delegations, detailed attention was given to the problems connected with the construction in the countries referred to of experimental nuclear reactors and accelerators of elementary particles, and to other problems relating to the organization of scientific research in nuclear physics and the use of radioactive isotopes in these countries.

Members of the delegations were given the opportunity to acquaint themselves with the scientific research being carried on in the Soviet Union in the peaceful uses of atomic energy, and with functioning nuclear reactors and accelerators of elementary particles.

In the Leningrad Physico-Technical Institute of the Academy of Sciences of the USSR, scientists of the countries receiving assistance from the Soviet Union observed the operation of a cyclotron and work being carried out with it. In the Physical Institute of the Academy of Sciences of the Ukrainian SSR at Kiev they watched work being done on the adjustment of a new cyclotron about to be started up. At the Kharkov Physico-Technical Institute of the Academy of Sciences of the Ukrainian SSR, the scientists were shown linear accelerators in operation. At the Moscow State University they were shown an operating experimental nuclear reactor using enriched uranium with ordinary water as moderator and coolant. At one of the laboratories of the Academy of Sciences of the USSR, scientists from China were shown an experimental reactor using heavy water as moderator.

Apart from the above installations, prototypes of which were recommended by Soviet scientists for design and construction in the countries receiving aid from the Soviet Union, the visiting scientists also familiarized themselves, in the course of the negotiations conducted with reference to scientific and technical assistance, with other work being carried out in the USSR in the sphere of nuclear physics and radiochemistry.

At Professor V. I. Veksler's laboratory in the Physical Institute of the Academy of Sciences of the USSR, the scientists examined an operating synchrotron designed to accelerate electrons to the energy of 250 Mev.

All the delegations visited the functioning atomic power station of the Academy of Sciences of the USSR. Many scientist members of the delegations also acquainted themselves with the work being carried out by Soviet scientific research institutions on the application of radioactive isotopes in various branches of science and technology, with the practical use of radioactive isotopes and with methods of fine radiochemical analysis.

After familiarizing themselves with the operation of accelerators and atomic reactors, members of the delegations discussed with Soviet specialists types of experimental atomic reactors and accelerators recommended by Soviet scientists for construction in their countries.

The Soviet scientists' recommendations were accepted by all the delegations of the countries concerned, and on the basis of these proposals agreements were concluded between the Soviet Union and the countries referred to. Under these scientific and technical assistance agreements, the Soviet Union will design and manufacture for Poland, Czechoslovakia, Romania, Hungary, Bulgaria and the German Democratic Republic 2000-kw nuclear reactors for the production of isotopes, and cyclotrons for the production of protons, deuterons and alpha particles with energy up to 25 Mev. By means of an alternative system of operation, using a phasotron, these same installations are capable of accelerating protons up to the energy of 30 Mev. A description of the reactor was given in a paper delivered by Mr. Y. G. Nikolayev at this Conference on 12 August. Work on the design of this equipment has already been put in hand. It will be delivered by the Soviet Union complete and installed with all the necessary instruments and apparatus. Specialists from the countries receiving these atomic reactors and accelerators will take part in the work of installing them.

In addition to carrying out this installation work, specialists from the Soviet Union will also give assistance in the adjustment, starting and operation of the atomic reactors and accelerators.

The nuclear reactors accepted for construction in the countries referred to uses enriched uranium with 10 per cent uranium-235 content as fuel, and ordinary water as moderator and coolant. A feature of the design is the provision of a large number of channels for the irradiation of samples of different types, including biological objects, and for the production of radioactive isotopes. The reactor can also be used for the engineering and physical testing of materials and for studying their behaviour under irradiation of varying intensity.

Each nuclear reactor is provided with a "hot" laboratory, equipped with manipulators for work with highly radioactive materials.

For the People's Republic of China an experimental nuclear reactor of thermal power up to 6500 kw is being designed. If necessary, the power of the reactor can be increased to 10,000 kw. It is designed for operation with uranium rods containing 2 per cent uranium-235, and heavy water as moderator and coolant. The design of this reactor is on view in the Soviet exhibit.

A cyclotron of the type described above is also being designed for the People's Republic of China.

In the construction of atomic reactors, a feature particularly stressed is a design permitting the simultaneous execution of the greatest possible number of experiments. For example, each reactor will be provided with 10 neutron beam ports.

The excess reactivity of the reactors is such that they can be used for the production of a large number of different types of radioactive isotopes. Using only half their excess reactivity, the nuclear reactors being designed for Poland, Czechoslovakia, Hungary, Romania, Bulgaria and the German Democratic Republic will each be able to produce such isotopes as radioactive cobalt in quantities up to 1500 curies per month and radioactive sodium in quantities up to 5000 curies per hour.

Thus the atomic reactors which are being designed by the Soviet Union for the above countries will enable them to produce many radioactive isotopes in quantities amply sufficient to meet all their requirements.

The production of radioactive isotopes by the reactors which are being constructed in the countries referred to will create the necessary conditions for the extensive application of radioactive isotopes in industry, medicine, agriculture and various branches of science and engineering.

It is well known, and has again been illustrated in some of the papers read at the present Conference, that radioactive isotopes can be used very effectively in medicine for the diagnosis and treatment for many diseases, and are already being widely used for treatment by medical establishments.

With their own atomic reactors of the above types, China, Poland, Czechoslovakia, Romania, Bulgaria, Hungary and the German Democratic Republic will be able to make extensive use of radioactive cobalt for the treatment of malignant tumours and of radioactive phosphorus for the treatment of certain diseases of the blood; they will be able to introduce into the practice of their medical institutes the use of radioactive iodine for the clinical diagnosis and treatment of diseases of the thyroid gland, and of radioactive sodium for the study of the permeability of blood vessel walls, the speed of blood circulation, the supply of blood to the organs, etc.

Using radioactive isotopes, biologists and agriculturalists will be able to carry out research impossible by any other method. By observing the path of tracer atoms we can now, as you know, follow the stages by which plants assimilate various elements introduced by fertilizers, and can determine what type of nourishment a plant most needs, and at what time. This opens up new possibilities for raising crop yields.

Radioactive isotopes are also being used successfully for food conservation, for the prevention of sprouting in potatoes and so forth.

Radioactive isotopes can also be used to test the quality of welding and casting work, to measure the thickness of many articles and the density of various materials, and to measure the levels of liquids or gas in vessels, for example in branches of production where measurements by the usual means are dangerous to the personnel carrying them out.

Until work on the construction and start-up of the atomic reactors has been completed, all the countries receiving assistance from the Soviet Union will be able to obtain radioactive isotopes produced in the Soviet Union.

Thus all these countries will be able to conduct research on the application of radioactive isotopes even before their own experimental atomic reactors have begun to operate and before their own production of radioactive isotopes has been organized. Radioactive isotopes are being supplied to these countries without any restrictions or special conditions whatsoever, on exactly the same terms as ordinary chemicals.

The Soviet Union will supply these countries with natural uranium, thorium, uranium-235, uranium-233, plutonium, tritium and heavy water in the quantities needed by their scientists for their physical and radiochemical research work.

With supplies of these substances and facilities for obtaining radioactive isotopes from the Soviet Union, the countries referred to will be able to develop their work in nuclear physics and radiochemistry at once, under favourable conditions, without waiting for the completion of the atomic reactors and accelerators.

Under the agreements concluded, the Soviet Union will also offer assistance in the training of the necessary scientific and technical personnel in these countries.

Soviet specialists will train not only students but also persons who have completed courses of higher education but have no experience of work with atomic reactors and accelerators.

Physicists and radiochemists from China, Poland, Czechoslovakia, Bulgaria, Hungary, Romania and the German Democratic Republic will be given the opportunity to acquire practical experience of work in nuclear physics, radiochemistry and the application of atomic energy at the Soviet Union's experimental installations in the physical and chemical institutes of the Academy of Sciences of the USSR, the Academy of Sciences of the Ukrainian SSR and other higher educational establishments in the Soviet Union.

Scientists from the above countries will be able

both to carry out their own researches, using the Soviet Union's reactors and accelerators and to participate in work being carried out by Soviet scientists.

To stimulate work on the application of radioactive isotopes in other countries, the Soviet Union is not only supplying isotopes and the necessary radiometric equipment, but has also organized courses of training on the technique of work with radioactive isotopes and on the handling of the various types of apparatus, instruments and devices used in such work.

The Soviet Union is also planning to supply the above-named countries with scientific information and technical literature on the peaceful uses of atomic energy.

The Soviet Union does not look on the assistance it is offering in the peaceful uses of atomic energy as a commercial undertaking. Although it has spent enormous sums on the development of atomic reactors and accelerators, the necessary scientific and technical information and the experience it has gained are being made available to other countries free of charge. These countries will pay only the actual cost of manufacture of the equipment to be supplied to them under the agreements concluded.

The assistance received from the Soviet Union will open up excellent opportunities for the development of a modern physical science in the countries concerned.

The experimental atomic reactors which are being built in these countries are the first necessary step on the road to the construction of atomic power plants. To be able to solve the more complex problems in engineering and physics, scientists must first have acquired practical experience in the construction of atomic reactors and the organization of the general intricate machinery of atomic plant layouts.

Thanks to the atomic reactors at present under construction, the countries receiving assistance from the Soviet Union will in future be able to design and construct atomic power stations more speedily and with less difficulty.

The Soviet Government has also expressed its willingness to consider furnishing assistance in the development of scientific research on the peaceful uses of atomic energy to a larger number of countries. The Soviet Union attaches great importance to the development of wide international co-operation.

In his message to the Conference, Mr. Bulganin, President of the Council of Ministers of the USSR, expressed the hope that this scientific and technical Conference would mark a substantial advance in the development of international co-operation in the peaceful uses of atomic energy.

The Soviet Government would like to see such conferences and meetings on the peaceful uses of atomic energy held regularly in future.

Mr. W. F. Libby (USA) read paper P/805, "International co-operation in atomic developments", as follows:

We have had a momentous and fruitful two weeks together at this first International Conference on the Peaceful Uses of Atomic Energy. The benefits of this meeting have been great. Scientists knowing the same things separately have increased their total knowledge in conferring with one another. Although possibly unable to tell one another anything new, the fact that another scientist has discovered the same knowledge working independently constitutes the final necessary scientific proof of essential truths. In this way has our total knowledge been greatly increased by this Conference. Let us hope that we shall meet again, perhaps in three years or so, to describe the progress made in the interval.

President Eisenhower, in his memorable address to the General Assembly of the United Nations on 8 December 1953, proposed that an international atomic energy agency be established under the aegis of the United Nations. He proposed such an agency as an instrument to spread throughout the world knowledge which had been acquired by those nations with advanced atomic energy programs. Last September the United States and a number of other nations, believing the world-wide sharing of atomic knowledge to be imperative, agreed to press forward with the creation of an international agency. Since that time, a draft statute has been prepared and discussed by those nations, and it is my understanding that this draft statute will be ready for consideration in the immediate future. These preliminary discussions were held by Australia, Belgium, Canada, France, Portugal, the United Kingdom, the Union of South Africa and the United States of America. However, the United States has taken steps to spread atomic knowledge in advance of the formation of the international agency.

During the last six months the United States has been disclosing to the world a good deal of its fund of information gained through the American people's immense outlay of time, treasure and energies.

We hope that the accomplishments of this Conference will increase the tempo of international co-operation in atomic energy. We are certain that this Conference has contributed in large measure to an improved understanding on the part of all nations of the present and future prospects for the peaceful uses of atomic energy. Such understanding is certain to be followed by constructive, co-operative action to develop these uses throughout the world.

Most representatives are aware of the effort which the United States is making to assist other peoples to develop their own atomic energy programs. However, the extent and the variety of the measures which we are taking may not be known fully to all. I should like to review the present status and future possibilities of American co-operation in the training of technical personnel and the exchange of technical data, materials and equipment. By bringing this to the attention of representatives now, we hope that in the months to come there will be a marked increase in the opportunities for co-operative endeavours presented to the United States.

Forty-seven countries now receive shipments of radioisotopes from Oak Ridge Laboratory—many of them since 1947. It is intended to facilitate this foreign distribution by an early substantial liberalization of the regulations applied to our shipments.

For some time the Oak Ridge Institute of Nuclear Studies has been offering a course in the handling of radioisotopes. In May of this year a special four-weeks course began at Oak Ridge with thirty scientists and technicians from twenty-one nations in attendance. The training which they received was identical to that given to American scientists at the same school. In the future a substantial percentage of the total enrollment in the course in radiation techniques will be reserved for students from countries other than the United States. The next course for foreign students will be offered in October.

There are many training courses offered in the United States on the utilization of atomic energy in the fields of biology, medicine and agriculture. These courses are open to students from all over the world. For example, pre- and post-doctorate training of from one to two years will be provided at Brookhaven National Laboratory, Argonne National Laboratory, Argonne Cancer Research Hospital and the United States Atomic Energy Commission projects at the University of California, the University of California at Los Angeles and the University of Rochester School of Medicine and Dentistry. Courses in the medical application of atomic energy are available at the Harvard University Medical Physics Laboratory, the New England Deaconess Cancer Research Laboratory and the Western Reserve University School of Medicine. The training offered by these institutions provides six to eighteen months of active participation with a research group. During this time the students gain experience under the direction of outstanding scientists in using the new tools which atomic energy has provided for their professions. American universities also give instruction in industrial hygiene for industries dealing with atomic materials in industrial medicine, and in radiological physics.

In the majority of instances the students pay for their training; however, when funds for training are not available, it may be possible to arrange for financial assistance through programs administered by the Department of State.

Many countries at the present time badly need more people possessing the basic technical training necessary for participation in specialized nuclear energy programs. Arrangements accordingly have been made for outstanding foreign students with scientific aptitude to receive one or two years of such basic training in American universities.

A few weeks ago in Washington, I had the pleasure of welcoming twenty-three distinguished physicians and surgeons from eleven countries who were about to begin a five weeks' tour of American cancer hospitals and laboratories. During the tour these doctors became acquainted with the research and clinical uses of radioisotopes and other weapons of atomic medicine in the battle against cancer. Two similar tours are planned for this fall.

As a means of disseminating information resulting from the programs of nuclear science in the United States, the United States Atomic Energy Commission has assembled technical libraries for presentation to those nations which desire them. A library which, at present, occupies the equivalent of 250 feet of shelf space, consists of about 6500 Atomic Energy Commission research and development reports, 28 bound volumes of the Commission's *National Nuclear Energy Series* and 6 other casebound books published by the Commission, 11 volumes of the Commission's journal, *Abstracts of Nuclear Science,* which contain over 50,000 abstracts of the open literature on nuclear energy published by the Commission everywhere in the world, and 55,000 catalogue cards indexing the entire collection. Periodic additions are made to these libraries. The United States only asks that the countries receiving these libraries provide in return their collections of similar official unclassified papers. The collection now on display at the United States exhibit has been given to the United Nations Library here in Geneva. A collection of works on particular aspects of nuclear science has already been provided to the European Center for Nuclear Research.

Since an increasing level of power generation is one of the prime factors in improving living standards, it is hardly surprising that the interest of people throughout the world is focussed on the utilization of nuclear energy in the production of electric power.

Remembering that this use of the atom is new, we must caution that the development of conventional power sources should not be neglected. For the next few years the atom will not be a major source of power. It is in the future—perhaps ten years from now—that we see it taking its rightful place as a primary source of power.

It is the aim of the United States to help other countries to proceed, as rapidly as possible, towards the economic production of electric power from the atom. Harnessing a nuclear chain reaction, however, is a highly complex undertaking. The design and operation of a reactor requires scientific and technical personnel who are familiar with this new and complicated technology.

In recognition of this need, the United States has established a School of Nuclear Science and Engineering at Argonne National Laboratory near Chicago. The purpose of the school is to provide advance instruction in reactor technology. The School opened in March of this year with thirty students from nineteen countries in addition to the American students in attendance. During the seven months' course, the students receive their practical experi-mental laboratory instruction in reactor physics, reactor engineering, the metallurgy of reactor materials, the chemistry of the lanthanide and actinide elements, the principles of separation processes, instruments, remote control, experimental reactor physics and analytical procedures. A second course will begin in November, and a third course next March. When present plans for expanding the training facilities are fulfilled, the school will be capable of accommodating 120 students. When these men return to their homes, they will form nuclei around which may develop indigenous groups of atomic specialists.

The Government of the United States has concluded agreements for co-operation in the civil uses of atomic energy with more than 25 nations and is prepared to conclude similar agreements with many more. The agreements call for exchanges of information on the application of atomic energy to biology, medicine and agriculture. In addition, under these agreements, the United States aids in the construction of research reactors, will contribute half the cost of the first reactor in each country and furnish the necessary fuel for these reactors. Nearly a year ago, the President authorized the Atomic Energy Commission to allocate 100 kg of enriched uranium-235 for use in research reactors abroad, and last June he increased this amount to 200 kg. Agreements for the sale of heavy water have been made with a number of countries at a price of $28 per pound. The enriched uranium used in these research reactors, containing as much as 20 per cent uranium-235, is to be leased at 4 per cent per annum on the basis of $25 per gram of contained U^{235}. A charge at this same rate—$25 per gram—will be made for U^{235} consumed. Ordinary uranium metal will be sold at $40 per kg. All of these prices and values are estimated so that the United States Government neither gains nor loses financially.

Research reactors, as you know, have many uses in themselves. These include production of radioisotopes, medical therapy, solid-state physics research, studies on nuclear properties of matter such as cross sections for capture or scattering of neutrons, gamma-ray spectrum induced by neutron capture and radiation attenuation, reactor physics measurements and reactor engineering experiments. The swimming pool reactor, which was shown at the United States exhibit and which has been sold and transferred today to the Swiss Government, is one of the types of research reactors which the United States will help to build.

I should like to emphasize that each of these bilateral agreements states that it is the hope and expectation of both parties that the initial agreement for co-operation will lead to consideration of further co-operation extending to the design, construction and operation of power reactors.

The United States has no wish that any nation be dependent on American technicians for the operation of a nuclear power program. Experience in the operation of research reactors should provide a reservoir of trained engineers and scientists in the countries where such specialists are now lacking.

President Eisenhower, in his notable speech of last June 11, said: "If the technical and material resources of a single nation should not appear adequate to make effective use of a research reactor, we would support a voluntary grouping of the resources of several nations within a single region to acquire and operate it together." There are regions throughout the world where governments well might consider the establishment of such co-operative ventures in the operation of research reactors.

The following countries have negotiated agreements for co-operation with the United States, received technical libraries or have had students participating in an active way in one or more of our training programs: Argentina, Australia, Austria, Belgium, Brazil, Burma, Canada, Chile, Republic of China, Colombia, Cuba, Denmark, Egypt, Finland, France, Germany, Greece, Guatemala, India, Indonesia, Israel, Italy, Japan, Republic of Korea, Lebanon, Mexico, The Netherlands, Pakistan, Peru, Philippines, Portugal, Spain, Sweden, Switzerland, Thailand, Turkey, Union of South Africa, United Kingdom, Uruguay and Venezuela.

Making the atom serve man is a long and laborious task. Atomic scientists and technicians must first be trained and given experience. This is the very first step. Experimentation and development work must be carried on continuously. The job is not a short one, but with large measure of patience, faith and imagination we can confidently anticipate the time when all men will realize the full potential of the atom.

The PRESIDENT: Item 24.1 is now open for comments. The programme has allowed twenty minutes for these comments. As we have more speakers than we can call upon in the time allowed in the programme, I propose to add the ten minutes allowed for Chairman's remarks in item 24.2 to the twenty minutes allotted to us in the programme for item 24.1. Even so, I fear that I shall be unable to call upon many of the delegates who have signified their desire to make comments on this item, and I shall call upon the speakers in the order in which their requests have been received. I call first upon Sir John Cockcroft from the United Kingdom.

Sir John COCKCROFT (UK): The United Kingdom delegation has been interested to hear of the plans of the United States and the Soviet Union for promoting international collaboration in atomic energy. We recognize the great help we have received in the past, particularly from the United States and Canada. We are equally willing to help in promoting such collaboration in the future, and we have presented a paper (P/1080) for the records of the Conference which describes what we have done in the past and expect to do in the future. In particular, we have established schools for isotopes

and reactor technology, and we welcome foreign students to our courses. We expect the reactor school will soon be much enlarged and that it will be supplemented by university post-graduate training open to students from other countries.

In Europe, we have co-operated with other countries in the founding of the European Atomic Energy Society, to promote regional and technical discussions of our problems by experts at the working level, and this has proved to be very valuable. In this way, we are helping to establish the normal pattern of collaboration in the scientific world in our subject.

Our present Conference will have a great effect in stimulating such interchanges in the future. We look forward also when our power programme is established to welcoming engineers from other countries to give them the benefit of our operating experience and actual costs, so that they will be able to judge the time at which it will be worth while to introduce nuclear power into their own countries.

We hope also that the other method of communication in science, by interchange of visits, will now become more general in our own field of work. We are looking forward to welcoming many delegates at Harwell next week and we are planning to make interesting return visits.

Our delegates have enjoyed this Conference and we have heard with pleasure of President Eisenhower's suggestion that another conference of this kind should be held. Speaking as scientists, we would welcome this in three or four years when we have accumulated more experience in this rapidly developing field.

Mr. CARRILLO (Mexico): Today marks the close of a Conference unique in history. The Mexican delegation came here in the hope of acquiring information which would enable it to use the knowledge of the most advanced countries in this field for the promotion of the Mexican people's well-being. We are leaving here with a feeling of profound satisfaction.

Because of the nature of nuclear research and the present stage of development of Mexican economy and industry, our work in Mexico has been limited to purely scientific study, to basic research. We are leaving satisfied and grateful. We agree with the speaker who said that the most important thing about this Conference is the fact that it has taken place.

It would seem at the end of this fortnight's work that scientists have more confidence in mankind than mankind has in scientists. The course of our discussions shows that there are good men here, men without fear. We are living through a very interesting phase of peace. Peace is undoubtedly the ideal of mankind. But to what extent can a peace founded mainly on fear be considered to fulfil that ideal? We consider that the ideal of mankind is not a material peace based on fear, but a spiritual peace based on mutual respect, on respect for the dignity of of man and respect for the dignity of nations.

The men of science who have been working here for the last two weeks have shown a respect for each other which has undoubtedly impressed the whole world. They have spoken with the traditional generosity of scientists the world over; they have spoken without fear; they have ranged over the future of the problems involved without giving any impression they are beset by a great fear. We believe that now as never before, mankind, thanks to science, has a wonderful opportunity to bring about an international settlement based not simply on material values, but on moral values, values which, like science itself, are not exclusive property of any one region of the world—another fact demonstrated at this unique Conference.

We wish to express our gratitude to all those responsible for the success of the Conference: to Mr. Bhabha, the President, to the representatives of the United Nations and to all the scientists who have taken part and whom we have come to know better. We leave with the memory that all the scientists, irrespective of their nationality, gave us their hand when we asked for it, gave us information when we requested it and gave us a confidence with which we shall return to our country, a quiet confidence that the work of the men of science who have foregathered here will make the world a better place to live in.

Mr. SHULKIN (Poland): The matters dealt with in the very interesting and comprehensive papers delivered by Mr. Lavrishchev and Mr. Libby are of great importance for the further development of the highly important science of nuclear physics. International co-operation in the peaceful uses of atomic energy is the goal to which we all aspire; and it is a goal which will, I hope, be fully achieved. That is best shown by our Conference, which has undoubtedly done much to draw us closer together and to promote mutual understanding and the exchange of experience among scientists from all parts of the world. The papers we have heard show that the scientific and technical assistance already being rendered is developing very successfully. This will create favourable conditions for extending substantially the range of scientific research, for the good of science and of mankind as a whole.

More specifically, let me say that the facilities now being created, thanks to assistance from the Soviet Union, in Poland and other countries, such as the People's Republic of China, Czechoslovakia, Hungary, Bulgaria, Romania and the German Democratic Republic will in the next 12 or 18 months make it possible—as Mr. Lavrishchev pointed out in his paper—to develop scientific research on a very much larger scale.

In my view, rapid and fruitful progress in this branch of science and in its application to the needs of man will be a characteristic feature of the period we are entering. The necessary condition for this,

however, is not only assistance, but complete co-operation and mutual understanding, and generous and concerted efforts by the scientists of all countries, great and small. The consolidation of the results achieved at this Conference must therefore be considered a matter of very great importance; and we must hope that in the future even closer co-operation between scientists from all parts of the world will be realized, with the help of the United Nations and through the efforts of all peoples and all scientists. For my part, I can assure you that the Polish Government and Polish scientists will do everything possible and necessary for co-operation and for the achievement of this high aim.

It seems to me that it would be most fitting for us to ask Mr. Hammarskjold, the Secretary-General of the United Nations, and Professor Bhabha, the President of our Conference, to place this important point on record as one of the achievements of the Conference and to emphasize our common wish for further co-operation and for ever deeper understanding between all scientists.

The events preceeding the Conference and the Conference itself show that we are on the right road, on the road which we have to follow for the progress of science. About two months ago a large number of scientists, from many countries, had the opportunity of participating in a session of the Academy of Sciences of the USSR devoted to problems of nuclear physics and its application in biology, medicine, technology etc., and also of visiting important Soviet laboratories and institutes. At this Conference we have received a kind invitation from the United Kingdom delegation to visit the research establishment at Harwell. It is to be hoped that in the future there will be even closer links, even more extensive co-operation of this kind, for such links and such co-operation are a necessary prerequisite for the rapid and effective development of science and serve the cause of peace and understanding among nations.

Our Conference is nearing its end, and we have every reason to consider that the results achieved justify us in regarding the future with optimism. Our further efforts should probably be directed along the following lines:

1. We must create the best possible conditions for the exchange of scientific information and experience.

2. We must organize visits by scientists of the various countries, on a reciprocal basis, and create the widest possible opportunities for young specialists to attend training courses at the leading scientific centres.

3. We must overcome the difficulties which still exist in certain areas in obtaining the measuring apparatus necessary for scientific work.

4. We must organize further scientific international meetings and conferences for the thorough and comprehensive study of a number of more narrowly delimited problems, such as the use of radioisotopes in medicine or agriculture.

A very important problem, which will need careful discussion, is the possibly dangerous influence of radioactive radiation on conditions of development in the organic world. I hope that Professor Bhabha, our President, who has guided our Conference with such ability, will touch on these questions in his closing address. I am sure that in his report to the United Nations on the results of our Conference Mr. Hammarskjold will consider it desirable to mention our views.

In conclusion, I should like to assure you that the scientists of Poland, who have every possible facility for the intensive development of scientific research in friendly co-operation with scientists throughout the world, will do their best to continue to make their contribution to the progress of world science.

Mr. TATSUKE (Japan): The speakers who have preceded me have already said everything I had intended to say. I shall therefore be very brief.

On behalf of the Japanese delegation I should like to say in a few words, on the occasion of the last meeting of this historic Conference, how happy we are to see that all the participating countries are firmly resolved to co-operate, in pursuance of the resolution adopted at the ninth session of the United Nations General Assembly, in developing the peaceful use of atomic energy.

We have no doubt that the aim of the Conference has been very fully achieved in an atmosphere of unprecedented cordiality and good feeling.

The Japanese delegation, convinced that the Conference has succeeded in laying a firm foundation for international co-operation in this field, would like to express its most sincere hope that this Conference will give rise to other meetings under United Nations auspices, and that it will lead to the setting up of an international atomic agency.

Before concluding, I should like to express my sincere thanks to the Secretariat and to all those who have contributed to the success of the Conference.

Mr. SAZIC (Yugoslavia): I think we all agree in recognizing the unusual importance of our Conference and of the results communicated in the course of our meetings; the only question is whether we are yet fully able to assess adequately the importance of these results and all the potentialities inherent in them.

It may, however, already be asserted without any exaggeration that the results of the Conference constitute a great contribution by science to the peace and prosperity of mankind.

This contribution by science to peace has been expressed in the common interest and daily practical co-operation of a large number of men of science, who have come here from all parts of the world, from countries of different social systems and at different levels of economic and technical development; and this means that our Conference—despite the disputes which trouble the world—has exercised a definite and undoubtedly salutory influence on the climate of international relations, one which has resulted in complete agreement of views being reached. It has laid the foundations for fruitful future co-operation in this field. Because of these results, in particular, my delegation, realizing as it does the permanent nature of the problems connected with the peaceful uses of atomic energy and their increasing importance for the development of the life of nations, will consider with the greatest interest, and will fully support any proposal to continue our efforts to develop these fruitful methods of work.

We met here to prevent the achievements of science from being used for purposes of hideous destruction and to help to create a bright future for mankind. This Conference has indeed opened up broad avenues of progress for humanity; more specifically, it has given us every reason to hope for a solution of the problems posed by the existing disproportion between levels of economic and technical development, i.e., by the situation of the underdeveloped countries and areas.

In conclusion, I have the honour to read to this Conference a message addressed to it by Marshal Josip Broz Tito, the President of the Federal People's Republic of Yugoslavia, on the occasion of its closing session:

"The Government of my country, and I myself, have followed the work of the International Conference on the Peaceful Uses of Atomic Energy with the greatest interest. I am deeply convinced that the positive results achieved in the course of the Conference are a first step towards further progress in fruitful international co-operation in this field, and that they fully justify those hopes and expectations of mankind which found expression in the course of the ninth session of the United Nations General Assembly. These results have further strengthened Yugoslavia's conviction that general co-operation, founded on democratic principles and on equality of rights within the framework and in the spirit of the United Nations and of the Charter, constitutes the best means of ensuring the harmonious development of international relations and of eliminating the terrible danger which the possible abuse of the great discoveries of contemporary science would represent for all mankind. For this reason, Yugoslavia will continue to give its full support to any initiative aimed at developing international co-operation in this and other fields, considering that such a policy will contribute to peace and to the favourable development of international relations.

"Seen in this light, the Geneva Conference has been more than a gathering of eminent scientists and Government representatives; it has assumed the character of an organ of moral and scientific control over the new forces which men have mastered, a control designed to ensure their use for the greater happiness and prosperity of mankind.

"I send my cordial greetings and my best wishes to the members of the Conference, and thank them for the generous efforts they have made to realize the Conference's high objectives.

"JOSIP BROZ TITO
"President of the Federal People's Republic of Yugoslavia"

Mr. G. RANDERS (Norway): Fellow atomic energy scientists, if any of you have become slightly discouraged in your aspirations for international co-operation by the immensity and formidability of this Conference, it may perhaps be some comfort and encouragement to be reminded that actual scientific technical co-operation is, in the end, a very simple and quiet process. For this reason I feel it may be worthwhile to return to the not-so-new story of the four and a half years' old co-operation which has been established on a modest scale between Norway and The Netherlands.

This co-operation, as most of you will know, began in 1951 when we had practically finished a heavy-water natural uranium reactor in Norway, all except for having the uranium. It turned out that The Netherlands had, by foresight, a stock of uranium from before the war, and in a very co-operative spirit they offered to give us this for use in the Norwegian reactor. As a result, a contract was signed in March, 1951, combining the atomic energy efforts of The Netherlands and Norway in one single effort. This was organized in the form of a laboratory called The Joint Establishment for Nuclear Energy Research at Kjeller, near Oslo, Norway. The laboratory was run by a joint commission of three scientific members from The Netherlands and three from Norway, and the staff is a combination of Dutch and Norwegian scientists. The money comes from the combined coffers of the Ministries of Finance in The Netherlands and in Norway. In addition, we have a considerable number of foreign members on the staff since, from the beginning, this project opened its doors to all kinds of interested people: the general public, industry and other countries.

Two years ago, in 1953, the world's first International Conference on Reactor Technology was called, and it was attended by eighteen nations.

Until this year the Kjeller reactor has been the only centre of this combination of effort. This year, however, The Netherlands Government has started a centre of their own for the development of atomic energy. This has led to rumours that the Norwegian-Dutch co-operation has been ruptured, and I thought this might be the right place to make it quite clear that this is not the case. On the contrary, the co-operation has been extended now to two centres, one in Norway and one in The Netherlands. The contract, which has recently been signed between The Netherlands and Norway prolonging the old one, calls for full co-ordination of effort between the two countries in this field, for the continued joint operation of the establishment at Kjeller, and for the pooling of all patents in this field. In the near future we will have a programme of reactor building which, we hope, will give us access within a couple of years to four reactors: a 20-megawatt materials testing reactor, which will be built shortly in The Netherlands under a contract agreement between the United States and The Netherlands Government; a 10-megawatt steam-producing boiling heavy-water reactor, which will be built on an industrial site in Norway; a 250-kilowatt suspension reactor experiment, now under development in The Netherlands; and finally our old reactor which has been running continuously for four and a half years.

Our future programme will also involve the continuation of isotope production and sending isotopes to several countries on a common basis.

I should also like to say here that we hope to be able to extend the possibility of having foreign members on our staff. We do not consider these usually as pupils or guests; they come and join our staff and learn in this way how to run a small establishment, which may be of use for some of those countries which do not have large resources.

In conclusion, I should like to give the three golden rules which The Netherlands/Norwegian combination has arrived at as essential for technical co-operation between atomic energy commissions.

1. The co-operation must be based on mutual need and desire. It must not have the aspect of relations between donor and recipient.

2. The co-operation must be full, comprehensive and whole-hearted without "keep-out" signs surrounding it.

3. We feel that scientific co-operation in the long run thrives in laboratories only and not in offices nor even in public meetings.

The PRESIDENT: Our time is up, but as a special request has been made I now call upon the last speaker in this discussion Mr. Henri Medi of the Holy See, to make his comments.

Mr. H. MEDI (Holy See): The delegation of the Holy See, representing at this Conference a spiritual power which unceasingly exhorts men to use the world's God-given resources for the benefit of one and all, through the greatest possible mutual co-operation, would like to emphasize what decisive progress the present Conference has made towards the realization of item 24.1 of our agenda. The pursuit of truth, generosity in communicating results obtained, and, above all, the conviction that in this field every discovery belongs to all men, so that they may use it for their welfare, such are the distinctive features that have ensured the success of this Conference; and they remain the essential conditions for any international co-operation in the peaceful uses of atomic energy.

Of course, the terms of reference of our Conference did not cover the whole range of the problem. In particular we still need to study, and to study very closely the social and economic factors necessary to ensure a fair distribution of our new wealth, so that it may serve first and foremost the poorest and materially most under-privileged peoples. We also need a concerted effort to ensure that the upheavals which the evolution of nuclear science may well bring in its train, respect the natural rhythm of man's life and do not shatter the surest foundations of human dignity. Technology will serve this end only if the fellowship achieved in the pursuit of truth is directed towards that authentic peace which is founded on love among men.

This being said, my delegation is thankful that with the help of God the first step has now been taken along the road to the peaceful use of atomic energy, that first step for which his Holiness the Pope prayed when, some sixteen months ago, he visualized the day when we should be able to see the wise men of this world turn their brilliant discoveries of the deep forces of matter to peaceful ends alone, so as to give men cheap power to supplement their scanty resources of wealth and labour, or to correct the uneven geographical distribution of those resources—and so that medicine and agriculture might be given new tools and the peoples new sources of prosperity and well-being.

The PRESIDENT: I regret that at this point I am compelled to close this discussion because our time is up. Many delegations, including my own, will be disappointed that they will be unable to make their comments on this subject.

The meeting here discussed Item 24.2 "Education and Training of Personnel in Nuclear Energy"—see Volume 1, these Proceedings.

The PRESIDENT: We now come to the final item on the programme. Before delivering my closing address I would like to draw your attention to the messages from the President of the Council of Ministers of the Bulgarian People's Republic and from the President of the Academy of Sciences of Bulgaria, the texts of which appear in this morning's Journal. These messages were received a few days ago, after the beginning of the Conference.

I would also draw your attention to the note in this morning's Journal concerning the credentials of the representatives at the Conference, which is included as called for in the Rules of Procedure.

Fellow delegates: This Conference started with great hopes and expectations, and the good wishes of the great statesmen of our time. The eyes of the world were upon it. Now that we have come to the end of our work, we have reason to be pleased with what has been achieved. It is the unanimous view of all concerned that this Conference has succeeded beyond all hopes and expectations.

A remarkable feature of this Conference has been the scientific and objective atmosphere which has prevailed throughout. A calm and objective atmosphere is natural at scientific meetings, but I cannot remember any scientific meeting in which these qualities were more conspicuous. This is all the more

remarkable when one considers that the delegates to this Conference have come to it as the representatives of their respective countries.

This is the largest conference ever organized by the United Nations. No scientific conference of this magnitude and importance has ever been held at any place at any time. Seventy-three nations have participated, and it has been attended by 1400 delegates and nearly as many observers from academic institutions and industry. It has been covered by over 900 correspondents.

The formidable task of organizing this Conference has fallen to the Secretariat of the United Nations both in New York and in Geneva, and 738 members of its staff have been directly engaged in this operation since its initiation in January.

The documentation for this Conference alone was a huge problem. One thousand and sixty-seven scientific and technical papers were submitted, all of which will be published in the proceedings: 450 of them have been orally presented during the last fortnight. Some 16,000 pages of documents in one language alone have been printed and distributed. In addition, each document has been or will be translated into four languages. In Geneva alone over two million copies of documents have been distributed. The verbatim records of the Conference amount to approximately 3000 pages, and the entire proceedings of the Conference were translated simultaneously in four languages. The translators and interpreters have had a particularly difficult task as they have had to handle scientific and technical material with which they were unfamiliar. I mention these facts to indicate to you the enormous magnitude of the job which the Secretariat has had to handle. I am sure you would all wish me to express our great appreciation of the work done so successfully and so unobtrusively by the Secretariat.

The success of the Conference has been due in no small measure to the skill with which the scientific material has been sorted and arranged, and the excellent way in which the programmes of the various sessions have been drawn up. We owe a great debt to the Conference Secretary-General, his Deputy, and their staff of 20 scientific secretaries, who have carried out this task. They have identified themselves wholly with the spirit of the United Nations and have done their work with an impartiality and an absence of national bias which has contributed in no small measure to the success of the Conference.

Its success is also due to the spirit and the manner in which all the representatives have played their part. From the very beginning meetings have begun and ended on time, and all the speakers have adhered to the time limits set in the programme. I am told that this is by no means a usual feature of international conferences. The difference can perhaps be attributed to the circumstance that in a scientific conference such as this, each speaker has something concrete to communicate. I suppose that when one has nothing concrete to communicate, there is no inherent reason why, having started speaking, one should stop.

In my opening address I drew attention to the importance of atomic energy in the broad perspective of human history and touched briefly on some of the problems which the Conference would consider. It would be natural at this point to summarize the conclusions which have emerged in the papers which have been communicated and the discussions which have taken place. Fortunately, this task has been done for me in large measure by Sir John Cockcroft in the excellent evening lecture he delivered yesterday. I will therefore content myself with merely picking out a few highlights.

The feasibility of generating electricity by atomic energy has been demonstrated beyond doubt. Indeed, one cannot but be impressed by the very large number of fundamentally different possibilities which lie before us in the design of atomic reactors, and by the boldness and imagination with which some of these possibilities are actually being tried out. As was anticipated, the sessions on reactor technology proved to be some of the most exciting.

The economics of atomic power generation have also been greatly clarified. While the capital costs of atomic power stations are still higher by 50 to 100 per cent than those of conventional power stations of a comparable size, the fuel costs are very much less, resulting in an estimated cost of between 5 and 7 mills per kilowatt hour of electricity generated by power stations of 100 to 200 megawatts of installed capacity. There are good reasons for expecting that the capital costs will come down during the next decade, thus still further reducing the cost of electricity. Even with present costs, atomic power stations would be economically competitive with power stations of a conventional type in many areas of the world where power costs are high.

The capital and operating costs of an actual power reactor in the United States with an installed capacity of about 2000 kilowatts was given. The cost of power from this small plant worked out at between 30 and 35 mills per kilowatt hour, which is less than double the cost of power produced by coal plants of the same size. It appears that there are many parts of the world where power would be acceptable at this price and small package power plants of this type may have wide-spread uses, especially in under-developed areas.

Several countries expect atomic energy to make a substantial contribution to their electricity generation during the next two decades. Thus, it is anticipated that nuclear power will provide 40 per cent of the total electric power requirements in the United Kingdom by 1975, replacing the need for 40 million tons of coal per annum.

It is likely that in making their plans for future power development many countries have not yet seriously considered the possibility of using atomic energy, because the technical and economic information was not available. One may expect that as a direct result of the information which has been made available in this Conference many countries will review their future power requirements, and this Conference may therefore well lead to a very considerable acceleration of the rate at which atomic energy is put to use for power generation in different parts of the world during the next two decades.

It came out clearly in the course of the Conference that when the development of a wide-spread atomic power industry takes place, ample supplies of uranium and thorium to feed it will be available. A highlight of the Conference was the demonstration of the importance of thorium for the production of atomic energy and possibility of a positive gain factor in the conversion of fertile to fissile material in the thorium-U^{233} system, which was shown to be superior to the uranium-238-plutonium system in several ways. The breeding of atomic fuel in fast neutron reactors also holds out exciting possibilities on which the prototypes now being built will throw more light in the next few years.

Another remarkable feature which the Conference brought to light was the parallel work which has been done in secrecy till now in several countries. For example, no less than five countries had independently developed the same techniques for the extraction of uranium from certain ores, while data on the fission process in uranium-233, uranium-235 and plutonium had been measured independently in France, the United Kingdom, the USSR, and the United States of America, with remarkable agreement among their results.

The sessions on biology and medicine have shown the great importance of isotopes in the study of the phenomena of life. The discussions indicated that all countries were alive to the direct biological hazards of radiation and that safe tolerance doses had been established. On the other hand, the discussion of the genetic effects of radiation clearly showed that we have not yet enough knowledge on which to base definite conclusions, and that a concerted and massive research effort on this problem is required, before we can be quite sure that no suffering will be caused to future generations through the production of deleterious mutations. There is no cause for alarm. But till the matter has been fully studied and understood, it would be wise, wherever possible, not to permit people to be subjected to more than about a tenth of the dose considered safe at present. While there is a difference of opinion among scientists on this and several other subjects, it is important to note that the differences showed no national pattern.

Credit for the excellent scientific atmosphere is due to the spirit in which the representatives of all countries have participated, but it was clear from the beginning that the scientific and technical contributions of all countries could not be the same. I wish particularly to express our great debt and appreciation to those very few countries, most advanced in this field, which have so whole-heartedly and generously placed before this Conference the knowledge which they have gained during the last decade through such strenuous efforts and at such great cost. The success of the Conference has depended largely on them.

This scientific Conference, which will inevitably have far-reaching political consequences, differs in one important respect from all political conferences. Knowledge once given cannot be taken back, and in organizing this Conference the nations of the world have taken an irreversible step forward, a step from which there is no retreat. The Proceedings of this Conference with all the papers submitted to it are to be published in four languages as a permanent record of the work that has been done, and will cover no less than 16 volumes.

Mr. Hammarskjold, the Secretary-General of the United Nations, whose other important duties did not permit him, to his great regret, to attend this Conference beyond the first few days, has asked me to convey to you his congratulations on behalf of the United Nations at the achievements of this Conference, and the gratitude of the Organization to all those who have contributed to its success. According to the decision of the General Assembly the Secretary-General will have to report to it on the Conference. The Secretary-General informs me that in this report he hopes to put forward such practical proposals as seem appropriate in view of the need to follow up the work so well begun at this Conference, and in order to equip the United Nations to meet such responsibilities in this field as may grow out of developments during the next session of the General Assembly. He expresses the hope that the Secretary-General will be able to count on the continued assistance of the Advisory Committee, whose help in the preparation of this Conference has been invaluable.

One of the most important contributions of this Conference is that in this important field it has re-established the channels of communication between men of science in different countries, channels which were interrupted with the outbreak of the Second World War. It has re-established that free exchange of knowledge among men of science which is one of the greatest glories of our civilization. It is clear that this exchange of knowledge must con-

tinue, and all are universally agreed that after an appropriate period another conference of this type should be held to continue the work which we have here initiated. I am happy to inform you that I received this morning a message from Mr. Bulganin, Chairman of the Council of Ministers of the Soviet Union, which should give us great satisfaction, and which I shall now read out.

"The International Conference on the Peaceful Uses of Atomic Energy, now drawing to its close in Geneva, is a significant step towards the establishment of international co-operation in the most important field of the utilization of atomic energy for peaceful purposes. The exchange of views and information which has taken place at the Conference represents a valuable contribution to further scientific and technical progress in this field.

"This Conference will undoubtedly serve the cause of peace and make for a further relaxation of international tension. The Soviet Government congratulates all those taking part in the Conference on the success achieved and expresses the hope that international cooperation in the field of the peaceful utilization of atomic energy, which has been so successfully inaugurated at this Conference, will be continued through the regular convening of similar meetings of scientists from all countries.

"Chairman of the Council of Ministers of USSR,

"(Signed) N. Bulganin."

I am also happy to inform you that I have been informed by Admiral Strauss, the leader of the United States delegation, that he received a message a few days ago from President Eisenhower, who is highly gratified by the success of the Conference, expressing his hope that a second conference will be convened at a later date to continue this great beginning of international co-operation.

After the close of this Conference we will all return to our work, which in one way or another is connected with furthering the peaceful applications of atomic energy. We can do so now with the satisfaction that we have in our modest way helped to make this historic Conference a success, and with the knowledge and determination that our labours will be directed and used towards bettering the conditions of life for all men, wherever they may be.

I now declare this International Conference on the Peaceful Uses of Atomic Energy closed.

Evening Lectures

LIST OF LECTURES

Physical Science and Man's Position

By Niels Bohr, Denmark

It is a great privilege to be given the opportunity of addressing this assembly convened by the United Nations in order to promote international co-operation on the use, for the benefit of humanity, of the vast new energy sources made accessible by the exploration of the world of atoms. I am also grateful for the invitation to speak, as an introduction to these evening lectures at which some broader aspects of our great subject will be discussed. I shall speak about the general lesson we have learned as observers of that nature of which we ourselves are part, by studying this new field of experience.

I shall not enlarge upon the great practical consequences of the development forming the main theme of our Conference, but we are, of course, all deeply aware of the responsibility associated with any advance of our knowledge resulting in an increased mastery of the forces of nature. Indeed, in the present situation, our whole civilization is confronted with a most serious challenge demanding an adjustment of the relationship between nations to ensure that unprecedented menaces can be eliminated and that all people can strive together for the fulfilment of the promises offered by the progress of science for promoting human welfare all over our globe.

For the appreciation of the common interests and for the furthering of a spirit of mutual confidence, it may be considered a good omen that we are dealing with consequences of endeavours which know no national borders. Truly, the fruits of scientific research, which through the ages have so largely enriched our life, are a common human inheritance. Moreover, the exploration of new fields of knowledge has steadily illuminated man's position, and in atomic science, so removed from ordinary experience, we have received a lesson which points far beyond the domain of physics. In stressing the necessity for a widening of our conceptual framework for the harmonious comprehension of apparently contrasting phenomena, I feel that this lesson may contribute to a broadening of our attitude on the relationship between human societies with different cultural traditions.

It is well known that the first vague ideas of the atomic constitution of matter go back to antiquity, but it was the great progress of physics and chemistry, which followed the Renaissance, that gave these ideas a firmer basis. Until very recently, however, the atomic theory was generally considered a hypothesis for which no direct proof could ever be given.

Indeed, it was belived that our sense organs and tools, themselves composed of innumerable atoms, were far too coarse to allow the detection of individual atomic particles. Still, the marvelous development of experimental techniques has not only made it possible to observe effects in single atoms but has even given us a far-reaching insight into the structure of the atoms themselves.

The development of modern atomic science is the outcome of intense international co-operation, in which the progress has been so rapid and the intercourse so intimate that it is often impossible to disentangle the contributions of individuals in the common enterprise. In this address I shall abstain from mentioning names of living scientists, but I feel that we are united in paying tribute to the memory of Ernest Rutherford who explored with such vigour the new field of research opened by the great discoveries of Roentgen, Thomson, Becquerel, and the Curies. We think not merely of Rutherford's fundamental discoveries of the atomic nucleus and its transmutability, but above all of the inspiration with which, through so many years, he guided the development of this new branch of physical science. On this occasion we also deeply miss Enrico Fermi whose name for all times will be associated with the advent of the "atomic age."

Notwithstanding the measure to which it has been possible by familiar physical approaches to extend and utilize our knowledge of atoms, we have at the

Mr. Niels Bohr

same time been confronted with unsuspected limitations of the ideas of classical physics which demand a revision of the fundamental ideas in order to provide for the unambiguous application of some of our most elementary concepts. As is well known, the first decisive step in this direction was the establishment of the relativity theory, by which Albert Einstein, whose recent death all the world deplores, widened the horizon of mankind and gave our world picture a unity surpassing all previous expectations. In return for the abandonment of customary ideas of absolute space and time the relativity principle offered means of tracing general physical laws independent of the observer. In this connection we applaud Einstein's recognition of the equivalence of mass and energy which has proved to be an unerring guide in nuclear research.

Still, to cope with the experience concerning atomic particles, it has been necessary to make further departures from the mechanical conceptions which had been the foundation for the account of physical phenomena since Newton's days. In so doing we have even led to the recognition of the limited applicability of deterministic description. Here I do not think merely of the recourse to statistical consideration in accounting for the thermodynamical properties of physical systems containing large numbers of atoms, but above all of the discovery of the universal quantum of action to which Max Planck, in the first year of this century, was led by his penetrating analysis of the laws of thermal radiation. In revealing an essential feature of wholeness in elementary processes pointing far beyond the old doctrine of the limited divisibility of matter, this epoch-making discovery showed that the theories of classical physics, according to which physical phenomena are described as a continuous chain of events, are idealizations applicable only to phenomena where the actions involved are sufficiently large to permit the neglect of the individual quantum.

While this condition is amply fulfilled for phenomena on the ordinary scale and even in the interpretation of the experiments permitting measurement of the masses and charges of atomic particles, we meet in proper quantum phenomena with regularities of quite a novel kind, responsible for fundamental properties of matter. The extent to which these regularities transgress the possibility of an analysis in classical physical terms is illustrated by the necessity of using such contrasting pictures as waves and corpuscles in attempts to visualize classically different aspects of the behaviour of atomic objects.

Particularly following the discovery of the atomic nucleus the accumulated evidence regarding the properties of the chemical elements became available for the further exploration of atomic processes. From the outset it was evident that the quantum of action afforded a clue to the understanding of the peculiar stability of the electron binding in the atoms, which resisted explanation within the framework of classical mechanics. Still, the establishment of a consistent interpretation of atomic phenomena presented a very difficult task which was only accomplished gradually by the concerted efforts of a whole generation of theoretical physicists.

In the mathematical formalism of quantum mechanics, which contains the classical physical theories as a limiting case, the kinematical and dynamical variables are replaced by symbolic operators subject to a non-commutative algorithm involving Planck's constant. The formalism thus defies pictorial representation and aims directly at the prediction of observations appearing under well-defined conditions. Corresponding to the circumstance that in a given experimental arrangement a number of different quantum processes may in general occur, these predictions are of essentially statistical character. In contrast to previous application of statistics for describing mechanical systems with many degrees of freedom, the use of probability considerations in quantum physics presents a direct departure from deterministic description inherently connected with the indivisibility of the elementary processes.

By means of the quantum mechanical formalism it has, as is well known, been possible to account in detail for an immense amount of experimental evidence concerning those physical and chemical properties of matter which depend on the binding of the electrons to the atomic nuclei. In particular, the peculiar periodic variation of these properties, the discovery of which we owe to Mendelejef's penetrating intuition, has been completely elucidated. Also as regards the constitution and properties of the nuclei themselves, great progress in the interpretation of the rapidly increasing experimental evidence has been made. In this connection we may particularly note how the law governing spontaneous radioactive decay which had been known for a long time is harmoniously incorporated into the statistical quantum mechanical description.

In spite of the power of quantum theoretical methods, the renunciation of accustomed demands on physical explanation has given rise to doubts in many minds as to whether we are dealing with an exhaustive description of atomic phenomena. Thus, it has been argued the statistical treatment should be regarded as a temporary approach, which will eventually be replaced by a more detailed deterministic theory. The lively discussion of this basic issue has stimulated the analysis of our position as observers of nature and forced us to be cautious in applying concepts adapted to our orientation under ordinary conditions to a completely new domain of knowledge.

Of course, even when the phenomena transcend the scope of classical physical theories, the description of the experimental arrangement and the recording of the observations must be given in plain language, suitably supplemented by technical terminology. This is a pure logical demand, since the very word "experiment" refers to a situation where we can tell others what we have done and what we have learned. In actual quantum phenomena, however, it is not possible to make sharp the separation so characteristic of the mechanical conception of nature, between the behaviour of the objects under investigation and their interaction with the measuring instruments. The recording of atomic phenomena involves an amplification device of essentially irreversible functioning, such as the production of a permanent mark on a photographic plate left by the impact of an electron. Further, any attempt to control the interaction between the atomic objects and the instruments serving to specify the experimental arrangement would imply a change in the observational conditions incompatible with the appearance of the very phenomenon in question.

The essential wholeness of the quantum phenomena makes it impossible to speak in an unambiguous way of attributes of the objects independent of the conditions under which they are observed. Thus, the evidence obtained under different experimental conditions may exhibit a type of relationship quite foreign to classical physics. Still, however contrasting the different phenomena may appear from the classical point of view, they must be regarded as complementary in the sense that only together do they exhaust all obtainable knowledge regarding the atomic objects.

Within its scope the quantum mechanical theory gives the appropriate mathematical formulation of the notion of complementarity. Thus, the non-commutability of the operators symbolizing the mechanical quantities of classical physics, which imply the indeterminacy relations of conjugate variables, corresponds to the mutually exclusive experimental conditions which permit unambiguous use of the corresponding classical concepts. In particular any quantum phenomenon which includes the registration of the position of an atomic particle at a given moment will involve an exchange of momentum and energy, which in principle is uncontrollable, between the particle and the instruments such as fixed scales and synchronized clocks serving to define the reference frame. Conversely, the account of phenomena governed by conservation of momentum and energy involves necessarily a limitation of space-time description.

The freedom of experimentation, presupposed in classical physics, is of course retained and corresponds to the variability of the experimental conditions provided for in the mathematical structure of the quantum mechanical formalism. While in classical physics, the assumed unlimited subdivisibility of the phenomena entails the unrestricted possibility of interfering and even reversing by suitable experiments the course of events, the wholeness of each quantum phenomenon implies a restriction on such interference. In particular, all features of reversibility are reduced to the statistical balancing implied in thermodynamical arguments.

The renunciation in quantum physics of the customary demands placed on physical explanation reminds us of the abandoning in relativity theory of the concepts of absolute space and time, the application of which is restricted by the upper limit of the rate of propagation of all physical signals, represented by the velocity of light. Similarly, the unsuspected lower limit for the unambiguous use of the mechanical concept of action excludes the unrestricted combination of space-time coordination and momentum and energy balance on which the deterministic description of classical physics depends. In both cases we have to do with irrevocable steps as regards the description of physical experience, based on the recognition of essential features of our situation as observers, which have demanded wider frames for the analysis and synthesis of natural phenomena.

The importance of the epistemological lesson which the exploration of the world of atoms has given us must be seen against the background of the impact of the mechanical conception of nature on general thinking through the centuries. Above all, the recognition of an inherent limitation in the scope of the deterministic description within a field of experience concerned with fundamental properties of matter, stimulates the search in other domains of knowledge for similar situations in which the mutually exclusive application of concepts, each indispensable in a full account of experience, calls for a complementary mode of description.

When leaving the proper domain of physics we meet at once with the old and much debated question of the place of the living organisms in the description of natural phenomena. Originally, no sharp distinction between animate and inanimate matter was made, and it is well known that Aristotle, in stressing the wholeness of the individual organisms, opposed the views of the atomists, and even in the discussion of the foundations of mechanics retained ideas like purpose and potency. However, with the great discoveries in anatomy and physiology at the time of the Renaissance, and especially the advent of classical mechanics in the deterministic description of which any reference to purpose is eliminated, a completely mechanistic conception of nature suggested itself.

It is true that the structure and functioning of the organisms involve an ordering of atomic processes which has sometimes been felt difficult to reconcile with the laws of thermodynamics, which imply a steady approach towards disorder among the atoms constituting an isolated physical system. If, however, sufficient account is taken of the circumstance that the free energy necessary to maintain and develop organic systems is continually supplied from their surroundings by nutrition and respiration, it becomes clear that there is in this respect no question of any violation of general physical laws. Still, as already noted by Boltzmann, it is important to recognize that the essential element of irreversibility involved in the description of the organic functions is the very basis for our notion of time direction.

In recent decades, great advances have been achieved in our knowledge of the structure and functioning of the organisms, and it has become evident that in many respects quantum regularities play a fundamental role here also. Such regularities are indeed basic for the remarkable stability of the highly complex molecular structures which form the essential constituents of the cells responsible for the hereditary properties of the species. Moreover, the induced mutations resulting from the exposure of the organisms to penetrating radiation offer a striking application of the statistical laws of quantum physics. The sensitivity of perceptive organs, so important for the integrity of the organisms, has been found to approach the level of individual quantum processes, and clearly amplification mechanisms, which remind us of the recording devices used in atomic physics experiments, play an important part in the transmission of nervous messages.

The whole development in these areas has again fostered a mechanistic approach to biological problems to the foreground although in a novel manner. At the same time the question has become acute whether a comparison between the organism and highly complex and refined physical systems, like modern industrial plants or electronic calculating machines, offers the proper basis for an adequate description of such self-regulating entities as living organisms.

Returning to the general epistemological lesson which atomic physics has given us, we must in the first place realize that the isolated phenomena studied in quantum physics are not directly analogous to biological processes which involve a continual exchange of matter and energy between the organism and its environment. Moreover, any experimental arrangement, which would allow a control of biological functions to the extent demanded for their exhaustive description in physical terms, would be prohibitive to the free display of life. Thus, notwithstanding the ever improving technique of studying metabolism especially by means of the ingenious atomic tracer method applying radioactive isotopes, we must realize that the possibilities for interfering with or reversing the course of events in organic life are still more limited than in the study of individual atomic processes. Incidentally, we may also recall that even the most effective medical treatment essentially aims at supporting the organism so that it may recover its health or resume its normal functions.

The emphasis on this point suggests an attitude toward the problem of organic life which provides an appropriate balance between the mechanistic and finalistic approaches. In fact, just as the quantum of action appears as an element which cannot be defined in classical mechanical terms in the account of atomic phenomena, so the notion of life is elementary in biological science in the sense that it applies to situations where the conditions for an exhaustive physical analysis are not fulfilled. Actually, we must recognize that the practical approach in biological research is characterized by the complementary way in which arguments, based on the full resources of physical and chemical science and concepts directly referring to the integrity of the organism transcending the scope of these sciences, are employed.

Similar situations regarding the comprehension of experience are met with in the study of the innate and conditioned behaviour of animals and man, which calls for the application of psychological concepts. Even in an allegedly behaviouristic approach it is hardly possible to avoid such concepts, and the very idea of consciousness impresses itself when we are dealing with behaviour of such a high degree of complexity that its description virtually involves introspection on the side of the individual organism. In this connection it is interesting to note that, while in the early stages of physical science one could directly refer to features of daily life events which permitted simple causal account, an essentially complementary description of the states of our mind has been used since the origin of language. In fact, the rich terminology adapted to this purpose does not point to an unbroken course of events, but rather to separate mutually exclusive experiences which remind us of the complementary phenomena in atomic physics. Just as these phenomena demand for their definition different experimental arrangements, the various psychological experiences are characterized by different placements of the separation between the content on which attention is focused and the background indicated by the word "ourselves."

From a purely biological point of view, we can hardly interpret the characteristics of psychical phenomena, except by concluding that every conscious experience, capable of being retained in the memory, corresponds to a residual impression on the organism, which amounts to an irreversible recording of the outcome of processes in the nervous system. Certainly, such recordings in which the interplay of numerous brain cells are involved are essentially different from the permanent structures in the single cells connected with genetic reproduction. On finalistic approach, however, we may stress not only the usefulness of permanent recordings in their influence on our reactions to subsequent stimuli, but also the importance that later generations are not encumbered by the actual experiences of individuals, but only rely on the reproduction of such properties of the organism as have proved serviceable for the collection and utilization of knowledge. In any attempt at pursuing the enquiry we must, of course, be prepared to meet increasing difficulties at every step, and it is suggestive that the simple concepts of physical science in an ever increasing degree lose their immediate applicability as we examine more closely the aspects of organic life related to the characteristics of our mind.

To illustrate such argumentation, we may refer to the old problem of the freedom of will. In an unrestricted deterministic approach this concept, of course, finds no place, but it is evident that the world volition is indispensable in an exhaustive description of psychical phenomena. Not only do we have the feeling of being able to make the best out of a given set of circumstances but also if we attempt to predict what another person will decide to do in a given situation, we must strive to know his whole background to such an extent that we shall actually be placing ourselves in his position. A logically consistent basis for speaking of the "freedom of our will" is provided by the recognition that the psychological situations in which we have a feeling of volition and those in which we ponder over the motives for our actions offer a typical example of complementary relationships. Thus, the proper latitude is also left for the use of words like aspirations and responsibility which separately are as little definable as other words which are indispensable in an account of the variety and potential of our situation.

Whenever I have entered into such general biological and psychological problems familiar to all, the intention has only been to remind you of common features of scientific enquiry and point to an attitude characterized by the striving for harmonizing apparently contrasting experiences by their incorporation in a wider conceptual framework. Such an approach may perhaps contribute to the promotion of the mutual understanding between human societies with different cultural traditions. Before concluding this address I shall allow myself to add some remarks concerning this question.

In this connection it may be pertinent to refer to the similarities and differences between animal and human societies. In animal life we meet with communities of very diverse kinds corresponding to the needs of the different species. Especially among insects we are sometimes confronted with a division of functions among the individuals carried to such extremes that the whole society in various respects resembles a single organism. In many species of birds and mammals who live in flocks more or less divided into families we have rather to do with an innate behaviour which reminds us of many habits in human communities serving the support of the individuals as well as the protection of the society.

The essential difference between such animal societies and the human communities is however that in our cultural traditions we have to do not with biologically inherited behaviour but with modes of reaction of the adult individuals which are carried from generation to generation by more or less consciously directed education. In this connection it is decisive to realize the extent to which instinctive behaviour is suppressed in human life. In the terminology suggested by modern science we may even say that words like "instinct" and "reason" have mutually exclusive complementary applications.

Human cultures developed in isolation from each other often exhibit deep-rooted differences not only as regards the adjustment to external conditions like climate and natural resources but also as regards the traditions which they have fostered and which often stand in the way of mutual understanding. Sometimes one has compared the various cultures with the different ways in which physical phenomena are described according to the standpoint of the observer. Still, the great scientific advance marked by relativity theory implies the possibility for any observer to predict, in terms of common concepts, how any other observer will account for physical experience. Just the difficulty of appreciating the traditions of other nations on the basis of one's own national tradition suggests that the relationship between cultures may rather be regarded as complementary. In all such comparisons it is, however, not taken into account that every culture is continually developing. Especially contacts between different cultural communities may influence the attitude of each to an extent which may even lead to a common culture with a more embracing outlook.

As an unifying element of human cultures, the development of science plays an ever more important role. Not only is any advance of knowledge, wherever gained, of benefit to all humanity, but co-operation in scientific research offers perhaps more than anything else opportunities for the furthering of close contacts and common understanding. These opportunities have a special significance at the present crucial stage of history. Indeed, the establishment of a co-operation in confidence between all peoples, which is now so urgently needed, depends essentially on the free access to all information and unhampered discussions of all problems of human interest.

We are all united in the hope that this Conference where representatives of so many nations are assembled for the exchange of knowledge will come to stand as a landmark for scientific and technological co-operation. We trust that the opportunity of intercourse and acquaintance offered us at this great occasion will promote the common striving for the elevation of culture in all its aspects.

High Current Accelerators

By Ernest O. Lawrence,* USA

In this distinguished gathering, which symbolizes so magnificently the international character of science and technology, it is hardly necessary to point out the fact that the remarkable development of particle accelerators, like all far-reaching scientific and technological advances, is the work of many people in many laboratories over the world. It was, for example, Cockcroft and Walton in England who first achieved the disintegration of lithium by accelerated protons, and it was my esteemed colleague of this evening Mr. Veksler of the Soviet Union who, in a classic paper on the theory of accelerators, was the first to describe the synchrotron, thereby pointing the way to much higher energies.

The bevatron, which for the moment is the largest proton synchrotron, is shown in Fig 1. The magnet is arranged in four quadrants and in the foreground may be seen the cavity-type linear accelerator which serves to inject pulses of 10 Mev protons into the synchrotron. The radio-frequency accelerating electrode and associated equipment is in the straight section on the right while the target area is in the straight section opposite the injector area, and hence hardly visible in the picture.

Figure 2 is a limited view of the injector quadrant of the bevatron. On the right is shown the housing of the 500 kv Cockcroft and Walton accelerator; the foreground shows the 10 Mev linear accelerator and on the left can be seen the strong focusing quadrapole magnetic lens which focuses the beam appropriately into the bevatron.

Figure 3 shows the power supply of the bevatron which provides 100,000 kw pulses which are switched by the array of ignitrons shown in the foreground.

I shall not undertake a more detailed description of the bevatron. For some time now, it has been in operation at full energy, 6.2 Bev.

I should like to note that this great machine is being utilized by scientists of many laboratories in America and abroad: indeed, about one-quarter of the operating time has been devoted to furthering work outside the United States. The many visiting scientists, especially from overseas, have been a real source of pleasure to all of us in Berkeley. Their presence has contributed greatly to the work in progress and we appreciate even more the fact that their collaboration is increasing enormously the flow of new knowledge which the bevatron makes possible.

Of course, the finest flowering of this kind of international collaboration is embodied in the CERN Laboratory now developing so auspiciously here in Geneva.

It is perhaps an understatement to say that the richness of the domain of the nucleus opened up for investigation by accelerator developments has exceeded all expectations. Those of us who have had the good fortune of participating in these developments during the past quarter century have indeed a vivid impression that each new door to a hitherto inaccessible region of nature opened by the development of an accelerator of new capabilities always leads to unexpected advances in knowledge of both scientific and technological importance. It is, of course, for this reason that accelerator developments over the world are proceeding at an ever increasing pace.

In his retiring address as President of the American Physical Society in 1954, Fermi humorously presented a logarithmic plot of the progress in accelerator developments towards ever higher voltages. He extrapolated the exponential progress of recent years to show that in a few more decades our accelerators would circle the earth and compete with very energetic cosmic rays!

In the same spirit, one may extrapolate the currents that will be produced. Taking a milliampere for cyclotrons in 1940, a microampere for synchro-cyclotrons in 1948 and a milli-microampere for the cosmotrons and bevatrons of 1956, we obtain a current of 5×10^{-4} particles per sec or 2 protons per hour when our energy should reach 10^{16} ev (Fig. 4)!

In a more serious vein, it is clear that the duty cycle limitation on beam currents imposed on all pulsed accelerators is a matter of concern. For it goes without saying that increasing beam intensities many fold opens up new possibilities for research just as ever higher energy opens new domains of investigation. If, for example, fifteen years ago cyclo-

*Director, Radiation Laboratory of the University of California.

Figure 1. General view of the bevatron

Figure 2. Bevatron injector

Figure 3. Bevatron magnet power supply

tron currents had been small fractions of microamperes rather than many microamperes, the discovery of neptunium, plutonium and other transuranium elements and their remarkable properties would surely have been delayed. Indeed, perhaps we would not be meeting here today! The problem of producing high currents of high energy particles is unquestionably an important one.

Many people have given thought to this problem and the story of their work is interwoven with that leading to higher energies. However, it is less well known to most physicists. It begins, at least for circular accelerators, with a paper published by L. H. Thomas in 1938 in which he showed that the energy limitations of an ordinary cyclotron (due to relativity mass increase with energy) can be overcome by inserting periodic azimuthal variations in the magnetic field so that the particle orbits depart from circular form, the departure becoming larger for the higher energy orbits of larger radius. This work of Thomas received but little attention for a period of more than ten years. This may be ascribed partly to the fact the cyclotron people had all they could do to develop and exploit the simpler and more straight-forward conventional cyclotron until they all became occupied with assisting in the defense of their various countries. After the war, it seemed simpler to raise cyclotron energies using the principle of phase stability of Veksler and McMillan as embodied in the synchrocyclotron.

However, a few years after the war, attention in our laboratory was drawn to the problem of producing high currents of particles accelerated to energies in the range reached by the synchrocyclotron, and in that connection my colleague McMillan came forward with an independent approach to the problem of a magnetic field which would be suitable for a high energy cyclotron.

There is not time here to discuss the relationship of McMillan's solution to that of Thomas, although they were basically similar in providing an azimuthal variation in the magnetic field to provide focusing. Nor is it possible to describe Judd's and later Richardson's contributions to the design of suitable

fields which made possible cyclotrons capable of continuous (in contrast to pulsed) operation of deuterons in the energy range above 700 Mev.

Figure 5 shows schematically the orbit of a particle in such a magnetic field which is a function of both azimuth and radius; n varies around the orbit as does the radius so that the focusing action is partly due to the variation in radius, which produces focusing like that of a wedge-shaped magnet, while the variable n gives the effect of alternating gradient focusing of Christofolis and Courant, Livingston and Snyder.

Now I should like to describe the experiments that have been carried out in our laboratory with an electron model of a clover-leaf cyclotron (socalled because of the shape of the magnet pole

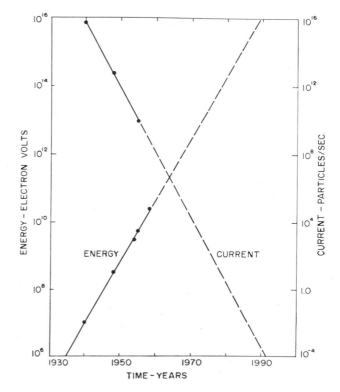

Figure 4. Extrapolation of accelerator energy and current output

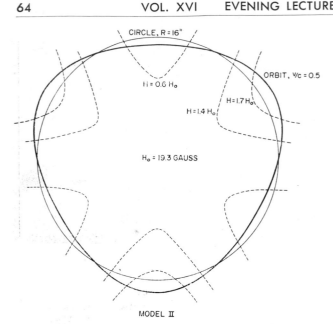

Figure 5. Particle orbit in Thomas-type cyclotron field

the average radial value of the field, while a number of coils in the valleys of the gap provide for azimuthal and radial variations.

With these orbit-correcting coils, it was possible to produce the desired field with the desired precision to tenths of one per cent everywhere.

With a suitable electron gun at the center, the model operated quite in accord with theoretical expectations. The measured threshold voltage to accelerate electrons was only 23 or 24 volts which corresponded to the energy gain required for electrons to miss striking the electron gun. It is estimated that the electrons required 2000 or 3000 revolutions to reach their final energy of 70,000 volts. This corresponds in an actual accelerator to an electrode potential of about 100 kv to accelerate deuterons to 300 Mev. Thus, it is clear that the Thomas-type field does indeed provide the necessary axial and radial stability and that, within the limits expected on theoretical grounds, the particles can stay in phase with the constant-frequency accelerating voltage.

It was observed that essentially the entire electron beam escaped from the machine in three divergent beams from each of the three hills, and by weakening the field on one of the hills it was found possible to produce a beam containing 90% of the total circulating energy from the hill in question. Using an external focusing magnet the external beam could be converged and altogether it appeared that this type of cyclotron had the admirable property of easy beam extraction along with high currents at high energy with very low voltages on the accelerating electrodes.

pieces) which have so beautifully substantiated the theoretical expectations.

Figure 6 shows one of the pole faces of the magnet of the electron model. Here the magnet diameter is 40 inches and the magnetic field chosen has a threefold symmetry.

Figure 7 shows a general view of the interior of the electron model. The variable magnetic gap is in view, as well as one of the three accelerating electrodes which occupy the three wide-gap regions between the poles.

Now in this electron model where the electrons reach final velocities equal to that of 300 Mev deuterons ($\beta = 0.5$) the magnetic fields are small —only about 20 gauss—and inhomogeneities of the iron make it difficult to produce the desired magnetic field. The mechanical problem of shaping the pole pieces accurately is also quite severe and in consequence field correcting coils are mounted on the pole pieces as shown in Fig. 8. As is seen, there is a considerable number of concentric coils to vary

At this stage, I should like to draw attention to yet another approach to the problem of high-current high-energy cyclotrons which is a by-product of the new and interesting set of proposals now under investigation by the accelerator design group of the Midwestern Universities Research Association, under the leadership of Kerst, whose interest lies primarily in the attainment of high energies in proton synchrotrons. Their work is so new that it

Figure 6. Electron model cyclotron pole face

Figure 7. Interior of electron model cyclotron

Figure 0. Electron model cyclotron pole face with field correcting coils

has not yet been put to practical test, although they are now engaged in constructing an electron model accelerator which will explore some aspects of their proposals. It is based on the observation by Keith Symon that a proton synchrocyclotron can be built with a magnet of small radial extent like that of a synchrotron provided that particles are injected with reasonable energy. This can be done by exploiting the alternating gradient focusing with its well known property of "momentum compaction" by which orbits of widely differing energies may be made to be very near each other in space. It certainly will be interesting to see whether such a scheme appears to be as attractive in practice as the alternating gradient modulated magnets being employed by the Brookhaven and CERN groups for machines in the 20–30 Bev range.

The MURA group have introduced the idea of spiraling the hills and valleys of the magnetic field so that particle orbits cross them at a rather steep angle instead of perpendicularly. Applying these ideas to betatrons, they predict that by using a greater flux change than necessary to attain the desired energy a betatron may be freed from its duty cycle limitation and its current increased ten thousand fold! Moreover, with the spirally rigid poles, it is possible to arrange matters so that orbits of all energies are geometrically similar with the frequencies of radial and axial oscillations remaining constant throughout the acceleration process. Therefore, in principle, troubles with resonance effects can be avoided. This MURA work, therefore, seems to constitute another improvement in the development of fixed-frequency cyclotrons.

All of this work has shown that the original energy limitations of the ordinary cyclotron can be surmounted in a variety of ways. This information can be applied directly to improve the performance or to lower the dee voltage requirement on existing cyclotrons by simply reshaping the poles. This proce-

dure has already been carried out under the direction of Keith Boyer on the Los Alamos cyclotron, and has resulted in very satisfactory operation with a greatly reduced loss of particles during acceleration. The present reasonable energy limit for high current cyclotrons producing currents of many milliamperes is not easy to establish, but it seems certain that it will increase with the development of accelerator technology that is certain to continue as long as physicists are interested in looking for new problems to solve!

Now returning to the accelerator development work in Berkeley during the last four or five years, along with the devolpment of the clover-leaf cyclotron, a greater effort was made to develop the linear accelerator, of the cavity resonator type devised by Alvarez, for high currents at high voltages. The over-all objective was what might be called a super power particle accelerator capable of producing thousands of kilowatts of high energy protons! The linear accelerator development appeared so promising that it was decided to abandon consideration of construction of a clover-leaf cyclotron which would involve a very large capital expenditure of funds and to concentrate on the design and construction of a linear machine, the first sections of which would not entail too great a capital outlay and would allow extension almost indefinitely to higher voltages as desired in the future.

Of course, the first problem was a source of protons of many amperes from which could be withdrawn 100 to 200 kv protons focused into a beam which would pass through an aperture about 5 cm in diameter. After that there was the problem of accelerating the beam in a first stage to about a half-million electron volts. Theoretical studies had shown that in a cavity-type accelerator operating at 48 Mc where solenoid focusing was used in the drift tubes there should be no great difficulty in accelerating such a 500 kv beam on up to many hundreds of millions of volts with little loss and at comparatively high efficiency. In other words, the technical problems seemed essentially that of bringing a large current of ions up to about a half-million volts or so, sharply focused and bunched for injection into the linear accelerator of the Alvarez type which we call the A-48 accelerator.

The arrangement has worked out very well, as is shown in Fig. 9. At the left is the injector consisting of an arc source in a solenoidal magnetic field mounted on insulators in a vacuum tank. The arc body is maintained at a positive potential up to 140 kv and has produced up to ¾ ampere of focused ion beam. Ions produced in the arc are accelerated by a single gap through a 4-foot length of beam tube and are brought to a focus on a collimating aperture by a large solenoidal magnet, through which the beam tube passes. The diameter of the ion beam is controlled by varying the magnet current, and the centering of the beam by orienting the magnet, which is flexibly mounted.

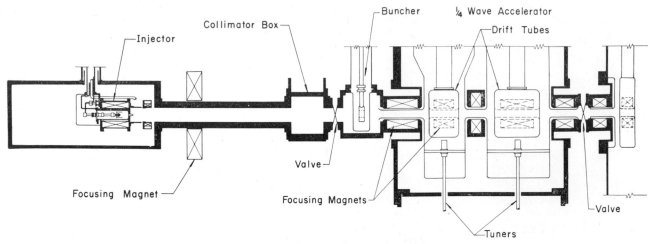

Figure 9. A-48 high current accelerator, low velocity end

Just beyond the collimating aperture, the ion beam passes through the buncher which applies a 24-megacycle ripple of 5 to 7 kev to the beam. As a result, a large fraction of the ions arriving at the first rf accelerating gap are bunched into a small phase angle of the 24-megacycle wave.

The next component shown is the 24-megacycle, quarter-wave accelerator. This machine consists of two quarter-wave resonant stems, the ends of which are drift tubes for 24-megacycle acceleration. Each drift tube and stem is housed in a separate cavity to reduce to a minimum the coupling between them. The gap spacings for each drift tube is $(\frac{3}{2})\beta\lambda$ and that between the two cavities is $1 \beta\lambda$, so that ideally the two stems should operate 180 degrees out of phase. Actually, the two stems and the buncher are all separately driven and the phases between them adjusted for optimum output.

In each drift tube and at positions before, between and after the drift tubes solenoidal magnets are located as shown to maintain beam focus throughout. Figure 10 is a view of the quarter-wave accelerator with one drift tube in place.

Deuterons are accelerated by the quarter-wave machine from 140 kev to about 1 Mev, for which energy the velocity is great enough so that the frequency can be increased from 24 to 48 megacycles for subsequent acceleration.

Figure 11 is a color photograph† of the ion beam from the injector as it passes from the beam tube into the collimating aperture. When this photograph was made a continuous beam of about ½ ampere of 100 kev protons was being injected through a 2½ inch diameter collimating aperture into the accelerator.

This part of the A-48 accelerator operates continuously and smoothly delivering several hundred milliamperes of one-half million volt protons or one million volt deuterons; thus several hundred kilowatts of nicely focused ions reach a target about one meter from the last accelerator electrode.

† Reproduced here in black and white.

The beam, of course, is bunched into short pulses (less than 10^{-8} sec) and the instantaneous currents therefore are of the order of one ampere. The energy distribution in the beam when protons are accelerated is shown in Fig. 12. It is seen that most of the beam is close to the desired energy and indeed is very close to theoretical expectations.

We are now building two sections of the A-48 accelerator to produce a quarter ampere of 7.8 Mev deuterons. Figure 13 is a view of the interior of one of the twenty-foot cavities looking in through a porthole in the side. The drift tubes are viewed from below and off to one side. The cavity tank is fabricated of copper-clad steel, the drift-tube shells

Figure 10. Quarter-wave accelerator with one drift tube in place

Figure 11. Half ampere, 100 kev proton beam entering input aperture of A-48 accelerator

of copper sheet and the supporting stems of heavy-wall steel tubing, copper plated on the exposed surfaces. Figure 14 is another view looking down the line of drift tubes showing the aperture through which the beam passes. The drift-tube volume is much larger than the beam aperture because of space requirements for water cooling and solenoidal focusing magnets.

The general arrangement of the A-48 high current accelerator is shown in a perspective drawing in Fig. 15. At the left are located the ion injector, the beam focusing and steering magnet, the 24-

Figure 13. Interior view through side porthole of A-48 cavity

megacycle buncher and the quarter wave accelerator as previously described.

The deuteron beam at 1 Mev from the quarter-wave accelerator then enters the first of two 48-megacycle resonant-cavity accelerator sections each 20-feet long. A portion of the side wall of the second cavity is cut away to show the drift tubes and supporting stems. As already mentioned, each drift tube contains a solenoidal magnet for maintaining beam focus throughout the machine. The gap spacings in both resonant cavities are $1 \beta\lambda$: that is, the ions receive one accelerating impulse during each rf cycle.

Since the design deuteron current output at 7.5 Mev is 0.25 ampere, the target system is designed to dissipate 2 megawatts of beam power. To prevent excessive power concentration at the target, the ion beam passes through a rotating magnetic field at the exit aperture so that the beam is slightly deflected and precessed over a target spot up to 3 feet in diameter. The target consists of a bank of overlapping tubes of aluminum, magnesium (Dow metal) or other metal with high velocity water flow to ensure good heat transfer.

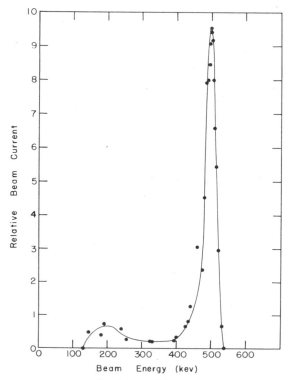

Figure 12. Energy distribution of beam from quarter-wave accelerator

Figure 14. Interior view of A-48 cavity through the beam output port

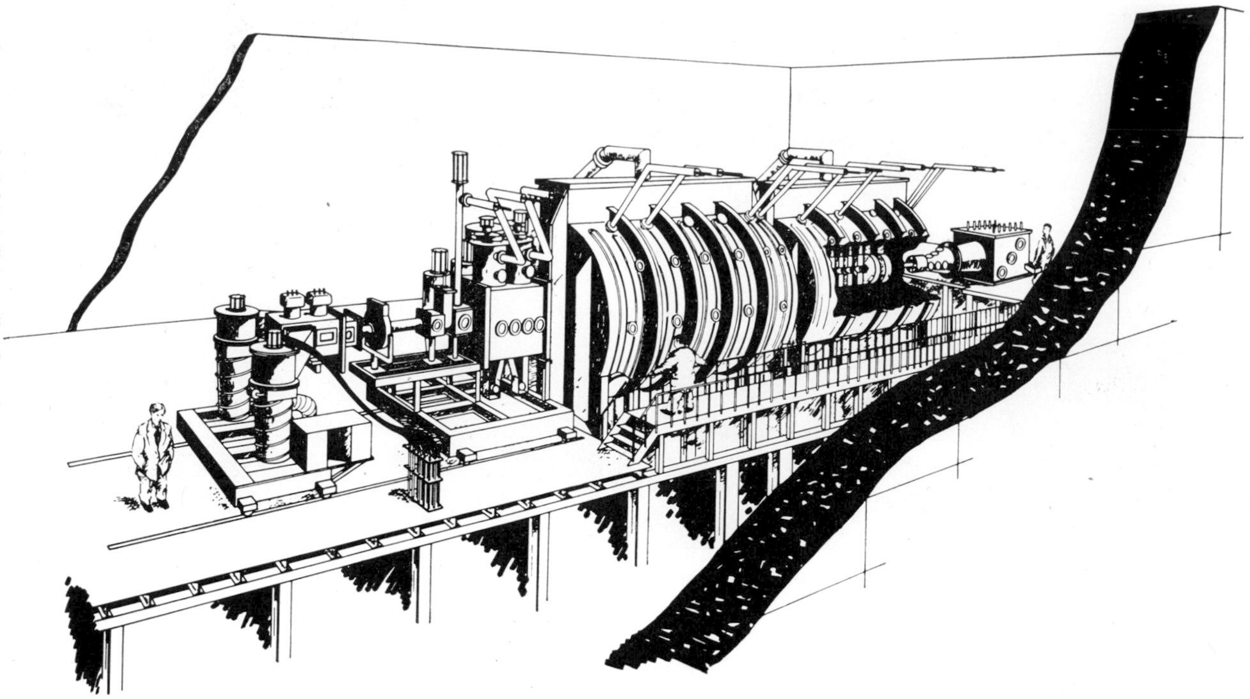

Figure 15. Perspective drawing of A-48 accelerator

Figure 16. View of A-48 accelerator during construction

The construction of this super-power accelerator is well along and we expect that it will begin operation next year. Figure 16 is a recent photograph of the present stage of construction. I cannot help but wonder what new knowledge will come from the availability in the laboratory of these very high currents of high energy particles. Just as it is certain that new things of great interest will indeed turn up, so we may be confident that plans will go forward to build additional accelerating sections for this machine for ever higher voltages!

In closing this all too brief account of high current accelerators, which surely will be a subject of increasing interest in the years ahead, may I express my appreciation of the honor of speaking this evening. Above all, may I express the hope that many of you whom I have had the pleasure of meeting for the first time here will give us the pleasure of a visit some day soon in California.

Principles of the Acceleration of Charged Particles

By Vladimir I. Veksler, USSR

During the past few years, the experimental physicist has solved the problem of producing in the laboratory particles with energies of the order of thousands of millions of electron-volts. Previously, such particles were observed only in cosmic rays, and then only in insignificant quantity. The artificial production of intensive beams of particles possessing such energy, the generation of which by direct acceleration would have needed electric fields of the order of thousands of millions of volts, made possible the discovery and study of a number of phenomena of fundamental importance in the physics of the atomic nucleus and elemental particles. A new branch of contemporary nuclear physics—perhaps the most promising of all—has been opened up: the physics of high-energy particles, based on the new methods of accelerating charged particles. The rate at which this new branch is developing is quite remarkable, discovery after discovery having been made during the last few years.

The newest accelerators have not only made it possible to produce and study the spallation of atomic nuclei, but have also revealed far-reaching prospects for developing the artificial synthesis of substances. Elements with greater atomic weights than uranium—the transuranic elements—have been created one after another. With the help of accelerators, a number of new particles have been produced artificially whose properties have been studied and a series of results of exceptional fundamental significance have been obtained. All these achievements owe their realization to the rapid development of experimental methods enabling charged particles to be accelerated up to enormous energies.

Cockcroft and Walton were the first to succeed, in 1932, in provoking nuclear reactions by means of protons accelerated directly in the permanent electric field of a high-voltage tube. Extensive use has been made of the Van de Graaff accelerator for nuclear research. However, it is not possible by such direct methods to accelerate particles up to energies of more than 5–10 Mev, since at very high voltages it is difficult to provide the necessary insulation and avoid breakdown. Physicists preferred to abandon the frontal attack on the problem in favor of an indirect approach. High voltages can be dispensed with if the particles to be accelerated are made to pass many times through a single relatively small potential drop so that they gradually gain the required energy.

There are several ways of doing this. Although it is possible that some of them, such as the linear accelerator, will be widely used in future, accelerators in which the particles follow closed or almost closed paths have so far been of the greatest value. Such machines are usually known as cyclical accelerators. From now on I shall confine myself to cyclical accelerators, because it is precisely these machines which have made it possible for us to penetrate into the field of ultra-high energies. Above all, I shall talk about the cyclotron.

As you know, the celebrated Lawrence cyclotron is a machine in which charged particles, moving under the influence of a magnetic field in almost closed orbits and continually returning, as a result of that movement, to the gap between the dees, across which there is a relatively small difference of potential, traverse the same unidirectional electric field many times and thus rapidly gain energy.

As the velocity of the particle increases, so the radius of the circle it describes through the uniform magnetic field, and hence the length of its path between successive traversals of the accelerating field, also increases.

The principle on which the cyclotron works is based on the fact that until the particle has gained a very considerable amount of energy, the time, T, which it takes to complete one circuit in the uniform magnetic field is independent of its velocity. The time is proportional to the ratio of the radius R of the circle in which the particle is moving to its velocity. As the radius itself is proportional to the velocity

$$R = \frac{MVC}{He} \qquad (1)$$

the ratio is independent of the velocity. Hence, if the frequency of the alternating electric field used to accelerate the particle is made equal to the frequency of revolution of the particles

$$\omega = \frac{He}{MC} = \omega_f \qquad (2)$$

the particles will move in resonance with the electric field and will continuously gain energy; the "rhythm" of the movement of the particles in the magnetic field and the rhythm of the electric field accelerating them (which periodically changes direction) then coincide.

The successes achieved with the help of the cyclotron, and with that of the betatron cyclical accelerator, which first appeared in 1940, but of which I cannot speak in detail for lack of time, were accompanied by a rapid improvement in these machines and more intensive study of the mechanics of their operation. As regards the betatron, this accelerator is not in practice suitable for accelerating heavy particles, and can be used only for accelerating electrons. But what the physicist really needed for the study of nuclear forces was projectiles capable of acting effectively on atomic nuclei, i.e., the nuclear particles: protons, deuterons, etc. The main hopes therefore naturally centered on the cyclotron. However, it was found relatively quickly that it is impossible with the cyclotron to impart very high energies to charged particles.

Actually, Equation 2 shows that the frequency of revolution of the particles in the cyclotron depends on their mass. As the energy increases, the mass of the particles, which in Equation 2 we assumed to be constant, also increases, in accordance with the laws of relativity, with the result that the resonance between the frequency of revolution and the frequency, ω_f, of the alternating electric field accelerating the particles is upset.

Owing to this disturbance of the resonance condition when higher energies are reached, the maximum energy which can in practice be imparted to, for example, protons accelerated in the cyclotron is of the order of 10–20 Mev.

Despite a number of attempts to solve the problem, the technique of accelerating particles in the cyclotron remained at the stage mentioned, with respect to the maximum attainable particle energy, for more than ten years. It seemed that the gateway to substantially higher energies was hermetically sealed. To all appearances—and this point of view was widely accepted—the increase in mass due to relativity effectively limited the possibility of accelerating charged particles by resonance.

However, I, and a little later, McMillan at Berkeley, California, succeeded in showing that this view was mistaken, and that the resonance acceleration method still held vast, unexploited possibilities.

I would like, if you will allow me, to describe this development in somewhat greater detail, and to try to explain the very simple considerations which made it possible eleven years ago to break this deadlock and lay the foundations of a new and, it must be admitted, highly complex technique of accelerating particles in the field of ultra-high energies.

I must go back a little. My feeling is that to some extent the doubts felt about the resonance method arose from the fact that, in analyzing the mechanics of acceleration in the cyclotron, those concerned always, in fact, stopped halfway. They always considered one part only of the complete cycle of movement of the particles—the part in which energy increases with time. No attention was paid to the fact that, taking the process as a whole, the change in a particle's energy in the cyclotron in no way repre-

sents a continuous upward movement in the energy scale, but corresponds much more closely to the behaviour of a pendulum, the kinetic energy of which alternately increases to a maximum and falls to zero. I shall now try to explain this, at first sight perhaps paradoxical, assertion.

Let us see how the process of changing the energy of particles in the cyclotron takes place. At first, as the energy increases, the velocity of the particles constantly rises. In addition, in accordance with the laws of relativity, their mass also increases. As a result, the radius of the circle in which the particles move increases rather more rapidly than their velocity, and hence the time T

$$T = \frac{2\pi \left(M_0 C^2 + \omega \right)}{Hec} \qquad (3)$$

taken by the particles to complete one revolution also gradually increases.

As a result of this increased period of revolution, the particles will traverse the gap between the dees at times such that the amount of energy they pick up at each traversal gradually diminishes. Finally, at the Nth revolution, the particles traverse the gap at a moment when the electrical field there is zero. This completes the acceleration cycle. During succeeding revolutions, the electric field will no longer be accelerating, but decelerating the particles, which will have to give up the energy they have gained. The process of deceleration will be completely symmetrical with that of acceleration, and the particles will therefore be decelerated to an energy level identical with that with which they began their journey through the acceleration cycle. After this (ignoring the possibility of particles striking the ion source) the whole process is repeated. Thus, the movement of the particles in the cyclotron will in fact be periodic. The particle will successively find itself at the crest of the accelerating voltage; in the neutral "phase," traversing the gap at moments when the accelerating voltage is zero; and finally, in the "phase" of the opposite sign, slowing down in the electric field between the dees. These changes in the "phase" will be periodic—I shall henceforward call them the phase oscillations of the particles. In addition, the energy and orbit radius of the particles will also increase and decrease periodically. Of course it could never have entered anyone's head to use a real cyclotron to play such a senseless game in which the energy gain won during the first half is completely lost in the second.

Naturally, physicists have always tried to bring the game to an end after the first half has gone in their favor. Hence the particles were used as soon as they had gained maximum energy. I shall now show, however, that the possibility of producing in accelerators a phase-oscillation condition of this kind is of fundamental importance and promises the patient player a far bigger profit than the cyclotron can ever give.

AUTO-PHASING

Let us suppose that we can draw up rules of play by which, after each complete cycle of phase oscillations, there is a gain in energy in the particles. It is obvious that it will then be to our advantage to go on with the game as long as possible. What must we do, then, to realize such an attractive prospect? To make the position clear, let us remember that in the cyclotron the average energy gain in each cycle of phase oscillations is zero only because the oscillations are symmetrical. When traversing the decelerating field, a particle loses exactly the same amount of energy as it gains while passing through the gap between the dees at moments when the field is accelerating it. The "point of equilibrium" around which the phase oscillations occur is therefore that value of the phase of the electric field at which the drop in potential between the dees is zero — the neutral phase. Let us now try to displace the point round which the phase oscillations occur into the region of the positive phase. It is easy to see that in this case, on completion of each cycle of phase oscillations, the particle retains a very marked energy gain.

Actually, the phase oscillations will now occur just as before, but in the process the particle either will not pass at all through the gap between the dees at moments when the electric field is decelerating the particles,* or gain energy during the greater part of the cycle and give it up only during the lesser part.

The energy gained during the first half will be greater than that given up during the second part of the cycle. Provided we can maintain such a condition for a sufficiently long time, the energy imparted to the particles can be raised to any desired level. What is required to create such conditions?

It appears (and this was not grasped for a long time) that in fact very little is required, and that the condition just described can be produced by a few very simple means.

It can be most simply produced by slowly changing in time, using the method of trial and error, any of the parameters of the accelerator, such as the strength of the magnetic field or the frequency of the accelerating electric field. Let us consider, for example, an accelerator in which the frequency is constant but the field increases (slowly in comparison with the period of revolution) with time.

It is at once clear from Equation 3 that in this case there will always be bunches of particles which, traversing the gap between the dees, will experience an increase in energy but will nevertheless be shifted in phase in opposite directions to one another. Actually, particles experiencing an increase in energy insufficient to compensate the reduction in the length of one revolution caused by the increase in

the magnetic field during that revolution, will undergo phase displacement towards the side of increasing energy gains. Conversely, particles gaining more energy than is required to maintain a constant period of revolution will be displaced to the side of diminishing energy gains. Thus it is obvious that the phases of both bunches of particles will oscillate about the point of stable equilibrium lying within the range of differences in potential accelerating the particles.

As the average gain in energy per cycle of phase oscillations is equal to the product of the number of revolutions completed during the cycle and the "equilibrium" potential difference, the increase in energy experienced by these particles will be the same as for those which may have been in the "equilibrium phase" from the outset of the process, and hence went through no phase oscillations. Obviously, this process of accumulating energy, i.e., of accelerating the particles, will continue until the phase-equilibrium point lies above zero, which will be when the magnetic field begins to increase at a uniform rate or the frequency of the electric field accelerating the particles begins to decrease.

The condition described has been given the name of "auto-phasing." It is evident that auto-phasing will work only where the magnitude of the drop in potential between the dees, accelerating the particles, is greater than the voltage corresponding to the point of equilibrium. It should be mentioned that the invention and construction of the betatron made a substantial contribution to the development of accelerators working on the auto-phasing system. The equilibrium energy gain acquired by a particle during one revolution in auto-phasing accelerators is very small as compared, for example, with the cyclotron, and therefore, as in the betatron, the particles have to travel a very long way in order to acquire very high energies. It follows that with these accelerators care must be taken to ensure that movement is stable and that, in the process of acceleration, particles do not stray from the straight and narrow path and destroy themselves on the walls of the vacuum chamber. The necessary conditions for that were already elucidated and put into practice in the construction of the betatron.

Auto-phasing has shown itself to be an unusually fruitful principle, which makes it possible to move up the energy scale exceptionally quickly.

Modern resonance accelerators based on the principle of auto-phasing have raised the upper energy limit obtainable in the cyclotron a thousandfold, enabling protons to be accelerated to energies of 10^9–10^{10} ev, and possibly to even higher orders. Resonance electron accelerators — synchrotrons — enable these particles to be accelerated up to 1000 Mev and apparently the limit here has not yet been reached. I shall go into this question in a little more detail and would now like to explain—very briefly, of course—the characteristic features of the basic types of cyclical resonance accelerators.

---

* Provided that the amplitude of the oscillations is less than the displacement of the phase-equilibrium point from neutral.

THE SYNCHROTRON

The synchrotron is a resonance electron accelerator. Its essential advantage over the other cyclical electron accelerator, the betatron, which we have already mentioned, is that it permits a striking reduction in the power and weight of the electromagnet, the poles of the magnet being made in the shape of a narrow annular ring. This is possible because, at the velocities at which the laws of relativity come into play, the mechanism of acceleration automatically keeps the electron orbit radius constant.

An essential part in the movement of electrons in cyclical machines, in contrast to that of heavy particles, e.g., protons, is played by the characteristic electromagnetic radiation emitted by the electrons.

The Soviet physicists Pomeranchouk and Ivanenko, and Pomeranchouk and Artsimovich, first called attention to the fact that this radiation upsets the operation of the betatron and sets a limit, of the order of several hundred Mev, to the energy thus attainable.

In contrast to the betatron, the resonance electron accelerator, the synchrotron, possesses the remarkable characteristic that the appearance of electromagnetic radiation does not upset the mechanism of acceleration since the radiation losses are automatically compensated. This compensation comes about because the radiation losses reduce the energy of the electron and consequently shorten the length of its revolutions. Therefore the equilibrium phase is shifted into the region of high accelerating voltages and some additional (by comparison with the absence of radiation) energy is imparted to the particles, thus compensating the losses.†

A number of fundamental problems of the physics of elementary particles could be explained if electrons and gamma-rays were available with much greater energies, of the order of several thousand Mev. It seems to me that it should now be possible to build a synchrotron designed to produce an electron beam with an energy of 5–10 thousand Mev.

There is, however, a limit to the energy attainable in the synchrotron. It is interesting that this limit is determined entirely by the quantum nature of radiation. This phenomenon, it seems, may serve as a first example of how often the laws of quantum mechanics that govern the microcosm lead to results of importance in engineering practice.

The Soviet physicists Sokolov and Ternov investigated, by quantum mechanics, the influence exerted by radiation on the trajectory of an electron moving in a magnetic field. The result of their work was rather unexpected. It turned out that at very high energies the radiation sharply increases the range straddle of the electron in a radial direction.

---

† Of course, this compensation can only go on until the point is reached at which the radiation losses per revolution exceed the maximum energy gain of the particles during the same period.

This effect, which might be called the "spread" of the trajectory, can also be quite easily produced and explained on the basis of the ordinary theory of the movement of particles in accelerators, if we simply allow also for the statistical character of the radiation. From this point of view, the emission of a quantum with an energy of $E = h\omega_i$ is accompanied by abrupt changes in the radius of the orbit in which the electron normally moves. Obviously, the amplitude of the oscillation also changes to a slight extent in the process. The statistical compounding of these random jumps results in the spreading of the trajectory. The position here is analogous to the oscillations of a pendulum subjected to random impulses on its point of suspension.

THE PHASOTRON

The principle of phase stability has made it possible to achieve very great successes in the acceleration of ions. There are two types of accelerators for heavy particles based on the application of this principle. One of them is very similar to the ordinary cyclotron, and is called in the Soviet Union a phasotron‡; the other is an unusual combination of synchrotron and phasotron, which we call a synchrophasotron.

The phasotron differs from the cyclotron in that in it the frequency of the electric field accelerating the particles is modulated in time.

In both cyclotron and phasotron the trajectory of the particles is an outward spiral. In the phasotron, however, the pitch of this spiral is very flat and at high energies amounts to only a few hundred microns. This is because at velocities of frequency modulation approaching one hundred cycles per second the equilibrium energy gain acquired by the particles each time they traverse the phasotron accelerator gap rises to the order of 10^4 ev. The flat pitch of the spiral makes it difficult to extract the particles from the phasotron. Usually only about 0.1 per cent of the particles can be successfully extracted. The effective extraction method developed by Dmitriyevski and others on the Soviet phasotron made it possible to extract 5 per cent of a beam of protons accelerated to an energy of 680 Mev.

About ten phasotrons are now in operation in various parts of the world, producing particle beams with energies of several hundred Mev. In the Soviet Union in particular is the biggest phasotron in the world, constructed under the direction of Meshcheryakov, Yefremov and Mints, giving proton beams with energies of 680 Mev. The magnet of this huge accelerator weighs about 7000 tons, the poles being 6 meters in diameter. The gap in the vacuum chamber is 60 cm wide. The accelerator can operate at various impulse frequencies, usually generating 80 impulses a second. The current of accelerated protons may be as great as 0.3 μa.

---

‡ In England and America this accelerator is called a synchrocyclotron.

The phasotron, used in general to produce π-mesons, is very effective, but the second accelerator I mentioned earlier, called a synchrophasotron, which combines certain features of both the synchrotron and the phasotron, is much more effective for accelerating ions to energy levels near the upper limit.

THE SYNCHROPHASOTRON

In the Soviet Union, "synchrophasotron" is the name given to an accelerator in which a magnetic field increasing with time is used to control the trajectory of particles, acceleration being effected by an intermittent electric field, the frequency of which also increases with time.

The accelerators built in America under the names of the bevatron and the cosmotron, and in England under the name of the proton synchrotron, are synchrophasotrons in so far as the principle on which they work is concerned.

So far as I know, the use of the synchrophasotron for accelerating heavy articles was first proposed by Oliphant.

Crane was the first to call attention to the fact that variation of the frequency of the electric field according to a rule, determined by the strength of the magnetic field in the gap of the magnet of the accelerator, allowed the orbit radius to be kept constant at all energies of the accelerated particles.

In this case, the pole of the magnet of the synchrophasotron can be made in the shape of a narrow annular ring. In all the big accelerators, e.g., the bevatron, cosmotron, etc., the radial width of the ring is about 5–10% of the value of the equilibrium radius of the orbit. This shape of pole makes it possible to reduce the weight of the magnet itself and the amount of power required to operate it many tens of times.

Modern synchrophasotrons are colossal engineering projects. Some idea of the scale of the works necessitated by the construction of such accelerators may be gleaned from a few data about the biggest synchrophasotron in the world, in the USSR, which is almost complete. The accelerator magnet consists of four quadrants with an average radius of 28 meters, separated by straight gaps each 8 meters long. The magnet weighs about 36,000 tons. The reactive power needed to operate it is 140,000 kva. To facilitate exhaustion, the chamber has been made double, with divided vacuum.

The protons will be injected with the help of a linear accelerator with an energy of 9 Mev. The protons are accelerated in the chamber for 3.3 seconds, gaining on an average 2200 ev of energy per revolution in two accelerating systems. The accelerating systems consist of stacked tubes each with a maximum effective voltage of 5 kv.

The frequency of the accelerating field is increased by $7\frac{1}{2}$ times, and its value is synchronized with the instantaneous strength of the magnetic field to an accuracy of up to 0.1 per cent. Having completed 4.5 million circuits of their orbit and travelled 2.5 times the distance from the earth to the moon, the protons will reach an estimated energy of 10,000 Mev.

Several problems connected with the operation of this synchrotron (injection, resonance, noise and modulation of the magnetic and accelerating fields, observation of the beam, etc.) have been studied under the direction of Professor V. A. Petukhov on a working model producing protons with an energy of 180 Mev.

Despite the great successes obtained in the study of elemental particles with the aid of accelerators, we are still far from the limiting energies possessed by cosmic-ray particles. I would like, therefore, in conclusion, to dwell on the problems, so intensively discussed during the past few years, of the construction of giant synchrophasotrons designed for accelerating protons to energies of the order of 50,000–100,000 Mev.

THE PROSPECTS OF DEVELOPING ACCELERATORS

In the ordinary synchrophasotron the magnetic forces which, as it were, hold the particles in their orbit and prevent their destruction on the walls of the chamber, are in fact very weak. It is easy to show that they are determined by the gradient of the magnetic field in the gap between the poles of the magnet. In ordinary synchrophasotrons this gradient is generally insignificant; accordingly, the quasi-elastic forces are weak and the range of oscillations of the particles is great. As a result, the dimensions of the gap between the poles must be relatively great. If the dimensions of the accelerator are increased, as they must be if we wish to increase the limiting energy of the particles, the width and height of the gap must themselves be correspondingly increased. Working on these lines, with contemporary experimental accuracy and the technical possibilities of industry, it will be hardly possible to reach energies exceeding 10,000 to 20,000 Mev. To continue along this path seems not only senseless, but ruinous.

In 1952, Livingstone, Courant and Snyder proposed a completely new and extremely ingenious way of solving the problem. The essence of their idea was a sharp increase in the magnitude of the forces constraining the particles to keep to their orbit.

For this it is necessary to make the gradient of the magnetic field in the gap between the poles of the synchrophasotron very large, both radially and vertically. Unfortunately, if the gradient of the magnetic field is chosen to ensure great vertical stability, then the radial movement becomes completely unstable, and vice versa.

Livingstone and his colleagues called attention to the circumstance that, by using a series of sectors with opposite gradient signs, general stability of movement could be achieved. This solution of the problem makes possible a sharp increase in the magnetic forces acting on the particle, and so reduces by from 10 to 15 times the size of the gap of the electromagnet required.

This method is called the strong focussing method. Unfortunately, it seems, nothing in this world can be got for nothing. The increase in focussing forces obtained by this method automatically increases the liability of particles to every form of perturbation.

In addition, another difficulty arises. At a certain rather high energy, usually called the critical energy, strong-focussing accelerators lose their auto-phasing capacity. This entails danger of the loss of accelerated particles. Still, it seems that all these difficulties can be overcome. An increase in accuracy in making and assembling electromagnets will obviously enable us to avoid dangerous perturbations in the movement of the particles. Rabinovich and Kolomenski, and also Vladimirski and Tarasov, have proposed an ingenious way of avoiding the critical energy.

In 1953, the Soviet physicists Petukhov, Rabinovich and Kolomenski suggested an interesting modification of the strong-focussing method based on the use of a constant magnetic field.

Quite recently a similar suggestion was published by Simon, Kerst and others.

Thus, in many countries intensive work is at present being carried out on the design and study of accelerators for the production of energies approaching the upper limit of the scale.

In the Soviet Union, plans are being made under the direction of Vladimirski to build strong-focussing accelerators for high energies. It is also proposed to avoid the critical energy by using a new method of regulating the frequency of the accelerating field (correlation with gradient of the magnetic field) etc. It seems to me, however, that no real progress in the production of ultra-high energies are to be expected from the use of such accelerators. It is a well known fact that the radius of the magnet of any cyclical accelerator is related by a simple equation to the energy of the particles obtainable in such a machine, namely: $W = 300\ HR$.

As contemporary magnetic materials do not allow a field of more than 10,000 to 20,000 oersteds to be produced, any increase in energy calls for a proportional increase in the radius of the electromagnet, which obviously, even in strong-focussing accelerators, in practice restricts the upper value of the energy to 50,000–100,000 Mev.

In so far as the potentialities of the usual proven methods appear to be exhausted, new ones will have to be looked for. For instance, we could make great progress if we could devise means of creating ultra-powerful magnetic fields, or of considerably increasing the maximum voltages of the electric field in linear accelerators. It is true that even ultra-powerful magnetic fields will not lead to a substantial increase in the upper limit of the energy of electrons, as this limit is in practice determined by radiation.

Therefore, my personal opinion is that we must seek out completely new approaches. There are several possibilities, I think. But it would be premature to discuss the problem here, as it still needs very thorough examination.

I do not doubt, however, that experimental physics will succeed in solving this problem too, and that we shall learn how to create artificially particles with enormous energies of the order of 10^{12} and 10^{13} electron-volts.

Radioactive Tracers and Their Application

By G. de Hevesy, Sweden

The early roots of the method of radioactive tracers, of radioactive indicators, go back to the Physics Department of the University of Manchester which was under the inspiring leadership of Lord, then Professor, Ernest Rutherford. Quite shortly prior to embarking on studies which led him to his discovery of the nucleus of the atom, Rutherford was greatly interested in the properties of radiation emitted by a number of radioactive bodies, including radium-D, and was anxious to obtain a strongly active sample of this radioelement. Radium-D is a disintegration product of radium emanation of radon and can be obtained from glass tubes in which radium emanation was kept and in which it decayed. Such radon-containing tubes were much used in cancer therapy.

A much more abundant source of radium-D is the large amounts of lead obtained when purifying uranium ores.

In those days, the only uranium mine was that of Joachimsthal in Bohemia, owned by the Imperial Austrian Government. The Austrian Government showed great generosity towards scientists engaged in the study of radioactivity. It presented Pierre and Marie Curie with a railway carload of pitchblende, enabling them to isolate radium shortly after their discovery of this element. All work carried out with radium by Rutherford and his school had to be done with a radium sample lent by the Austrian Government which also presented Rutherford with many hundreds of kilograms of lead chloride prepared from pitchblende containing the precious radium-D, which was useless, however, due to its contamination with very large amounts of lead.

One day in 1911, when I met Rutherford in the basement of his institute, where the lead chloride was stored, he addressed me in his usual unconventional way, telling me that if I were worth my salt I should separate radium-D from all that disturbing lead. I was then a young man (they are always optimists) and did not doubt for a moment that I would succeed. I failed entirely and had to conclude, correspondingly, that radium-D and lead belong to the group of "practically inseparable substances," as such bodies were called prior to the coining of the word isotope which was of later date. Since my extended separation attempts were a total failure, I tried to find consolation in the possibility of labeling lead by adding pure radium-D prepared from emanation tubes to a known amount of lead, and

tracing the path of lead atoms by means of radioactive measurements.

The only institute which in those days handled large amounts of radium emanation, and thus of radium-D, was the Vienna Institute of Radium Research; this fact induced me late in 1912 to go to Vienna, where I was fortunate enough to meet Dr. Paneth, an assistant to this Institute, who had carried out equally extensive experiments to separate radium-D from lead, and who received the same negative result. We worked together on tracer experiments with radioactive lead and bismuth. Radioactive tracers were for the first time applied early in 1913 to the determination of the solubility of slightly soluble salts as lead sulfide and lead chromate in water, using radium-D as an indicator for lead. These experiments were soon followed by numerous applications of radioactive lead and bismuth isotopes as tracers in the study of problems of inorganic and physical chemistry. A study of the laws of electrochemistry at very low concentrations of lead and bismuth ions was carried out. The interaction of atoms of metallic lead and lead ions contained in a surrounding aqueous solution and the

Mr. G. de Hevesy

interaction between the ions located in the surface layer of solid salts as lead sulfate and the lead ions of the solution in which they were immersed were investigated.

When, almost a century ago, Maxwell was faced with the task of calculating the rate of diffusion of gaseous oxygen into gaseous nitrogen, he made the assumption — to simplify the calculation — that the size and mass of the nitrogen and oxygen molecules are identical, calculating thus the diffusion rate of oxygen into oxygen which he called "self-diffusion." The possibility of labeling lead enabled us to turn this mathematical fiction into a reality and to measure the self-diffusion both in liquid and solid metallic lead and lead compounds. Very numerous and extended studies on self-diffusion and diffusion in solids were made in the later years, when radioactive isotopes of almost every element became available, and these studies broadened considerably our knowledge of the solid state of matter.

A few years later, Paneth, making use of labeled lead and bismuth, discovered the existence of volatile hydrides of these elements and also the existence of free radicals, and in this way made advances of great importance.

By means of isotopic indicators we can trace the paths of atoms and molecules. Since their path is most intricate in living organisms, radioactive tracers have found by far their most extensive applications in life sciences. The first application of radioactive tracers to biology was the study of the uptake of lead ions labeled by addition of its radioactive isotope thorium B, prepared from radiothorium isolated from thorium-containing minerals. Not only was the path of lead in the plant followed by radioactive measurements, but the extent and the speed at which lead ions are released by the plant when placing it in a culture solution containing inactive lead salts was also studied. Thus it was possible to distinguish between lead ions taken up by the plant at different times and from different sources. When, a quarter of a century later, radioactive phosphorus became available, such a possibility proved to be of great importance to agriculture. It was now possible, for example, to distinguish between phosphorus taken up by barley, from fertilizers added to the soil and from the soil proper.

A great number of similar studies have been carried out and I wish to mention the results obtained by Spinks and his colleagues in Canada. They added P^{32}-labeled phosphorus fertilizers (12 kg P_2O_5 per acre) of different types and of known radioactivity to the soil and determined both the phosphorus content of the plant and its radioactivity. If, for example, 1 mg of the plant phosphorus was half as radioactive as 1 mg of the phosphorus of the added fertilizers, they could conclude that half of the phosphorus of the plant originated from the fertilizer and half had to come from the soil. The results also showed that more than 60 per cent of the phosphorus of barley harvested in June was supplied by the fertilizer, and somewhat less of the phosphorus of wheat. When harvesting the barley in August, the share of the fertilizer phosphorus in the total phosphorus of barley was reduced to about 30 per cent. The rate of supply of fertilizer phosphorus declines thus in the later part of the season. While, in the early stages of development, the fertilizer supplies the major part of the plant's phosphate requirement, in the later stages the share of the soil phosphorus in the phosphorus uptake of the plant increases. This is presumably due to the fact that the root system expands with time and the plant thus can avail itself of an increasing amount of competing soil phosphorus. They further obtained a comparison of the effectivity of different phosphorus compounds as fertilizers. Ammonium phosphate proved to be the most, dicalcium phosphate the least effective compound among those investigated.

From the very numerous applications of radioactive tracers in agriculture and botany I wish to mention just one more, viz., the tracing of the path of the atoms of pollen in fertilized seed.

Pollen labeled with P^{32} can easily be obtained by placing, for example, an aspen branch shortly before pollen formation into water containing radioactive phosphate. The radioactive phosphate diffuses into the branch and participates in the formation of the pollen. Active pollen, emitting several β-particles per microgram, were obtained in experiments carried out in Stockholm after keeping an aspen branch for 7 days in a solution containing 1 mc of P^{32}. Even the preformed leaves took up appreciable amounts of phosphorus–32.

Female aspen were fertilized with the labeled pollen. The fruits were collected three weeks later and the radioactivity of a known number of seeds compared with that of a known number of pollen. One seed was found to contain the labeled phosphorus atoms of 8 and 9 pollen grains. At first sight, this is a puzzling result, since the formation of a seed requires one fertilizing pollen only, just as in the animal organism the fertilization of an egg requires one sperm. However, in the animal organism, not only the atoms of the fertilizing sperm may participate in the formation of the offspring but also those of many millions more sperms; the very numerous sperms which did not participate in the fertilizing process are degraded in the female organism, reach the circulation, and have an opportunity of participating in the formation of the fetus. In a similar way, as the above-mentioned results demonstrate, also atoms of pollen which do not participate in the fertilizing process may contribute to the formation of the seed.

The tracing of the path of ancestral atoms through different generations is a fascinating task. A fraction of maternal atoms, varying considerably from element to element, is replaced by atoms taken up by the food and excreted before the offspring is born; another fraction, though present, may be prevented from taking part in building up the offspring.

By applying radioactive tracers the size of these fractions can be determined.

In the extracellular fluid of a human subject weighing 80 kg, about 55 gm of sodium circulates. If we administer radioactive sodium of negligible weight, the circulating sodium will be momentarily labeled almost uniformly. We find 4 per cent of the activity administered to be excreted in the course of the first day and can thus conclude that 4 per cent of all the circulating sodium left the organism as well and was replaced by food sodium. Half of the sodium atoms present at the start of the experiment are lost in the course of about a fortnight. The body contains about 30 gm of cellular sodium as well, and these sodium atoms are preserved longer than the circulating sodium, 10 gm being deeply imbedded in the mineral frame of the skeleton and almost quantitatively retained during life.

It was the subject of the first investigation carried out in Copenhagen very shortly after Joliot-Curie's fundamental discovery of artificial radioactivity to determine if and to what extent the atoms of the mineral frame of the fully grown skeleton are replaceable, are renewable. It was found that, only a few minutes after introducing labeled phosphate into the circulation, thus labeling the plasma phosphate, P^{32} is located in the skeleton of the rat. In recent years, the technique of autoradiography has made great advances and the rapid uptake of P^{32} by the bone tissue has also been demonstrated by this method.

If all skeletal phosphate were replaced by plasma phosphate with time, we ought to find 1 mg of skeletal phosphate to have the same radioactivity as 1 mg of plasma phosphate. This is far from being the case. In experiments in which the radioactivity of the plasma phosphate of the rabbit was kept at a constant level by daily repeated injections, after the lapse of 50 days the activity of 1 mg of the phosphate of the soft bone reached only 30 per cent of that of the plasma phosphate, and that of the hard bones still less, the result obtained indicating that through the lifetime of the rabbit not more than about $\frac{1}{3}$ of the mineral constituents of the skeleton is accessible to renewal.

Similar considerations permit us to determine to what extent the phosphorus atoms incorporated in the numerous phosphorus compounds present in the living organism are replaced, thus the rate of renewal of these types of molecules. The determination of the turnover rate of such compounds was the subject of many hundreds of investigations. While half of the terminal phosphorus atoms of the ATP molecule is renewed in the course of seconds only, a very slight renewal of the phosphorus atoms incorporated into DNA present in the nervous system, for example, is observed in the course of a month, the molecules of other phosphorus compounds in the body being renewed at an intermediate rate.

In the body, much harassed phosphorus and also other types of atoms find a safe abode in the skeleton only. Some of the mineral constituents of the skeleton, a part of the bone apatite is dissolved by plasma of lymph and new apatite is crystallized from these liquid phases. In this process only a part of the mineral frame is involved, the rest having no opportunity to get into contact with the solvent or not availing itself of this opportunity. Due to this fact, we cannot label a fully grown organism through and through. We can, however, obtain completely labeled animals by administering labeled food to the mother, a procedure which results in the formation of completely labeled offsprings. We fed pregnant mice food containing radioactive calcium with the result that a litter of mice was obtained which contained—even in their skeleton—labeled calcium only. All members of a litter had about the same calcium content. By sacrificing the different members of the litter, shifted after birth to an inactive foster mother, at various dates within an interval of a year or two, we obtain information about the percentage of the maternal calcium conserved in the animal during lifetime. Half of the maternal calcium atoms are preserved during the life of the mouse. Ninety-nine per cent of the body calcium is present in the skeleton, and a large share of this is to be found in the inaccessible part of the bone apatite.

If we continue feeding the litter on radioactive food after birth until it reaches about 100 days and sacrifice different members at different dates, we find that in the course of a year or two, thus almost through life, 33 per cent, i.e., $\frac{1}{3}$ of the labeled calcium atoms of the skeleton are lost, the rest being incorporated into inaccessible skeletal parts.

Out of the atomic heritage of the mouse about 1/300 goes over to the offspring and, as this is the case for each following generation, we arrive at the result that the eleventh generation of mice does not contain a single ancestral calcium atom, a result which demonstrates beautifully the known fact that heredity does not involve atomic kinship.

While we can locate ancestral calcium atoms in the tenth generation of the mouse, half of the water molecules of the mouse is replaced by water molecules taken up by the animal in the course of 2.5 days, and after the lapse of 159 days no maternal water molecule is any longer present in the animal.

For many years after the discovery of artificial radioactivity, radioactive hydrogen, tritium, was not available and such experiments were carried out with heavy water as an indicator. Tritium, however, is a very much more sensitive tracer than deuterium. We can dilute 1 millimol of tritium 10^{12} times or more and still ascertain its presence, while the presence of deuterium cannot longer be detected after a 10^6 times dilution. With tritium-labeled water the replacement of labeled body water molecules through inactive ones could be followed for a very long time with the result that after many days a three-day interval does not suffice to replace half of the water molecules of the mouse.

This result is to be interpreted in the following

way. In the course of the experiment a minor part of the labeled hydrogen atoms of the water is incorporated at a low rate into organic compounds of the body and is correspondingly released at a low rate in a later phase of the experiment, forming labeled water molecules again. After replacement of most of the labeled water molecules originally present in the body by inactive water molecules, these resurrected water molecules—during resurrection they found a new oxygen partner—make themselves noticeable and are responsible for the fact that 1/100,000 of the administered tritium is present in the mouse as water even after the lapse of 280 days.

That hydrogen atoms of the body water can be incorporated into organic compounds as, for example, into fatty acids was already observed in Schoenheimer and Rittenberg's classical investigation using deuterium as a tracer. Though deuterium found a most useful application in many studies, the availability of a radioactive hydrogen isotope was a great advance in view of its much greater sensitivity, and also because it can be more conveniently determined than deuterium.

In early days after the discovery of artificial radioactivity, radioactive tracers were prepared under the action of neutrons emitted by mixtures of radium and beryllium. By using 1 gm of radium, a few microcuries of P^{32} of high specific activity and a few other radioactive isotopes could be prepared. The application of a cyclotron for the same purpose a few years later was an immense advance. From then on it was possible to obtain 10^5 times more active preparations than by using neutrons emitted by radium-beryllium mixtures; also radioactive isotopes of the great majority of elements became available for tracer work. For those investigators who applied naturally radioactive isotopes as indicators at an early date, the discovery of Frederic and Irene Joliot-Curie opened a fairyland, the size of which was immensely enlarged by Ernest Lawrence's construction of the cyclotron. Not only did the cyclotron prepare radioactive substances of prodigious activities, they were also with the greatest generosity put at the disposal of those working with these new tracers by Dr. Ernest Lawrence.

The next great advance was the construction of the pile. Radioactive isotopes of almost every element and of prodigious activity became available, among them tritium and C^{14} which could not formerly be supplied. Radiocarbon found wide application to metabolic and related studies, as well as to dating investigations, due to the ingenious discovery of Libby, the results of which he will present. I just want to mention one of these which, though possibly not the most important, is a very instructive one.

Chaikoff and his colleagues injected into the circulation of the rat, glucose containing C^{14} of negligible weight, thus labeling the circulating glucose of the blood. By determining the radioactivity of 1 mg of glucose secured from the blood at different time intervals they could follow the speed at which those glucose molecules which had been present, at the start of the experiment, left the circulation. By collecting the CO_2 exhaled and determining its radioactivity they could, furthermore, follow the rate at which the carbon of these glucose molecules was converted into CO_2. The results showed that half of the glucose molecules present at the start of the experiment was no longer in the circulation after the lapse of 70 min.

The exhaled air is found to be radioactive a few minutes after injecting labeled glucose. Since more and more of the glucose is being burned the activity of the air increases for the first ¾ hours, whereafter it declines hand in hand with the radioactivity of the blood. From the data obtained it follows that 45 per cent of the CO_2 exhaled by the rat originate from the burning of glucose, the residual 55 per cent from that of fats and other body constituents.

Ions of sodium, potassium, chlorine, phosphate and so on, present in the blood plasma, are replaced by extravascular ions at a very much more rapid rate than glucose. Half of the sodium ions present in the plasma leaves the circulation in the course of 1 or 2 minutes. The very great rapidity with which these and also many other types of ions interchange was only revealed when radioactive tracers became available. On the other hand, it takes several days for proteins to be half replaced. Many hundreds of studies deal with the turnover of the constituents of blood plasma.

Very beautiful results were obtained in the study of the turnover of the circulating plasma iron, a problem of great importance for medical diagnosis; usually, minute amounts of iron are taken up from the food. The study of this uptake was immensely facilitated by using radioiron as a tracer. Paul Hahn, Whippel and their colleagues demonstrated, shortly after cyclotron-prepared iron became available, that the uptake of iron from the intestinal tract is governed mainly by the iron requirement of the body. Tedious chemical analyses could be replaced by feeding labeled iron and determining after the lapse of several days the radioactivity of red corpuscles, in which most of the iron taken up by the body concentrates with time. Later, John Lawrence and his colleagues, and numerous others, studied the rate at which labeled iron atoms present in the plasma leave the circulation and are replaced by others coming from various organs and, to a minor extent, from the food. Of the about 4 mg iron present in the human blood plasma half is no longer to be found in the circulation after the lapse of 90 minutes. Slightly more than half, thus about 18 mg daily, is making its way into the marrow, to be utilized for the formation of hemoglobin of the red corpuscles, while the other half is taken up by the liver and other organs.

The disappearance rate of the iron atoms from the plasma is accelerated, for example, at high altitudes, where the rate of formation of the red corpuscles is a more rapid one than on sea level. It is depressed in numerous diseases as in refractory anemia. Lawrence and his colleagues have demonstrated how with time the iron atoms present at the start of the experiment are to a very large extent in the red corpuscles of a healthy human, not, however, in that of one suffering from myeloma.

A very effective way to interfere with hemoglobin formation and thus with the path of the circulating plasma iron is exposure to inonizing radiation. This interferes with the formation of new marrow cells and may destroy even those already present. The *milieu* in which hemoglobin is laid down being now absent, hemoglobin formation and utilization of iron for this purpose cease.

That irradiation interferes with the formation of desoxyribonucleic acid was first demonstrated when radiophosphorus, and later also radiocarbon, were used as tracers. It was also found that this interference is highly specific; synthesis of proteins, for example, continues in the exposed tissue. When, for example, a marrow cell, in which the formation of other constituents continues after exposure, not however that of DNA formation, recovers its synthesizing capacity later on and divides, the division can easily become fatal, leading to the death of the marrow cells.

Radioactive tracers can not only be administered to the organism, they can also be produced *in situ* by exposure to neutrons. The stable arsenium present in the body can, with a comparatively good yield, be turned into radioarsenium. After poisoning with arsenic an appreciable part of arsenium concentrates in the hair and remains in it. By cutting the hair of a victim of such a poisoning, exposed previously to irradiation with neutrons, and determining whether the hair sample is radioactive or not we can — as the growth rate of hair is known — determine at which date the poison was administered.

In view of the very numerous applications of radioactive isotopes in metabolic and related studies, many of which are highly fascinating, one is tempted to discuss many more of them. I have, however, had to restrict myself to the discription of very few examples.

Besides the easy availability of radioactive tracers, their very extended application is to a large extent due to the great convenience with which radioactive measurements can be carried out which compete with the easiest procedures of analytical chemistry.

Of all the radioactive tracers, C^{14} has found the most extended application. Due to the prodigious efficiency of the US, British and Canadian piles many hundreds of labeled carbon compounds are at the disposal of workers in this field. Results of greatest importance for biochemistry and physiology were obtained by using pile-made C^{14}. The most fascinating experiments with C^{14} were, however, carried out with C^{14} found in nature applied by Dr. Libby in his beautiful dating studies which will be the subject of his lecture.

Radiocarbon Dating

By W. F. Libby,* USA

The bombardment of the Earth by the cosmic radiation produces neutrons by the disintegration of nuclei of the air atoms. If Geiger counters are sent aloft one observes[1] that the neutron intensity rises to a maximum at some 50,000 feet and then falls abruptly at higher altitudes, as though the neutrons were not present in the incident primary radiation but were produced by collisions of the primary cosmic rays with the air. The decrease in intensity of the neutrons at the very top of the atmosphere is due to their escaping from the earth after being formed in the initial collisions of the cosmic rays. About one-third of them thus escape. This supposition that the neutrons are secondary in origin is reasonable since the neutron is known to be unstable, decaying with a half-life of about 13 minutes to form a proton,[2] and could hardly live long enough to traverse the great distances of interstellar space, though it could just reach the Earth from the Sun. Careful measurements made with the balloon technique have revealed an average rate of 2.4 neutrons/cm^2/sec produced on and not escaping from the Earth's surface, strong variations with latitude[3] being averaged out. As the neutrons produced by cosmic rays seldom ever reach the Earth's surface, some absorptive process must occur in the air, and the question arises of what nuclear species neutrons will be produced by the reaction with air.[4,5] In the laboratory, oxygen is observed to be almost completely inert to neutrons, but nitrogen, the principal constituent of air, has a strong interaction (the nuclear cross section for thermal-energy neutrons is $1.7 \times 10^{-24}\,cm^2$). This interaction is almost exclusively due to a single reaction:

$$n + N^{14} \rightarrow C^{14} + p$$

Various other possibilities exist. One of these is the production of radioactive hydrogen (tritium) at a small fraction of the radiocarbon yield,[5] but the principal product of the cosmic-ray bombardment of air, at least that involving neutrons as an intermediary, must be radiocarbon. We can conclude that 2.4 radiocarbon atoms are produced each second for each square centimeter of the Earth's surface on the average at the present time.

If this rate has obtained in times past, especially during the last several lifetimes of radiocarbon (5568 ± 30 years half-life, or 8030 years average life), we can say with complete certainty that a sufficient store of radiocarbon must exist on the

Earth for a steady-state balance to be assured; that is, there must be enough radiocarbon for exactly 2.4 radiocarbon atoms to disappear each second per square centimeter, to ensure that the rate of formation is just equal to the rate of disappearance. Therefore we can calculate with equal certainty that there should be some 74 metric tons of radiocarbon on the Earth. The rates of radioactive disintegrations are immutable, and under no conditions yet obtained in the laboratory have any appreciable alterations of these rates been observed. We therefore can expect with very considerable confidence that the rate at which radiocarbon reverts to N^{14} by beta-decay is independent of whether it is present in a living organism or in limestone rock or as carbon dioxide in the air.

Where should one expect to find this large quantity of radiocarbon, and why has it not long ago been observed? Returning to the mechanism of genesis, we observe that the radiocarbon atoms are formed at an altitude of about 6 or 7 miles on the average. It therefore seems reasonable to suppose that the radiocarbon atoms will burn in the air soon after their birth, to form radioactive carbon dioxide. Therefore we conclude that the cosmic rays introduce radioactive carbon dioxide into the air, and that this is probably mixed by the winds so that all the atmospheric carbon dioxide is contaminated at

Mr. Willard F. Libby

---

*Atomic Energy Commission, Washington, D. C.

the rate of 2.4 molecules of $C^{14}O_2$ per second for each cm^2 of the Earth's surface. It is, of course, well known that atmospheric carbon dioxide is the main source of plant carbon, through photosynthesis. Therefore we conclude that all plant life must contain radiocarbon. It is obvious also that since animal life lives on plant life it too must contain radiocarbon. In addition the carbonate and bicarbonate and other inorganic carbonaceous materials dissolved in the sea, which are in interchange equilibrium with atmospheric carbon dioxide, must contain radiocarbon. The total diluting reservoir apparently contains about 8.3 gm of elemental carbon per cm^2 of the Earth's surface. The bulk of it is the dissolved inorganic material in the sea, which amounts to 7.25 gm, and the remainder is 0.12 gm of atmospheric carbon dioxide and some 0.9 gm of living matter all over the earth, together with dissolved but dead organic matter in the sea-water. Since the bulk of the reservoir is inorganic matter in the sea, which is particularly easy to determine accurately, we are entitled to assume that the total figure, 8.3, is probably accurate to about 10 per cent, even though the estimation of the total amount of living matter on the Earth is not known accurately. If it is correct that there are 8.3 gm of carbon involved or being mixed with the atmospheric carbon dioxide on a time-scale of the order of the 8000-year average life of radiocarbon, we can immediately calculate that the specific activity of living matter should be 2.4 divided by 8.3 disintegrations per second or 17.3 per minute per gram of carbon contained. The experimentally observed value for organic matter is 15.3 per minute.

This satisfactory agreement leads us to believe that the postulate of the constancy of the cosmic radiation in the last 20,000 years or so, and the implied but not specifically stated postulate that the volume of the reservoir has not changed, are probable both correct. It would seem extremely unlikely that the cosmic-ray intensity should be casually related to the volume of the sea, for two less cognate physical quantities could hardly be imagined. Therefore we take it that, since our determination depends on the ratio, the agreement between the calculated and observed specific activity means that both the cosmic rays and the carbon content of the sea have been relatively constant for the last 10,000 or 20,000 years.

Since the cosmic-ray neutron intensity varies considerably with latitude[6] one might expect living matter at the equator to be less radioactive than that in the northern and southern regions, the cosmic ray neutron intensity at 50–60 degrees north geomagnetic latitude being some four times that at the equator. On second thought, however, one realizes that this is not likely to be so, for on the average radiocarbon atoms live 8000 years and therefore have this great length of time to be evenly distributed by winds and ocean currents. Direct tests have shown that this prediction is correct, and that all over the Earth's surface all forms of living matter possess the same radiocarbon activity per gram of contained carbon to within the error of measurement.

Radiocarbon dating is based on the above postulates and the fact that at the time of death the assimilation of radiocarbon ceases. The radiocarbon present in the body at the time of death then proceeds to disappear at its immutable rate of one-half every 5568 years. Therefore, we expect that a 5600-year-old mummy or piece of tree or cloth or flesh will show one-half the specific radioactivity observed in living organic matter at the present day and that one 11,200 years old would show one-quarter, etc. The radiocarbon content of dead matter accordingly reveals the age of the specimen, the age being taken as time elapsed since death rather than, as in normal usage, time elapsed since birth. The error of measurement is determined by the accuracy with which the specific radioactivity can be measured. Direct comparison with organic matter of known age back to 5000 years, the oldest material of known age available, appears to confirm these postulates and deductions. Utilization of the method in the great periods of prehistory has resulted in a series of dates which display some element of consistency and give reason for belief in the validity of the dating technique.

METHODS OF MEASUREMENT

The radiocarbon content of living matter is so low that its measurement is somewhat difficult. The procedures used in our laboratory consist of the conversion of the sample to pure carbon and the measurement of the radioactivity of the latter. Pure carbon is used, since any diluent atoms will reduce the measurable effect by absorbing the very soft radiocarbon radiation. The measurement of the pure carbon is accomplished by a Geiger counter in which the sample of carbon lines the cylindrical wall. (Fig. 1) This places the sample in a most advantageous position, where the radiations have a high probability of being recorded. The actual probability attained with a 400 cm^2 area of carbon sample weighing 8 gm in all is 5.46 per cent. Since, on the average, we find 15.3 disintegrations per minute per gram of carbon in modern organic matter, we can expect $8 \times 15.3 \times 0.0546$, or 6.7, counts per minute for modern material in our special Geiger counter.

A counter of the size used normally has a background of five or six hundred counts per minute, this background being due to laboratory contamination by naturally radioactive materials and to cosmic radiation. It is obviously necessary, therefore, that the background be reduced to a very small fraction of its normal value if we are to hope to measure the radiocarbon content of even modern organic matter. Since the background is due to two different types of radiation, namely, the cosmic rays and the natural radioactivities, we use two types of shielding. For the natural radioactivities a shield of several

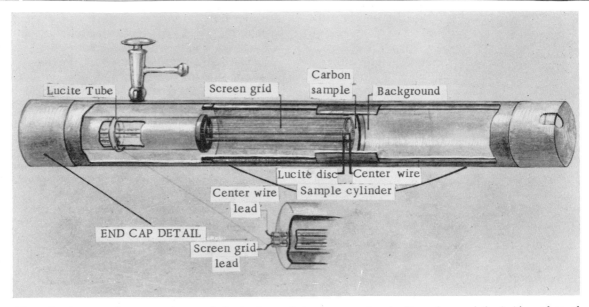

Figure 1. Screen wall counter. The sample in the form of elementary carbon is disposed around the inside surface of a movable cylinder surrounding a grid, defining the sensitive Geiger counter volume. The two possible positions of the cylinder correspond to the carbon sample being alternately over the grid and removed from it, so the difference in counting-rate is a direct measure of the radiocarbon activity

inches of iron is employed (Figs. 2, 3); this reduces the unshielded background from 600 to 100 counts per minute. The residue of 100 counts per minute is very little reduced by the further addition of iron. As much as 20 feet seems to reduce it by only 20 or 30 per cent. It is clear, therefore, that the cosmic rays cannot be absorbed, and some device for eliminating their effect must be employed. A ring of protecting counters in close contact with one another is placed around the central Geiger counter in which the carbon sample is being measured. They are then electronically connected in such a way that each response in the protecting ring renders the central counter inoperative for a very small fraction of a second. Since the cosmic radiations will penetrate several inches of iron, there is little doubt about their

ability to penetrate the fraction of an inch of brass or copper involved in the counter bundle, and any radiation passing through the central counter must necessarily pass through one of the shielding counters, unless it passes directly down the length of the counter. With this device the background is reduced to about 5 counts per minute. A further shield of mercury encased in iron has been shown by Dr. Kulp to reduce the background to 2 or 3 counts per minute. One might worry about the loss of efficiency due to the fact that the central counter is turned off by the action of the protecting counters operating in anti-coincidence. The aggregate count-rate of the shielding counters when located inside the 8-inch iron shield is only 900 counts per minute, and since each impulse turns off the central counter for only a fraction of 1

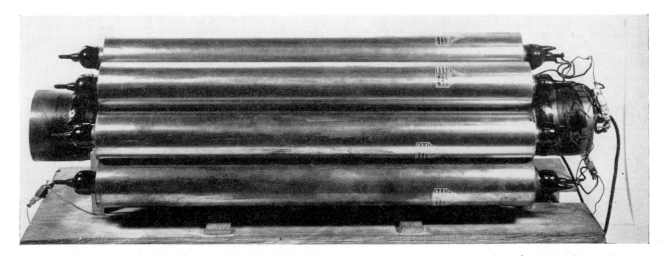

Figure 2. Side views of the screen-wall counter surrounded by the shielding counters used to cancel out the penetrating cosmic rays. The box contains four counters underneath, making a total of eleven, as shown in Fig. 3

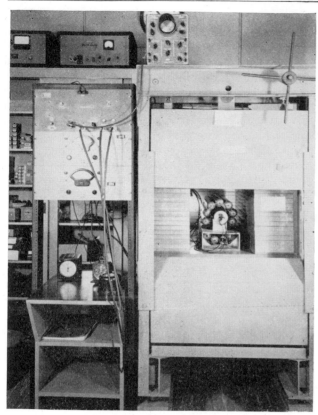

Figure 3. The complete apparatus, consisting of the iron shield (with the door open), the counter bundle in place, and the associated electronic apparatus. The shield has at least 8 inches of iron in all directions and weighs some 6 tons

metal. Magnesium turnings are placed in an ordinary iron tube about 3 feet long and 1 inch in diameter, connected to the vacuum line. The air is removed, some of the carbon dioxide is introduced, and the tube is heated to the melting point of magnesium, 651°C. At this point the reduction reaction begins vigorously, and care must be exercised to prevent holes being burned in the iron tube. With reasonable care the fire can be kept going until the storage bulbs are exhausted. Normally, about 1 gram-atom of carbon is involved, i.e., some 24 liters of carbon dioxide.

After the reduction is complete, the solid products are removed from the iron tube and extracted with hydrochloric acid, to remove the excess of metallic magnesium and the magnesium oxide produced in the reaction. This extraction takes 24 to 48 hours and produces a carbon black of better than 90 per cent purity, the remaining materials being magnesium oxide—which for some obscure reason is difficult to remove completely by hydrochloric acid extraction—and about 5 per cent non-carbonaceous but volatile matter which probably is absorbed water. The samples are analyzed for carbon, and an appropriate correction of the observed count-rates is made.

More recently other laboratories have developed methods of measuring the radiocarbon content of organic matter by different techniques maintaining the sample in the gaseous state. The two most highly developed procedures consist in a method which uses acetylene gas in the one case, and carbon dioxide gas in the other case. The acetylene gas technique was developed by H. Suess in America, and A. R. Crathorn in England. Acetylene is prepared by the conversion of the sample to strontium carbide by heating a mixture of magnesium metal and strontium carbonate—strontium carbonate having been prepared from the sample to be measured. The acetylene technique appears to have a superior sensitivity and to extend the dating range of the radiocarbon method back to perhaps 30,000 years. The second major gas counting technique was developed first in Holland by deVries and Barendsen and later at several laboratories in Europe and America. The results strongly indicate that the carbon dioxide counting technique may rival the acetylene method and that probably both constitute an advancement over the solid carbon procedure developed in our laboratories.

millisecond at most, one is certain that not more than one second is lost out of each minute. It is true in principle, however, that this type of shielding-arrangement has limitations if the over-all size of the assembly is increased greatly. The advantage of putting the shielding counters within the iron shield will also be clear. It is well to note that the radiations from the radiocarbon itself will not be cancelled by the shielding counters, for they are not sufficiently penetrating to pass through the walls of the central Geiger counter. An ordinary sheet of paper stops the radiocarbon radiation practically completely.

With material such as wood or peat, conversion of the samples to elementary carbon is accomplished by combustion to carbon dioxide. With inorganic material such as calcium carbonate, acidification is sufficient to liberate carbon dioxide, which is thus produced for all types of samples. The carbon dioxide needs purification from radon, since small amounts of uranium and radium can be expected in most materials, and both the combustion and the acidification operations will carry the radon along with the carbon dioxide. The purification is accomplished by precipitating calcium carbonate and washing and drying it. The purified calcium carbonate is then acidified with hydrochloric acid and carbon dioxide is produced again. This carbon dioxide is dried and stored in bulbs. Reduction to elementary carbon is accomplished by reaction with pure magnesium

WORLD-WIDE DISTRIBUTION OF RADIOCARBON

E. C. Anderson[7, 8, 9] in our laboratory studied the present distribution of radiocarbon throughout the world. As expected, the strong variation in production rate with latitude was found to be completely masked by the long lifetime of radiocarbon and the consequent opportunity for world-wide mixing. The data, given in Table I, show no significant variation from the mean for the woods assayed from widely scattered points on the Earth's surface. In examining this table it is well to remember that, as previously mentioned, the cosmic-ray intensity and, therefore, the radiocarbon production rate are about one-fourth as great at the equator as at the latitude of 50 or 60 degrees geomagnetic north or south. The further point should be recalled that, the average life of radiocarbon being 8000 years, the radiocarbon atoms now present in living organic matter and in the dissolved carbonaceous material in the sea have been on the Earth for 8000 years on the average, and have therefore had abundant opportunity to circulate throughout the life cycle and to be moved about in the ocean currents and in the winds of the atmosphere.

The absolute radiocarbon content thus appears to be in reasonably good agreement with the present rate of production of radiocarbon, if we assume that the ocean is mixed with radiocarbon essentially to its full depth. The amount of carbon involved in living forms on land is negligible relative to the inorganic carbon in the sea. In other words the 2.4 atoms being produced per second per cm² on the average at the present time, when divided by the 8.3 gm of carbon in the ocean and in the life cycle, agree to within 10 per cent with the observed radiocarbon content at the present time. This plainly indicates that in the course of some 8000 years uniform mixing of the waters of the sea occurs, even at great depths—a point of interest to oceanographers. It indicates further that the present cosmic-ray intensity is not far different from that which obtained 8000 years ago. This latter point is of course vital to the radiocarbon dating method, in that we must assume that the radiocarbon content of living matter at the present time has been its content at all times, and that a piece of wood measured now has the same radiocarbon content as a comparable piece would have had in Egypt 5000 years ago. As we shall see later, there is further confirmatory evidence for this in the apparent agreement found among the radiocarbon contents of carbonaceous samples of historically known age.

RADIOCARBON DATING

The possible utilization of natural radiocarbon for dating was one of the principal goals throughout the early stages of the research. These consisted in the discovery of natural radiocarbon in Baltimore sewage methane with A. V. Grosse and his collaborators,[10] the development of the measurement techniques, and the world-wide assay. We then approached the interesting and crucial stage of testing the dating method with considerable care. J. Arnold joined the group as principal collaborator in this phase of the research. The American Anthropological Association and the Geological Society of America appointed a committee on carbon-14, consisting of F. Johnson (Chairman), D. Collier, F. Rainey, and R. F. Flint, to advise on the selection of samples for measurement and, most important, to organize a comprehensive test of the method. The Wenner

Gren Foundation for Anthropological Research, under its director P. Fejos, gave generous financial support to the research. Part of the development of the low-level counting technique was conducted under contract with the United States Air Force.

The advisory committee decided that it would be possible to test the method against samples of known age back to about 5000 years. This was done, and the results are shown in Fig. 4. The curve drawn is the exponential decay curve fixed by the laboratory determination of the half-life and the world-wide assay of modern organic matter for radiocarbon (Table I). The errors indicated are standard errors as determined solely by the counting statistics. That is, they are essentially governed by the square root of the total number of counts measured. Experience has indicated that this is the principal source of random error in the measurement, in that repeated measurements on a given sample have shown scatter not too inconsistent with this single measure. The materials used as samples of known age are given in Table II.

It is clear that with one or two exceptions the agreement is satisfactory. These exceptions may be acceptable statistically. One of the most interesting of the "knowns" is the redwood sample. This giant tree apparently has heartwood still containing the carbon originally deposited there when the wood

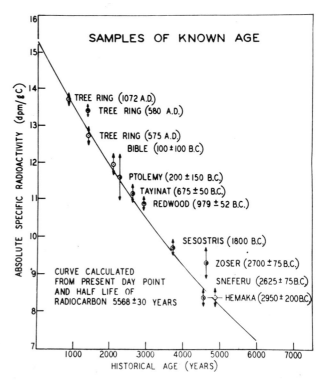

Figure 4. Samples of known age. The solid curve is calculated from the assay for modern wood and the laboratory measurement of the half-life of radiocarbon. The individual points are the specific radioactivities of various pieces of organic matter, principally wood, of known age. The errors indicated are the standard deviations (which ensure 2 out of 3 chances), and are calculated solely on the basis of the number of counts taken; they do not include any other errors, such as that arising from contamination

Table I. Activity of Terrestrial Biosphere Samples

Source	Geo-magnetic latitude	Absolute specific activity (disintegrations per minute per gram)
White spruce, Yukon	60°N	14.84 ± 0.30
Norwegian spruce, Sweden	55°N	15.37 ± 0.54
Elm wood, Chicago	53°N	14.72 ± 0.54
Fraxinus excelsior, Switzerland	49°N	15.16 ± 0.30
Honeysuckle leaves, Oak Ridge, Tennessee	47°N	14.60 ± 0.30
Pine twigs and needles (12,000 feet), Mount Wheeler, New Mexico	44°N	15.82 ± 0.47
North African briar	40°N	14.47 ± 0.44
Oak, Sherafut, Palestine	34°N	15.19 ± 0.40
Unidentified wood, Teheran	28°N	15.57 ± 0.34
Fraxinus mandshurica, Japan	26°N	14.84 ± 0.30
Unidentified wood, Panama	20°N	15.94 ± 0.51
Chlorophora excelsa, Liberia	11°N	15.08 ± 0.34
Sterculia excelsa, Copacabana, Bolivia (9000 feet)	1°N	15.47 ± 0.50
Ironwood, Majuro, Marshall Islands	0°	14.53 ± 0.60
Unidentified wood, Ceylon	2°S	15.29 ± 0.67
Beech wood (Nothofagus), Tierra del Fuego	45°S	15.37 ± 0.49
Eucalyptus, New South Wales, Australia	45°S	16.31 ± 0.43
Seal oil from seal meat from Antarctic	65°S	15.69 ± 0.30
AVERAGE		15.3 ± 0.1*

* Error of calibration of counter raises error on absolute assay to 0.5.

was formed. This result—very acceptable to most botanists, we understand—seems to be somewhat astonishing chemically. The fine filaments which constitute the cell walls, though made of cellulose molecules which of course are extremely inert, appear to have been in contact for thousands of years with enzymatically active sap.

The radiocarbon deposited at the beginning of history still has more than half the modern assay, so it was obviously necessary to consider how the great periods of prehistory could be used to check the method, and *vice versa*. The committee attacked this problem by setting up a network of projects so designed as to afford the maximum number of internal cross-checks. They arbitrarily excluded certain areas of the world and periods of history in order the more to concentrate, temporally and geographically, the prehistoric problems being investigated. They then assembled a team of collaborators in geology and archaeology, who proceeded to furnish samples for the study. The results now number between 700 and 1000, including those obtained at other laboratories, though the committee has been advisory to our group alone. It is impossible this evening to list all the dates, but some are given in Table III.

It is somewhat difficult to judge the significance of this group of dates. It seems that one of the principal conclusions is that the ice sheet last covered both northern North America and northern Europe some 11,000 years ago. It would seem that these dates are evidence that the northern regions of Europe and of North America were covered simultaneously.

It is interesting that, according to the radiocarbon evidence, the earliest men in North America, Northern Britain, and Denmark appeared roughly contemporaneously some ten thousand years ago. We were afraid that we should find man older than the last ice age, and had agreed that this would constitute sufficiently conclusive evidence to discredit the whole method; we felt that glaciers sweep very clean and that there should be no evidence of earlier human occupation left. So in England, which was completely glaciated in the north, there should be no evidence of human beings older than the time of the last ice sheet. One notes that the Lascaux cave (Dordogne), sample 406, apparently was occupied, and that its paintings were executed, some 5000 years before the last ice sheet. Other samples not listed have revealed the existence of man around the Mediterranean basin long before the last ice sheet. Such evidence has not appeared yet in conclusive form in the Americas. This may of course be a fortuitous circumstance, but it does seem significant that some evidence of a 10,000-year threshold appears.

We learn that the complicated history of glaciation in the North American Continent has been somewhat elucidated, with the dating of ice sheets preceding the last one. The phenomena of the formation of the Great Lakes and the enormous changes of the terrain in the Northern Hemisphere during the last 30,000 years due to the action of the glaciers is perhaps better understood.

We learn of the correlation of the calendars of the ancient Babylonians and Mayans with our Christian calendar. We see that the oceans of the world probably have risen in water level at a leisurely and stately pace as the glaciers melted. Further

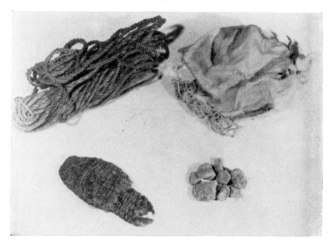

Figure 5. Typical samples used for measurement. Left foreground, rope sandal from Fort Rock Cave, Oregon, 9000 years old. Left rear: 2000-year-old rope from Peru. Right rear: 2000-year-old cotton cloth from Peru. Right foreground: 10,000-year-old faeces of the extinct giant ground sloth (Northrotherium shastense) from Gypsum Cave, Nevada

Table II. Samples of Known Age

Sample No.	Description	Age (years) by C¹⁴ dating	Average
108A	*Sequoia trunk*, clean borings in growth-rings between year A.D. 1057 and 1087, i.e., known age 880 ± 15 years	800 ± 600 900 ± 200 1030 ± 200 900 ± 200	
			930 ± 100
103	*Broken Flute Cave, New Mexico (Tree Ring)*. Douglas fir wood excavated in 1931 from Red Rock Valley, Room 6, Broken Flute Cave. Inner ring, A.D. 530; outer ring, A.D. 623. Known age thus 1330 – 1423 years	973 ± 200 1070 ± 100	
			1042 ± 80
108B	*Sequoia trunk* (108A), rings A.D. 570 – 578, i.e., known age 1377 ± 4 years	1520 ± 170 1300 ± 200	
			1430 ± 150
576	*Bible*. Dead Sea Scrolls. Book of Isaiah; linen wrappings used. Found in cave near Ain Fashkha in Palestine. Thought to be first or second century B.C.	1917 ± 200	
62	*Ptolemy*. Wood from mummiform coffin of Egyptian Ptolemaic period. Age 2280 years, according to John Wilson	2190 ± 450	
72	*Tayinat*. Wood from the floor of a central room (I–J–1st) in a large hilani ("palace") of the Syro-Hittite period in the city of Tayinat in north-west Syria. Age 2625 ± 50 years, according to R. J. Braidwood	2696 ± 270 2648 ± 270 2239 ± 270	
			2531 ± 150
159	*Sequoia*. Wood from the heart of the giant redwood known as the "Centennial Stump," felled in 1874, with 2905 rings between the innermost, and 2802 rings between the outermost, portion of the sample and the outside of the tree. Therefore known age was 2928 ± 51 years	3045 ± 210 2817 ± 240 2404 ± 210	
			2710 ± 130
81	*Sesostris*. Wood from deck of funerary ship from tomb of Sesostris III. Age 3750 years, according to John Wilson	3845 ± 400 3407 ± 500 3642 ± 310	
			3621 ± 180
1	*Zoser*. Acacia wood beam in excellent state of preservation from tomb of Zoser at Sakkara. Age 4650 ± 75 years, according to John Wilson	3699 ± 770 4234 ± 600 3991 ± 500	
			3979 ± 350
12	*Sneferu*. Cypress beam from tomb of Sneferu at Meydum. Age 4575 ± 75 years, according to John Wilson	4721 ± 500 4186 ± 500 5548 ± 500 4817 ± 240	
			4802 ± 210
267	*Hemaka*. Slab of wood from roof beam of tomb of the vizier Hemaka, contemporaneous with King Udimu, Dynasty I, at Sakkara. Accepted age 4700 – 5100 years, according to Braidwood	4803 ± 260 4961 ± 240	
			4883 ± 200

With the exception of samples 108A and 108B, which were determined by J. L. Kulp and his group at Columbia University,[11] the data are to be found in the author's book "Radiocarbon Dating".[9]

Table III. Radiocarbon Dates

I. MESOPOTAMIA AND WESTERN ASIA

Sample No.	Description	Age (years)	Average
	A. Egypt		
463	*Middle Predynastic.* Charcoal from point A–15 of the house floors at El-Omari near Cairo, Egypt. A typological assessment of the position of El-Omari would be about midway between the time of the Upper K pits of the Fayum (Nos. 457, 550, and 551) and Hemaka (No. 267)	5256 ± 230	
C–753	*Shaheinab charcoal*	5060 ± 450	
C–754	*Shaheinab shell.* Bivalve shells from Shaheinab, apparently in fairly unaltered condition. This ancient site may provide a clue to whether some elements in Egyptian civilization came from Africa northward. The site is about 1200 miles from the Egyptian Fayum (samples 457, 550, 551 — the Egyptian granaries, which dated 6240 years), and the archaeological connection with the Fayum Neolithic is close	5446 ± 380	
457	*Fayum A (Upper K).* Wheat and barley grain uncarbonized with no preservatives added, from Upper K pit 13 of the Fayum A material	6054 ± 330 6136 ± 320	
			6095 ± 250
550 and 551	*Fayum A (Upper K).* Wheat and barley grain from Upper K pit 59, Jar 3, and another of the Upper K pits (number lost) of the Fayum A material	6391 ± 180	
	B. Iraq		
113	*Jarmo.* Land-snail shells fairly well preserved from the basal levels 7 and 8 at Jarmo	6707 ± 320	
C–742	*Jarmo (Jarmo II).* Charcoal. Jarmo is an early village site midway between the towns of Kirkuk and Sulimaniyah. This site is Early Neolithic and exhibits the earliest traces of an established food-producing village economy in the Near East. Only the upper third of the site yielded portable pottery. An excavation labelled I was made clear to virgin soil near one edge of the mound. Eight floors were found. A second excavation, labelled II, was made at the highest point. This went down 4 m through the sixth floor, which is still 3.2 m above virgin soil. The sixth floor of II is equivalent to the third floor of I, and the second floor of II is equivalent to the first floor of I. The earlier Jarmo sample (113), consisting of shell, came from the seventh floor of I	6606 ± 330	
C–743	*Jarmo (Jarmo III).* Charcoal from fifth floor of excavation II (cf. samples 742 and 113)	6695 ± 360	
C–752	*Nippur.* This sample is to date the time of Hammurabi of Babylon. The problem is approached by dating the associated kings Ibi-Sin and Shu-Sin, who lived about 250 years before Hammurabi, but at a time accurately known on the Babylonian Calendar. The sample itself came from a roof beam of a house built not later than the Year 3 of Ibi-Sin, or earlier than Year 1 of Shu-Sin (a range of 12 years). From other evidence the date of this house should be between 1975 and 2375 B.C. We therefore conclude that the younger of the possible calendars which constitute this range of historical dating is strongly favoured by the radiocarbon dating	3945 ± 106 (1887 to 2100 B.C.)	
C–818	*Hazer Merd.* Ancient cave dwelling in Sulimanizah, Iraq. Charcoal ash from human campfires	Older than 25,000	
	C. Afghanistan		
C–815	*Mundigak.* Beginning of the Bronze Age in Afghanistan	4720 ± 270 4439 ± 280	
			4580 ± 200
	II. WESTERN EUROPE		
	A. France		
406	*Lascaux.* Charcoal from the Lascaux cave in the Dordogne	15,516 ± 900	
	B. Germany		
337	*German Allerod.* Peat with birch remains from pollen zone IIb, the younger Allerod, from Wallensen-im-Hils, north-western Germany	11,044 ± 500	

Table III. Radiocarbon Dates (continued)

Sample No.	Description	Age (years)	Average
	II. WESTERN EUROPE (continued)		
	C. Denmark		
432	*Danish Boreal (Danish Boreal II).* Pine cones from Denmark. They are from pollen zone V, thought to be 8500 years old	7583 ± 380	
433	*Danish Boreal (Boreal IV).* Hazel-nuts from Denmark. The nuts are from one single summer dwelling, belonging to the late boreal age, pollen zone VI, thought to be about 8000 years old	9935 ± 440 9927 ± 830	
			9931 ± 350
434	*Danish Boreal (Boreal III).* Charcoal from the same summer house as No. 433 Expected age about 8000 years	8631 ± 540	
435	*Danish Boreal (Danish House).* Birchwood from the same area as Nos. 433 and 434. From House 2. Probably a few years younger than House 1	9425 ± 470	
	D. Ireland		
355	*Irish mud.* Lake mud from Knocknacran, County Monaghan. Late Glacial, pollen zone II	11,310 ± 720	
356	*Irish Post-glacial.* Lake mud, Lagore, County Meath. Early Post-glacial, zone IV	11,787 ± 700	
C–877	*Irish Cooking Place.* Ancient Irish cooking place made by lining hole in the ground by oak planks	3506 ± 230	
C–878	*Irish Cooking Place.* Second place at Killeens, County Cork	3713 ± 270	
	E. England		
353	*Yorkshire.* Wooden platform from Mesolithic site at Lake Pickering. Pollen zone IV	10,167 ± 560 8808 ± 490	
			9488 ± 350
444	*Neasham.* Lake mud from Neasham, near Darlington. Pollen zone II, correlated directly with last Glacial stage	10,851 ± 630	
341	*Hawks Tor.* Peat from Hawks Tor, Cornwall, late Glacial, pollen zone II, 9 feet to 9 feet 4 inches at site 1, middle of lower peat	9861 ± 500	
602	*Stonehenge.* Charcoal sample from Stonehenge, Wiltshire. Late Neolithic	3798 ± 275	
	F. Iceland		
C–749	*History of the Geomagnetic Field, Reykjavik, Iceland (Iceland Peat).* The direction of the earth's magnetic field is recorded by solidifying lava, at the time of solidification, by the permanent polarization of the lava. Near Reykjavik, a lava flow occurs with polarization roughly parallel to the present geomagnetic field. It happened to flow over Post-glacial peat, which constitutes the sample. Its date correlates directly with that of the flow	5300 ± 340	
	III. UNITED STATES		
	A. Louisiana, Mississippi, Nebraska, and Texas		
558	*Folsom Bone.* Burned bison bone from Lubbock, Texas from the Folsom Horizon	9883 ± 350	
	B. Arizona, California, and New Mexico		
440 and 552	*California Early Horizon.* Charcoal from near Sacramento, site SJo–68; culture Early Central California Horizon	4052 ± 160	
C–631	*California Crude I.* Crude oil taken from depth of 1100 feet in the Tulare formation, Upper Pliocene age, at the South Belridge field, California	Older than 24,000	
C–632	*California Crude II.* Crude oil from the upper or middle Pico formation, Upper Pliocene age, from the Padre Canyon field, California. This, and sample 631, constitute the youngest crude oil samples measured	Older than 27,780	
C–898	*Guano from Carlsbad Caverns, New Mexico.* Compacted guano from New Cave. The layer is about 2 feet below the flow-stone cap forming the present floor. Contains numerous remains of an extinct three-tailed bat, Tadarida	Older than 17,800	

Table III. Radiocarbon Dates (continued)

Sample No.	Description	Age (years)	Average
	III. UNITED STATES (continued)		
	C. Nevada, Oregon, and Utah		
221	*Gypsum Cave.* Dung of giant sloth (Fig. 5) from Gypsum Cave, Las Vegas, Nevada. Collected in 1931 from room 1, dung layer 6 feet 4 inches from surface	10,902 ± 440 10,075 ± 550	
			10,455 ± 340
599	*Leonard Rock guano.* Bat guano taken from immediately next to the Pleistocene gravels in the Leonard Rock Shelter, Nevada	11,199 ± 570	
298	*Leonard Rock Shelter (Leonard Rock II).* Atlatl (throwing-stick) foreshafts of Sarcobatus, greasewood	7038 ± 350	
247	*Mazama, Oregon.* Charcoal from a tree burned by the glowing pumice thrown out by the explosion of Mount Mazama (this formed Crater Lake). The pumice is about 75 feet deep at this point, and about 40 feet of pumice overlies the portion of the tree from which these samples came. The impression was that the tree was still very nearly in an upright position	6389 ± 320 7318 ± 350 5938 ± 400 6327 ± 400	
			6453 ± 250
428	*Fort Rock Cave, Oregon.* Several pairs of woven rope sandals found in Fort Rock cave, which was buried beneath the pumice from the Newberry eruption in Oregon	9188 ± 480 8916 ± 540	
			9053 ± 350
609	*Danger Cave I, Utah.* Charcoal, wood, and sheep-dung from Danger Cave, near Wendover	11,453 ± 600	
610	*Danger Cave II.* Same as No. 609, wood	11,151 ± 570	
C–611 and C–635	*Danger (Lamus) Cave.* Floor of cave was dated at 11453 ± 600 and 11151 ± 570 years by sheep-dung and wood fragments respectively, which were found in the sand (samples 609 and 610)		
C–611	*Danger Cave III.* Charcoal from just above the sand in the lowest layers of the 15–foot deposit of garbage and debris found at the cave mouth	9789 ± 630	
C–635	*Danger Cave VII.* Charred bat guano, plant stems, and twigs from 18 to 24 inches below the current surface of the pile of debris	1930 ± 240	
	D. Minnesota, Wisconsin, and Wyoming		
308 365 366 536 537	*Two Creeks.* Wood and peat samples from Two Creeks forest bed, Wisconsin. Forest bed underlies Valder's Drift (Thwaites). Apparently the spruce forest was submerged, pushed over, and buried under glacial drift by the last advancing ice sheet in this region. Thought to be Mankato in age		
	Sample 308 (spruce wood) 365 (tree root) 366 (peat in which root, 365, was found) 536 (spruce wood) 537 (peat)	10,877 ± 740 11,437 ± 770 11,097 ± 600 12,168 ± 1500 11,442 ± 640	
			11,404 ± 350
C–630	*Kimberly, Wisconsin (Neenah).* Glacial wood from Kimberly, Wisconsin. This consisted of a tree stump about 9 feet × 5 feet, found about twelve years ago. The site is almost in a direct line with the Pointe Beach site of Two Creeks, and is thought to be of Mankato age (cf. samples 308, 365, 366, 536, 537, 444, and 355–7)	10,676 ± 750	
302	*Sage Creek, Wyoming (Yuma).* Partially burned bison bone with high organic content	6619 ± 350 7132 ± 350	
			6876 ± 250
C–795	Horner Site. Butchering site of ancient Indians in Wyoming. Hundreds of buffalo skeletons found here. Animals were slain in the fall of the year	6151 ± 500 7690 ± 850	
			6920 ± 500
	IV. SOUTH AMERICA		
484	*Mylodon Cave, Chile.* Dung of giant sloth from Mylodon Cave, Ultima Esperanza, Chile (51° 35′ S). Not associated with human artifacts, though sloth and man were found together in three caves 125 miles distant (cf. No. 485)	10,800 ± 570 10,864 ± 720	
			10,832 ± 400

Table III. Radiocarbon Dates (concluded)

Sample No.	Description	Age (years)	Average
	IV. SOUTH AMERICA (continued)		
485	*Palli Aike Cave, Chile.* Burned bone of sloth, horse, and guanaco, associated with human bones and artifacts	8639 ± 450	
	V. OTHER AREAS		
548	*Japanese.* Charcoal from Ubayama shell mound, about 10 miles west of Tokyo. Charcoal was part of structural remains in a house area in the bottom levels of the mound. Thought to be oldest house site in Japan	4850 ± 270 3938 ± 500	4546 ± 220
603	*Late Jomon.* Charcoal from the early Late Jomon (Horinouchi Stage) Horizon at the Ubayama shell mound (cf. No. 548), Japan	4513 ± 300	
C-688	*Chaney Seeds.* Wood from a canoe in which viable lotus seeds were found near Tokyo, indicating viability of the seeds of this age	3052 ± 200 3277 ± 360	3075 ± 180
C-613	*Zimbabwe.* Large log from the famous prehistoric site of Zimbabwe in southern Rhodesia. Zimbabwe is generally thought to date from the fourteenth or fifteenth centuries A. D., but may be as early as the ninth century A. D.	1415 ± 160 1344 ± 160 1271 ± 260	1361 ± 120
C-669	*Chalan Piao Site, Saipan Island (Saipan).* Oyster shell found 1.5 feet below the surface at the Chalan Piao Site, about ½ mile inland from the shore line. Conjectural date, 3000 – 4000 years	3479 ± 200	
C-721	*Blue Site, Tinian Island (Tinian Blue Site).* Shell (Tridacna) from the Blue Site on Tinian in the Marianas Islands, from Test A at a depth of 1.9 feet	1098 ± 145	
C-948 C-949	*Mayan.* Carved lintels from Tikal, Guatemala, bearing the Mayan date 9.15.10.00. This Mayan date would, on the one correlation, (Goodman-Thompson) be June 30, 741 A. D. and of another correlation with a Christian calendar (Spinden) would be October 30, 481 A. D.	1503 ± 110 (451 ± 110 A. D.)	

1, 12, 62, 81, 267, Cf. Table II

measurement of the depths of the ancient sea shores should help us to further understand this rate of rise. This should lead to new conclusions as to the geography of the earth in ancient times and it seems that most interesting historical results may follow this study.

We see that ancient man in North America was wide-spread. We find him from the State of Washington to the southern tip of South America nearly 10,000 years ago as soon as the great ice sheet receded. We see him making the most artful types of basketry. I show you this evening one of the most remarkable bits of human handwork of this ancient time (Fig. 5). We see here a shoe woven of grass rope by an ancient artisan, some 9000 years ago in western America — in the State of Oregon. This shoe was found together with its sister as a pair — as one of 300 pairs neatly stacked in a cave which, by accident, was buried by the eruption of an ancient volcano. We find this shoe to have been made some 9000 years ago. Other samples are on display. The entire sweep of ancient history with its breathtaking story of the development of man may be displayed somewhat better for the light radiocarbon dating sheds.

The ultimate question of the validity of the absolute dates given by the radiocarbon method is not yet completely answered. The evidence seems to be favorable, but only the passage of time, with its further accumulation of dates and its further digestion of the results obtained, can furnish us with a final answer.

REFERENCES

1. Yuan, L. C. L., *Phys. Rev., 74,* 504 (1948).
2. Robson, J. M., *Phys. Rev., 83,* 349 (1951).
3. Ladenburg, R., *Phys. Rev., 86,* 128 (1952).
4. Korff, S. A., *Terr. Magn. atmos. Elect., 45,* 133 (1940).
5. Libby, W. F., *Phys. Rev., 69,* 671 (1946).
6. Simpson, J. A., Jr.,*Phys. Rev., 73,* 1389 (1948)
7. Anderson, E. C., *Natural Radiocarbon,* Doctoral thesis, University of Chicago (1949).
8. Anderson, E. C. and Libby, W. F., *Phys. Rev., 81,* 64 (1951).
9. Libby, W. F., *Radiocarbon Dating,* University of Chicago Press, Chicago (1952) ; Second Ed. (1955).
10. Anderson, E. C., Libby, W. F., Weinhouse, S., Reid, A. F., Kirshenbaum, A. D. and Grosse, A. V., *Science, 105,* 576 (1947).
11. Kulp, J. L., Feely, H. W. and Tryon, L. E., *Science, 114,* 565 (1951).
12. Kulp, J. L., Tryon, L. E., Eckelman, W. R. and Snell, W. A., *Science, 116,* 409 (1952).
13. Libby, W. F., *Science, 116,* 673 (1952).

Elementary Particles. I. Light Mesons

By H. A. Bethe,* USA

HISTORICAL

Our interest in mesons originated from the desire to explain nuclear forces. Yukawa suggested in 1935 that nuclear forces are transmitted by particles having a rest mass of about 200 electron masses, in a similar way as electric forces are transmitted by light quanta. By assuming that the particles transmitting the force have a nonvanishing rest mass, Yukawa was able to explain the short range of nuclear forces. In fact, he obtained for the interaction between two nucleons the expression

$$V \sim \frac{e^{-\mu r}}{r} \qquad (1)$$

where $1/\mu$ is the Compton wave length of the meson. In order to explain exchange forces, he postulated that the mesons should be charged. Three years later, Kemmer showed that also neutral mesons should be present in order to explain the charge independence of nuclear forces.

In 1938, Anderson, Neddermeyer, Street and Stevenson found particles in cosmic radiation which seemed to have the properties postulated by Yukawa. They have a mass of 207 electron masses, and exist with both positive and negative charge. They were subsequently proved to constitute the main part of cosmic radiation at sea level and below ground. However, a closer examination of their properties showed that they do not strongly interact with nucleons and, therefore, cannot be the mesons transmitting the nuclear force. This was shown strikingly by the experiment of Conversi, Pancini, and Piccioni in 1947. These cosmic-ray particles are now known as μ mesons.

The particles which do transmit the nuclear force were finally discovered in 1947 by Powell, Lattes and Occhialini in Bristol, using nuclear emulsions. In the next year it was shown that they could also be produced by the 300 Mev Berkeley Cyclotron. This was accomplished through the help of Dr. Lattes who brought to Berkeley the nuclear emulsion technique developed at Bristol.

FREE π MESONS

By means of cyclotrons and other high-energy accelerators, π mesons can now be produced in large numbers, and collimated and monoenergetic beams can be obtained. By these means, it has been possible to study π mesons extensively, determining their

* Cornell University, Ithaca, New York.

properties as free particles, as well as their interaction with nucleons.

Let us first consider the properties of the free π meson (Table I). This particle exists with unit positive and unit negative charge and also in a neutral form, as Yukawa and Kemmer had predicted. There is ample evidence that the three charge forms are merely three different modifications of the same particle. Within experimental error the two charged mesons have the same mass, 273 electron masses. The neutral meson is about nine mass units lighter, and this small mass difference can easily be interpreted as due to secondary effects such as the electromagnetic self-energy of the charged mesons. The mass of the charged mesons is most accurately determined by measuring the curvature of their path in a magnetic field, and then their range in a photographic plate. The mass of the neutral meson is measured by means of the reaction

$$H + \pi^- = N + \pi^0 \qquad (2)$$

using negative mesons bound in the hydrogen atom to start the reaction and then measuring the velocity of the outgoing neutral meson.

The only point in which neutral and charged mesons differ appreciably is their decay. However, this does not substantially affect their properties while they exist, due to the fact that the decay is very slow compared to the time characteristic of the free π meson which may be defined as $\hbar/mc^2$ which is about 10^{-23} second. Therefore, during the life of a π meson, and also when considering its interaction with nuclear particles, we may disregard its decay properties.

A charged π meson decays into a μ meson and a neutrino. Its lifetime is 2.5×10^{-8} seconds. While long compared with $\hbar/mc^2$, this time is short enough so that essentially all π mesons formed by cosmic radiation in the atmosphere will decay into μ mesons, only very few will disappear by colliding with nuclei in the air. This is the reason for the great abundance of μ mesons in sea-level cosmic radiation. Changes in temperature will affect the balance between nuclear collisions of π mesons and decay into μ mesons, and

Table I

	Charged	Neutral
Mass (electron masses)	273.3 ± 0.2	264.5 ± 0.6
Mass (Mev)	139.6	135.2
Lifetime (sec)	2.5×10^{-8}	$\sim 5 \times 10^{-15}$
Decay into	$\mu + \nu$	2γ
Spin	0	0

have been found to influence the intensity of cosmic radiation at sea level and underground. The decay of π into μ mesons must be attributed to a special interaction which seems to be closely related to the β decay of nuclei and has been the subject of many theoretical investigations.

The neutral π mesons decays into two γ rays. If the π meson is at rest, the two γ rays go in opposite directions and each takes one half of the rest energy mc^2 of the meson. These γ rays are used to detect the neutral meson. The lifetime of the neutral meson is exceedingly short, it is between 2 and 15×10^{-15} seconds. This decay is 10,000,000 times faster than that of the charged π meson, but still 100,000,000 times slower than the characteristic time $\hbar/mc^2$. It is also slow enough so that there is only a negligible probability that a neutral π will decay within the nucleus in which it is created.

In the case of the neutral meson, the mechanism of the decay is well known. It is related to the existence of anti-nucleons, i.e., particles which are related to the ordinary nucleon, in the same manner as the positron is related to the negative electron. It is a firm prediction of every relativistic theory that there should be a counterpart to any charged particle. Thus there should be an anti-proton having unit negative charge, which can be created or annihilated together with an ordinary proton. Similarly, there should be an anti-neutron. There is strong reason to believe that the total number of nucleons is conserved; so whenever the negatively charged anti-proton is created an ordinary nucleon, either proton or neutron must be created as well. It is entirely impossible that an anti-proton transforms into a regular neutron by emission of an electron or a negative π meson; such a transformation would contradict the law of conservation of heavy particles which seems to be strictly obeyed.

Some doubt has been raised about the existence of the anti-proton because it has not been observed as yet. There are good experimental reasons why this particle has never been observed and why it is difficult to observe. At present a systematic search for the anti-proton is being made on the Berkeley Bevatron. I have no doubt that the search will succeed.

A neutral π meson, since it interacts strongly with nucleons, must be able to create a pair of nucleons, either an ordinary proton and an anti-proton or else a neutron and an anti-neutron. These particles will, of course, be created only in a virtual state since there is not enough energy available to create them actually. On the other hand, the proton and anti-proton can, of course, annihilate each other in the same manner as a positive and negative electron, i.e., by emitting two γ rays going in opposite directions. By this mechanism then the neutral π meson decays into the two γ rays.

Unfortunately, a quantitative calculation of the lifetime of the neutral π has not been successful.

It yields a lifetime of 5×10^{-17} seconds, about 100 times too short. However, there are other phenomena, for instance meson scattering, which indicate that the production of nucleon pairs by low-energy π mesons is far smaller than a straightforward application of the theory would indicate. A decay probability 100 times smaller than straightforward theory is quite in accord with this other theoretical evidence. Presumably one should conclude that also the probability of creation of an actual nucleon pair is much smaller than any simple theory would indicate, but it should not be zero.

The fact that the neutral meson decays into two γ rays rather than into three, has been used to deduce its spin. Its spin must be even, and theoretical arguments as well as the similarity of the neutral and the charged π, lead one to assign a spin of zero to this particle.

The spin of the charged meson has been measured by observing the reaction in which mesons are produced,

$$H + H = D + \pi^+ \qquad (3)$$

and its inverse reaction at the same energy. Using the principle of detailed balance, it has been shown that the spin of the positive π meson is zero. There is no doubt that the same value is also valid for the analogous negative meson.

An important property of any particle of integral spin is its parity. The concept of parity is familiar from atomic and nuclear physics. Even parity means that the wave function of a system remains unchanged upon inversion, that is in an operation in which the sign of all three spatial coordinates is changed. An odd-parity wave function changes sign upon inversion. The intrinsic parity of a Bose particle like a meson is defined by the effect which its absorption or emission has upon the wave function of the absorbing or emitting system.

If the parity of the system changes in such a process, then the parity of the particle is said to be odd. Now it has been found that slow mesons will cause the reaction

$$D + \pi^- = N + N \qquad (4)$$

which is closely related to reaction 3. By using the Pauli principle for the two neutrons emerging from this reaction, it can be shown that reaction 4 is only possible if the parity of the nuclear system changes, i.e., if the two neutrons have a parity opposite to the initial deuteron. This shows then that the parity of the meson is odd. A particle of zero spin and odd parity is called a pseudoscalar particle.

In this manner all the properties of the π meson in the free state have been derived by direct experiment. The particle then is to be described by the Klein-Gordon wave equation quantized according to the theory of Pauli and Weisskopf. Its coupling to the nucleon must be described taking into account the pseudoscalar nature of the π meson. The simplest coupling conceivable under these conditions is the so-called pseudoscalar coupling in which the interaction energy is given by

$$G \, \overline{\psi \gamma_5 \psi} \phi \qquad (5)$$

where ψ is the nucleon and ϕ the meson wave function, and γ_5 the Dirac operator. It can be shown that this is the only interaction which can be renormalized in the sense of modern field theory.

INTERACTION OF π MESONS

Since π mesons are supposed to be responsible for nuclear forces, it is important to study their interaction with nucleons. The best tool for such studies is the observation of the scattering of π mesons by nucleons. In this case only one state of the meson-nucleon system is involved, of one particular energy which can be described by a single wave function. The next simplest phenomenon is that of production of mesons by γ rays; in this case two wave functions are involved, that of the original nucleon and that of the final state, meson plus nucleon. The external agent, the electromagnetic field, is sufficiently well known to cause no essential complication. These two processes are by now reasonably well understood, at least up to energies of about 400 Mev.

By contrast the production of mesons in the collision between two nucleons is far more complicated, and has only been qualitatively interpreted up to the present. Production in complex nuclei presents further complication. Thus the process of production by nucleons is not a good way to study the meson-nucleon interaction, but it has so far proved to be the best method to obtain an intense meson beam for scattering experiments.

The most extensive experiments on meson scattering so far have been done at the University of Chicago, initiated by the late Enrico Fermi. Several other American groups and a Russian group have made important contributions. Our experimental knowledge of the photoelectric production of mesons also is due to many groups of physicists.

Before the scattering experiments were started the theoretical cross section was calculated using the pseudoscalar interaction, given previously in Equation 5, and also another interaction known as the pseudovector or gradient coupling interaction,

$$\frac{G}{2M} \, \overline{\psi} \, \vec{\sigma} \psi \cdot \nabla \phi \qquad (6)$$

where σ is the ordinary spin operator of the nucleon. Using the pseudoscalar interaction and perturbation theory, a cross section was derived which showed no remarkable features: the cross section was high, approximately 500 millibarns, at zero kinetic energy and then gradually decreased with increasing meson energy. With gradient coupling the cross section should be zero at zero energy, should then increase as the square of the kinetic energy and reach extremely high values at high energy.

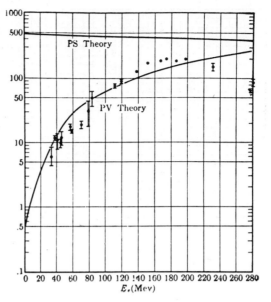

Figure 1

Figure 1 represents the predictions of these two theories and also some of the experimental data. It is seen that the pseudoscalar perturbation theory does not in any way agree with experiment. The pseudovector or gradient theory agrees rather well from about 40 to 200 Mev. At higher energies, however, the experimental cross section decreases while the theoretical one continues to increase. Similarly the cross section at zero energy is not negligible, about 3 millibarns, whereas the pseudovector theory would predict zero. Even more striking disagreements were found when the angular distributions and the relative probabilities of various possible scattering processes were investigated. The conclusion from this first comparison is that perturbation theory cannot be applied to the calculation of meson-nucleon cross sections. This is not surprising since all evidence indicates that the coupling constant, $G^2/\hbar c$ has a value somewhat greater than 10, in contrast to electromagnetic theory where the corresponding quantity, the fine structure constant $e^2/\hbar c$ has the value $1/137$.

To make progress it is best to look in an unbiased way at the experimental results. Figure 2 gives the observed cross section for the scattering of positive mesons by protons. It is seen that it has a high maximum, of about 200 millibarns, at an energy of about 200 Mev, and falls off sharply to both sides. This behavior strangly suggests a resonance. It is therefore, reasonable to expect that there is one quantum state in which there is a particularly strong interaction between meson and nucleon. We must now find out the nature of this quantum state.

One clue in this investigation is the scattering of negative π mesons by protons, which is shown in Fig. 3. It has a maximum at the same energy as the scattering of positive mesons, thus confirming the idea of a resonant state. However, the cross section at the maximum is only about 65 millibarns,

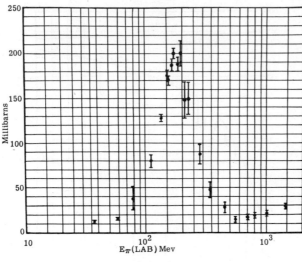

Figure 2

whereas for positive mesons it was 200. The ratio is about 1 to 3, a result which will be useful to us presently.

A further clue is obtained from the angular distribution. This is shown on Fig. 1 for an energy close to the resonance. The fact that this distribution is not isotropic shows that we are dealing with an orbital angular momentum of the meson greater than zero. Since the interaction between meson and nucleon is likely to be restricted to very small distances, of the order of 10^{-13} cm or less, and since the wave length of the meson is also about 10^{-13} cm, it is reasonable to consider only very small angular momenta. Since zero is excluded, an orbital momentum of one unit, that is a p state, is the most likely choice. Since the nucleon has a spin of $\frac{1}{2}$, we still have the choice between a $p_{\frac{1}{2}}$ and $p_{\frac{3}{2}}$ state. The former would give an isotropic angular distribution so that the experiments lead uniquely to the choice of a $p_{\frac{3}{2}}$ state. The angular distribution expected for such a state is $1 + 3\cos^2\theta$, and this is indeed the angular distribution found experimentally at energies close to the resonance.

Further confirmation of this choice of angular momentum is provided by the total cross section for positive meson scattering at its maximum. It has

a value very close to $8\pi\lambda^2$ which is just the resonance cross section expected for a $p_{\frac{3}{2}}$ state. This gives also further evidence in favor of the resonance idea as such.

For the next step in the analysis, it is most helpful to remember that nuclear forces are charge independent. Over twenty years ago, this fact lead nuclear physicists to introduce the concept of isotopic spin, and to assign to the nucleon an isotopic spin $T = \frac{1}{2}$, since it exists in two modifications. We introduce an isotopic-spin space and consider the isotopic spin of the proton as pointing in the positive direction in this space, and that of the neutron as pointing in the negative direction. Now if nuclear forces are due to mesons, charge independence should be valid also for the coupling between mesons and nucleons. This, indeed was the basis of the symmetrical meson theory proposed by Kemmer in 1938. Isotopic spin should then also be useful for mesons and it is easy to see that we have to assign to the meson an isotopic spin of one unit, and to the positive, neutral, and negative mesons' isotopic-spin components in the "positive" direction of $+1, 0$ and -1.

Now if the isotopic spin is a good quantum number, as it should be in order to obtain charge independence, and if the meson has isotopic-spin 1, and the nucleon $\frac{1}{2}$, then the system composed of both particles should have two possible values of the total isotopic spin, namely $\frac{3}{2}$ and $\frac{1}{2}$. If we have a positive meson plus a proton, then the isotopic-spin component is $\frac{3}{2}$, and, therefore, this system must have a total isotopic spin $T = \frac{3}{2}$. So if there were a resonance in a state of $T = \frac{1}{2}$, this could not manifest itself in tne scattering of positive mesons by protons but only in that of negative mesons. Thus we are forced to assume that the experimental resonance at 200 Mev is due to a state of isotopic spin $\frac{3}{2}$ if indeed it is due to one single state. A simple calculation shows that for $T = \frac{3}{2}$ the cross sections for positive mesons should be just three times that for negative mesons, which is exactly the ratio found experi-

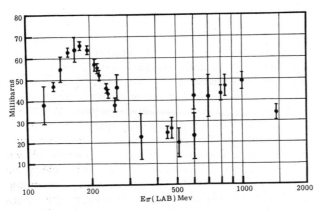

Figure 3

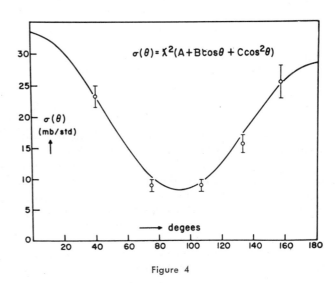

Figure 4

mentally. This is beautiful confirmation of the charge independence hypothesis and of the assignment of isotopic spin $T = \frac{3}{2}$.

Moreover, for $T = \frac{3}{2}$ the theory predicts that negative mesons should in the majority of cases not be scattered, but should undergo the charge-exchange reaction

$$\mathrm{H} + \pi^- = \mathrm{N} + \pi^0 \qquad (7)$$

Experiments show that this charge exchange is about twice as frequent as elastic scattering of the negative meson, again in accord with theoretical expectation.

At this point one might consider the problem as qualitatively solved and proceed to an evaluation of the coupling constant G. Unfortunately, the situation did not prove to be so simple. The next step in any theoretical analysis of scattering experiments is the determination of phase shifts of the partial waves which together make up the wave function of the system. Unfortunately, this analysis did not give a unique result as is shown in Fig. 5. Figure 5 gives the phase shift for the $p_{\frac{3}{2}}$ state of isotopic spin $T = \frac{3}{2}$, as a function of energy. Three curves are shown, all of which fit the experimental data equally well; they are denoted as solutions 1, 2 and 3. Solutions 1 and 2 show a resonance, i.e., the phase shift goes through 90°. Solution 1, known as the Fermi solution behaves more smoothly than solution 2, known as the Yang solution. Solution 3 has no resonance at all.

Figure 6 shows the results for some of the other phase shifts for solutions 1 and 3. The two lower curves represent the phase shift for the s state of $T = \frac{3}{2}$ in which the meson after all must be expected to have *some* interaction with the nucleon. It is seen that this interaction is repulsive corresponding to a negative-phase shift. In solution 1 the s-phase shift is a very smooth function of energy. The interaction can then simply be taken to be a strong repulsion in a region of radius of about 2×10^{-14} cm, and no interaction outside this region. On the other hand, in solution 3 the s-phase shift suddenly drops very rapidly above 150 Mev. This is a very unusual behavior which would be extremely hard to explain theoretically, and which makes solution 3 very suspect.

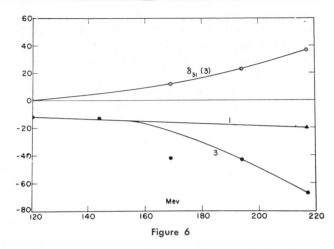

Figure 6

The upper curve gives the phase shift for the $p_{\frac{1}{2}}$ state of isotopic spin $\frac{3}{2}$. In the case of solution 1, this phase shift is essentially zero at all energies, which is in good accord with theoretical expectation. For solution 3, however, this phase shift, while still zero at low energy, rises very abruptly above 150 Mev, again a strange behavior. For all these reasons, solution 3 has been regarded as incorrect for over a year; but from purely experimental arguments, it could not be excluded.

Recently it has been possible, however, to show conclusively that solution 3 is incorrect and solution 1 is the right one. This was achieved by Goldberger on the basis of a dispersion theory which is an extension of the Kramers-Heisenberg dispersion formulae to the case of particles (mesons) which have a finite rest mass and are charged. Figure 7 gives the result of this theory. It represents the quantity

$$S = \sin 2\delta_3 - \sin 2\delta_{31} - 2 \sin \delta_{33}$$

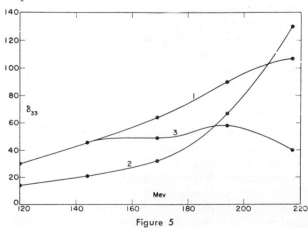

Figure 5

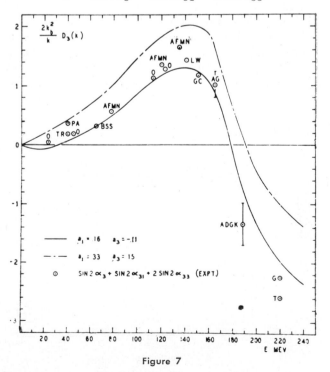

Figure 7

where the δ's are the phase shifts of the three partial waves s, $p_{1/2}$ and $p_{3/2}$ which contribute to the scattering of positive mesons. The solid curve is obtained from Goldberger's theory using only the measured total cross sections as a function of energy. To derive this curve, neither the measured angular distributions were used nor any phase-shift analysis. This solid curve is seen to go through zero at about 180 Mev, and gives surely the correct value of the quantity S.

This correct value may now be compared with the value of S obtained from the three solutions of the phase shift analysis which we previously mentioned. If the phase shifts of solution 3 are selected, then S will not go through zero, but will remain positive at all energies. If, however, the resonant solution 1 is chosen, then the dominant phase shift δ_{33} will go through 90° at the resonance, hence its contribution to S, sin $2\delta_{33}$, will go through zero at this energy. Since the other two contributions are small, S itself will go through zero, in accord with the prediction of Goldberger's dispersion theory. This theory, therefore, decides in favor of solution 1. The points on the slide represent the values of S deduced from the phase shifts of solution 1 which are, of course, based upon the analysis of the measured angular distribution.

An interesting question is that of the sign of the phase shifts. We have so far tacitly assumed that the principal nuclear interaction between nucleon and meson is attractive. To determine the sign of the interaction experimentally, one can investigate the interference between the nuclear scattering of mesons and that due to the Coulomb field whose sign is known. Figure 8 gives the result of experiments by Orear on the scattering of positive mesons by protons at 120 Mev. Similar results were obtained by Puppi in Italy. The Coulomb interaction is repulsive in this case. The Coulomb scattering dominates at small angles, the nuclear scattering at large angles. At intermediate angles the two types of scattering interfere. The slide shows that the interference between the Coulomb scattering and the nuclear scat-

tering is destructive, which, therefore, shows that the nuclear scattering is indeed attractive, as we have assumed. This is confirmed by experiments at lower energy. At higher energy the interference of nuclear with Coulomb scattering gives additional evidence for the existence of a resonance in the nuclear scattering.

THEORETICAL ANALYSIS

For a long time it was believed that the main problem in the theoretical analysis was to decide between the pseudoscalar interaction 5, and the gradient coupling 6. It is now believed that for all practical purposes, at moderate energies, the two types of coupling give identical results. This leaves us free to choose the pseudoscalar interaction which is the only type which can be renormalized.

Until recently the only method for a theoretical treatment of scattering was that of Tamm and Dancoff, in which the wave function is analyzed into states of varying numbers of virtual mesons. All calculations so far have taken into account only states containing up to two virtual mesons. It is difficult to justify the neglect of states with more virtual mesons, but we shall see shortly that the method has given good results, nevertheless.

During the last nine months, Low of the University of Illinois has developed a method which is largely free from the objectionable features of the Tamm-Dancoff method. In this method the Heisenberg representation is used, i.e., one considers only real mesons present in the field, not virtual ones. Now two real mesons can only be formed at all at energies above 300 Mev and the formation will become important only at about 500 Mev or more. For low-energy experiments, it should, therefore, be permissible to neglect the possibility of formation of additional real mesons.

Low succeeded in deriving an integral equation between the amplitudes for finding one real meson of varying momentum. He used mostly symmetry arguments in his derivation. Very recently it has been shown that Low's equations can be derived almost entirely from dispersion theory, i.e., merely from the requirement of causality. These equations may, therefore, be considered as quite firmly established.

A final solution of the Low equation has not as yet been obtained; however, some general features of the solution have been deduced. Low and Chew have shown that the quantity

$$F = \frac{k^3 \cot \delta_{33} - \mu^3}{\omega} \qquad (9)$$

should be a nearly linear function of the meson energy ω. In this equation k is the momentum of the meson, μ its mass and δ the phase shift for the resonant state. Figure 9 shows the best straight line which can be drawn to fit the experimental points. The experimental points themselves are also shown and it is seen that they give a remarkably good fit

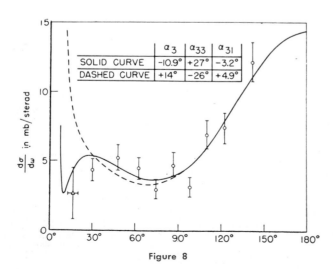

	α_3	α_{33}	α_{31}
SOLID CURVE	-10.9°	+27°	-3.2°
DASHED CURVE	+14°	-26°	+4.9°

Figure 8

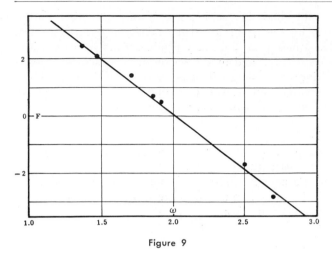

Figure 9

to the straight line. This straight line should be regarded as semi-empirical; it is not the result of a theoretical calculation, but expresses merely the fact that the range of the forces between nucleon and meson is small compared to the wave length of the meson. This, in turn, is due to the fact that a pseudo-scalar meson interacts with the nucleon most strongly when it has a high momentum, i.e., at small distances.

It can also be made plausible that the theory of Low and Chew should give results similar to the Tamm-Dancoff theory. The latter was developed, including relativistic corrections, at Cornell University. Kalos of Cornell has carried out the required numerical integrations with the help of the high-speed computer of the UNIVAC type at New York. His results for the phase shift are shown in Fig. 10, as a function of energy, together with the experimental points. The agreement is very good, much better than might be expected from the crude assumptions of the Tamm-Dancoff theory. The faint curve on the same slide represents similar calculations carried out earlier with insufficient numerical accuracy; the agreement in this case was poor.

In Kalos' calculations only one parameter is adjustable, namely the coupling constant. For this

Kalos has found the value 15.5. This agrees quite well with the most recent evaluation of the photo-electric production of mesons in the s state. The latter evaluation gives the most reliable value of the coupling constant because it has been shown that in this case perturbation theory is nearly exact.

There is still considerable lack of understanding of the scattering of mesons by nucleons in the s state. It is known experimentally that this scattering is small, but not zero. It proceeds by a similar mechanism as the decay of the neutral π meson, namely by the formation of a virtual pair of nucleon and anti-nucleon in the intermediate state. The s scattering is, therefore, additional evidence for the fact that nucleon pair formation is less probable than an elementary theory would predict but, nevertheless, does occur.

With the interaction between meson and nucleon rather well understood, we may now return to the starting point and ask what this means for nuclear forces. In this respect, meson theory has not yet been very successful. Figure 11 shows, however, those main features of nuclear forces derived from meson theory on which most theoretical physicists would agree. There is a strong repulsive interaction between two nucleons at very small distances, up to about $\frac{1}{2} \times 10^{-13}$ cm. This repulsive core was first predicted by Maurice Levy and is of great importance for the saturation of nuclear forces. Outside of it there is a region of extremely strong attraction. Both central and tensor forces are predicted by the theory, the latter giving rise to the strong polarization of nucleon scattering at high energy. On the details of the forces as the function of distance,

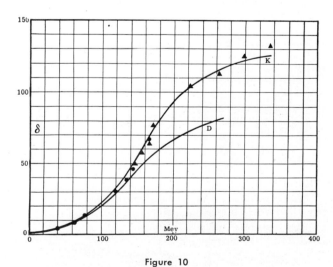

Figure 10

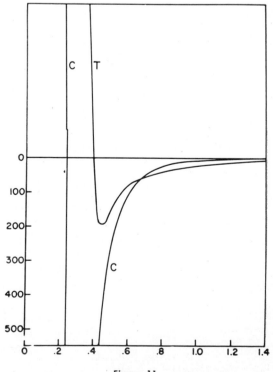

Figure 11

there is as yet no agreement between various theories; Fig. 11 corresponds to the theory of Brueckner and Watson.

μ MESONS

Finally, let us return to the meson which was first discovered, the μ meson. Table II shows the main features of this particle, in comparison with the π meson. Its mass is smaller, its lifetime much longer than that of the π. It decays into an electron and two neutrinos and this process is responsible for most of the electrons in cosmic radiation. The decay process again is closely related to the β disintegration of nuclei. The spin of the μ meson is $\frac{1}{2}$. When it is absorbed by the nucleus, another particle of spin $\frac{1}{2}$ must be emitted, namely a neutrino. It can be shown that the neutrino, having small mass, receives most of the energy released. This makes stars caused by μ meson capture quite small.

Table II

	μ	π
Mass	206.9	273.3
Lifetime	$2.22 \cdot 10^{-6}$	$2.5 \cdot 10^{-8}$
Decay	$\epsilon + 2\nu$	$\mu + \nu$
Spin	$\frac{1}{2}$	0
Star production	10^{-29}	10^{-25}
Star production due to	electromagn.	nuclear

The main interaction of μ mesons with other matter is by means of its electric charge. By this means, a μ meson in flight may produce stars in nuclei close to its path and may even produce π mesons of relatively low energy. This is the cause of the hard showers in cosmic rays underground. There is no positive evidence for any nuclear interaction of the μ meson but the upper limit which can be set on such nuclear interaction is still rather high, namely the nuclear coupling constant is certainly not larger than the fine structure constant.

Perhaps the most interesting feature of the μ meson is its decay. Many accurate observations have been made of the continuous spectrum of the electrons resulting from the decay. It is now well established that the spectral intensity does not go to zero near the maximum energy, a fact which is of theoretical importance.

It is as yet not understood what role the μ meson plays in the structure of the universe, and it is not clear why such a particle should exist at all. On the basis of our present understanding it would be entirely satisfactory if there were only π mesons apart from nucleons, electrons and neutrinos. Indeed, it now seems very likely that a satisfactory theory of nuclear forces can be constructed with π mesons and with π mesons alone.

The "Strange Particles": Heavy Mesons and Hyperons

By Louis Leprince-Ringuet, France

The first information concerning heavy mesons appeared at about the same time as the pi meson was discovered, or even shortly before; but progress in the study of these particles has been much slower. The main reason for the delay is that much greater energy is required to produce them than to produce π mesons; hence they are harder to obtain from cosmic radiation. Phenomena in which an energy of the order of 500 Mev to 1 Bev is available are very rare, and scarcely one heavy meson in a hundred is found. Moreover, they could not be produced in the machines built before the Brookhaven cosmotron and the Berkeley bevatron. Until recently, therefore, the study of heavy mesons was confined to cosmic rays; but the field is now widening considerably, especially since the bevatron has made it possible to produce beams of these radiations.

Thus less is known about heavy mesons than light mesons, and my paper will not be so well-ordered and positive on many points as that of Professor Bethe. It will be much more in the nature of an examination and discussion of the observed facts and concomitant uncertainties—a review which is not final, but shows the present state of progress in this rapidly changing field. It will also be purely experimental, first because at this stage of progress only attempts at theoretical interpretation can be made and secondly because I am essentially an experimental worker. We shall see, moreover, why the theoretical problems raised by these particles are difficult. Heavy mesons cannot be treated as super-pi mesons; their production, their mode of disintegration and other properties make it necessary to observe them with a particularly fresh and attentive eye.

We shall have to distinguish between two classes of particle which are widely different in appearance, but resemble each other in certain properties: heavy mesons and hyperons. The former are designated by the letter k, the latter by capital Y. Within these two groups, particles of which the essential properties are known will be indicated by Greek small letters for heavy mesons, and Greek capital letters for hyperons.

(*a*) k mesons all have a mass in the neighbourhood of 1000 times that of the electron; they may be positively charged, negatively charged or neutral. They cannot be produced without an energy corresponding to their rest mass, at least, and there are probably other more restrictive conditions attached to their creation. The mean life of charged heavy mesons does not appear to vary greatly according to

type, and is of the order of 10^{-8} seconds. The mean life of neutral heavy mesons, on the other hand, is much shorter, namely, 10^{-10} seconds. We shall have to examine the problem of the mass of these particles, their process of spontaneous decomposition, their mode of production and their interaction.

(*b*) Hyperons, on the other hand, appear to be particles composed of a nucleon and a light meson, or sometimes more complex in structure. But there is always a pre-existing nucleon; hence the energy required to produce these particles, whose mass is greater than that of the nucleon, does not correspond to their mass, but merely to that of the light meson or mesons involved, plus a certain quantity of energy called Q, which defines the excitation of the hyperon. Thus the best known, Λ^0, requires for its formation an energy of 140 Mev, corresponding to the pi meson, plus an excitation of 37 Mev. From the small amount of this energy, namely 177 Mev in all, it might be supposed that hyperons could be produced by the ordinary synchro-cyclotron, but this is not the case; it is probable that they cannot be produced alone, but can be produced in pairs of particles, the other particle being, not another Λ^0, but a heavy meson. The mean life of typical hyperons is of the order of 10^{-10} seconds. There are hyperons with charges of both signs and at least one neutral type.

FIRST DEVELOPMENTS

The first publications are concerned with Wilson cloud-chamber photographs:

(*a*) In 1944 an isolated case of collision, presumably elastic, between a positively charged penetrating particle and an electron of the gas in the cloud chamber produced a mass $(990 \pm 100)\ m_e$, where m_e is the mass of the electron.

(*b*) In 1947 two remarkable photographs provided the first examples of neutral V and charged V (disintegration in flight) for heavy particles, thus showing their instability.

(*c*) In 1948 photographic emulsions sensitive to fast electrons began to contribute with brilliant result: the first picture of a tau meson disintegrating at rest into three charged pi mesons.

(*d*) In 1951 heavy mesons, observed at rest, producing a single light meson (*S* events), appeared in multiple-plate cloud chambers and on emulsions at the same time.

Since that time, these particles have been studied in many laboratories, mainly with photographic emulsions or cloud chambers; various devices comprising complex arrangements of scintillators and Cerenkov counters have also been used with success.

The particles normally appear in one of two ways, disintegrating either at rest (*S* events) or in flight (*V* events).

TECHNIQUES USED
Photographic Emulsions

The first emulsions sensitive to fast electrons were used by Bristol with glass support. They were rarely thicker than 600 microns and the tracks were usually observable only in the thickness of a single emulsion, as the presence of the glass made it impossible to follow the track in the other plates in the packet. A considerable improvement was obtained when it became possible to use unsupported emulsions: a packet could then consist of a number of sheets of emulsion stacked without intervening glass. A fast particle will pass through a number of sheets, and after development the track can be followed from sheet to sheet. Thus, instead of short tracks of a few thousand microns at the most, tracks several tens of centimetres long will be available. Thus it will be possible to follow the secondary track of a heavy meson from beginning to end; the length will be known and hence, with some precautions, the energy. The nature of the particle and often its sign can also be ascertained by observing the phenomena produced by its spontaneous disintegration or its nuclear effects. Recent experiments with very large packets (some 30 kilogrammes of emulsion) exposed to cosmic rays, made during the last year by an important group of European laboratories (*G* stack) and those carried out elsewhere with the bevatron, sometimes using several tens of kilogrammes of emulsions, have made it possible to obtain information of the first importance in a short time.

The masses of particles stopped in the emulsion can be measured by various methods, based on the increase of ionization and of multiple scattering as the speed of the particle decreases. On one individual particle the degree of precision attainable for a mass of the order of 1000 rarely corresponds to a standard deviation of less than 70 m_e. Errors due to the method may also arise, so that direct measurements of mass are never very accurate; the results obtained in the past four years have not shown with certainty whether different types of heavy meson have differences in mass of the order of 30 m_e.

The charged secondary particles can be studied by measuring ionization and scattering at their departure. The measurements made before the advent of unsupported emulsions were somewhat confused in the case of high-energy secondary particles, only the first few millimetres of whose range were visible. Using large packets of unsupported emulsions the ranges of these secondary particles can now be obtained directly, and thus either lines or continuous spectra can be determined for them. In the case of a line, i.e., for a monokinetic meson, the range can

be very accurately determined, but the energy, which must be known in order to determine the disintegration process and the mass of the primary particle, is less accurately known owing to the uncertainty regarding the relationship between the range and the energy. Very detailed discussions took place on this subject at the recent Pisa Congress, and certain disparities between the results obtained by different methods can be explained by these uncertainties.

Nevertheless, owing to its exceptionally favourable properties one of the heavy mesons has had its characteristics very precisely defined: this is the tau meson, which produces three charged pi mesons by spontaneous disintegration.

As the kinetic energy taken up by the three pi mesons together is only 75 Mev, these secondary mesons are relatively slow and are stopped fairly soon in the emulsion. From the energy and impulse balance for this emission, it has been possible to calculate the mass of the tau meson, which is defined with the exceptional precision of an electronic mass, assuming that the mass of the pi meson is accurately known:

$$\text{Mass of } \tau = (965.5 \pm 0.7)m_e$$

taking the mass of pi meson as 273 m_e.

It should be noted that photographic emulsions are very well suited to observation of the phenomena produced by the stopping of an unstable particle; a time of flight greater than 10^{-12} seconds is enough. They are less suitable for observation of *V* events; in particular, they cannot be used to reconstruct a phenomenon of high-energy nuclear interaction, with its charged and neutral components, as can be done in the cloud chamber under certain favourable conditions. When a *V* from a neutral particle is observed in emulsions, it is usually very difficult to ascertain the origin of the particle, as all the events recorded on the emulsion during irradiation are intermingled without distinction.

Wilson Cloud Chambers

By the use of a large multiple-plate chamber without a magnetic field, very significant information can be obtained concerning *S* events and the charged or neutral particles accompanying the rest decomposition of a heavy meson, but the sign of the primary particle cannot be ascertained, nor can its mass be accurately measured. On the other hand, cloud chambers with a magnetic field provide a means of studying *V* events and obtaining information on the dynamics of disintegration in flight, but they do not generally show the nature of the products (pi or mu mesons or electrons). Using a magnetic chamber and a multiple-plate chamber in conjunction, more definite information can be obtained; this photograph shows such an assembly and indicates some of its possibilities. In the case of an *S* event taking place in the multiple-plate chamber, the mass and sign of the primary particle can be measured directly from the curvature in the magnetic chamber and the range in the screens. In the case of a V event taking place in the magnetic chamber, the curvatures of the secondary particles will be measured and, if they pass through the plate chamber, additional information can be obtained, e.g., the range, in the case of a stoppage, or the occurrence of a nuclear interaction.

An important improvement has recently been introduced with the possibility of counting the cloud droplets with some precision. In favourable cases, both the impulse and the ionization of a particle can thus be ascertained in a magnetic chamber by measuring the curvature and counting the droplets. Hence the nature of the particle can sometimes be determined with a fair degree of accuracy.

The great advantage of the cloud chamber is that a selected individual phenomenon of nuclear interaction can be studied by means of a more or less complex arrangement of counters, without losing the emitted neutral particles. Pure absorbers (such as copper screens) can be used, whereas emulsions are composed of a fairly large number of elements, which complicates the interaction problem.

With machines, but not with cosmic rays, other techniques can be applied. For example diffusion chambers can be used: by filling them with hydrogen under pressure and using a magnetic field it is possible to study nuclear interactions under particularly good conditions for observation.

Also in conjunction with machines, the bubble chamber with liquid hydrogen or helium will probably become a first-rate detector, but it does not appear to be readily usable in its existing form for the study of cosmic radiation.

While most of the discoveries concerning heavy mesons and hyperons made up to this year have been obtained from cosmic radiation, very valuable information has been gained with the aid of machines in the last few months. The possibility of producing beams of positive or negative heavy mesons through the action of magnetic fields and suitable screens should make it possible to find an answer to most of the fundamental questions raised by heavy mesons and hyperons.

FEATURES PECULIAR TO HEAVY MESONS

The Tau Meson

(a) There is a heavy meson called the tau meson, which disintegrates in the following manner:

$$\tau^{\pm} \rightarrow \pi^{\pm} + \pi^{\mp} + \pi^{\pm} + 75 \text{ Mev} \qquad [M = 965 \, m_e]$$

It has been observed mainly in emulsions, by its disintegration at rest. In some cases it has been possible to follow the three pi mesons up to their termination; there are always two positives and one negative, indicating a positive tau. It has also been seen to disintegrate in flight, in cloud chambers, and in this case often appears positive. A few negative tau particles have also been seen with certainty to disintegrate in flight, but these have not been

observed directly in emulsions. There are some negative heavy mesons which produce a nuclear absorption star when stopped in emulsion; these are probably tau mesons, though this is not certain.

In every case of disintegration at rest into three charged pi mesons, coplanarity has been confirmed and the Q value is compatible with 75 Mev. Only one case has been reported in which there was no coplanarity and the Q value was too low. This can be explained by the addition of a γ-ray to the three charged pi mesons.

The mean life of the tau meson is of the order of 10^{-8} second.

(b) This particle is also known to disintegrate as follows:

$$\tau^{\pm} \rightarrow \pi^{\pm} + 2\pi^0$$

The observation of photographic emulsions gives good evidence of the above mode of disintegration. The ratio between the proportions of these two modes of disintegration is of the order of unity but has not been determined very accurately.

(c) It may be asked if there is any evidence for a neutral tau which would give

$$\tau^0 \rightarrow \pi^+ + \pi^- + \pi^0$$

The existence of this neutral counterpart of the tau is uncertain, but various abnormal Q values found during study of the neutral meson θ^0 may be explained by the existence of the neutral tau.

The Neutral θ^0 Meson

There is a neutral heavy meson which disintegrates as follows:

$$\theta^0 \rightarrow \pi^+ + \pi^- + Q \qquad Q = 214 \text{ Mev}$$

This particle has been identified mainly by cloud-chamber observations. It has a mass of $966 \, m_e$, with a standard deviation of approximately $10 \, m_e$. There is no significant difference in mass between the θ^0 meson and the tau meson. The mean life of the neutral heavy meson is 1.5×10^{-18} second.

Certain abnormal values found for Q suggest other modes of disintegration. The existence of the neutral tau meson may explain some, but not all of these values; the others could be explained by the formula

$$\theta^0 \rightarrow \pi + \mu + \nu \qquad (\nu \text{ neutrino})$$

The $K\mu$ (or η) Meson

Among the charged heavy mesons producing a single charged secondary particle, the $K\mu$ has been identified by S events observed in cloud chambers. The emission of this particle has been confirmed very recently, by the use of large packs of unsupported emulsions. The observed $K\mu$ mesons are positive; the existence of a negative $K\mu$ meson is uncertain. Disintegration takes place as follows:

$$K\mu^+ \rightarrow \mu^+ + \nu + Q \qquad Q \sim 375 \text{ Mev}$$

The charged particle is certainly a mu meson. The neutral particle is of very small or zero mass and does not produce any electron sheaves; hence it is not a photon and is assumed to be a neutrino.

According to the cloud-chamber results, the range of the charged secondary particle is:

$$R = 75.8 \pm 1.2 \, \text{gm/cm}^2 \text{ of copper,}$$

and according to the emulsions, $R = 78.2 \pm 1.4$ gm/cm² of emulsion. These two values agree closely, the stopping power of the emulsion being substantially equivalent to that of copper.

The mass of the $K\mu$ meson is now being studied and discussed in detail. Experiments with cloud chambers give a mass $M = (935 \pm 15) \, m_e$, whereas experiments with emulsions give a mass very close to that of the tau meson. This important problem has not yet been solved, but probably will be solved by the methods of differential measurement with beams of K mesons now coming into use.

The χ Meson

Assumed to exist since 1951 as a result of work with emulsions and more clearly defined by the cloud chamber, the χ meson has been rediscovered in large packs of unsupported emulsions. It disintegrates as follows:

$$\chi^{charged} \rightarrow \pi^{charged} + \pi^0 + Q \qquad Q \sim 212 \, \text{Mev}$$

The χ meson has a mass close to the mass of the tau meson; cloud-chamber experiments show it to be approximately $20 \, m_e$ greater than the mass of the $K\mu$ meson. Emulsion experiments also give a mass close to that of the tau meson. The range of the secondary pi meson is 44.2 ± 1.4 gm/cm² of copper in cloud chambers and 44.7 ± 0.8 gm/cm² of emulsion.

The χ mesons observed by their disintegration at rest are all positive, where the sign is known. In the cloud chamber, the sign is positive for an observable event, which is interpreted as the emission in flight of a π^+ and four electrons produced by disintegration of the π^0.

The mean life of the χ meson has not been measured very accurately, but there is no definite reason for supposing that it is less than that of the $K\mu$ and the tau, i.e., of the order of 10^{-8} second.

The Kappa Meson (κ or κμ3)

The mode of disintegration has been observed. As a result of disintegration at rest, a heavy meson produces a μ meson, the energy of which is not always the same. There is a continuous μ spectrum, so that at least two neutral particles must be involved. The nature of these particles is not known, nor is the upper limit of the spectrum of the emitted μ meson. All that is known is that this spectrum reaches a value corresponding to a momentum of 120 Mev/c for the μ, and that if we go further, its intensity is very low. The mass of the kappa meson is not very certain, but it probably differs little from that

of the tau. Observations made with emulsions on the disintegration of a kappa meson at rest are all compatible with its having a positive sign.

The mean life of the kappa meson is not well known, it may be similar to that of the tau or possibly shorter.

The κβ

A charged heavy meson has been observed to disintegrate as follows: $\kappa\beta \rightarrow$ electron $+ 2$ or more neutral particles.

Relevant information is scarce, but it seems certain that this mode of disintegration occurs. The emitted electrons do not all have the same energy, and the possibility of two or more neutral particles accompanying this disintegration must be considered. The maximum energy of the spectrum of the electrons exceeds 100 Mev, but its limit is uncertain. The mean life of this particle is not known.

It should be noted that this mode of disintegration has not yet been observed in cloud chambers, but it may be that they have a disadvantage for this purpose (e.g., thickness of the screens).

Other Heavy Mesons

Some information has been published concerning the existence of particles with a mass said to be $1400 \, m_e$, but so far it does not appear to justify general acceptance.

SOME GENERAL PROBLEMS RELATING TO HEAVY MESONS

Have They All the Same Mass?

As is shown by what I have already said, the masses of the various distinct heavy mesons do not differ very much. If there is indeed a difference, it cannot exceed 30 electronic masses, i.e., 3%. Then again, the measurements which seem to show a characteristic difference of mass are mainly those obtained with the Wilson cloud chamber on $K\mu$: they give $(935 \pm 15) \, m_e$; this result differs significantly from tau without however being incompatible with it. One of the causes of our inability to obtain more precise results is the uncertainty about the curve relating range to energy for high energies. Exact experiments should be made on this problem in research centres which have available pi mesons of high energy (100 to 200 Mev).

The new methods which have made it possible at Berkeley to make comparative measurements of the masses of the various heavy mesons have already yielded interesting preliminary results, described at the Pisa Conference, showing that, if there is a difference in mass, it is very small. These methods ought soon to give a more definite answer to this fundamental question.

Have They All the Same Mean Life?

If all the occurrences of charged heavy mesons correspond to the different ways in which the same particle can disintegrate, the mean life observed for each manner of disintegration should be the same. But as yet there are no sure signs either for or against an identical mean life. The lives which have been most accurately measured, i.e., those of $K\mu$ and τ, are of the same order of magnitude; in fact, some observations hardly seem to support the hypothesis that all charged heavy mesons have an identical mean life, but it is not out of the question that this may be due to certain experimental errors.

We may hope soon to obtain valuable information on the mean lives of the different heavy mesons by comparing their proportions for various times of flight, providing that they are produced under identical conditions.

Proportions of the Various Modes of Disintegration

Experimenters have naturally studied the proportion of the different modes of disintegration we have discussed. The main results refer to large packs of emulsion irradiated with cosmic rays or to multiple-plate cloud chambers. The proportions can also be determined in meson beams produced in machines.

When large packs of emulsion are exposed to cosmic rays we find:

51% of $K\mu$; 28% of χ; 12% of κ; 9% of $\kappa\beta$

These values are not very exact; they must also be treated with some caution because of difficulties of observation which introduce experimental errors. For example, a $K\mu$ can easily be missed if the development of the pack is not carried very far, since at departure the μ possesses almost minimum ionization, which makes it hard to see; with the kappa, observations will be more reliable if the μ secondary has low energy, and there will be less risk of missing it. With the χ, whose pi-secondary has a slightly greater initial ionization than the μ of $K\mu$, the risk of a miss will be less than with the $K\mu$. Besides, it is not easy to place numerical value on the experimental errors introduced with the emulsions for the detection of the various phenomena: decomposition on stopping, with emission of one or more secondaries, nuclear absorption in the form of a sigma star, end of range with no visible development, etc. Psychological factors also play a part: even an excellent observer, intent on a certain line of research, will miss more easily observable phenomena on which her attention is not concentrated.

With the cloud chamber, the proportion of $K\mu$ is greater, but it should be noted that this apparatus requires a minimum time of flight of 10^{-9} seconds, or of 5×10^{-9} seconds, according to whether one large, multiple-plate chamber is used, or a combination of two chambers.

Sign Asymmetry in Heavy Mesons

One important problem that has recently cropped up in connexion with heavy mesons is the asymmetry in the sign of their charge. If we examine each type of meson, we see that, generally speaking, they are observed with only one sign of which we can be certain: for $K\mu$, χ, and the kappa only positive signs have been identified. Tau is an exception, and it is certain that τ^- exists. True, it is more difficult to observe τ^- than τ^+: the primaries of low energy, disintegrating in flight, which it is easier to identify and to measure with greater precision, are generally τ^+. Taken as a whole, the results suggest that τ^+ and τ^- are not emitted in the same way; it is not impossible that at the relatively low energies available only τ^+ is emitted, τ^- appearing at higher energies. Neither is it out of the question that the positive heavy mesons can escape more easily from the nuclei than the negative ones.

In the case of the other heavy mesons, disintegration at rest allows us to distinguish the particle when it is positive. A particle with strong nuclear interaction, however, must be absorbed at rest and produce a star when it is negative. It cannot, therefore, be distinguished by its decomposition except when the phenomenon occurs in flight. In fact, sigma stars are observed which are caused by the nuclear absorption of negative heavy mesons at rest, and the positive heavy mesons as a whole can be compared to these K^-.

These results show a ratio K^-/K^+ of very much less than unity. In addition, the ratio varies according to whether cosmic rays or machines are used. It must be remembered that the energy available for creating these particles is not the same in the case of machines and in that of cosmic rays: the latter permit the observation of rare phenomena of ultrahigh energy which the machines cannot provide. If, for example, K^- are produced mainly in such phenomena, a greater proportion of them will be seen in cosmic radiation.

Nuclear Interaction of High-Speed Heavy Mesons

A start has been made on the study of these interactions in emulsions. K^+ have an effective cross section of the order of one-third of the geometric cross section and their interactions provide relatively low energy. K^- have a greater effective cross section, of the same order of magnitude as the geometric cross section, and the interactions produced often release an energy greater than the kinetic energy of K^-. It seems therefore that the nuclear behaviour of K mesons varies according to their sign.

HYPERONS

Hyperons are unstable particles of greater mass than the nucleon, which, in disintegrating, produce a nucleon, a pi meson or, sometimes, a meson and another hyperon. As we have already said, the nucleon does not have to be created; it is taken from a nucleus. Hyperons are produced in high-energy nuclear interactions, either in the free state or in the bound state (hyperfragments). They may also be observed in the nuclear absorption of negative heavy mesons.

The Λ^0 Hyperon

This well-known particle disintegrates into a proton and a negative pi meson. First observed in the cloud chamber, it has since frequently been found in emulsions, and the Q of the reaction has been very accurately measured. The formula is:

$$\Lambda^0 \rightarrow p^+ + \pi^- + Q \quad Q = 37 \text{ Mev} \quad M = 2180 \, m_e$$

The mean life of Λ^0 is $(3.8 \pm 0.5) \times 10^{-10}$ second.

Some measurements of Q do not give the above value, and may be explained by another type of decomposition, producing $p + \mu + \nu$. It is highly probable that another type of disintegration of $\Lambda^0 \rightarrow n + \pi^0$ exists; but it is difficult to detect because the three particles are neutral. Nevertheless, the γ emitted by the π^0 can be observed.

Charged $\Sigma^{\pm}$ Hyperons

Charged hyperons disintegrating into a nucleon and a pi meson have been identified. The Σ^+ may disintegrate in either of the two following ways:

$$\Sigma^+ \Big\langle \begin{array}{l} p + \pi^0 + Q \quad Q = 116 \text{ Mev} \quad M = 2327 \, m_e \\ n + \pi^+ + Q' \quad Q' = 110 \text{ Mev} \end{array}$$

The two manners of disintegration are equally certain, and the value of Q has been accurately determined. Data have been mainly obtained with the help of photographic emulsions.

The mean life is short, of the order of 5×10^{-10} second. Since, in a large proportion of cases, the phenomena were observed as disintegration in flight, it was not always possible to give the sign.

The Σ^- negative hyperon, whose existence was not very certain at the end of last year, now seems to have been confirmed, mainly as a result of certain occurrences observed through disintegration in flight in cloud chambers and also in emulsions.

The mean life would appear to be less than 10^{-10} second.

The Ξ^- Hyperon

The hyperon family must be rather complicated; for we already know with certainty the Ξ giving the following formula:

$$\Xi^- \rightarrow \Lambda^0 + \pi^- + Q \quad Q \sim 60 \text{ Mev}; \quad M \sim 2570 \, m_e$$

The number of cases observed amounts to only some ten; but the general picture is very convincing. The measurement of Q is sometimes inexact, owing to the high energy of the primary; the true value seems to be about 60 Mev. The charged secondary is certainly a pi meson, because it has been observed producing a nuclear interaction.

The mean life is certainly very short, about 10^{-10} second; but it has not yet been measured.

Hyperfragments

In some nuclear disintegration stars, what is called a "hyperfragment" has been observed. This is a light nuclear fragment emitted with great energy, like the usual rays of the star (helium, lithium, hydrogen, etc.) but with the neutron replaced by a Λ^0. This fragment stops after a flight lasting usually about 10^{-12} second, and gives birth to a small secondary star. In some cases a pi meson with low energy is then emitted; in others, only nuclear fragments are observed: this is explained either by the spontaneous decomposition of the bound Λ^0, with the emission of its pi meson, or by the same phenomenon as that in which the pi meson is absorbed by the nucleus and does not emerge.

Many problems arise in connexion with these hyperfragments: how does the Λ^0 fit into the nucleus? Does it replace a neutron, or is it superimposed on an existing nucleus? Can a hyperon heavier than Λ^0 exist in these hyperfragments? What are the other rays of a star that includes the hyperfragment? Is one of these rays always a heavy meson or a hyperon? Partial or preliminary answers have already been given to most of these question.

COMBINED PRODUCTION OF HEAVY MESONS AND HYPERONS

One of the very remarkable characteristics of these strange particles is that they seem to be produced in pairs: this is of capital importance for theory (Gellman and Pais). Experimenters must therefore study it with the greatest care. A great variety of experiments is made, during which interesting associations can be observed: on the one hand, during creation, several strange particles are often noticed; on the other hand, when one such particle is absorbed in a nucleus another is emitted.

Association During Production

In a high-energy interaction several heavy mesons and hyperons are sometimes observed; but that is not necessarily valid proof that they are produced in pairs, if the disintegrated nucleus is complex. Nevertheless pairs of such particles have been observed with considerable frequency in the cloud chamber, in which the observation of neutral particles is relatively easy. The most decisive experiments should entail production in hydrogen. However, very few results have so far been obtained by the reaction of π^- on the protons of a diffusion chamber containing hydrogen under pressure; but there are none the less a few convincing cases of production in pairs: either Λ^0 and θ^0, or charged hyperon and charged meson K.

One of the most conclusive experiments concerning the creation of these particles is now being carried out at Berkeley: the production threshold of when the energy of the protons in the bevatron is increased, is found to be approximately 1.6 Bev which corresponds neither to the production of a solitary Λ^0, nor to that of two Λ^0 or of one Λ^0 and another hyperon, but does correspond to the production of a $\Lambda^0 + K$ pair.

Among the associations during production hyper-fragments have been seen that have come from stars in which a K was produced.

Other Associations of Heavy Mesons and Hyperons

Hyperons are observed in certain phenomena, particularly in nuclear absorptions of heavy negative mesons. It is thus possible to see in the cloud chamber heavy negative mesons absorbed then stopped by the screens, from which some Λ^0 emerge. In emulsions, when a K^- stops and produces a star, a neutral or a charged hyperon is sometimes observed. In a few cases the phenomenon occurs with great simplicity: from the edge of a heavy meson a charged hyperon emerges, alone, probably accompanied by invisible neutrons.

In a small number of fortunate cases, the phenomenon observed can be explained by the absorption of the K^- by one of the protons of the emulsion. The reaction, which seems to be proved, is then

$$K^- + p \rightarrow \Sigma^+ + \pi^-$$

the two particles being emitted in opposite directions.

This brief summary shows that many new and fascinating problems have been raised by the discovery of the "strange particles". They are being feverishly studied in the principal cosmic-ray laboratories and the two great research centres of Brookhaven and Berkeley. There is not the slightest doubt that impending important results will lead us to discuss and to define more accurately a number of essential ideas, such as the criterion of simplicity of a sub-atomic particle, the identity of two particles with different behaviour and many others. These results will stimulate the attempts to evolve theory, which are already beginning to take shape and appear rich in promise.

Modification of Radiation Response

By Alexander Hollaender,* USA

Protection and recovery from radiation damage is a subject of great importance for the intelligent use of radioisotopes and for the use of radiation in general.

In a consideration of the effects of radiation on individual cells and groups of cells, the first effort is to visualize what actually takes place when radiant energy, like X- or γ-rays, penetrates living tissues. Usually, the discussion falls back to the effects of radiation on water and simple chemical compounds. This is not because the need for understanding the effects of radiation on more complicated compounds and macromolecules is overlooked, but because so little information is available for such molecules. The decomposition of water by ionizing radiations, as now understood, involves the production of a number of such radicals as H, OH, and HO_2, and of hydrogen peroxide. The effect of X- and γ-radiation on water can be modified by the removal of oxygen, by low temperature, and by other factors. Removal of oxygen causes very little, if any change in the effect of α- radiation, and its effect on neutron irradiation is intermediate between those of α- and γ-radiations.

Even though good experimental data for the production of radicals and hydrogen peroxide are available, how these findings actually fit into the picture of the biological damage, which is finally recognized by rather crude methods, is not easy to show. Toxicity of these radicals and of peroxide is quite well established. As a matter of fact, it has been found that certain organic peroxides can produce genetic as well as toxic effects. Evidence of the effectiveness of these radicals in biological material is indirect and is best illustrated by the knowledge that many of the ways employed to modify the effects of X- or γ-radiation on water will also change the X-ray sensitivity of biological materials. However, it should be pointed out that the concentration of hydrogen peroxide which can be measured after X-irradiation of water can account for only a small part of the biological effects of radiation.

Before the modification of radiation resistance is discussed, the tremendous variation in the radiation sensitivity of living organisms should be emphasized. The most sensitive measurable function is the rate of mitosis, which can be altered by as little as one roentgen of X-rays. Another very sensitive

biological reaction was discussed by Latarjet (this conference) on the basis of the paper by Markovitch.[19] This is in sharp contrast to the resistance of *Paramecium,* which can take as much as 500,000 r with little effect on survival. Certain bacteria which grow on meat will resist doses of more than a million roentgens. The X-ray LD_{50} (the dose required to kill 50 per cent of a population) for mammals, varies from 200 to 800 r for different species and strains. The response to radiation is not necessarily influenced by the size but rather by the complexity of the organism, at least at the extremes of sensitivity. The interdependence of the various systems in an organism as complicated as a mammal may explain its sensitivity. This interdependence is conditioned by the most sensitive essential tissues in mammals, for example, the blood-forming organs, bone marrow, the spleen, or the lining of the intestine. Destruction of the function of these tissues causes death. Other tissues might be more sensitive to radiation but, since they are not so essential to life, their loss is less serious. Studies conducted in many laboratories have revealed many interesting ways to modify radiation response.

PROTECTION FROM RADIATION INJURY
Modification of X-ray Sensitivity by Treatment before and during Exposure
Reduced Moisture Content

Reduced moisture content increases resistance to radiation. The effect of this treatment can be demonstrated with seeds of certain plants and especially with the spore forms of certain microorganisms. Ninety per cent reduction of the moisture content of these organisms will increase their radioresistance several-fold. Typical results are shown in Fig. 1. At this conference it has been shown that the sensitivity of certain seeds does not necessarily decrease with reduction of moisture content but varies with certain conditions.[4] Although this technique is unsuitable for use with mammals, it has important practical application, especially in the industrial and agricultural use of ionizing radiation.

Reduced Temperature

It was to be expected that cells would become more resistant if irradiated at subfreezing temperatures. This method has been very successful, especially with microorganisms, which can withstand liquid nitrogen temperatures. The crucial tempera-

---

* Biology Division, Oak Ridge National Laboratory, Oak Ridge, Tennessee.

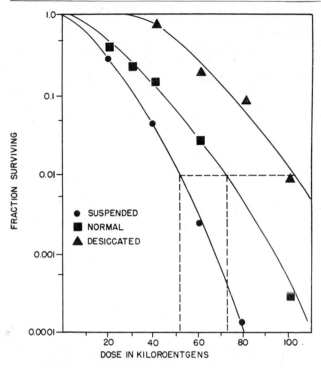

Figure 1. Dose dependence on water concentration

ture range in radiation resistance seems to be around the freezing point. It was found that super-cooled suspensions of yeast are more sensitive than the same suspensions permitted to freeze.[31] Especially interesting data on low-temperature effects were obtained with bacteria, where the resistance continued to increase as the temperature was lowered from the freezing point to liquid nitrogen temperature.[24, 29] Resistance varies little for treatments from freezing point to room temperature. Unfortunately, higher organisms, especially mammals, cannot withstand very low temperatures.

Reduced Oxygen Tension

One of the most important means of modifying radiation sensitivity is by the removal of oxygen. This approach is not only extremely interesting from the theoretical point of view, but also has considerable promise for practical applications. Theoretically, X- and γ-rays, in the presence of oxygen, will produce a number of oxidizing radicals which can become toxic, either directly or in combination with biologically important compounds, to produce conditions which will cause a serious disturbance in the metabolism of the cell or other changes which could be of a permanent nature. The effect of oxygen on X-ray resistance was recognized soon after the discovery of X-rays but investigation was neglected until about 1940. Ionizing radiation has again become an important tool for research. Microorganisms show the increase of sensitivity with increase of oxygen concentration only up to 10 per cent. The effect of oxygen may be increased by increasing the pressure. Reduction of oxygen tension to below the normal (this is for most organisms living in

atmospheric air below 21 per cent) increases the resistance of the organism, often proportionally to the decrease of oxygen concentration (Fig. 2). The limit of 21 per cent oxygen as the maximum of increase of sensitivity applies only to mammals and certain types of plants. This effect is shown most easily in plants having large chromosomes which are few in number. The question is whether the oxygen affects the number of breaks produced by radiation or the healing-up process of broken chromosomes (Fig. 3). It is possible to keep mammals, mostly mice, for a short time in 5–7 per cent oxygen if the residual gas is helium. The LD_{50} for mice can thus be changed from 500 to about 900 r.[8] This technique is not applicable to man because lack of oxygen leads to serious consequences. However, individual tissues may be sensitized to X-rays by increasing the concentration of oxygen in the tissue. This technique has some promise in the treatment of cancer tissue, as Gray and his co-workers have shown.[12]

Chemical Protection

Reducing compounds. It was mentioned that the oxygen concentration may be reduced by replacing it with an inert gas. Interesting work in the field has also been published by Graevsky.[11] Another way of accomplishing this is by using reducing compounds. One of the most effective compounds is sodium hydrosulfite ($Na_2S_2O_4$), which has a strong enough attraction for oxygen to remove it from inside the cell. A plot of the concentration of sodium hydrosulfite against the survival ratio of *Escherichia coli* exposed to X-rays is an exact reversal of a graph of the concentration of oxygen versus survival, demonstrating that the protective ability of sodium hydrosulfite is based on its ability to absorb oxygen. This compound is effective with microorganisms but is toxic to mammals. One of the first compounds found to protect mammals was cysteine, an amino acid with a SH group. At certain pH's, this compound, being water soluble, has the ability to remove oxygen readily from mammalian tissues. The X-ray LD_{50} for mice may be

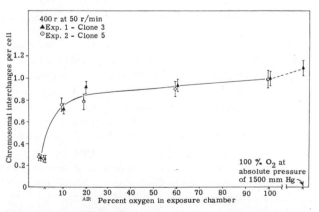

Figure 2. Relation between percentage of oxygen in exposure chamber and frequency of chromosomal interchanges per cell in *Tradescantia* microspores

NORMAL CELL, IN PROCESS
OF DIVIDING

RADIATED CELL, SHOWING
BROKEN CHROMOSOMES

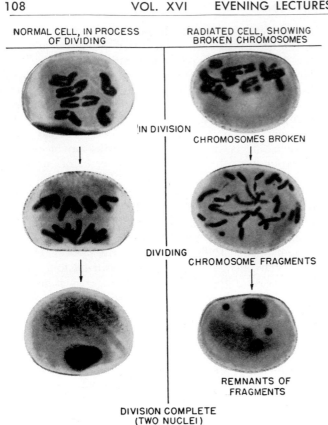

IN DIVISION

CHROMOSOMES BROKEN

DIVIDING

CHROMOSOME FRAGMENTS

REMNANTS OF
FRAGMENTS

DIVISION COMPLETE
(TWO NUCLEI)

Figure 3. The effect of radiation on chromosomes in the flowering plant, *Tradescantia*. Left column, control; right column, irradiated

almost doubled by giving cysteine in proper concentration shortly before exposure. The protective activity of cysteine may be reversed by keeping the animal under slightly positive pressure in high concentration of oxygen.[27]

Compounds which use up oxygen during metabolism. A number of compounds, during their metabolism by the cells, give some protection to microorganisms and somewhat less to mammals. This group includes the glycols, glucose, succinate, and alcohols. Their protective ability can be interfered with by metabolic inhibitors; for example, cyanide. Here again, quantitative titration can be made of the concentration of cyanide versus the protective ability of those compounds which require metabolism for protection. Their protective value for mammals, in which they may produce toxic effects, is small, owing to the necessity for rather high concentration. This is especially true of alcohols.

Compounds which slow down respiration. Anesthetics and related compounds which slow down respiration and make it difficult for oxygen to reach an area where it might be effective are somewhat dangerous to use; but they do give some protection.

Compounds which produce methemoglobinemia or which affect blood flow. Compounds which produce methemoglobinemia, e.g., PAPP, cyanide and related compounds, protect to a moderate degree but their toxicity prevents their effective application to man. Another group of compounds that might pro-

tect are those which reduced blood flow through their action on the capillaries.

Estrogens. Protective compounds which are little understood in their action are the estrogens. Some investigators believe that these compounds will constrict the capillaries but others think that their function is dependent on hormonal activity. However, the practical usefulness of the compounds is limited until more is known about their mechanism of action.

Some compounds having practical use. Of a large number of other compounds which have been reported to be more or less protective, three which appear to have some practical use will be discussed; namely, cysteine, β-mercaptoethylamine (cysteamine), and S,β-aminoethylisothiuronium·Br·HBr (AET). Cysteine has been reported by Patt[23] to be effective; cysteamine was first reported to be protective by Bacq and Herve;[1] and the last compound has been developed by Doherty.[6] Cysteamine has considerable promise as a protective compound, but certain characteristics make it somewhat dangerous to use. More than 100 derivatives of this compound have been prepared in this Laboratory. Characteristic of all these compounds is the presence of the NH_2 group (Fig. 4). The SH group, which is free in the first two compounds, is covered in AET. In an attempt to determine the important groups in these compounds, Doherty covered each group individually. When the NH_2 group was covered, all activity was lost. Apparently this group must be left free, at least for mammals. The reducing ability of the SH group is excellent for protection against radiation damage. Cysteine and cysteamine become quite toxic close to concentrations necessary for protection. The latter compound is especially unstable and must be kept under nitrogen before use in order to preserve its protective ability. For this and the following reasons, AET now appears, at least from studies in this Laboratory, to be the most promising. It can be stored in powder form in air, and solutions prepared whenever they are necessary. It can be given intravenously or orally. It has some interesting effects on the blood pressure, which can be controlled by certain drugs. In a cooperative inves-

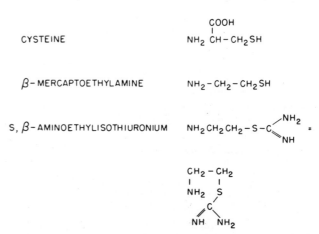

Figure 4. Structural formulas of three protective compounds

tigation with the University of Rochester, toxicity studies are being extended for the purpose of obtaining information about the practical application of this compound to man. At least another year or two of work will be required to settle questions pertinent to human application.

All the compounds discussed must be given before irradiation, or at least must be present during exposure. When given after exposure, they are of no known value. A phenomenon which should be mentioned here, since it may have significant basic implications, is that oxygen, when present in the cell in fairly high concentration, even in the absence of radiation, will produce changes similar to radiation effects. This can best be demonstrated in *Tradescantia* pollen grains, where it will break the chromosomes similarly to radiation.[5] A mechanism of this type may be involved in a large part of spontaneous chromosome breaks and mutations. The typical oxygen poisoning, which is known in mammals, can be counteracted by the same chemicals which protect against radiation damage.[10]

Shielding of the Spleen or Other Parts of the Body

Another approach which was developed during study of treatment after exposure has been used in several of the US Atomic Energy Commission laboratories and elsewhere.

It has been observed that, if certain parts of the body are protected against X-radiation by lead shielding, the animal can take considerably higher doses than if the irradiation is to the entire body. This can be demonstrated readily by shielding one leg. Especially striking results were obtained when the spleen was shielded.[16] This finding led to the technique of transplanting the spleen from a nonirradiated animal into an irradiated one, with a noteworthy increase in survival.

RECOVERY FROM RADIATION DAMAGE

a. Recovery Phenomena

A modest amount of progress has been made during the last few years in studying means of helping the living organism to recover from radiation damage. That recovery after irradiation is a normal process has been known for many years, since interrupted exposures under certain conditions permit the animal to tolerate higher amounts of radiation than if the total amount of radiation is given in one dose. This applies to survival and physiological effects; the problem is somewhat different in regard to mutation rate.

b. Recovery by Treatment After Exposure

Reduced Temperature

Recovery from radiation damage in bacteria can be increased if the bacteria are kept, after exposure, at suboptimal temperatures, especially in the presence of certain complete media. For example, 37°C is the optimal temperature for growth of non-

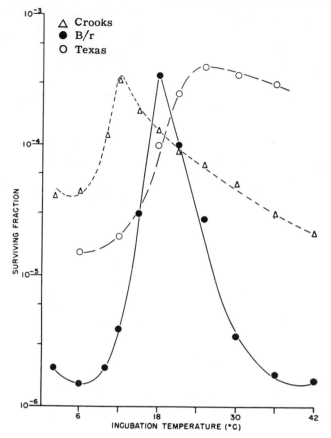

Figure 5. Survival of three strains of *E. coli* at 80 kr at various temperatures

irradiated *E. coli*, whereas irradiated cells show maximal survival if incubated at 18°C, following X- or γ-irradiation (Fig. 5).

Stimulation of Enzyme Activity and "Slowed-down" Cell Division

Apparently, these reduced temperatures slow down cell division but still allow some enzyme activity. One interpretation is that the process of cell division puts so great a strain on the enzymes and nutritional sources of the cell that any slowing down of the synthesis of essential compounds during cell division causes death of the cell. But if the cell is permitted to replenish its enzyme supply and redevelop the mechanism of enzyme production which has been upset by radiation before cell division is initiated, the cell can recover from radiation damage. Some basis for this idea is that the cells require for recovery certain types of tissue extracts like yeast or spleen extract.

Hemopoietic Tissue Transfers

Jacobson et al.[16] found that spleen transplanted from nonirradiated to irradiated mice permitted many of them to recover from radiation damage. The basic action of this treatment is the prevention of radiation infection, hemorrhage, leukocytopenia and anemia by causing damaged tissues to recover. Similar results have been obtained with injections of bone marrow.[18] In addition, *rat* bone marrow was shown to prevent death of the irradiated *mouse,* indicating that the responsible agent may not be species specific. Some of these tissues not only cause recovery from radiation damage, but also prevent leukemia induction by radiation.[17] The last observation was soon extended to include reduction of incidence of spontaneous leukemia in the mouse.[18] Preservation for 83 days of the activity of the ground-up tissues against radiation injury by storing the breis in frozen glycerine was demonstrated by English workers.[2]

Treatment of leukemia by total-body irradiation has been severely limited by the lethality of the radiation. By use of bone marrow injections to cause recovery from the lethal injury, Hollcroft *et al.*[13] obtained permanent regression of certain leukemias in mice and prolonged regressions in leukemic guinea pigs.

Many attempts have been made to isolate specific chemical substances from nonirradiated tissues, but as far as mammals are concerned, these have shown no effect on recovery. However, the story is somewhat different in bacteria, where cell-free extracts of yeast or spleen were found to be as effective as breis made of these tissues. After many tedious attempts to isolate specific substances that would favor *E. coli* recovery, it was finally found that three chemical compounds, i.e., glutamic acid, uracil and guanine, would simulate spleen and yeast extracts under certain conditions in their ability to make the bacteria recover from radiation damage.[28] As a matter of fact, with certain strains of bacteria, the protection by cysteamine is dependent to about 90 per cent on the presence of these so-called recovery factors in the medium in which the bacteria are incubated after X-ray exposure. This is probably the first demonstration of the dependence for chemical protection on the supply of recovery factors after exposure.[7, 15] This interdependence of chemical protection and recovery might very well be much more general than is now suspected.

Antibiotics

Antibiotics given to mice and other mammals after X-ray exposure will change the surviving fraction in the LD_{50} range and increase the life span at higher exposures. The antibiotics will inhibit bacterial invasion, often a serious consequence of overexposure where the lining of the intestine is destroyed.[20] The beneficial effects of antibiotics may also contribute toward a nutritional support of the irradiated animal, even though direct experimental evidence is not now available to support this contention.

Nutritional Support

The recovery produced by spleen extract and certain chemical compounds in bacteria can be looked upon as a nutritional support; that is, they supply to the bacteria nutrients which are required for recovery.

The truth of this can be shown by the finding that recovering organisms synthesize nucleic acids at a more normal rate than the nonprotected irradiated ones. Many interesting aspects of this problem lend themselves to experimental tests which are especially well adapted to the use of radioisotopes. The remarkable thing about bacteria is that, if they contain the enzyme systems for the production of radiation-sensitive intermediates, they do not require special chemicals after irradiation. For instance, if *E. coli* is grown before irradiation on a simple medium consisting of inorganic salts and glucose, it will not require elaborate nutritional support after exposure. However, if the cells are grown on a complete medium consisting of yeast or beef extract, they will not grow on minimal medium after irradiation but require the so-called recovery factors.

It has also been possible, in a few isolated cases, to extend the survival time of irradiated mice by supplemental feedings of certain nutritionals. There is no convincing evidence that this alone will increase the total survival after massive irradiation. Similar results may be expected when certain vitamins and some fatty acids are supplied. The whole problem of nutritional support and proper treatment after exposure of mammals is still in a very unsettled state; it is an excellent field for irradiation studies, especially in the hands of nutrition experts.

Combined Treatments

What happens in mice when chemical protection before and during irradiation is combined with spleen transplantation or bone marrow injections after exposure? A number of such tests have been conducted but little of the work has been reported in the literature. Several groups of investigators at the Argonne National Laboratory found that cysteine given before irradiation of the mice and spleen injected after irradiation apparently give additive results. Still better results have been obtained with cysteine and estrogen before exposure and spleen afterward. In this manner, the LD_{50} was raised from 600 to about 1400 r. Extensive experiments were conducted in this Laboratory by Burnett[3] who gave AET, a relatively low-toxicity compound, before exposure, bone marrow shortly afterward, and an injection of streptomycin daily for ten days. This seems to be the most effective combination. It was possible to raise the LD_{50} for certain hybrid mice which have considerable radiation resistance from 800–850 r to about 2400 r; in other words, the LD_{50} was tripled. Similar results were obtained with several inbred strains of mice. The mice which recover from these relatively large amounts of radiation appear fairly normal but show early graying and loss of hair. This is especially true for mice which have received only bone marrow. The protection by a chemical appears to be more general; that by the tissue transplantations is more specific.

The entire field of radiation recovery is still in its infancy. There are many possibilities, especially for combined treatments, which have not yet been explored.

GENETIC IMPLICATIONS OF RADIATION PROTECTION AND RECOVERY

Certain plant cells, such as the microspores of *Tradescantia* and the root of *Vicia,* are excellent materials for radiation studies since their chromosomes are large and few in number. The chromosomes, of course, go through certain cycles of condensation, rearrangement, doubling, and separation of the two sets of chromatids. Their sensitivity can therefore be studied at different stages of development and the results of radiation damage to one chromosome or chromatid can easily be followed. Chromosome breaks caused by radiation will stay open for a certain period, then the broken ends may heal together again; or if the break stays open too long, they may heal over without rejoining. If two neighboring chromosomes are damaged, there is a possibility of interjoining of different pieces of chromosomes, or a ring formation, with elimination of pieces of the chromosome. All this can be measured which helps to clarify what happens when the chromosome has absorbed the energy during the process of irradiation.

Removal of oxygen will reduce the number of recognizable breaks produced by radiation (usually, the DRF† is close to 3) which is similar to the effect of oxygen removal on the killing of other cells. However, the size of the DRF depends to a great extent on the types of aberrations and the mode of treatment. A number of chemicals produce the same effect on chromosome breaks as oxygen removal. This has been demonstrated with cysteine by Forssberg and Nybom,[9] with sodium hydrosulfite by Riley[25] and by Wolff and Luippold,[30] and with AET by Wolff and Luippold.[30] The question has arisen as to whether the oxygen removal affects the immediate, direct effect of radiation on the number of breaks produced or whether it favors the healing-up of chromosomes which are broken. It has been found that the process of reunion of radiation-broken chromosomes is closely controlled by the energy sources of the cell. The addition of adenosine triphosphate (ATP) will favor the healing-up of the chromosomes.[30] Extensive loss of parts of chromosomes by breakage leads to death of the cell. Such cell death may be an important basic cause of the various symptoms of radiation sickness. In addition, when produced in the sperm, chromosome losses may lead to death of the developing embryo. Smaller losses may cause smaller but nonetheless serious impairment of functions.

† "Dose-reduction factor" is defined as the ratio of energy necessary to produce an effect in the presence of a protective agent, to that necessary to produce an effect in the absence of the factor; e.g., if twice the dose is required to kill a mouse in the presence of cysteine as in its absence, the DRF is 2.

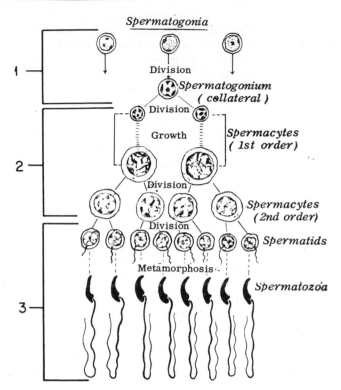

Figure 6. Development of spermatozoa from spermatogonia. (From Lacassagne, Arch. inst. Radium.) For convenience, in this paper, stages have been divided into three parts

This damage to the chromosomes can be observed by certain techniques used by geneticists to recognize dominant changes in the following generation. These changes are not to be confused with gene mutations in the cell.

Figure 6 illustrates the development of the sperm from the spermatogonia to the spermatozoa. The basic illustration has been taken from a publication of Professor A. Lacassagne and modified for the purpose of illustrating these points. The development of the sperm goes through definite stages, from the early spermatogonia through the spermatocytes, spermatid stage, and finally to the completed sperm. For simplification, development has been divided here into three stages. Cells in the first stage, spermatogonia, are very sensitive to radiation—as little as 25 r may inactivate them. Cells in the second stage are considerably more resistant and will be inactivated by about 600 r, in mice. Spermatozoa are very resistant and may survive as much as 1000 to 1500 r. Oakberg[22] has found that the spermatogonia stage can be protected against radiation damage by reduced oxygen tension enough to double the LD_{50}. This is of considerable interest since it may furnish a means of protecting some of the stages of sperm formation against radiation damage. As far as is known, it is not possible to protect mature sperm against radiation damage. One reason is that the sperm probably exists in anaerobic conditions. In a mammal irradiated with 200–300 r, the fully formed sperm used immediately after exposure will continue its fertilizability even when it contains considerable chromosome damage; it will transmit to the following generation certain dominant changes which may express themselves in stillbirth or other deleterious effects. Since the spermatogonia are so extremely sensitive, most of them will be killed; which, in part, accounts for the sterile period which usually follows the initial fertility and may last for several weeks, depending on the amount of radiation exposure. Then, when new spermatogonia are formed, the fertility may return. These conditions point up the extreme importance of avoiding conception for several weeks after exposure to radiation.[26]

Only the dominant changes have been discussed. These differ from the more insidiously dangerous gene mutations or recessive changes, which usually cannot be recognized microscopically in the structure of the chromosome. Recessive mutations cause, when mated with a similar recessive gene, the appearance of mutations of a dangerous type. Practically all gene mutations are detrimental; a beneficial one is extremely rare. This phenomenon causes the concern felt by many geneticists in regard to radiation damage. The mention that the recessive gene has to pair with another recessive gene before it can express itself is really not entirely correct. It is now quite well established that many recessive genes are not absolutely recessive but that most of them are in reality partially dominant; they may express themselves, even without pairing with another recessive gene, in decreased vitality or in physiological or mental shortcomings (for review of this entire subject, see Muller[21]).

It is usually accepted that mutation changes increase linearly with increasing amounts of radiation and that they are accumulative. It makes little difference whether the radiation is given as one acute dose or is spread over the period of reproductive life of the mammal. From the point of view of protection, only in bacteria is there significant data. In bacteria, the number of mutations (nutritional reversions are referred to here) increases linearly with increasing doses, just as in higher organisms. What happens to the bacterial mutations when the cells are protected by chemicals or when they recover from radiation damage by proper treatment after exposure? Certain strains of bacteria, which are protected by chemical means or which recover by proper treatment after exposure, show a mutation rate which is proportional to the number of cells recovering, not to the amount of radiation to which they have been exposed.[14] Several interpretations of these data are possible; one of them is that the mutation process requires considerable time after irradiation has been absorbed for its completion; during this time, it is possible to modify it. A high percentage of the mutations can be prevented by treatment either before or after exposure. The data on this problem are very limited but more experiments are in progress. Experiments to check this problem on mammals have been started but

several years will be required to obtain even preliminary data.

SUMMARY AND CONCLUSIONS

It is quite justifiable to state that damage from X- or γ-radiation may be modified by reducing the oxygen concentration within the cells and that this can be accomplished by treatment with certain chemicals, most of which are reducing compounds. Chemical treatment must be used before or during irradiation. Hemopoietic tissue transfer after irradiation will increase survival of mammals. In bacteria, glutamic acid, uracil, and guanine will simulate the effects of tissue extracts. It appears that chemical protection and supply of recovery factors are effective by somewhat different mechanisms—the chemical protection is more general, the tissue transfer more specific. These phenomena are well established in mice and some are effective in other mammals. On the basis of present knowledge, the use of chemicals gives considerable promise as a protective technique. The problem of tissue transfer is not so near clarification.

All the factors mentioned apply to survival and physiological damage from radiation. Much less well defined is the repair of radiation-protected chromosomes. As far as is known, this has been demonstrated only in specific biological materials in regard to postirradiation modification of mutation production. Scant data are available on this material; less is known concerning *Drosophila* than for *E. coli*. Whether these findings can be applied to mammals remains to be seen. In any case, tools are now available for studying the protection and recovery phenomena, and a moderate degree of optimism seems justified on the basis of the findings discussed. However, extensive work at many laboratories will be required for their application to practical use.

The wide use of atomic energy as a power source will result in world-wide distribution of reactors; and the extensive use of radioisotopes as powerful research tools in medicine and in industry make an understanding of the basic mechanism of radiation damage to living cells extremely important. Such an understanding should enable the investigator to develop practical methods for protecting man against radiation, by physical as well as by some biological means. It also behooves the scientist to study means of aiding the recovery of people who have been accidentally exposed to radiation; accidents should be very rare but will not be entirely avoidable. It is satisfying to investigators in the radiobiology field to find the wide interest in these problems and the conviction that extensive work is going on in laboratories all over the world. This conference should encourage an exchange of opinion in this field, and through the mutual understanding among scientists, the field of study of radiation protection and recovery should be widely extended.

REFERENCES

1. Bacq, Z. M. and Herve, A., Protection chimique contre le rayonnement X, *Bull. Acad. roy. med. Belg., 18:* 13-58 (1952).

2. Barnes, D. W. H. and Loutit, J. F., The radiation recovery factor: preservation by the Polge-Smith-Parkes technique, *J. Natl. Cancer Inst., 15:* 901-905 (1955).

3. Burnett, W. T., Jr. and Doherty, D. G., Additive effect of S,β-aminoethylisothiuronium·Br·HBr, bone marrow, and streptomycin on gamma-irradiated mice, *Radiation Research* (in press), (Radiation Research Soc., New York City, May 1955).

4. Caldecott, R. S., Reduction of X-ray sensitivity of seeds by hydration, *Nature, 176:* 306 (1955).

5. Conger, A. D. and Fairchild, L. M., Breakage of chromosomes by oxygen, *Proc. Natl. Acad. Sci. U.S., 38:* 289-299 (1952).

6. Dotherty, D. G. and Burnett, W. T. Jr., Protective effect of S,β-aminoethylisothiuronium · Br · HBr and related compounds against X-radiation death in mice, *Proc. Soc. Exptl. Biol. Med., 89:* 312-315 (1955).

7. Doudney, C. O. and Hollaender, A., Studies on the chemical protection of *Escherichia coli* from X rays by cysteamine and mercaptoethanol. In preparation.

8. Dowdy, A. H., Bennett, L. R. and Chastain, S. M., Protective action of anoxia against total-body roentgen irradiation of mammals, *Radiology, 55:* 879-885 (1950).

9. Forssberg, A. and Nybom, N., Combined effects of cysteine and irradiation on growth and cytology of *Allium cepa* roots, *Physiol. Plantarum, 6:* 78-95 (1953).

10. Gerschman, R., Gilbert, D. L., Nye, S. W., Dwyer, P. and Fenn, W. O., Oxygen poisoning and X irradiation: A mechanism in common, *Science, 119:* 623-625 (1954).

11. Graevsky, E. J., A study of the protection of the animal organism against the deleterious effect of ionizing radiations, *Proc. Atoms for Peace Conf. of the Acad. Sci. USSR* (Moscow, July 5-10, 1955), volume on Biological Sciences, pp. 34-50.

12. Gray, L. H., Conger, A. D., Ebert, M., Hornsey, S. and Scott, O. C. A., The concentration of oxygen dissolved in tissues at the time of irradiation as a factor in radiotherapy, *Brit. J. Radiol., 26:* 638-648 (1953).

13. Hollcroft, J., Lorenz, E., Congdon, C. C. and Jacobson, L. O., Factors influencing the irradiation treatment of experimental lymphoid tumors, *Rev. Mex. Radiol., 7:* 115-124 (1953).

14. Hollaender, A., Billen, D. and Doudney, C. O., The modification of X-ray-produced mutations in *Escherichia coli* by pre- and post-treatment, *Radiation Research* (in press), (Radiation Research Soc., New York City, May 1955).

15. Hollaender, A. and Doudney, C. O., Studies on the mechanism of radiation protection and recovery with cysteamine and β-mercaptoethanol, Radiobiol. Symposium (Proc.) 1954, ed. Z. M. Bacq and P. Alexander. Butterworths Scientific Publications, London, pp. 112-115.

16. Jacobson, L. O., Marks, E. K., Gaston, E. O., Dobson, M. J. and Zirkle, R. E., The role of the spleen in radiation injury, *Pro. Soc. Exptl. Biol. Med., 70:* 740-742 (1949).

17. Kaplan, H. S., Brown, M. B. and Paull, J., Influence of bone marrow injections on involution and neoplasia of mouse thymus after system irradiation, *J. Ntl. Cancer Inst., 14:* 303-316 (1953).

18. Lorenz, E., Congdon, C. C. and Uphoff, D. Modification of acute irradiation injury in mice and guinea pigs by bone marrow injection, *Radiology, 58:* 863-877 (1952).

19. Markovitch, H., P/371, The problem of the biological action of low doses of ionizing radiation, Volume II, Session 12, these Proceedings.

20. Miller, C. P., Hammond, C. W. and Tompkins, M., The role of infection in radiation injury, *J. Lab. Clin. Med., 38:* 331-343 (1951).

21. Muller, H. J., The manner of production of mutations by radiation, *In* Radiation Biology, Vol. I, ed. A. Hollaender. McGraw-Hill Book Co., Inc., New York, pp. 475-627 (1954).

22. Oakberg, E. F., Sensitivity and time of degeneration of spermatogenic cells irradiated in various stages of maturation in the mouse, *Radiation Research, 2:* 369–392 (1955).

23. Patt, H. M., Protective mechanisms in ionizing radiation injury, *Physiol. Rev., 33:* 37-76 (1953).

24. Rajewski, B., The limits of the target theory of the biological action of radiation, *Brit. J. Radiol., 25:* 550-552 (1952).

25. Riley, H. P., Preliminary report on the effect of certain chemicals on radiation damage to chromosomes, *Genetics, 37:* 618 (1952).

26. Russell, W. L., Genetic effects of radiation in mammals, *In* Radiation Biology, Vol. I, ed. A. Hollaender. McGraw-Hill Book Co. Inc., New York, pp. 285-859 (1954).

27. Salerno, P. R. and Friedell, H. L., Further studies on the relationship between oxygen tensions and the protective actions of cysteine, mercaptoethylamine, and p-aminopropiophenone, *Radiation Research, 1:* 559 (1954).

28. Stapleton, G. E., Billen, D. and Hollaender, A., Recovery of X-irradiated bacteria at suboptimal incubation temperatures, *J. Cellular Comp. Physiol., 41:* 345-358 (1953).

29. Stapleton, G. E. and Edington, C. W., Temperature dependence of bacterial inactivation by X rays, *Radiation Research, 1:* 229-230 (1954). (Also paper in preparation).

30. Wolff, S. and Luippold, H. E., Metabolism and chromosome break rejoining, *Science, 122:* 231-233 (1955).

31. Wood, T. H., Influence of low temperature and phase states on X-ray sensitivity of yeast, *Radiation Research, 1:* 234 (1954).

Radioactive Elements in the Study of Plant Life

By Andrei L. Kursanov, USSR

The brilliant successes of nuclear physics have had a tremendous influence on the development of other branches of science and technology, even those which seem at first sight to have no connexion with atomic fission.

In our day, machines for generating electricity, or doing any other kind of useful work, are being driven by the energy released in radioactive disintegration. Radioactive elements and ionizing radiations are used for controlling many production processes, for measuring the age of geological formations, for establishing the chemical structure of substances, for studying the processes which go on in the human body and in animals and plants, for changing the nature of living organisms, and even for determining dates in history connected with the cultures of antiquity and the development of society.

The Geneva Conference on the Peaceful Uses of Atomic Energy, which has attracted so much attention, has shown us many fine examples of the utilization of atomic energy in different fields of man's intellectual activity.

However, we are still only on the threshold of that new era which will rightly be called the age of the peaceful use of atomic energy. Thus it is hardly possible for us to foresee at the present time all that we shall be able to achieve with the help of radioactive elements.

This is particularly true of a branch of knowledge very dear to me—biology, where the new opportunities offered by modern nuclear physics are far from exhausted. Nevertheless, in a very short space of time, the use of radioactive elements as a research tool has carried us so far forward in our understanding of the metabolism of organisms, that already, behind the old conceptions built up by the painstaking work of many decades, we can descry the outlines of more complete and accurate conceptions, reached in a short time with the help of tracer atoms.

In his lecture my distinguished colleague, Professor Hollaender, dwelt mainly on problems connected with the action of ionizing radiations on organisms, and revealed to us the profound metabolic changes that can be brought about in living creatures by the use of this powerful weapon.

I, by contrast, or, perhaps, rather as a supplement to that work, shall try to throw light on another aspect of the use of radioactive elements in biology,

namely, their use as *labelled atoms* in the study of plant nutrition and metabolism. The unique feature of the labelled-atom method is that it makes it easy to distinguish between substances containing a radioactive or a non-radioactive isotope in any biological medium, and even in an organism as a whole. This makes it possible to observe the movement and transformations of the tracer substances and, by analogy, to draw conclusions about the normal course of transformation, since the tagged substances, when only slightly radioactive, take part in the general metabolic processes together with the non-radioactive compounds.

To illustrate these possibilities by more practical examples, I shall try in my lecture to paint a picture of plant nutrition as it appears to us now after several years' use of labelled atoms. I chose this particular subject because the use of radioactive elements in the form of labelled atoms makes it easier than with any other method to observe how plants make use of nutritive elements and how different compounds move through their tissues, and to observe the most subtle reactions going on in those tissues. As a result, many new discoveries about plant nutrition have been made in recent years, opening up new prospects for the practical improvement of agricultural methods—a statement with which I hope my audience will agree as it becomes better acquainted with the problem.

It has long been established that the roots of plants absorb from the soil water and mineral salts which pass into the organs above the ground and are there used in the metabolic processes. The greater part of the synthesizing functions of plants were originally ascribed to the leaves, the roots being generally regarded as intermediaries between soil and leaves, and as the organs which anchor the plant to the ground, thus playing only a subordinate role. In some cases the roots were also regarded as receptacles in which the organic substances originating in the leaves could be stored. At the same time, earlier works usually failed to take sufficient account of the ability of the roots themselves to synthesize many complex compounds, or to analyse in the necessary detail the significance of these processes for the life of the plant as a whole.

True, at the beginning of the century Prianishnikov, followed by others, showed that the ammonia nitrogen absorbed from the soil is utilized to make asparagine in the roots themselves, so that the latter are not mere transmitters of inorganic substances

Original language: Russian.

from the soil to the leaves, but can themselves effect their primary transformations. Later the ability of the roots to synthesize certain alkaloids (Shmuk, Ilyin, Mothes, Dawson) and other nitrogenous compounds (Mothes, Kursanov, Kolosov) was discovered. Nevertheless, the role of the root as an organ which, by its biochemical activity, shared in the plant's general metabolism was still not entirely clear.

At the same time, during the period in question the leaves were considered responsible not only for the primary formation of organic substances by photosynthesis, but also for the secondary synthesis of most of the products met with in plants. Thus, according to earlier ideas, the synthesizing functions of plants were, so to speak, concentrated in the leaves, from whence the various substances could pass into the other parts of the plant.

The relationships between plant leaves and roots as then conceived may be illustrated by a diagram (Fig. 1) showing two unconnected and opposite stream of substances: one ascending, carrying inorganic substances and water from the soil, the other descending from the leaves and supplying the other parts of the plant with the necessary organic substances.

In essence, this diagram gives us a true picture of the basic sources of plant food, but it reflects the internal links between the various organs quite inadequately, and therefore gives a very poor idea of the laws governing the movement, distribution and transformation of substances inside the plant.

Important new successes have been achieved in this field in recent years, mainly through the use of labelled atoms.

The research carried out by Vennesland, Ochoa and some other American scientists, using radioactive carbon dioxide, has proved that in animal and plant tissues there exist widespread special enzymatic systems which bring about the combination of carbonic acid gas with organic acids independently of photosynthesis. Poel and others, carrying this work further, have shown that a plant's ability to fix carbon dioxide in darkness is particularly marked in the root tissues. It was also proved that the process is related to the oxidizing degradation of organic substances in the cells, but the physiological significance of this phenomenon in plant life remained rather obscure.

The explanation came from the Soviet Union after a number of workers, including Kursanov and Kuzin, working on roots of whole plants with radioactive carbon dioxide, had discovered a new physiological function of the root system. This function consists in the absorption by the roots of carbon dioxide from the soil and its translocation to the leaves, where, in the light, it can be used, just like the carbon dioxide absorbed from the air, for the synthesis of sugars and other products. The entire process usually takes place so quickly that within a few minutes of the roots being brought into contact with carbon dioxide solution tagged with radioactive carbon, C^{14}, can be identified in all parts of the plant, occurring especially abundantly in the leaves. Figure 2 illustrates this, and shows a young bean plant photographing itself, so to speak, by means of the radioactive carbon which has penetrated into its tissues through the root.

Thus, with the help of labelled carbon, a supplementary source of carbon nutrition was discovered, whose existence had hitherto been unsuspected. This fact also has its practical significance, in that it brings out the important part played by the carbon dioxide formed in the soil by microbiological processes when natural fertilizers are used. The role of the carbon dioxide entering through the roots is obviously of minor importance in the general carbon-dioxide nutrition of plants, but that role may vary quite considerably according to circumstances—a fact of practical interest that deserves serious study. At

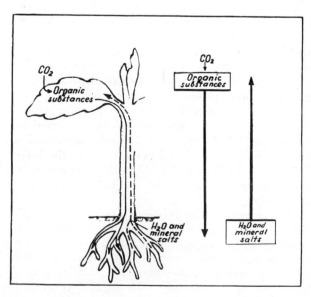

Figure 1.

Figure 2.

the present time we do not have enough data to attempt a final judgment on the effectiveness of feeding plants with carbon dioxide through the roots. However, experiments carried out by Grinfeld in the Latvian SSR have recently shown that fertilizing with ammonium carbonate instead of ammonium sulphate increases the weight of sugar beets by 14-16% without lowering their sugar content. Similar results were obtained in the experiments I carried out with Tamman in the Moscow region in 1953 and 1954. Figure 3 gives some idea of the influence of carbon-dioxide fertilizers (carbonates) on yields of barley and potatoes.

Here we have a concrete example of how the use of radioactive carbon in the study of plant life helps us to devise new practical methods of increasing yields.

With the help of radioactive carbon (C^{14}), we succeeded in making a fairly detailed study of the internal mechanism of this phenomenon. Figure 4 is a schematic representation of a plant, accompanied by chemical formulae showing the course of the transformations in which the carbon dioxide from the soil takes part.

By contrast with the first diagram, we now see that carbon dioxide — that basic source of carbon nutrition—enters the plant from two opposite ends, through the leaves and through the roots. We know well that the sugar formed in the leaves by the assimilation of CO_2 from the atmosphere moves downwards through the plant and reaches the roots. The speed of this downward movement, which previously could not be determined by any existing method, can now be easily and accurately measured with the help of substances tagged with radioactive elements. The speed varies from 40 to 100 centimeters an hour, the products of photosynthesis formed in the leaves reaching the roots in 30–40 minutes in most agricultural plants.

In young active rootlets, which have not yet lost their capacity for absorbing nutritious substances from the soil, the sugar is subjected to glycolytic

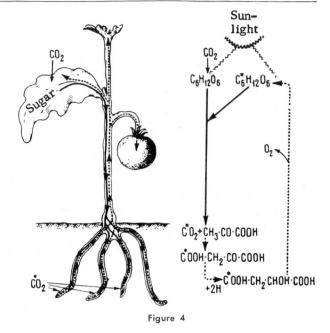

Figure 4

decomposition, with the formation of pyruvic acid. This substance takes up the carbon dioxide in the soil with the help of carboxylating enzymes, and turns it into oxalacetic and, by simultaneous reduction, malic acid. These acids are the first stable compounds, carrying in one of their carboxyl groups the carbon dioxide absorbed from the soil. Later, as a result of the mutual transformation of organic acids and further carboxylation, the soil carbon dioxide may enter into the composition of other acids.

It must be remembered, of course, that this introduction of carbon dioxide into organic compounds cannot in itself be considered as the *feeding* of the plant with carbon dioxide, as in this process the free energy of the compounds in question shows virtually no increase. However, as has been established with the aid of radioactive isotopes, the organic acids do not remain in the roots, but rise through the plants to the leaves at a speed which may reach as much as two metres per hour. Thus the soil carbon dioxide contained in them quickly reaches the green tissues, where it is again released through the action of the decarboxylating enzymes and converted by photosynthesis into carbohydrates, albumins and other products rich in energy.

Part of the sugars formed in this way pass in their turn into the roots, there to be converted into pyruvic acid and thus enabled to take up new doses of CO_2 from the soil and carry them to the leaves. This is the fundamental cycle in this particular process linking the activity of the roots with that of the leaves.

We can prove the existence of the cycle by different methods, for example by immersing the roots of plants in a solution of radioactive carbon dioxide and at the same time inhibiting the photosynthetic action of the leaves by shading them.

Under these conditions, the organic acids arriving from the roots are subjected in the leaves to

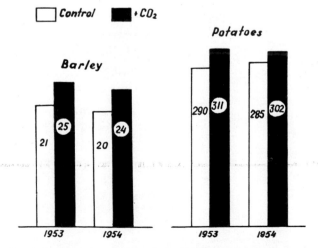

Figure 3. The influence of soil fertilization with carbonates on the yield of some plants

strong decarboxylation, which liberates the soil carbon dioxide, which, finding itself with no part to play in the process of photosynthesis, passes into the surrounding atmosphere. Thus, when there is insufficient light, the cycle described is broken off at the stage of photoconversion, the process becoming unidirectional and entailing the "pumping" of the soil carbon dioxide through the body of the plant into the surrounding air. The active emission by plants of carbon dioxide through their leaves when there is insufficient light, or when the metabolism has broken down, has often been described in scientific literature, being known under the name of "CO_2 fountains." We now think that this phenomenon is connected with the excretion of soil carbon dioxide.

However, a number of complementary phenomena are superimposed upon the cycle we have been discussing; these link carbon dioxide nutrition via the roots with other aspects of the plant's physiological activity. In particular, it is easy, by observing, with the help of tagged carbon, the movement of organic acids from the roots to the leaves, to see that a certain amount of the soil carbon dioxide incorporated in the acids breaks off and is used for photosynthesis in the stems by the green cells, which are usually grouped along the conducting tubes, contiguous to active parts of the skin. As a result, in dense tissues, to which the outside air can penetrate only with difficulty, a large quantity of the oxygen necessary to sustain the very active respiration of the conducting tissues is formed. This interesting phenomenon is illustrated in Fig. 5.

As a proof of the importance of normal oxygen respiration of the conducting cells in the trans-

location of organic substances within the plant we can cite experiments carried out in our laboratory with the help of radioactive carbon. These experiments showed that when the oxygen respiration of the conducting tissues is inhibited, e.g., by means of carbon monoxide (CO), the translocation of sugars and other organic substances comes to a standstill (Fig. 6).

Thus the use of labelled atoms has enabled us to elucidate the role of the chlorophyll-bearing cells which so constantly accompany the conducting tissues.

As a result, we come to the conclusion, paradoxical at first sight, that the oxygen respiration of dense tissues, to which the outside air can penetrate only with difficulty, is carried on with the help of carbon dioxide which comes to them through the roots.

However, the absorption of CO_2 from the soil is also directly related to such important functions of the root system as nitrogen and phosphorus nutrition, and these relationships themselves are obviously the most important in the process of assimilation by the plant of soil carbon dioxide.

Not long ago Tueva, Kolosov and some others proved that the synthesis of many amino-acids, the basic constituents of proteins, is carried out in the roots.

So far, about fifteen different amino-acids formed in the roots have been isolated and studied. In addition, Mothes and his co-workers have demonstrated the capacity of roots to synthesize allantoin, cytillin and some other more complicated nitrogenous compounds. Thus it has been shown that in addition to its absorptive functions, which have for long been the subject of study, the root system has a second important role connected with the protein metabolism of the whole plant.

At first it seemed that this aspect of the activity of the roots was an independent function unconnected with their absorptive activity, but with the use of labelled atoms it has gradually become clear

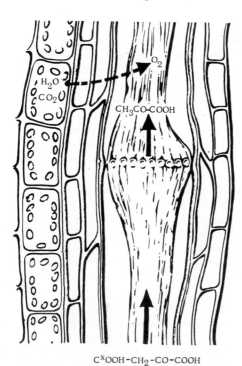

CH₃CO-COOH

C^XOOH-CH₂-CO-COOH

Figure 5

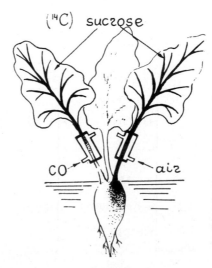

(¹⁴C) sucrose

CO   air

Figure 6

that this is actually the direct mechanism used by the roots to take up ammonia fertilizers from the soil.

Prianishnikov, and later Kretovich, together with a number of other workers, have proved that the primary absorption of salts of ammonia by the plant is carried out by direct amination, i.e., the combination of NH_2-groups with certain organic acids continually being formed in the roots. Later, as Braunstein showed, transamination occurs, giving rise to various amino-acids. Like the organic acids, the amino-acids quickly travel from the roots into the organs above the ground, where they are used for renewing proteins, and, in young growing tissues, for forming new masses of protein compounds.

Experiments with radioactive carbon dioxide have shown that the role of soil carbon dioxide in the primary synthesis of amino-acids consists in carboxylating the products of the incomplete degradation of the sugars, which leads to the formation of those organic acids (oxalacetic and α-keto-glutaric acid) which are the main acceptors of nitrogen from ammonia fertilizers.

Finally, this system can function in the roots only in the presence of phosphoric acid, as phosphorus takes a direct part in the conversion of the sugar entering the roots into the essential organic acids, and even in the fixation of the carbon dioxide. Therefore, if a plant lacks phosphorus fertilizer, the formation of organic acids in its roots is slowed down, with a consequential reduction in its capacity to absorb carbon dioxide from the soil (Fig. 7). Such plants make only slight use of nitrogenous fertilizers even when the soil is rich enough in them.

With phosphorus starvation, the movement of sugars from the leaves to the roots goes on, although more feebly. However, the sugars do not find in roots starved of phosphorus the conditions necessary for their transformation into organic acids, and therefore accumulate there, or return unused with the ascending stream. Thus, when there is insufficient

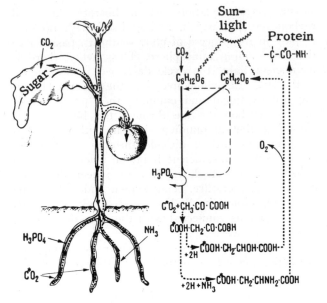

Figure 8.

phosphorus in a plant, a kind of "vicious circle" is set up, in which the circulating sugars take no part in the metabolic reactions proper to normal plants.

Thus, beginning with the use of radioactive carbon for the study of the elementary reactions of carboxylation, and using the method for further investigation, the biologists of the Soviet Union, the USA and other countries have in a short space of time explained the complex picture of the circulation of substances in plants, by which the activities of the various organs are integrated and the conditions created for normal plant nutrition. The entire picture is illustrated in Fig. 8.

Comparing this picture with our original conception of plant nutrition, illustrated in Fig. 1, we rightly draw the conclusion that labelled atoms have enabled biologists to achieve considerable successes in the study of plant nutrition in a very short time.

The quintessence of all this is, of course, the discovery that there is a rapid circulation of organic substances covering the entire body of the plant from its uppermost leaves to the tips of its roots. This circulation is also interesting in that it is accompanied by transformations of the constituents taking part in it and proceeds by bringing the soil carbon dioxide into the reaction. Thus we can no longer accept the earlier idea that ascribed to the roots a humble role as transmitters of mineral substances and water from the soil to the organs above ground. On the contrary, on the basis of the data cited, we may ascribe to the roots a leading part in those complex transformations that the substances taking part in the main cycle undergo.

If a leaf still attached to the plant is placed in a glass vessel containing radioactive carbon dioxide for a few minutes and exposed to light, radioactive sugars and other products of photosynthesis are immediately formed in the leaf tissues. Observing, with the help of a dosimeter-counter or by contact

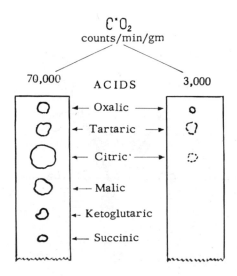

Figure 7.

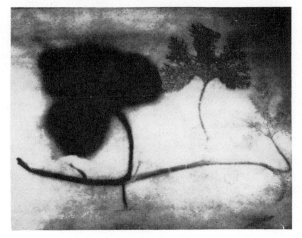

Figure 9.   Figure 10

radiography, how the radioactivity spreads from the leaf into the other organs, we can watch the direction and speed of movement of the assimilation products in the plant. This shows that by far the greatest part of the products of photosynthesis move from the leaves down through the stem even when the leaves are near to the crown or are situated not far from growing fruits or shoots.

Figures 9 and 10 reproduce the contact radiographs of one such experiment carried out on a pumpkin, which provide documentary proof of what has just been described.

After a rather longer period, we can see also the radioactive assimilates reaching the roots. Here they undergo various transformations connected with the absorptive function of the root system and its specific activity. Thence, in the form of a mixture of new products, including carbon dioxide and nitrogenous compounds from the soil, organic substances return to the growing fruits, shoots and leaves.

Thus, with the help of radioactive carbon, we can observe with our own eyes the regulating function of the roots, which allow a considerable part of the products of photosynthesis to pass through them, subjecting them to the necessary transformations before they are used by the other organs of the plant.

Radioactive isotopes, like labelled atoms, are rendering invaluable service to contemporary biologists by making it possible to solve complex problems more easily and more quickly. However, hardly any other aspect of plant life has become so readily accessible to study as the phenomenon of translocation, i.e., those processes with which we have, hitherto been able to deal only through indirect evidence. If we reflect that it is precisely the translocation of substances, both organic and inorganic, in solution or in the gaseous state, upon which the correct nutrition of different parts of plants and the accumulation of valuable reserve substances depends, then it is obvious that direct observation of the flow of the substances is of great importance for biology and agriculture alike.

We have just considered a case where, with the help of radioactive carbon, we have discovered in the plant, which outwardly appears so still, a rapid circulation of substances linking the activity of all its organs.

However, in addition to this central process, which we may rightly call "the major circulation of substances", there goes on in individual organs of the plant a private, or "minor" circulation, which plays an important role in the life of the particular organ. This discovery, which is very recent, was also made with the aid of labelled atoms.

I shall mention here only one such private process — the circulation of substances in green fruits recently discovered by V. Pontovich in Moscow.

Figure 11.

By adding to the air contained in the vacuole of an unripe, still green, poppy fruit a small quantity of carbon dioxide tagged with radioactive carbon, Pontovich discovered that the carbonic acid gas emitted abundantly by developing seeds in respiration does not accumulate in the vacuole of the fruit, but quickly penetrates into the tissues of the green wall where, with the help of chlorophyll and sunlight, it is again transformed into sugar and other products of photosynthesis. Investigating with labelled atoms the behaviour of the organic substances thus formed, Pontovich showed that they are translocated to the pericarp to which the seeds are attached, and, passing quickly through its colourless tissue, again enter the growing seeds (see Fig. 11).

Thus in the green fruit of the poppy (and of other plants) there is a local circulation of substances which quickly removes the harmful excess of carbon dioxide in the vacuole, supports a high concentration of oxygen, necessary for the synthesis of lipoid and other substances, and restores the organic substances lost by the seeds in respiration.

Since this "minor circulation" takes place with the help of photosynthesis, in which the carbon dioxide produced in respiration is transformed into organic substances, it is easy to understand the physiological role of the chlorophyll which is so constantly found in the walls of unripe fruit. We must emphasize once more that all this was quickly and accurately discovered with the help of labelled atoms.

Radioactive elements enable successes to be achieved in the case of many other problems of plant nutrition also. Particularly great progress has been made with their help in the study of photosynthesis, that most complex, and at the same time unique in respect of its energy balance, process, which stores up the energy of light in organic compounds by converting it into chemical energy. Naturally, countless scientific papers have been devoted to the study of this process, for it was discovered almost two hundred years ago. However, the more it was studied, the more complex the general picture of the phenomenon appeared, and the harder it seemed to reproduce this complex process outside a green plant.

And yet the mastery of the photochemical processes conducing to the steady accumulation of the energy of light in the substances formed would mean for mankind a new era in power production prospects, that would probably be even wider than in the age of atomic energy.

We may say with some satisfaction that the radioactive elements which have been widely used in recent times for studying photosynthesis have brought us considerably nearer to a solution of this remarkable enigma. This gives grounds for hoping that, perhaps even in the not too distant future, the possibility may arise of the practical application of photosynthesis outside the plant. Very real successes have been achieved in this field by United States scientists; especially prominent in recent years have been Calvin, Benson and their co-workers, who with the aid of radioactive carbon have shed much new light on the preliminary reactions that precede the reduction of carbon dioxide, and on the primary products of photosynthesis. The work of Arnon is also exceptionally promising; in this, the use of radioactive phosphorus has revealed the possibility of stable accumulation of the energy of light in amounts of the order of macro-ergs in adenosinetriphosphoric acid. Thus we can see that the rational use of atomic energy is already paving the way to the mastery of the energy of light.

However, labelled atoms are not only helping us to prepare future successes, but are already proving of real worth in man's practical activities. This is the case in agriculture, where many problems of farming techniques and plant nutrition are now being solved with the help of radioactive isotopes. In my discourse, I have already mentioned some practical prospects for agriculture opened up by the study of plant life with the help of labelled atoms. However, the chief practical application is in the matter of fertilizers—the most accessible and controllable means of influencing crop yields. Radioactive isotopes of phosphorus, sulphur, calcium, cobalt and other elements are now being widely used in the experimental stations of the USSR, the USA, England and other countries, to solve problems relating to the avidity of plants for one or another type of fertilizer, the most advantageous distribution of fertilizer in relation to sowing, the critical periods, the needs of plants in mineral nutritive elements and so on.

The experiments with radioactive isotopes are showing agricultural workers the surest way to high and sustained harvests, the way to a secure and quiet life for man. The peoples of all countries now realize this, which constrains them to look with respect and trust on the work being carried on by scientists with the aid of radioactive elements. Our duty now is to justify that trust.

The Future of Atomic Energy

By Sir John Cockcroft, UK

To many of us this Conference has been a celebration of a very great achievement of the scientific world—the harnessing of the energy of atomic nuclei to serve the future needs of man. This is the culmination of scientific work of men of genius in many nations. It is fitting therefore that representatives of the great majority of countries should have come together to present their contributions to this work and to discuss how this new source of power can help the future development of their countries and the whole human race.

We have had described to us the first experimental atomic power stations and have heard that they are working well. We have also heard of the rapid progress of construction of the first full-scale nuclear power stations. Within two years they will be delivering very substantial amounts of electricity to industry and we will begin to gain experience in their operation and economics. These early stations will be closely followed by successors of different and generally improved designs, so that within five years we are likely to have at least ten nuclear power stations generating up to 200 megawatts in a single unit operating in different parts of the world.

These will all be pioneering or demonstration stations built to test the technology on which all depends and to compare the relative advantages of the ten most promising types both from the point of view of economics and also of reliability and safety in operation. So most of the next decade will be occupied in laying a sound basis from which nuclear power can expand rapidly to become in the end the major power source of the world. Until we have achieved satisfactory operating experience we will not be justified in embarking on a more rapid expansion.

This new industrial development has the advantage of a very great and unparalleled concentration of scientific and engineering ability driving it forward with imagination and enthusiasm—as you can judge from the papers which have been presented to this Conference. So the speed of development will be rapid and the nuclear power stations of 1970 will look as different from those of 1957 as a modern motor car differs from a Model T Ford.

The papers presented to the Conference have shown that we must not expect the cost of nuclear power to be cheaper in the next decade than power from coal. The concensus of opinion is that capital costs will be appreciably higher—50 to 100 per cent higher—than the capital costs of coal stations, but that fuel costs will be less than half that for coal. So on balance there should be little difference in the cost of power, with nuclear power slightly more expensive than conventional power.

But to many countries that is not the *important* point. The important point is to obtain an *additional* source of energy to our conventional energy resources where they are becoming overstrained.

Nevertheless the whole history of engineering development shows how rapidly capital costs fall in the early stages of important new developments, and there is good reason to believe that in the second decade the cost of nuclear power will fall below that of power from coal and oil.

Our second major objective is progressively to increase the amount of energy we can extract from each ton of uranium and thorium. We believe, although we have not yet proved the point, that in the early stations we can extract from one ton of uranium the heat equivalent of about 10,000 tons of coal in a single fuel cycle; but we have also heard of the promise of recycling the fuel in thermal reactors several times so that the energy extraction can be increased five- or ten-fold. We have also heard of the more ambitious *final* goal of achieving the nuclear physicist's dream of making use of the breeding principle, and so extracting a great part of the fission energy of the whole uranium. In this

Sir John Cockcroft (UK) and Mr. D. V. Skobeltzin (USSR), two of the vice-presidents of the Conference, discuss a written question

way we expect to make one ton of uranium do the work of at least a million tons of coal. The engineer has still to convert the physicist's dream into large-scale practical power stations but we have heard during the Conference of the building of large-scale experimental breeder reactors both of the homogeneous and fast reactor types. Both have difficult engineering problems but sometime during the second decade breeding is likely to be an important characteristic of nuclear power stations.

Our economists and statisticians have looked ahead to the years 1975 and 2000 and they have predicted that by these years our energy requirements will increase by at least 1½ times in 1975 and by 3 times in the year 2000. So by the end of the century the world is likely to require the energy equivalent of 7 or 8 milliard tons of coal a year as compared with our present usage of 1.7 milliard tons a year. (By milliard I mean 10^9.) Almost one-half of this energy will be required for generating electricity. Hydro-electricity should by then be fully developed, but even so will only do the work of 1 milliard tons of coal a year. It will be a great help to the human race if by the year 2000 nuclear energy can generate the remainder of the electricity and so do the work of 2 to 3 milliard tons of coal a year.

We have heard the forecast of uranium supplies — how it occurs throughout the world, not only in concentrated deposits but in abundant gold ores, shales, phosphate rocks. In seven countries alone there is reported to be available at least one million tons of uranium, whilst costs of uranium toward the end of the next decade have been predicted to be as low as 10 dollars a pound. The evidence presented to this Conference suggests that in the 1960's there will be more than enough uranium for the nuclear power development of that decade. If we look further ahead and combine the forecast of nuclear energy produced in the year 2000 with the forecast of the achievement of breeding, we can see at once that only a few thousand tons of uranium or thorium a year would be required for this task. So there would appear to be ample uranium and thorium available to accept the economists' predicted task and if necessary to do even more than this, carrying a still greater share of the world's energy needs until we achieve our final goal and produce by fusion reactions in the *light* elements an inexhaustible power source for the world.

If we look into the middle distance — the 1970's — the use of nuclear power is likely to vary greatly from nation to nation. Some countries such as Norway, blessed by abundant and cheap hydro-electric power, will still be developing these resources as their primary source of energy. Many other nations such as France, Italy, Portugal and Sweden with important hydro-electric development still to come, will by then have completed this development and will be turning to nuclear power.

Great Britain is an example of a highly industrialised country with small hydro-electric resources, with poor prospects of any substantial increase in coal production and with a rapidly increasing demand for electricity and other forms of energy. So *early* nuclear power development is essential for Britain—it comes only just in time for us—and we believe that by 1975 almost half our electricity will be developed from nuclear energy.

The United States presents a *different* picture of a great industrial country with very great reserves of easily worked coal. Their speakers have said that the use of nuclear energy in *their* country will depend mainly on its cost relative to power from coal. So they think that by 1975 the production of power generated from nuclear energy will be between one per cent and 15 per cent of their total power depending on whether costs are 9 mils a unit or 6 mils a unit. The Canadian position seems to be very similar.

The situation in the so-called "under-developed" countries is different again. India is a typical example of an "under-developed country" since its real income per head is only one-tenth of that of Britain. It seems also that India's energy consumption per head is in the same proportion, that is, one-tenth of that of Britain. Dr. Bhabha's paper points out that 80 per cent of this comes from the burning of dung which would no doubt be better used for increasing the productivity of agriculture. The production of electricity per head in India is at present 80 times less than in Britain but is now planned to increase seven-fold by 1975. So electrical capacity will have to increase from 3½ million kilowatts to 25 million kilowatts installed by that time. The potential hydro-electric capacity is about 35 million kilowatts so that this would be exhausted in the succeeding decade. Dr. Bhabha has said that, since the capital cost of hydro-electric development is likely to be less than that of nuclear power development, the most important part of the electrification will initially be carried by hydro-electricity. On the other hand, nuclear energy will have a specific role to play in areas where hydro-electric development is likely to be slow because of it being combined with irrigation plans which require very large capital expenditure. There are also special areas in India where the construction of thermal stations is at present justified and this part of the load may in future be taken by nuclear power stations particularly where cost of transport of coal is very high.

The development of such countries depends a good deal on the availability of capital resources. Nuclear power may therefore have some special advantages when capital costs of reactors fall since it avoids the heavy capital expenditure on coal mines and on special facilities for transport of fuel. Nevertheless we must recognize that nuclear energy by itself is not a magic key to prosperity for under-developed countries. The main requirements are the provision of capital and the development of the technology and agriculture of these countries.

Nuclear energy will ensure that sufficient energy is available to allow these developments to take place.

Besides these general aids to development, nuclear energy may have a special part to play in some regions. One of these may be in the development of arid zones. We have heard, for example, that one-third of the power used in Israel today is devoted to irrigation—for pumping water—and that Israel is planning a fourfold increase in irrigated areas in the next decade. So the uranium in their phosphate rocks should be very important in providing fuel for this increased pumping power.

Dr. Schonland has suggested that in Southern Africa the semi-arid Karoo could become a well watered region if the waters of the swamps of Northern Bechuanaland could be pumped to the Karoo. Nuclear power may help.

Professor Oliphant has suggested that the tropical parts of Australia, particularly the central and western areas, could support much higher populations if life there could be made more attractive and work be made more efficient by a wide-spread adoption of air conditioning. This has already been shown to have a marked effect in other tropical countries. These areas are remote from sources of fossil fuels and are short of water. Here, then, is a role for the so-called "packaged reactor" driving gas turbines since gas turbines do not require large amounts of cooling water. Reactors producing power in blocks of about 10 Mw seem likely to have important applications in remote areas and under-developed areas.

It seems also that recent developments in the demineralisation of sea water offer prospects that nuclear power may one day be used to produce large quantities of fresh water from the sea at a reasonable cost for waterless areas near the sea such as SW Africa.

Nuclear energy will have another special role to play in providing power for industrial and mining areas remote from coal mines and hydro-electric supplies. In South Africa coal from the Transvaal and Natal has to be transported to the Cape by an already overloaded railway system over a distance of 1000 miles so that the cost of power is twice that at the source of coal and is about 0.8d. per unit. In the Federation of Rhodesia and Nyasaland, coal is transported from Wankie 400 to 500 miles over an overloaded railway system to the copper mines of Northern Rhodesia. By 1962 the Rhodesias will need 4 million tons of coal a year for power generation alone and this is the whole predicted output of the mines at that date. Some help will indeed come from the hydro-electric development of the Kariba Gorge but this is 250–300 miles from the mines and transmission costs are likely to be abnormally high and will double the cost of power at the source. So Dr. Schonland suggests that by the 1970's nuclear power stations of considerable size—perhaps up to 1000 megawatts—could be contemplated, in the copper belt itself. By this time nuclear power is likely to be important also at the Cape.

There are many other regions in the world where mines are remote from fuel sources. Thus in Canada the present cost of diesel-generated power at Port Radium and Beaver Lodge is four times the normal cost. Similar cost levels prevail in mining areas of Australia such as Broken Hill. The local application of nuclear power should encourage the production at the mine itself of highly refined metals by electro-lytic and electro-thermal processes. In this case capital investment might be diverted from the building of railway systems to carry coal to mining areas and ores and crude metal products back to industrial areas, and instead the capital might be used for nuclear power units. Nuclear power units for such areas would have to be built in a transportable form and would probably have to use enriched fuel with provision for some regeneration of fuel. Such units could probably be built within 5 years to produce power at about twice the cost of power from full-scale stations. In such areas, however, these costs would be acceptable.

There are *other* processing industries, such as cement, or pulp or paper, often located away from fuel sources where the energy of high temperature heat is required. Reactors producing high temperature gas might be developed for such purposes.

Industries such as aluminium could absorb the output of the largest-scale nuclear power plants now contemplated. These plants may produce power at costs well below that for coal stations in the second decade, though they are unlikely to compete with the lowest cost hydro-power. Nevertheless, in the long run their use may lead to large-scale shifts in the location of metallurgical industries.

We have not discussed in the Conference the possible application of atomic energy to transport which today consumes about 8 per cent of the energy of the world. The United States has already shown that the nuclear propulsion of ships is technically feasible but only a limited amount of information on the economics of nuclear propulsion is available. A fairly recent discussion in the United States Congressional Committee suggested that present nuclear propulsion systems would lead to costs about ten times normal commercial costs. On quite general grounds it would appear that commercial nuclear propulsion of ships is not likely to develop until the cost of heat energy from pure fissile material is less than that of fuel oil at £6 per ton. This obviously requires that plutonium or U^{233} should become available as a by-product of reactor operations at a cost of appreciably less than £6 per gram. Regeneration of fuel and high burn-up in fuel elements will help. Thus if plutonium becomes available at £3 per gram, and 50 per cent burn-up and 33 per cent thermal efficiency is achieved, this would lead to fuel costs of 0.3d per kwh, which would be commercially interesting.

It seems quite possible that these conditions will be reached by the time large-scale breeding is achieved. But many other technical considerations have to be taken into account in determining the desirability of commercial nuclear ship propulsion. The engineers responsible must in particular be specially concerned with potential hazards due to leaks of radioactivity in such confined quarters. For such reasons I do not myself predict a rapid development of commercial nuclear propulsion.

In the present state of nuclear technology, chemical and metallurgical operations play a major part and their role is likely to become more important as we progress towards the development of breeding, for by then nuclear fuel costs will be due almost entirely to chemical processing costs. Some of the homogeneous nuclear power plants of the future may indeed be chemical plants of highly specialised nature. Even with solid fuel reactors there are considerable possibilities for reducing recycling costs by simpler processes in which some of the important radioactive waste products which poison the chain reaction are removed without dissolving the fuel elements in acids or solvents. Since the spent fuel elements will be highly radioactive, remotely controlled operations will be necessary—here is a good application for the automatic factory.

The development of nuclear energy will inevitably lead to the production of large quantities of radioactive fission products. At present they are looked upon as a nuisance and a problem for the future since they have to be stored for long periods of time. However it seems that the radiation from these waste products will find important uses. The gamma-radiation from spent fuel elements can be used in the first few months after their withdrawal from the reactor, and we have heard of several such applications. Our discussions on waste disposal have shown that the long lived useful products radiocaesium and radiostrontium will be separated from the rest of the fission products and concentrated into radioactive sources. The radioactivity of the remaining fission products will be concentrated and stored until the activity decays to low enough levels for discharge to the sea or fixation. The cost of this storage has been estimated to be less than two per cent of the cost of nuclear power and will probably be offset by revenue from the sale of the useful radiocaesium and strontium, which will become available in source strength varying from kilocurie sources of radiocaesium for radiotherapy to megacurie sources for industrial applications.

Work on the application of radiation needs to be pursued on a much wider front before its possibilities can be properly evaluated. It already seems certain that sterilisation of pharmaceuticals and some medical supplies could be carried out with safety as soon as processed fission products are made available in quantity. The sterilisation of food has already been strikingly demonstrated, but the processes require much further study and trial before it can be certain that it is acceptable and safe for general use.

A most promising field of application of radiation is in insect control. Successful large-scale experiments have been reported from the USA on the eradication of the screw-worm by liberating large numbers of males rendered infertile by suitable doses of gamma radiation. In this conference we have also heard of the control of the parasitic disease trichinosis which is transmitted by larvae in pork. Irradiation of hog carcases sterilises the female and breaks the disease cycle. In Great Britain, joint studies by the Forest Products Research Laboratory and the UK A.E.A. have shown that the life of insects infesting wood can be markedly shortened and their ability to lay fertile eggs prevented, by doses much smaller than those needed to kill the beetles and larvae (*Lyctus* species). The eggs of the death watch beetle are rendered infertile by doses of a few thousand roentgens. The preservation of historic timber and valuable furniture is an exciting possibility. Entomologists ought to look for other applications in this field.

Chemical synthesis is an application that could use large quantities of fission products. It is accepted that chain reactions offer the best hope of economical utilisation. The fields of polymer modification and polymerisation have been studied actively. The very high conversion rates observed in some emulsion polymerisations should be noted. Halogenation and oxidation have been neglected relatively. It is not to be expected that industry will set aside well-established processes unless the use of radiation offers some well-marked advantage. Too much current effort is devoted to existing fields of production. In Great Britain, industry is studying such fields with a view to improvements and new products. We are also sponsoring basic research in radiation chemistry and less profound studies in the organic chemistry field. The irradiation of concentrated solutions, non-aqueous solvents, new approaches to chlorination and molecular rearrangements are being studied. Clear selective reactions of decomposition and oxidation have been revealed and high yields suggestive of chain processes have been observed in unexpected places. New pathways in sugar synthesis and degradation have been found, but it is too early to say that economic application is proven. The systematic study of organic radiation chemistry is still in its infancy, but seems to offer the best hope of progress. Radiation may also be applied in future to the fixation of nitrogen if it becomes really plentiful and cheap.

Professor Hevesy has spoken in his evening lecture of the important part radio-active elements are playing in the development of our knowledge of living organisms. So I do not need to speak about this myself except to say that I believe this will be a major contribution to the development of our understanding of the biological world and this in turn will inevitably contribute to human health and well being.

In planning the development of nuclear energy during the next two decades we have a great responsibility to see that it is developed in such a way that it is an essentially safe industry and that it does not produce a substantial new hazard to the general population of the world.

We have been fortunate so far in having been able from the beginning to lay a sound scientific basis for health protection by the devoted labours of our biologists and health physicists. I do not think that any other new industry has had the advantages of such preparation. The immediate effect of radiation on living organisms has been studied by very large numbers of experiments on animals and as a result of this the International Commission on Radiological Protection has prepared a list of safe levels of radiation and of the amounts of radioactive materials which can be ingested. These recommendations have been incorporated into the working practice of all well run atomic energy organizations and should form the basis of world-wide Codes of Practice to be promulgated by the World Health Organization.

We have also a responsibility to the general public in our own countries in seeing to it that possible accidents to reactors cannot produce an appreciable hazard to surrounding populations. Here again Codes of Practice are being drawn up by experts who really know the hazards and the problems of control. The next step is to compare experiences and ideas of different countries and to agree on International Codes of Practice. Whilst we are accumulating experience of reactor operation much can be done to reduce these risks by adopting a policy of enclosing reactors in buildings which are so constructed that they could contain any large scale leakage of radioactivity resulting from a reactor accident.

The still larger problem of the long-term effects of raising the world wide level of radiation by the dispersal of fission products has been discussed in our chemical and biological sessions. Our knowledge of the genetic effects of radiation on human beings is at present much less than our knowledge of the effects on animals and we should press on with research on human genetics and in the meantime adopt a cautious policy. We have some yardstick to guide us in the general background level of radiation due to cosmic rays, potassium in our blood, and radium in the walls of our houses and in the ground. This gives us all a radiation dose during our reproductive period varying from about 3 roentgens to 6 roentgens depending on the locality. Investigations are proceeding in Britain and the United States by Committees of the Medical Research Council and National Academy of Science which should help us to decide by how much the general background level of radioactivity may be allowed to increase without appreciable harm. This

may well be followed by international discussion of this problem. We may then hope to prepare International Codes of Practice which will determine the amounts of radioactive gases which may be safely discharged to the atmosphere and of radioactive liquids and solids which may be safely discharged to the ocean.

I am quite sure that by such means we can carry out this great new development in a far safer way than has been the case in any other new activity of the human race.

We have still to discuss in our closing session the important question of how international co-operation can help in speeding up this vital new development. Atomic energy by its world-wide effects in the field of public health can for this reason alone benefit by international co-operation.

We must also not lose sight of the fact that its products—the fissile elements—are potentially very dangerous materials, not only to public health but also because of their explosive possibilities. International co-operation in preventing the diversion of such materials to explosive uses could therefore be of the greatest importance.

In Western Europe we have made a beginning in a modest way in the European Atomic Energy Society in discussing our common scientific and technical problems. This has proved valuable.

The United Nations Organization is in process of giving birth to a much more ambitious offspring —the International Atomic Energy Agency. We must all hope that its birth will not be too painful or too long delayed. The Agency, wisely guided, could do a great deal to ensure that the inherent dangers in our development are prevented.

Having looked into the cloudy crystal ball with my imperfect eyes I feel quite sure that the real picture 25 years hence will be very different. For scientific and technological progress is today so rapid that our predictions must be subject to great uncertainties. Rutherford in 1937 could not predict fission and did not believe that nuclear power was likely. Now power from fission reactions is assured. I would like tonight to have been able to predict when the exciting prospect of power from fusion reactions would be achieved. But although we are working seriously on this problem in Britain, my vision is not good enough for that. I am not as bold as our President. The experimental physicist must inevitably have a greater appreciation of the problems and difficulties than the theoretical physicist. However, my faith in the scientist's creative ability is so great that I am sure that this will be achieved long before it is essential for man's needs.

We must all hope that the statesmen who control our destinies and whose vision has made this Conference possible will continue to liberate the creative ability of the scientific world and so enable it to produce these benefits which I have so imperfectly attempted to predict.

Exhibits

The Canadian exhibit: general view

Part of the Canadian exhibit

Part of the Belgian exhibit

Part of the Norwegian exhibit

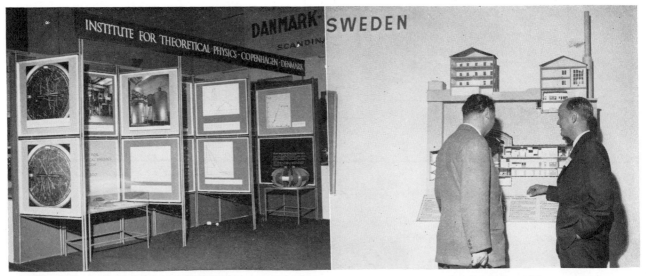

Part of the Danish exhibit

Part of the Swedish exhibit

USSR exhibit: model of an atomic power station   USSR exhibit: model of an experimental heavy water reactor

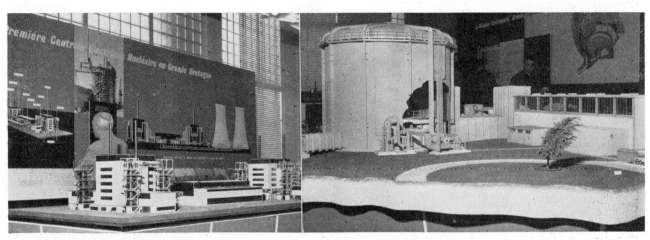

UK exhibit: model of the Calder Hall nuclear power station   UK exhibit: model of the site of reactor E.443

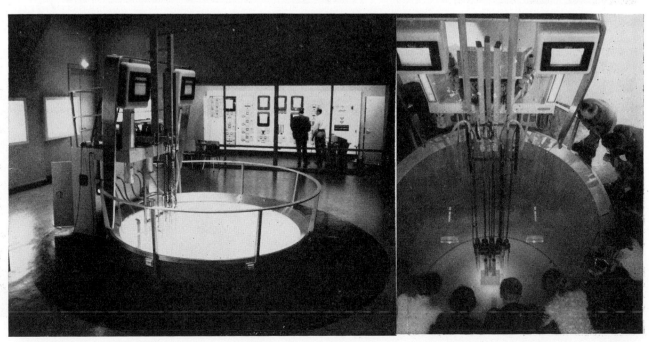

US exhibit: swimming-pool reactor glowing during operation *(Photo Union Carbide)*   Public visiting the reactor *(Photo Union Carbide)*

US exhibit: general view *(Photo Union Carbide)*   US exhibit: model of an experimental boiling water reactor

French exhibit: model of a proton-synchrotron   Demonstration of remote-control equipment

USSR exhibit: short focal gamma ray apparatus for therapy   General view of the commercial exhibition

Annexes

The president and vice-presidents of the Conference. Left to right: Mr. W. B. Lewis (Canada) Mr. F. Perrin (France) Mr. I. I. Rabi (USA); Mr. H. J. Bhabha (India) President; Mr. D. V. Skobeltzin (SSR); Sir John Cockcroft (UK); Mr. B. de Mattos (Brazil)

ANNEX I

LIST OF OFFICERS, DELEGATIONS AND CONFERENCE SECRETARIAT

Officers of the Conference

President

Dr. Homi Bhabha (India)

Vice-Presidents

General Bernardino C. de Mattos (Brazil)
Dr. W. B. Lewis (Canada)
Professor Francis Perrin (France)

Academician D. V. Skobeltzin (USSR)
Sir John Cockcroft (UK)
Dr. I. I. Rabi (USA)

Conference Secretary-General

Professor Walter G. Whitman

Deputy Conference Secretary-General

Dr. Viktor S. Vavilov

National Delegations

ARGENTINA

Captain of the Navy D. Pedro E. IRAOLAGOITÍA
Engineer D. Otto O. M. GAMBA
Dr. D. GERMÁN MENDIVELZÚA
Dr. D. Fidel ALSINA FUERTES
Dr. D. Arturo CAIRO

Dr. Mario Raúl PICO, Counsellor of Embassy
Dr. Eduardo de ANTUENO, Secretary of Embassy
Dr. Américo RONCAROLO, Assistant
Dr. D. Constantino NUÑEZ
Engineer D. Victorio ANGELELLI
Dr. D. Mauricio BUHLER
Dr. D. Kurt FRAENZ
Engineer D. Juan U. KOPPEL
Dr. D. Walter SEELMAN-EGGEBERT
Dra. Dña. Ilse G. DE FRAENZ
Dr. D. Eusebio MANCINI

AUSTRALIA

Professor J. P. BAXTER, Australian Atomic Energy Commission
Professor Marcus OLIPHANT, Australian National University
Mr. R. L. HARRY, Department of External Affairs
Dr. C. E. EDDY, Department of Health
Mr. S. E. HUDDLESTON, Electricity Trust of South Australia

Dr. C. N. WATSON-MUNRO, Australian Atomic Energy Commission
Dr. G. L. MILES, Australian Atomic Energy Commission
Dr. K. F. ALDER, Australian Atomic Energy Commission
Dr. G. C. J. DALTON, Australian Atomic Energy Commission

Mr. R. G. THOMAS, Commonwealth Scientific Industrial Research Organization
Mr. D. L. ANDERSON, Department of National Development
Mr. V. J. F. BRAIN, Electricity Commission of New South Wales
Mr. D. R. GRIFFITHS, Electricity Trust of South Australia
Mr. F. SYKES, Electricity Commission of New South Wales

AUSTRIA

Dr. Franz MATSCH, Envoy Extraordinary and Minister Plenipotentiary, Chairman of the Austrian Atomic Energy Commission
Professor Dr. Berta KARLIK, Director of the Institute of Radio-Research
Dr. Wilhelm KOVATS, Ministerial Councillor
Ing. Franz GRILL, Ministerial Councillor
Dr. Josef NAGLER, Director of the Technical Museum

Dr. Herbert VETTER
Dipl. Ing. Richard POLACZEK, Councillor of Section
Dr. Adalbert ORLICEK, Councillor of Section
Professor Dr. Maximilian LEDINEGG, Director, Federal Experimental Establishment Arsenal
Dr. Ferdinand CAP, Professor, University of Innsbruck
Dr. Karl LINTNER, Institute of Radioresearch
Dr. Heinrich GLEISSNER, Secretary of Legation
Dr. Gustav ORTNER, Professor of Nuclear Science
Dr. Heimo HARDUNG-HARDUNG
Dr. Richard KIEFER, Director of the Plansee Metallic Plant
Mr. Eugen VUCINIC, Director of the Elin Electric Firm
Dipl. Ing. Dr. Roland KEMETSMÜLLER, Director of the Establishment Waagner-Biro
Dipl. Ing. Franz HINTERMAYER

Dipl. Ing. Wolfgang HAHN

Dipl. Ing. Dr. Leopold BAUER

Dipl. Ing. Dr. Heinz SCHMIDL

Dr. Friedrich OSZUSZKY

Prof. Dr. Ludwig MUSIL, Director of the Styrian Hydro-electric Company

Senatsrat Dr. Ing. MOKESCH, Electricity Plants of Vienna

Dipl. Ing. Dr. KAINDL

Dr. Otto SMETANA, Chief-chemist of Treibacher chemical plants

Dipl. Ing. Friedrich JANICEK, Austrian Drau Werke A. G.

Dr. Ing. Karl SEDLATSCHEK, Plansee Metal Plant Ges.m.b.H., Reutte/Tirol

Dr. RIGELLE, Vereinigte Osterreichische Eisen — und Stahl-werke, Linz

BELGIUM

M. PIERRE RYCKMANS, Gouverneur Général Honorarie du Congo belge, Commissaire à l'Energie atomique

M. Paul de GROOTE, Président du Conseil d'Administration de l'Université Libre de Bruxelles, Membre du Conseil d'Administration du Centre d'Etudes pour les Applications de l'Energie Nucléaire

M. Louis DE HEEM, Directeur Général du Centre d'Etudes pour les Applications de l'Energie Nucléaire

M. Jacques ERRERA, Professeur à l'Université de Bruxelles, Conseiller de la Délégation permanente de la Belgique auprès des Nations Unies

M. Jean WILLEMS, Président du Conseil de l'Institut Inter-universitaire des Sciences Nucléaires

M. Gaston ANDRE, Directeur du Département Radium de l'Union Minière du Haut Katanga

M. Zénon BACQ, Professeur à l'Université de Liège, Membre de la Commission scientifique du Conseil supérieur de la Sécurité civile

M. Paul CAPRON, Professeur à l'Université de Louvain

M. Albert CLAUDE, Professeur à l'Université Libre de Bruxelles, Membre de la Commission scientifique de l'Institut Interuniversitaire des Sciences Nucléaires

M. Marcel de MERRE, Administrateur, Directeur Général de la Société Métallurgique de Hoboken

M. Maurice D'HONT, Attaché au Centre d'Etudes pour les Applications de l'Energie Nucléaire

M. Pierre ERKES, Attaché au Syndicat d'Etudes de l'Energie Nucléaire

M. Maximilien FRESON, Docteur en sciences naturelles, Secrétaire de l'Institut Interuniversitaire des Sciences Nucléaires

M. Edgard GILLON, Professeur à l'Université de Louvain

M. Julien GOENS, Directeur au Centre d'Etudes pour les Applications de l'Energie Nucléaire

M. Georges GOFFIN, Ingénieur en chef, Directeur du Service de l'Energie électrique au Ministère des Affaires économiques

M. Pierre GOSSELIN, Administrateur-Délégué au Syndicat d'Etudes des centrales atomiques

M. Georges GUEBEN, Professeur à l'Université de Liège, Membre de la Commission scientifique du Centre d'Etudes pour les Applications de l'Energie Nucléaire

M. René LEDRUS, Professeur à l'Ecole Militaire, Membre de la Commission scientifique du Centre d'Etudes pour les Applications de l'Energie Nucléaire

M. Joseph MAISIN, Professeur à l'Université de Louvain, Membre de la Commission scientifique du Conseil supérieur de la Sécurité civile

M. Herman ROBILLART, Vice-Président du Centre d'Etudes pour les Applications de l'Energie Nucléaire, Président du Syndicat pour l'Etude de l'Energie Nucléaire

M. Edgar SENGIER, Président du Comité permanent de l'Union Minière du Haut Katanga

M. Ch. SILLEVAERTS, Général-Médecin, Président de la Commission de la Protection civile au Ministère de l'Intérieur

M. Pierre SMITS, Président du Syndicat d'Etudes des centrales atomiques, Président du Comité d'exécution du Centre d'Etudes pour les Applications de l'Energie Nucléaire

M. Pierre STANER, Inspecteur Royal des Colonies

M. Guy TAVERNIER, Attaché au Centre d'Etudes pour les Applications de l'Energie Nucléaire

M. Denis TYTGAT, Attaché au Centre d'Etudes pour les Applications de l'Energie Nucléaire

M. Julien VERHAEGEN, Professeur à l'Université de Gand, Membre de la Commission scientifique du Centre d'Etudes pour les Applications de l'Energie Nucléaire

M. Jean VAN DER SPEK, Directeur du Syndicat d'Etudes de l'Energie Nucléaire

M. R. VAN MELE, Ingénieur, Directeur du Service d'études de la C.P.T.E. (Société pour la Coordination de la Production et le Transport de l'Electricité)

M. Jean LEROY, Conseiller de Légation, Représentant permanent de la Belgique auprès des Nations Unies à Genève, Secrétaire Général

M. Pierre van HAUTE, Secrétaire d'Ambassade, adjoint

M. Marcel van de KERCKHOVE, Attaché de Légation, adjoint

Mlle Simone HERPELS, Secrétaire

BOLIVIA

V. Ismael ESCOBAR, Dr. Sc., Director of the Cosmic Physics Laboratory at Chacaltaya and Professor at La Paz University, Professor at the Centro Brasileiro de Pesquisas Fisicas, President of the National Commission for the International Geophysical Year and President of the Bolivian Association for the Advancement of Science

BRAZIL

General Bernardino de MATTOS, Civil and Electrical Engineer. Member of the National Research Council and Chairman of its Atomic Energy Commission

Professor Joaquim da COSTA RIBEIRO, Member of the National Research Council and of its Atomic Energy Commission. Professor of Experimental Physics, University of Brazil. Member, Brazilian Academy of Sciences

Professor Elysiário TÁVORA, Professor, Mineralogy and Petrography, University of Brazil. Member of the National Research Council and of its Atomic Energy Commission. Mineralogist, National Department of Mineral Production. Member, Brazilian Academy of Sciences

Professor Marcello Damy da SOUZA SANTOS, Head, Department of Physics, University of São Paolo. Vice-President, Brazilian Academy of Sciences, Member of the National Research Council and of its Atomic Energy Commission

Professor Ernani da MOTTA REZENDE, Director, Electrotechnics Institute, University of Brazil. Member, National Water and Electric Power Council. Member of the Atomic Energy Commission, National Research Council

Dr. Alfredo Teixeira VALLADAO

Dr. Heitor Pinto MOURA

Dr. J. GOLDENBERG, Assistant Professor of Experimental Physics, University of São Paolo.

Mr. Silvio V. GUEDES, Geologist, Air Survey Company, Rio de Janeiro

BULGARIA

Academician Guoergui Stefanov NADJAKOV

Engineer Yordai Boyanov DIMITROV

Professor Gotze Christov TENTCHEV

Professor Engineer Nikola Stoyanov KALITZINE

Assen Zakhariev TRIFONOV, Counsellor

BURMA

Dr. Freddy BA HLI, Acting Director, Union of Burma Atomic Energy Centre

U HLA NYUNT, Deputy Director, Union of Burma Atomic Energy Centre

Dr. MAUNG MAUNG KHA, Consultant to the Union of Burma Atomic Energy Centre

BYELORUSSIAN SOVIET SOCIALIST REPUBLIC

Dr. V. F. KUPREVICH

Dr. A. N. SEVCHENKO

Dr. V. I. STEPANOV

Dr. T. I. GODNEV

Dr. A. F. PROKOPCHUK

Professor O. K. KEDROV-ZIKHMAN, Member of the Academy of Sciences of the Byelorussian SSR

Mr. I. W. LEBEDEV, Candidate of Science

Mr. B. V. KUDRYAVTSEV, Secretary

Mr. V. S. KOLBASIN, Interpreter

Mr. V. N. KOVALENKO, Interpreter

CANADA

Mr. W. J. BENNETT, President, Atomic Energy of Canada Ltd.

Dr. W. B. LEWIS, Vice-President, Research and Development, Atomic Energy of Canada Ltd.

Dr. A. J. CIPRIANI, Director, Biology and Radiation Hazards Control Division, Atomic Energy of Canada Ltd.

Dr. A. H. LANG, Chief, Radioactive Resources Division, Biological Survey of Canada Branch, Department of Mines and Technical Surveys.

Dr. J. W. T. SPINKS, Dean of Graduate Studies, University of Saskatchewan.

Dr. D. G. HURST, Reactor Research and Development, Atomic Energy of Canada Ltd.

Mr. A. G. WARD, Reactor Research and Development, Atomic Energy of Canada Ltd.

Dr. D. E. McKENZIE, Chemistry Division, Atomic Energy of Canada Ltd.

Dr. John DAVIS, Associate Director, Economic Division, Department of Trade and Commerce

Dr. C. A. MAWSON, Biology Research and Radiation Hazards Control Division, Atomic Energy of Canada Ltd.

Dr. A. THUNAES, Director of Research, Eldorado Mining and Refining Ltd.

Dr. R. F. ROBERTSON, Head of Radiation Chemistry Section, Atomic Energy of Canada Ltd.

Dr. C. H. JAIMET, Chemical Director, Department of Medical Research, McMaster University

Dr. R. L. HEARN, Chairman of the Board, Ontario Hydro-Electric Power Commission

Mr. H. A. SMITH, Director of Nuclear Power Project, Ontario Hydro-Electric Power Commission

Dr. D. H. COPP, Professor of Physiology, University of British Columbia

Dr. L. YAFFE, Professor of Chemistry, McGill University

Professor Frank FORWARD, Director of Mining and Metallurgy, University of British Columbia.

Dr. F. D. SOWBY, Medical Officer, Department of National Health and Welfare

Dr. Paul E. GAGNON, Dean of the Graduate School, Laval University

Dr. A. B. LILLIE, Commercial Products Division, Atomic Energy of Canada Ltd.

Mr. C. C. KENNEDY, Public Relations Officer, Atomic Energy of Canada Ltd.

Mr. R. H. BULL, Sales Manager, Commercial Products Division, Atomic Energy of Canada Ltd.

Mr. Fraser ABRAHAM, Commercial Products Division, Atomic Energy of Canada Ltd.

Mr. R. THOMAN, Vice-President, General Manager, Canadian Vickers Limited

Mr. Aubrey MONTGOMERY, Vice-President, John Inglish Company

Mr. K. B. YOUNG, Orenda Engines Limited

Mr. H. M. TURNER, Chairman of the Board, Canadian General Electric Company Limited

Mr. I. F. McRAE, Civil Atomic Power Development, Canadian General Electric Company Limited

Mr. J. M. THOMSON, President and General Manager of Ferranti Electric Limited

Mr. E. M. LEAVER, President and General Manager of Electronics Associates Limited

Mr. J. A. CAMPANARO, General Manager, Commercial Development, Canadian Westinghouse Limited

Mr. J. G. NOTMAN, President of Canadair

Mr. M. J. LAVIGNE, Department of Mines and Technical Surveys

Mr. J. E. WOOLSTON, Atomic Energy of Canada Limited

Mr. D. D. STEWART, Atomic Energy of Canada Limited

Mr. Keith MacLELLAN, Secretary to the Delegation

CEYLON

H. E. Sir Claude COREA, High Commissioner for Ceylon in The United Kingdom

Dr. C. J. ELIEZER, Dean, Faculty of Science; and Professor of Mathematics, University of Ceylon

CHILE

Mr. Carlos RUIZ, Under-Secretary for Mines

Mr. Humberto DIAZ-CASANUEVA, Permanent delegate to the European Office of the United Nations, Geneva

Mr. Mayor Enrique LACKINGTON, Professor in the Faculty of Arts and Sciences and Education, University of Chile, Santiago

Mr. Gabriel ALVIAL, Head of the Physics Department in the Pedagogic Institute, University of Chile, Santiago

Mr. Ferdinand OBERHAUSER, Head of the Chemistry Department in the Pedagogic Institute, University of Chile, Santiago

Mr. Roberto MULLER HESS, Professor at the University of Chile, Santiago

Mr. Francisco STEEGER, Member of the Production Promotion Board

CHINA

Dr. Hsioh-ren WEI, Physicist. Alternate representative of China on the United Nations Disarmament Commission. Formerly, professor of physics and dean, College of Science, University of Nanking, and alternate representative of China on the United Nations Atomic Energy Commission.

Dr. Ching WU, Radiologist. Professor of Radiology, National Defense Medical College, Taipei, Taiwan. Formerly, professor of Radiology, Peking Union Medical College, and exchange professor, Medical College, Tokyo University

Dr. Kan-hou LIH, Chemist. Director, Ordnance Research Institute. President Chinese Association for the Advancement of Natural Science. Formerly, professor and head of Chemistry Department, Chekiang University; Director of the Research Institute of Applied Chemistry.

Dr. Shi-mou LEE, Electrical Engineer. Chairman, Science Education Council, Ministry of Education. Formerly, professor and dean, College of Engineering, Chekiang University; professor and dean, National Chiao-Tung University; UNESCO representative in Japan.

Mr. Jin-Tai SHEN, Chemical Engineer. Director of Union Industrial Research Institute, Ministry of Economic Affairs. Formerly, Vice-President of Chinese Petroleum Corporation.

Professor Yuin-kwei TAI, Physicist. National Taiwan University, Chairman of Physics Department, Honorary Fellow of University of Minnesota, Visiting Professor, University of California. Formerly professor of University of Nanking and National Central University.

Mr. CHENG Hsi-ling, Second Secretary, Permanent Delegation of China to the United Nations.

COLOMBIA

Ambassador Eduardo ZULETA ANGEL

Dr. Mario LASERNA, Vice-Rector of the University of Andes, Colombia

Dr. Alvaro LUQUE, Cancer Specialist

Dr. Luis GONZALEZ BORROS, Representative of Colombia to the European Office of the United Nations

COSTA RICA

Mr. Antonio QUESADA

Mr. Herman HERRERA

Mr. Aristide DONNADIEU, Permanent Representative of Costa Rica at the European Office of the United Nations, and Consul General in Geneva

CUBA

Ambassador Dr. Emilio NUÑEZ PORTUONDO

Dr. Avelino CANAL Y BARRACHINA, Cuban Ambassador to the Federal Republic of Germany

Dr. Antonio O. PÉREZ Y ARA, Chief Medical Officer of the Cuban Army, Member of the National Commission for the Uses of Atomic Energy

Dr. Marcelo ALONSO ROCA, Technical Adviser to the Delegation

CZECHOSLOVAKIA

Mr. František ŠORM, Secretary-General of the Czechoslovak Academy of Sciences

Engineer Cestmir ŠIMÁNĚ, Czechoslovak Academy of Sciences

Professor Dr. Václav VOTRUBA, Correspondent Member of Czechoslovak Academy of Sciences, Professor of Charles University in Prague

Engineer Jan NEUMANN, Expert in Chemical Industry

Professor Dr. Ferdinand HERČÍK, Czechoslovak Academy of Sciences

Professor Engineer Josef BĚCVÁR, Professor of Technical Institute

Dr. Miroslav BEZDĚK, University in Brno

Engineer Dr. Jiři GUT, Czechoslovak Academy of Sciences

Engineer Rudolf HENYCH, Expert in Metallurgical Industry

Engineer Vladimír JÁRA, Expert in Chemical Industry

Engineer Miroslav MACH, Expert in Health Welfare

Engineer Jaromír MALÝ, Czechoslovak Academy of Sciences

Engineer Dr. Agustin ŠEVČÍK, Doctor of Technical Sciences

Dr. Ladislav TRLIFÁJ, Candidate of Physical Sciences, Czechoslovak Academy of Sciences

Phmr. Jan URBANEC, Czechoslovak Academy of Sciences

Dr. Ladislav DVOŘAK, Expert

Dr. Gejza MENCER, Chief of Division, Ministry of Foreign Affairs (Secretary)

DENMARK

Professor Niels BOHR, Institute of Theoretical Physics, University of Copenhagen

Professor Robert HENRIKSEN, Director, The North Sealand Power and Tramway Co., Ltd.

Professor J. C. JACOBSEN, Institute of Theoretical Physics, University of Copenhagen

Mr. H. H. KOCH, Permanent Under-Secretary of State, Ministry of Social Affairs and Ministry of Economy and Labour

Mr. Haldor TOPSØE, Civil Engineer

Mr. K. A. BAK, Director, The Copenhagen Gas and Electricity Services

Dr. Aage BOHR, Institute of Theoretical Physics, University of Copenhagen

Dr. Borge CHRISTENSEN, Deputy Superintendent, Finsen Institute, Copenhagen

Dr. Aage GRUT, Senior Physician, Factory Inspection, Copenhagen

Professor Tage KEMP, University of Copenhagen

Dr. Hilde LEVI, University of Copenhagen

Mr. Jens MØLLER, Director, Vestkraft Power Co., Esbjerg

Professor Jens NIELSEN, Senior Physician, Radium Center, Copenhagen

Professor R. E. H. RASMUSSEN, The Technical University of Denmark, Copenhagen

Professor Hans USSING, University of Copenhagen

Professor Sven WERNER, Institute of Physics, University of Aarhus

Mr. Anker HANSEN, Industrial Attaché, Ministry of Foreign Affairs

Mr. Chr. L. THOMSEN, Assistant Head of Section (Secretary)

DOMINICAN REPUBLIC

Brigadier-General Alexander KOVACS, Director General of the Technological Services of the Ministry of War, Navy and Aviation

Major Dr. Rafael Blas GONZALEZ MASSENET, Director of the Military Hospital

Major Alfredo F. VORSHIRM, Assistant to the Director General of the Technological Services of the Ministry of War, Navy and Aviation

ECUADOR

Ambassador Jaime NEBOT VELASCO

EGYPT

Professor Mostafa NAZIF, Rector of Ein-Shams University, Member of the Atomic Energy Commission

Dr. Ahmed Riad TORKY, Dean, Faculty of Science, Cairo University, President of the National Research Council, Member of the Atomic Energy Commission

Dr. Ibrahim Helmi Abdel RAHMAN, Secretary-General of the Council of Ministers, Secretary-General of the Planning Commission, Member Secretary to the Atomic Energy Commission

Mr. Mohsen IDRIS, Member of the Atomic Energy Commission

Mr. Abdel Rahman MAKHIOUN, Member of the Atomic Energy Commission

Dr. Mahmoud MOKHTAR, Professor of Physics, Cairo University

Dr. Mahmoud El KOCHEIRI, Professor of Electronic Engineering, Cairo University

Professor Hamman Mohamed MAHMOUD, Professor of Electronic Engineering, Cairo University

Dr. Mahmoud Ahmed El SHERBINI, Professor of Physics, Alexandria University

Dr. Nasri SHUKRI, Professor of Geology, Cairo University

Dr. Mohamed GAMAL EL DINE NOUH, Assistant Professor of Physics Ein-Shams University

Dr. Abdel Aziz AMIN, Assistant Professor of Chemistry, Cairo University

Dr. Mohamed El CHAHAT AWAD, Assistant Professor, Chemistry, Cairo University

Dr. Afaf SABRI, Lecturer, Applied Mathematics, Cairo University

Dr. Fathi El BEDEWI, Lecturer, Physics, University of Alexandria

Mr. Ismail FAHMY, Permanent Egyptian Delegation to the United Nations, New York

Mr. Abdel Maaboud El GUEBELY, Chemist, Radium Institute of Paris

Mr. Hassan AFIFI, Research Physiologist, University of Paris

EL SALVADOR

Lt. Colonel Oscar A. BOLAÑOS, Secretary-General of the Presidency

Dr. Victor ORTIZ, Chemical Sciences

Dr. Ruben DARDANO, Medical Sciences

ETHIOPIA

Ato Gachaou ZELLEKE, His Imperial Majesty's Envoy Extraordinary and Minister Plenipotentiary to the Government of the Union of Soviet Socialist Republics in Moscow

Fitawrari Tsehai INKO-SELLASSIE, Vice-Minister for Public Health of the Imperial Ethiopian Government

Ato Yohannes MENKIR

Ato Shimellash BEKELLE, Secretary

FINLAND

Prof. Erkki LAURILA

Prof. Risto NIINI

Prof. Sakari MUSTAKALLIO

Mr. Heikki LEHTONEN, Managing Director

Mr. Pekka JAUHO, Assistant Professor

Mr. K. E. SALIMAKI, B. A.

FRANCE

M. Pierre GUILLAUMAT, Administrateur Général, Délégué du Gouvernement au Commissariat à l'Energie Atomique

M. Francis PERRIN, Haut-Commissaire à l'Energie Atomique

M. Bertrand GOLDSCHMIDT, Directeur chargé des Relations Extérieures et du Département de Chimie au Commissariat á l'Energie Atomique

M. Pierre AILLERET, Directeur des Etudes et Recherches à l'Electricité de France, Membre du Comité de l'Energie Atomique

M. Louis BUGNARD, Directeur de l'Institut National d'Hygiène, Membre du Conseil scientifique

M. Gaston PALEWSKI, Ministre, Délégué à la Présidence du Conseil

M. B. EPINAT, Ministre plénipotentiaire, Membre de la Délégation française permanente à New York

M. R. TURPIN, Membre de la Délégation franćaise permanente à New York

M. Georges BORIS

M. Louis ARMAND, Directeur Général, Président du Conseil d'Administration de la Société Nationale des Chemins de Fer Français, Président du Comité de l'Equipement Industriel

M. Pierre BASDEVANT, Service des Pactes au Ministère des Affaires Etrangères

M. Maurice BAYEN, Directeur-Adjoint de l'Enseignement Supérieur

M. Roger BELIN, Maître des Requêtes au Conseil d'Etat, Chargé de mission au Secrétariat général du Gouvernement, Membre du Comité des Mines

M. Lambert BLUM-PICARD, Président de la Commission Consultative pour la Production d'Electricité d'Origine Nucléaire

M. Jean-Marc BOEGNER, Directeur de Cabinet du Ministre délégué à la Présidence du Conseil, Membre du Comité de l'Energie Atomique

M. Roger BRARD, Ingénieur Général de la Marine

M. Duc Maurice de BROGLIE, Président du Conseil Scientifique

M. Robert COURRIER, Membre du Conseil Scientifique, Professeur au Collège de France

M. Emile de CURTON, Délégué Permanent de la France auprès de l'Office Européen des Nations Unies à Genève

M. Gaston DUPOUY, Directeur du Centre National de la Recherche Scientifique, Membre du Comité de l'Energie Atomique

M. Raymond GASTAMBIDE, Conseiller d'Ambassade au Ministère des Affaires Etrangères

M. Louis LEPRINCE-RINGUET, Professeur à l'Ecole Polytechnique, Membre du Comité de l'Energie Atomique

Dr. Jean MABILEAU, Ministère de la Santé

M. Albert ROBIN, Rapporteur général de la Commission de l'Energie, Commissariat Général au Plan

M. Yves ROCARD, Professeur à la Faculté des Sciences de l'Université de Paris, Membre du Comité de l'Energie Atomique

M. Marcel ROUBAULT, Président du Comité des Mines

M. André SAINT-MIEUX, Conseiller technique auprès du Ministre délégué à la Présidence du Conseil

M. Louis SAULGEOT, Directeur du Gaz et de l'Electricité au Ministère de l'Industrie et du Commerce

M. Yves AUBINEAU, Chef du Service Documentation du C.E.A.

M. Maurice AICARDI, Secrétaire général du Commissariat Général au Plan de Modernisation et d'Equipement

M. Henri BAISSAS, Adjoint au Directeur du Centre d'Etudes Nucléaires de Saclay

Dr. Michel BERGER, de la Faculté de Médecine et Pharmacie, Laboratoire Biophysique de Lyon

Dr. André BERTHELOT, Chef du Service de Physique Nucléaire; C.E.A.

M. Denis BRETON, du C.E.A.

M. Gérard CABANNE, du C.E.A.

M. Roger CAILLAT, du C.E.A.

M. Paul CHAMBADAL, de l'Electricité de France

Dr. A. CHEVALLIER, Professeur à la Faculté de Médecine

Dr. Jean COURSAGET, Chef du Service de Biologie; C.E.A.

Dr. Pierre Descans, Chef du Service des Etudes Mécaniques; C.E.A.

Dr. Charles Eichner, Chef du Département de Métallurgie et Chimie appliquée; C.E.A.

Dr. Charlie Fisher, Chef du Service des Radioéléments artificiels; C.E.A.

Dr. Pierre Fromageot, C.E.A.

Dr. Robert Galley, C.E.A.

Dr. Emmanuel Grison, Adjoint au Chef du Département de Métallurgie et Chimie appliquée; C.E.A.

Dr. Jules Guéron, Directeur du Département de Physico-Chimie, Directeur des Programmes Généraux du C.E.A.

Dr. Jean Guilhamon, Electricité et Gaz d'Algérie

Dr. Hermann Hering, Chef du Service de Chimie physique; C.E.A.

Dr. Jules Horowitz, Chef du Service de Physique mathématique; C.E.A.

Dr. Pierre Hubert, C.E.A.

Dr. Jacques Hure, C.E.A.

Dr. Bernard Jacrot, C.E.A.

Dr. Henri Jammet, Chef du Service de Protection contre les Radiations; C.E.A.

Dr. Henri Joffre, C.E.A.

Dr. Jacques Labeyrie, C.E.A.

Dr. Hubert de Laboulaye, C.E.A.

Dr. Raymond Latarjet, Professeur à la Faculté de Médecine

Dr. Jean Lecoq, Adjoint au Directeur des Recherches et Exploitations Minières; C.E.A.

Dr. Maurice Lemoigne, Professeur à l'Institut Pasteur

Dr. André Lenoble, Chef du Service des Recherches; C.E.A.

Dr. Pierre Lévêque, C.E.A.

Dr. Jacques Mabile, Directeur des Recherches et Exploitations Minières; C.E.A.

Dr. Michel Magat, Maitre de Recherches au C.N.R.S., Laboratoire de Chimie-Physique de la Faculté des Sciences de Paris

Dr. Guy Mayer, C.E.A.

Dr. Gerard Milhaud, chargé du Laboratoire des Isotopes de l'Institut Pasteur

Dr. Jules Moch, Membre de l'Assemblée Nationale

Dr. François Morel, C.E.A.

Dr. Pierre Mouret, C.E.A.

Dr. Francis Netter, C.E.A.

Dr. Maurice Pascal, C.E.A.

Dr. Henri Piatier, Chef du Cabinet du Haut-Commissaire à l'Energie Atomique

Dr. Victor Raievski, C.E.A.

Dr. Pierre Regnaut, Chef du Service du Plutonium; C.E.A.

M. Jean Renou, Adjoint au Directeur des Relations Extérieures; C.E.A.

M. Maurice Roques, Chef du Service de Concentration des Minérais; C.E.A.

M. Etienne Roth, C.E.A.

M. Marc Salesse, Adjoint au Chef du Département de Métallurgie et Chimie Appliquée; C.E.A.

M. Jacques Stohr, Chef du Service de Technologie; C.E.A.

M. Maurice Surdin, Chef du Service des Constructions Electriques; C.E.A.

M. Pierre Taranger, Directeur Industriel; C.E.A.

M. Georges Vendryes, Chef du Service de Neutronique Expérimentale; C.E.A.

M. Paul Vertes, Directeur de l'Usine du Bouchet; C.E.A.

M. Lucien Vuchot, Directeur du Service Exploitation; C.E.A.

M. Jacky Weil, C.E.A.

M. Jacques Yvon, Chef du Département des Etudes de Piles; C.E.A.

M. Brachet, Ingénieur en Chef du Génie Maritime

M. Raymond Braconnier, Directeur de l'Institut National de la Recherche Agronomique

M. Crescent, Ministère de l'Industrie et du Commerce

M. Raymond Maillet, C.E.A.

M. Julien Martelly, C.E.A.

M. Anatole Muhlstein

FEDERAL REPUBLIC OF GERMANY

Professor Dr. Otto Hahn, President of the Max-Planck Society, formerly the Kaiser-Wilhelm Society for promotion of Sciences, Göttingen

Professor Dr. Wolfgang Gentner, Director of the Institute of Physics of the University of Freiburg

Professor Dr. Karl Winnaker, Director General of Farbworke Hoechst

Professor Dr. Carl Friedrich Ophuls, Ambassador in the Foreign Office

Dipl. Eng. Walter Hinsch, Ministry of Economic Affairs

Professor Dr. Erich Bagge, State Institute for Physics, Hamburg

Professor Dr. Michael Bauer, University of Bonn

Professor Dr. Josef Becker, Institute of Radiology of the University of Heidelberg

Doz. Dr. Erwin Becker, Institute of Physics of the University of Heidelberg

Professor Dr. Groth, Institute of Physical Chemistry, Bonn

Professor Dr. Otto Haxel, Institute of Physics of the University of Heidelberg

Professor Dr. Kurt Illies, Technical Institute for Shipbuilding of the Technical College, Hannover

Doz. Dr. Leopold Kuchler, University of Frankfurt

Professor Dr. Langendorff, Institute of Radiology of the University of Freiburg

Professor Dr. K. L. Lauterjung, Max Planck Institute for Medical Research, Institute of Physics of the University of Heidelberg

Professor Dr. Josef Mattauch, Max Planck Institute for Chemistry, Mainz

Professor Dr. Friedrich Paneth, Max Planck Institute for Chemistry, Mainz

Professor Dr. Boris Rajewsky, Max Planck Institute for Biochemistry, Frankfurt

Professor Dr. Wolfgang Riezler, Institute for Ray and Nuclear Physics of the University of Bonn

Professor Dr. Fritz Strassmann, Institute for Inorganic Chemistry of the University of Mainz

Professor Dr. Karl Wirtz, Max Planck Institute for Physics, Göttingen

Dr. Günter Harkort, Senior Counsellor, Ministry of Foreign Affairs

Mr. Henning Thomsen, Senior Counsellor, Ministry of Foreign Affairs

Dr. Heinz Hädrich, Cousellor, Ministry of Foreign Affairs

Frl. von Neurath, Attachée with the Embassy of the Federal Republic of Germany in Berne

Dr. Karl Pretsch, Oberregierungsrat in the Ministry for Economic Affairs

Dr. Karl Schmidt-Amelung, Oberregierungsrat in the Ministry for Economic Affairs

Dr. Emil Pohland, Oberregierungsrat in the Ministry for Economic Affairs

Dr. Franz FRANK, Lawyer, Ministry for Economic Affairs

Dr. Hans STEPHANY, Ministerialdirigent in Ministry of Labour

Professor Dr. BARTHOLOME, Badische Anilin- und Soda-fabrik, Ludwigshafen

Dr. Wilhelm BOVERI, Brown Boveri, Mannheim

Dr. DUHM, Bayer, Wuppertal

Dr. DUNKEL, Leyboldt, Karlsruhe

Professor Dr. FINKELNBURG, Siemens, Erlangen

Dipl. Ing. FLEISCHER, Deutsche Verbundgesellschaft, Heidelberg

Professor Dr. HOUDREMONT, Krupp, Essen

Professor Dipl. Ing. LÖBL, Rheinisch-Westfälische Elektrizitätswerke AG

Professor Dr. MAYER-LEIBNITZ, Institut für Technische Physik der Technischen Hochschule, München

Direktor RUTHARDT, Heraeus, Hanau

Direktor SCHIMMELBUSCH, Degussa, Frankfurt

Dr. Ing. SCHULT

Dr. TELSCHOW, Max Planck Gesellschaft, Göttingen

Mr. ULRICH, Graphitwerke Kropfmühl AG

Mr. Ludwig ROSENBERG, Allgemeiner Deutscher Gewerkschaft

Mr. Karl OSTERKAMP, Gewerkschaft Transport und öffentlicher Dienst

Dr. Hans-Dieter BECKEY, Bonn

Dipl. Phys. BECKURTZ, Göttingen

Dr. Peter BRIX, Heidelberg

Dr. HARDE, Bonn

Dr. Joachin HEINTZE, Heidelberg

Dr. W. HERR, Mainz

Dr. B. ZIEGLER, Karlsruhe

Dr. K. G. ZIMMER, Hamburg

Dr. A. SCHRAUB, Frankfurt

Dr. G. HERRMANN, Mainz

Doz. Dr. HINTENBERGER, Mainz

Dr. A. KLEMM, Mainz

Dr. O. KNECHT, Heidelberg

Dipl. Phys. Hans A. KUNKEL, Hamburg

Dipl. Phys. MEISTER, Göttingen

Dipl. Phys. MEYER, Göttingen

Dr. Otto OSBERGHAUS, Bonn

Dr. Kurt Ernst SCHEER, Heidelberg

Dr. H. SCHOPPER, Erlangen

Dr. Rudolf SCHULTEN, Göttingen

Dr. Heinrich SCHULTZ, Göttingen

Dipl. Ing. Tasso SPRINGER, Munich

Dr. WEIMER, Göttingen

Dr. Karl WILDERMUTH, Munich

GREECE

Mr. Dimitri ARGYROPOULOS

Professor Th. G. KOUYOUMTZELIS, Physics

Professor K. D. ALEXOPOULOS, Physics

Professor Const. Th. KAWASSIADES, Inorganic Chemistry, Vice-Rector of University of Salonica

Professor Th. VLISSIDIS, General Biology

Professor G. PANTAZIS, Zoology

Major-General G. PAPATHEODOROU

Professor K. MALAMOS

Mr. J. TSAMBIRAS

GUATEMALA

Mr. Edgar S. WUNDERLICH

HASHEMITE KINGDOM OF JORDAN

Professor Kadri TUKAN, President of the Jordan Society for Sciences

HOLY SEE

Professeur Henri MEDI, Directeur de l'Institut National de Géophysique, Rome

R. P. Henri de RIEDMATTEN, Geneva

HONDURAS

Arturo LÓPEZ RODEZNO, Engineer

HUNGARY

Janos SEBESTYEN, Engineer, Deputy Minister of Chemical Industry and Power

Lajos JANOSSI, Academician, Scientific Secretary of the Hungarian Academy of Sciences

Lenard PAL, Candidate of Physics, Head of Department at the Central Research Institute for Physics

Karoly SIMONY, Candidate of Physics, Head of the Department of Nuclear Physics at the Central Research Institute for Physics Advisers

Ferenc SZABO, Head of Industrial Department of the Council of Ministers

Tibor HOFFMANN, Physicist, Head of Department of the Hungarian Institute for Telecommunication Advisers on behalf of the Ministry for Foreign Affairs

Gyoergy LORAND

Istvan MOLNAR

ICELAND

Mr. Kristján ALBERTSON, Counsellor of Legation

Mr. Thorbjörn SIGURGEIRSSON, Scientist

Mr. Magnús MAGNÚSSON, Scientist

INDIA

Dr. H. J. BHABHA, F.R.S., Secretary to the Government of India, Department of Atomic Energy, Chairman, Indian Atomic Energy Commission, and Director, Tata Institute of Fundamental Research

Dr. K. S. KRISHNAN, F.R.S., Member, Indian Atomic Energy Commission, and Director, National Physical Laboratory

Dr. V. R. KHANOLKAR, Director, Indian Cancer Research Centre, and Chairman, Biological and Medical Advisory Committee, Department of Atomic Energy

Shri Arthur S. LALL, Permanent Representative of India at the United Nations

Dr. D. N. WADIA, Geological Adviser, Department of Atomic Energy

Dr. A. R. GOPAL-AYENGAR, Biology Division, Department of Atomic Energy

Shri N. B. PRASAD, Engineering Division, Atomic Energy Establishment

Dr. R. RAMANNA, Nuclear Physics Division, Atomic Energy Establishment

Shri A. S. RAO, Electronics Division, Atomic Energy Establishment

Dr. Jagdish SHANKAR, Radio Chemistry Division, Atomic Energy Establishment

Shri H. N. SETHNA, Works Manager, Indian Rare Earths Limited

Dr. G. S. TENDOLKAR, Metallurgy Division, Atomic Energy Establishment

Dr. V. T. Athavale, Chemistry Division, Atomic Energy Establishment

Shri V. P. Duggal, Nuclear Physics Division, Atomic Energy Establishment

Dr. K. G. Vohra, Air Monitoring Division, Atomic Energy Establishment

Shri V. N. Meckoni, Chemical Engineering Division, Atomic Energy Establishment

Dr. K. C. Bora, Biology Division, Department of Atomic Energy

Shri L. S. Kothari

Shri K. Sahai

Shri Maheshwar Dayal

Shri D. N. Chatterjee

Shri D. C. Verma

Shri A. E. Ribeiro

Shri N. Ranchod

INDONESIA

Dr. R. A. Asmaoen, Chairman of the Delegation with the rank of Ambassador Extraordinary and Plenipotentiary, Director General of Foreign Economic Affairs concurrently Head of the Directorate of Foreign Economic Relations of the Ministry of Economic Affairs

Professor Dr. Bahder Djohan, President of the University of Indonesia

Mr. Izak Mahdi, Head of the United Nations Section of the Ministry of Foreign Affairs

Dr. Siwabessy, Head of the Department of Radiography of the Central General Hospital

Professor Dr. Johannes, Dean of the Faculty of Technical Science of the University of Gadjah-Mada

Dr. Sudjito Danusaputro, Lecturer in physics at the Faculty of Medicine of the University of Indonesia

Dr. Kaslan A. Tohir, Head of International Relation Department of the Ministry of Agriculture

Dr. F. J. Inkiriwang, Head of the Directorate for Energy and the Coordination of State Electric Power

IRAN

Dr. Kamal Jenab, Professor of Physics in the Faculty of Science at the University of Teheran

Dr. Gholam Ali Bazargan, Professor of Chemistry and Physics in the Faculty of Engineering at the University of Teheran

Mr. Javad Mansour

IRAQ

Dr. Sabeeh Al-Wahbi, ex-Minister of Health

Mr. Sheeth Numann, Director of Scientific and Industrial Research and Director-General of Industry

Mr. Abdul Karim Hilmi, Research Chemist, Directorate-General of Industry

Dr. Salah Izzet Tahseen, Department of Physics, College of Arts and Sciences

Dr. Louay Tahseen Kadry, acting Director, Field Crops Division, Ministry of Agriculture

Dr. Mohammed Kashif Al-Ghita, Nuclear Physicist and Senior Process Engineer, Baghdad

Mr. Abdul-Malik Al-Zaibag, United Nations and Conferences Section, Ministry for Foreign Affairs

IRELAND

Mr. Hugh McCann, Minister Plenipotentiary and Envoy Extraordinary of Ireland at Berne

Professor E. J. Conway, D.Sc., M,B, B.Ch., B.A.O., F.R.S. Professor of Bio-Chemistry and Pharmacology, University College, Dublin

Professor Thomas E Nevin, D.Sc., Professor of Experimental Physics, University College, Dublin

Professor E. T. S. Walton, Ph.D., Professor of Experimental Physics, Trinity College, Dublin

Dr. Thomas A. McLaughlin, D.Sc., B.E., Electricity Supply Board

ISRAEL

Mr. Walter Eytan, Director General, Ministry for Foreign Affairs

Professor Dr. Ernst David Bergmann, Chairman, Atomic Energy Commission

Professor Dr. Israel Dostrowsky, Director of Research, Atomic Energy Commission

Dr. Amos De Shalit, Head of Physics Department, Weizman Institute of Science, Rehovot

Dr. Haim Cats, Director, Department of Economic Research and Statistics, Palestine Electric Corporation

Professor Giulio Racah, Professor of Theoretical Physics, Hebrew University

Dr. Sally Cohen, Lecturer in Experimental Physics, Hebrew University

Dr. Menahem Kahany, Permanent Delegate of Israel to the European Office of the United Nations, Geneva

Mr. Michael Doron, Technical and Industrial Attaché, Embassy of Israel, Paris

ITALY

Dr. Professor Francesco Giordani, President du Comité National des Recherches Nucléaires; Professeur Ordinaire de Chimie Générale à l'Université de Naples

Ministre Plénipotentiaire Renzo Carrobbio Di Carrobbio Ministère des Affaires Etrangères

M. Aldo Silvestri Amari, Directeur Général des Affaires Générales au Ministère de l'Industrie et Commerce Membre du C.N.R.N.

Professor Ing. Felice Ippolito, Professeur Ordinaire de Geologie Appliquée à l'Université de Naples Membre du C.N.R.N.

Professor Bruno Ferretti, Professeur Ordinaire de Physique Théorique à l'Université de Rome Membre du C.N.R.N.

Professor Mario Ageno, Physicien à l'Institut Supérieur de Santé à Rome

Professor Edoardo Amaldi, Membre du C.N.R.N.—Professeur Ordinaire de Physique Expérimentale à l'Université de Rome

Dr. Paolo Baggio, Géologue du C.N.R.N.

Dr. Annetta Baroni, Service de Documentation du C.N.R.N.

Dr. Alberto Bessone, Association Italienne Hydrocarbures (E.N.I.)

Dr. Germano Bodo, E.N.I.

Professor Giuseppe Bolla, Professeur Ordinaire de Physique Expérimentale au "Politecnico" de Milano—Consultant Technique au C.I.S.E. (Centre Italien Etudes et Expériences)

Dr. Alberto Bracci, C.I.S.E.

Ing. Alberto Cacciari, C.I.S.E.

Ing. Claudio Castellani, Directeur du Département de l'Energie à la Société Montecatini

Dr. Enrico Cerrai, C.I.S.E.

Dr. Giorgio Cortellessa, Physicien à l'Institut Supérieur de Santé

Dr. Nicola D'Angelo, Physicien à l'Institut Supérieur de Santé

Professor Ugo Facchini, C.I.S.E.

Dr. Carlo FIZZOTTI, C.I.S.E.

Ing. Gianfranco FRANCO, C.I.S.E.

Professor Sergio GALLONE, C.I.S.E.

Ing. Silvio GARRONE, Fonctionnaire du Ministère du Travail et de la Prévoyance Sociale

Professor Emilio GATTI, C.I.S.E.

Dr. Elio GERMAGNOLI, C.I.S.E.

Dr. Guglielmo GIANNELLI, C.I.S.E.

Dr. Alessandro MALVICINI, C.I.S.E.

Professor Giovan Battista MARINI-BETTOLO, Chimiste à l'Institut Supérieur de Santé

Dr. Pietro MARINO-CLARELLI, Société Romaine d'Electricité (S.R.E.)

Dr. Michele MATTEO, Directeur Général de l'Association Nationale des Sociétés Productrices et Distributrices de l'Energie Electrique (A.N.I.D.E.L.)

Ing. Luciano ORSONI, C.I.S.E.

Dr. Ferdinando PASSALACQUA, Département de Radio-biologie à l'Institut d'Anatomie Pathologique de Milan

Ing. Alberto PEDRETTI, C.I.S.E.

Dr. Marcello QUINTILIANI, Radiologue à l'Institut Supérieur de Santé

Professor A. Mario ROLLIER, C.I.S.E. Institut de Chimie Générale du "Politecnico" de Milano

Professor Carlo SALVETTI, Professeur de Radioactivité à l'Université de Milan et Consultant du C.I.S.E.

Dr. Gian Tommaso SCARASCIA, Directeur du Département de Génétique à l'Institut Scientifique Expérimental du Tabac

Ing. Vito SCHIRONE, E.N.I.

Professor Mario SILVESTRI, C.I.S.E.

Ing. Luigi USONI, Inspecteur Général minéraire près du Comité National Recherches Nucléaires—Directeur du Centre pour la préparation des minéraux

Dr. Edoardo ZIMMER, C.I.S.E.

Professor Dr. Ing. Arnaldo Maria ANGELINI, Directeur Général Adjoint de la Société TERNI-A.N.I.D.E.L.

Dr. Ing. Vittore ANTONELLO, Directeur Central de la "Società Adratica di Elettricità" A.N.I.D.E.L.

Dr. Aldo ASCARI, C.I.S.E.

Ing. Aurelio ASCOLI, C.I.S.E.

Dr. Maria ASDENTE, C.I.S.E.

Ing. Antonio BAGLIO, Chef Division Energie Atomique, Ministère de l'Industrie

Dr. Sergio BARABASCHI, C.I.S.E.

Dr. Bruno BRIGOLI, C.I.S.E.

Dr. Ing. Mario BRUNI, Directeur Technique de la Société "La Centrale"—A.N.I.D.E.L.

Dr. Ing. Constantino BUONOCORE, Chef du Bureau d'Etudes de la "Società Meridionale di Elettricità" A.N.I.D.E.L.

Dr. Ugo Lucio BUSINARO, C.I.S.E.

Ing. Adriano CAPERLE, Direction Générale Mines, Ministère de l'Industrie

Dr. Giuseppe CAGLIOTI, Institut de Physique à l'Université de Rome

Dr. Ing. Gerolamo CALABRIA, Directeur de la "Società Termo Elettrica Italiana" A.N.I.D.E.L.

Dr. Ing. Filippo CARATI, Directeur Général de la "Azienda Elettrica Municipale"

Dr. Ing. Franco CASTELLI, Directeur de la Section Centrales Thermiques de la Société Edison A.N.I.D.E.L.

Dr. Ing. Gianfranco CASTELLI, Société Edison A.N.I.D.E.L.

Dr. Ing. Guido CERILLO, Directeur Général de la Société Méridionale d'Electricité A.N.I.D.E.L.

Dr. Claudio COCEVA, C.I.S.E.

Ing. C. COSTADONI, Compagnie Générale d'Electricité Milan

Professor Dr. Ing. Agostino DALLA VERDE, Directeur Général Adjoint de la "Società Idroelettrica Piemonte" A.N.I.D.E.L.

Dr. Ing. Vittorio DE BIASI, Conseiller délégué de la Société Edison A.N.I.D.E.L.

Ing. Sergio FINZI, C.I.S.E.

Dr. Mario FORTE, C.I.S.E.

Dr. Ing. Teo LEARDINI, Società Adriatica di Elettricità A.N.I.D.E.L.

Ing. Piero GIUSTINIANI

Professor Dr. Ing. Mario MAINARDIS, Directeur Central de la "Società Adriatica di Elettricità" A.N.I.D.E.L.

Professor Dr. Ing. Roberto MARIN, Directeur Central de la "Società Adriatica di Elettricità" A.N.I.D.E.L.

Dr. Ing. Alfonso MODICA, Directeur des Services de la Production de la Société Générale Electrique de la Sicile A.N.I.D.E.L.

Dr. Ing. Luigi MOLTENI, Directeur Administratif de la Société Edison A.N.I.D.E.L.

Dr. Luigi MONGINI, C.I.S.E.

Professor Dr. Ing. Giovanni Giuseppe MOTTA, "Azienda Elettrica Municipale" de Milan

Dr. Federico NORDIO, C.I.S.E.

Ing. Giovanni PERONA, C.I.S.E.

Dr. Ing. Carlo PERRONE, Directeur Général de la Société Vizzola A.N.I.D.E.L.

Professor Aldo PERUSSIA, Chargé de cours à l'Université de Milan et Privat-Docent de radiologie médicale

Professor Dr. Ing. Giuseppe QUILICO, "Società Idroelettrica Piemonte" A.N.I.D.E.L.

Dr. Ruggero RENZONI, C.I.S.E.

Dr. Ing. Marcello RODINO, Conseiller délégué, A.N.I.D.E.L.

Dr. Angelo ROSSI, Chargé de cours à l'Institut de Physique de l'Université de Milan A.N.I.D.E.L.

Dr. Ing. Bartolomeo ORSONI, Société Montecatini

Professor Francesco SCANDONE, A.N.I.D.E.L

Dr. Ing. Cesare SCIMENI, Directeur Général de la Société Générale Electrique de la Sicile A.N.I.D.E.L.

Dr. Lucio SELMI, C.I.S.E.

Dr. Carla TAMAGNINI, C.I.S.E.

Dr. Ing. Giuseppe TARDINI, Société Edison A.N.I.D.E.L.

Dr. Sergio TERRANI, C.I.S.E.

Dr. Ing. Giorgio VALERIO, Conseiller délégué de la Société Edison

Professor Dr. Ing. Giancarlo VALLAURI, Società Idroelettrica Piemonte" A.N.I.D.E.L.

Professor Vittorio VALLETTA, Directeur Général de la F.I.A.T.

Dr. Stelio VILLANI, C.I.S.E.

Dr. Luigi BERRUTI, Directeur de la F.I.A.T. à Genève

Dr. Giorgio BERRUTI, Ingénieur-chimiste

JAPAN

Mr. Keiichi TATSUKE, Permanent Delegate of Japan to the International Organizations, Geneva; Consul General of Japan at Geneva

Dr. Koichi AKI, Vice Chairman, Resources Council, Prime Minister's Office

Dr. Yoshio FUJIOKA, Professor, Faculty of Science, Tokyo University of Education

Dr. Sakuji KOMAGATA, Director, Agency of Industrial Science and Technology, Ministry of International Trade and Industry

Dr. Masao TSUZUKI, Professor Emeritus of Tokyo University; Director of Japan Red Cross Central Hospital

Dr. Sakae YAGI, Professor, Faculty of Engineering, Tokyo University

Dr. Shingo MITSUI, Professor, Faculty of Agriculture, Tokyo University

Dr. Seizo OKAMURA, Professor, Faculty of Engineering, Kyoto University

Dr. Eiichi TAKEDA, Professor, Faculty of Engineering, Tokyo Institute of Technology

Dr. Masao KATO, Assistant Professor, Metallurgy Division, Institute of Industrial Science, Tokyo University

Dr. Masatake HONDA, Assistant Professor, Faculty of Science, Tokyo University

Mr. Shigetada ABE, Technical Official, Prime Minister's Office

Mr. Hideo KITAHARA, Assistant Permanent Observer of Japan to the United Nations in New York

Mr. Ohtori KURINO, Secretary, Ministry of Foreign Affairs

Dr. Tamaki IPPOMMATSU, Managing Director, Kansai Electric Power Co. Ltd.

Dr. Katsumi OKUDA, Deputy-Chief, Technical Department, Mitsubishi Shipbuilding & Engineering Co. Ltd.

Dr. Tokuzo KAMBARA, Member, Hitachi Central Laboratory, Hitachi Ltd.

REPUBLIC OF KOREA

Dr. Chulchai PARK, Director, Bureau of Technological Education in Seoul

Professor Dong Suk YUN, Associate Professor, College of Technology, Seoul National University

Professor Kee Uk LEE, Associate Professor in Physics, Seoul National University

LEBANON

Dr. Salwa C. NASSAR, Chairman of the Physics Department, Professor of Physics at the American University of Beirut, Lebanon

LIBERIA

Dr. T. O. DOSUMU-JOHNSON, Director, College of Liberal Arts, University of Liberia

Hon. John L. COOPER, Inspector of Communication, R. L.

LUXEMBOURG

M. J. P. KREMER, Conseiller de Légation au Ministère des Affaires Etrangères

M. Henri THILL, Professeur de physique aux Cours supérieurs à Luxembourg

MEXICO

Dr. Nabor CARRILLO, Rector of the National University of Mexico

Dr. Manuel SANDOVAL VALLARTA, Scientific Research Director National University of Mexico

Dr. Alberto BARAJAS, Co-ordinator of Scientific Research National University of Mexico

Dr. Carlos GRAEF FERNANDEZ, Director of the Institute of Physics at the National University of Mexico

Sr. Joel VAZQUEZ MENDOZA, Chief of the Department of Law at the National University of Mexico

Sr. Tomás GURZA, Public Relations Adviser to the National University of Mexico

Sr. Jorge CASTAÑEDA, Counsellor to the Foreign Relations Secretariat

PRINCIPALITY OF MONACO

Mr. César SOLAMITO, Private Cousellor to His Most Serene Highness the Prince

Dr. Etienne BOERI, Director of Hygiene and Public Health

Mr. René BICKERT, Consul General in Geneva

Dr. André FISSORE

Mr. Pierre NOTARI, Consul General, "Chargé de Mission" with External Affairs Department

Mr. Robert MARCHISIO, "Chargé de Mission" with External Affairs Department

NETHERLANDS

Dr. C. J. GORTER, Professor at the University of Leyden, Chairman of the Foundation for Fundamental Research of Matter, Chairman of the Delegation

Dr. J. H. DE BOER, Professor at the Technical University of Delft, Scientific Adviser, Netherlands State Mines in Limburg, Geleen

Dr. J. M. W. MILATZ, Professor at the University of Utrecht, Director of "Reactor Centrum Nederland"

Dr. B. G. ZIEDSES DES PLANTES, Professor at the Municipal University of Amsterdam

Mr. H. F. ESCHAUZIER, Director-General for Political Affairs, Ministry of Foreign Affairs

Dr. H. M. HIRSCHFELD, Chairman, Board of Governors, "Reactor Centrum Nederland"

Dr. E. L. KRAMER, Director-General for Industrialization and Energy, Ministry of Economic Affairs

Mr. J. MEIJER, Deputy Head of the International Affairs Department, Ministry of Foreign Affairs

Dr. A. H. W. ATEN, JR., Chief Scientist, Institute for Nuclear Energy Research, Amsterdam, Professor at the Municipal University of Amsterdam

Dr. F. BARENDREGT, Professor, Chief Scientist, Foundation for Fundamental Research of Matter (FOM), Utrecht

Dr. T. J. BARENDREGT, Head, Chemical Department, Norwegian-Netherlands Joint Establishment for Nuclear Energy Research, Kjeller, Norway

Dr. F. BOESCHOTEN, Scientist, Foundation for Fundamental Research of Matter (FOM), Utrecht

Dr. M. BOGAARDT, Scientist, Foundation for Fundamental Research of Matter (FOM), Utrecht

Mr. E. F. BOON, Professor at the Technical University of Delft

Dr. H. DE BRUYN, Scientist, Netherlands State Mines of Limburg

Mr. M. BUSTRAAN, Scientist, Norwegian-Netherlands Joint Establishment for Nuclear Energy Research, Kjeller, Norway

Dr. H. B. G. CASIMIR, Professor at the University of Leyden, Director, Philips' Research Laboratories, Eindhoven

Dr. W. J. D. VAN DIJCK, Professor, Special Advisor N. V. Bataafse Petroleum Maatschappij (Royal Dutch Shell)

Dr. K. VAN DUUREN, Scientist, Philips' Research team, Institute for Nuclear Energy Research, Amsterdam

Mr. J. KOOI, Scientist, Norwegian-Netherlands Joint Establishment for Nuclear Energy Research, Kjeller, Norway

Mr. H. KRAMERS, Professor at the Technical University of Delft

Mr. K. P. M. NEUERBURG, Deputy Director-General for Industrialization and Energy

Dr. W. J. OOSTERKAMP, Chief Scientist, Philips' Research Laboratories, Eindhoven

Mr. J. PELSER, Scientist, Norwegian-Netherlands Joint Establishment for Nuclear Energy Research, Kjeller, Norway

Mr. H. POLAK, Scientific Attaché, Netherlands Embassy, Washington, D. C.

Dr. A. C. SCHUFFELLEN, Professor at the Agricultural University of Wageningen

Mr. A. SOMERWIL, Chief Physicist, Radio-Therapeutic Institute, Rotterdam

Dr. E. C. WASSINK, Professor at the Agricultural University of Wageningen

Dr. J. J. WENT, Head, Physics Department of the N. V. KEMA, Arnheim

Mr. H. H. WOLDRINGH, Scientist, Foundation for Fundamental Research of Matter (FOM)

Dr. W. J. BEEKMAN, Director, Bureau Foundation for Fundamental Research of Matter (FOM), Scientific Secretary of the Delegation

Mr. G. W. BENDIEN, Senior Officer, Ministry of Foreign Affairs, General Secretary of the Delegation

NEW ZEALAND

Dr. W. M. HAMILTON, Secretary of the Department of Scientific and Industrial Research

Mr. M. G. LATTA, Chief Engineer of the State Hydro-Electric Department

Mr. R. F. D. RITCHIE, Project Engineer of the Ministry of Works

Professor Darcy WALKER, Professor of Physics, Victoria University College, Wellington

Dr. F. J. M. FARLEY, Senior Lecturer in Physics, Auckland University College, Auckland

Dr. V. ARMSTRONG, New Zealand Government Scientific Liaison Officer, London

Mr. G. D. L. WHITE, Staff of the New Zealand High Commissioner in London

NORWAY

Mr. O. DAHL, Doctor

Mr. F. VOGT, Director-General

Mr. R. MAJOR, Director

Mr. E. SAELAND, Chief of Research

Mr. R. EKER, Director

Mr. Hans ENGEN, Norwegian Permanent Delegation to the United Nations, New York

Mr. U. BEEN, Scientist

Mr. K. CARLSEN, Scientist

Mr. L. ELDJARN, Chief Physician

Mr. V. O. ERIKSEN, Scientist

Mr. N. HIDLE, Chief of Research

Mr. P. LIEN, Scientist

Mr. A. LUNDBY, Chief of Research

Mr. K. MICHAELSEN, Scientist

Mr. A. PAPPAS, Doctor

Mr. T. SIGGERUD, Geologist

Mr. T. SIKKELAND, Scientist

Mr. S. AASS, Scientist

Mr. Th. HVINDEN, Chief of Research

Mr. Gudbrand JENSSEN, Scientist

Mr. O. R. KÅSA, Engineer, Secretary

PAKISTAN

Dr. Nazir AHMAD, Chairman, Atomic Energy Committee and Chairman, Tariff Commission

Dr. Bashir AHMAD, Director, Punjab University Institute of Chemistry and Director, Regional Laboratories, Council of Scientific and Industrial Research

Dr. Rafi M. CHAUDHARI, Professor and Head of the Physics Department and Dean of the Faculty of Science, Government College, Lahore

Dr. Mohammed Abdur RAHMAN, Professor of Physiology, Dacca Medical College, Dacca

Mr. H. RAHMAN

Mr. Manzoor AHMAD, Secretary, Officer on Special Duty (Power) Ministry of Industries

PANAMA

Mr. Bernardo LOMBARDO

PERU

General Jorge SARMIENTO, President of the Controlling Board of Radioactive Substances

PHILIPPINES

Mr. Felixberto M. SERRANO, Ambassador Extraordinary and Plenipotentiary, Permanent Representative to the United Nations

Dr. Joaquin MARAÑON, Director, Bureau of Science

Dr. Armando CLEMENTE, Dean, Chemical Engineering, University of the Philippines

Dr. Casimiro del ROSARIO, Director, Weather Bureau

Col. Florencio MEDINA, Armed Forces of the Philippines

Dr. Ricardo PASTOR

Mr. José TORRES

Dr. Ricardo SEBASTIAN

PEOPLE'S REPUBLIC OF POLAND

Professor Dr. Leopold INFELD, Member of the Presidium of the Polish Academy of Sciences, Director of the Institute of Physics of the Warsaw University

Professor Dr. Pawel SZULKIN, Deputy Scientific Secretary of the Polish Academy of Sciences, Professor of Warsaw Polytechnic

Dr. Juliusz KATZ-SUCHY, Professor of Warsaw University, Minister Plenipotentiary, Director of the Polish Institute of International Affairs

Professor Dr. Andrzej SOLTAN, Member of the Polish Academy of Sciences, Professor of Warsaw University

Professor Dr. Henryk NIEWODNICZANSKI, Member of the Polish Academy of Sciences, Professor of Cracow University

Mr. Zygmunt BIEGUSZEWSKI, Engineer-Chemist

Mr. Bronislaw BURAS, Docent-Physicist

Mr. Marian DANYSZ, Professor of Physics

Dr. Andrzej HRYNKIEWICZ, Docent-Physicist

Dr. Wladyslaw JASINSKI, Docent, Academy of Medicine

Mr. Edward KOWALSKI, Docent-State Institute of Hygiene

Mr. Wladyslaw NEY, Engineer, Ministry of Power

Mr. Mieczyslaw PEREC, Engineer-Chemist

Dr. Ignacy REIFER, Professor-Biologist

Mr. Jerzy ROMAN, Engineer, Ministry of Power

Mr. Stefan SWIERCZEWSKI, Engineer-Physicist

Mr. Mieczyslaw TAUBE, Engineer-Chemist

Mr. Zdzislaw WILHELMI, Associate Professor of Physics

PORTUGAL

Ingénieur José Frederico ULRICH, Président de la Junta de Energia Nuclear, (Commission pour l'Energie Nucléaire)

Ingénieur Manuel ROCHA, Directeur du Laboratório Nacional de Engenharia Civil

Professor Carlos BRAGA, Professeur de Physique de la Faculté des Sciences de l'Université de Porto

Professor António Herculano de CARVALHO, Professeur de Chimie de l'Institute Superior Técnico de Lisbonne

Dr. Rui Brás MIMOSO, Ministère des Affaires Etrangères

Professor Ingénieur Alberto Abecasis MANZANARES, Professeur d'Hydraulique de l'"Instituto Superior Técnico" de Lisbonne

Professor Antonio SOUSA DA CÂMARA, Directeur de la "Estaçao Agronomica Nacional"

Professor Edmundo LIMA BASTO, Faculté de Médecine de Lisbonne

Ingénieur Minas Carlos Pires LOBATO

Ingénieur Fernando Marques VIDEIRA

Dr. Victor Hugo FRANCO

Ingénieur El. Rui José PACHECO DE FIGUEREDO

Ingénieur Luis Almeida ALVES, Companhia Uniao Fabril

Ingénieur Pedro Lobo MACHADO, Sociedade Anónima Concessionaria da Refinacao de Petroleos em Portugal

Ingénieur António Gouveia PORTELA, Companhia Uniao Fabril

Ingénieur Henrique PESSOA ARAUJO, Sociedades Reunidas de Fabricaçoes Metálicas

Ingénieur Carlos CARVALHO DIAS, Sociedades Reunidas de Fabricaçoes Metálicas

Ingénieur José Rola PEREIRA, Hidro-Electrica de Zezere

Ingénieur Joaquim Sabino DOMINGUES, Hidro-Electrica de Cávado

Ingénieur Antonio Nunes COELHO, Companhia Nacional de Electricidade

Ingénieur Manuel Gaspar de BARROS, l'Amoniaco Portugês

Ingénieur José Maria Mercier MARQUES, Fábrica Portuguesa de Fermentos Holandeses

Dr. Carlos CACHO, Boursier de l'Instituto de Alta Cultura

ROMANIAN PEOPLE'S REPUBLIC

Mr. Gheorghe GASTON MARIN, Chairman, Nuclear Energy Commission of the Romanian People's Republic

Professor Dr. Horia HULUBEI, Nuclear Energy Commission, Director, Institute of Physics, Bucarest Member of the Academy of the Romanian People's Republic

Professor Dr. Stefan MILCOU, Member and First Secretary of the Academy of the Romanian People's Republic, Director, Romanian Institute of Endocrinology, Bucarest

Dr. Alice SAVULESCU, Member of the Academy of the Romanian People's Republic, Institute of Agronomy, Bucarest

Professor Dr. Raluca RIPAN, Member of the Academy of the Romanian People's Republic, Head of the University of Cluj, Director, Institute of Chemistry

Professor Bucur SCHIOPU, Vice-Chairman of the Romanian State-Planning Commission

Mr. Alexandru LAZAREANU, Director, Ministry of Foreign Affairs

Mr. Mihail PETRI, Director-General, Ministry for Foreign Trade

Professor Dr. Alexandru SANIELVICI, Member of the Academy of the Romanian People's Republic, Institute of Physics, Bucarest

Professor Dr. Eugen PORA, Member of the Academy of the Romanian People's Republic, Institute of Physiology, Cluj

Professor Dr. Iosif AUSLÄNDER, Institute of Physics, Bucarest

Dr. Octav COSTACHEL, Director, Institute of Oncology, Bucarest

Professor Adrian GEORGESCO, Director-General, Ministry of Electrical Energy

Professor Iosif DRIMUS, Director, Ministry of Chemical Industry

Professor Stefan MANTEA, Director, Centre of Metallurgical Research, Bucarest

Mr. Paul DRAGHICESCO, Institute of Physics, Bucarest

Mr. Mihail PACEPA, Secretary of the Delegation, Romanian State-Planning Commission

Mr. Constantin MUNTEANU, Secretary of the Delegation, Ministry of Foreign Affairs

REPUBLIC OF SAN MARINO

Dr. Boris LIFSCHITZ, Envoy Extraordinary and Minister Plenipotentiary, Geneva

Dr. B. WARTANOV

Mr. H. RAYNAUD, Secretary

SPAIN

Mr. José María OTERO NAVASCUÉS, Vice-President of the Nuclear Energy Commission

Mr. Pedro CORTINA MAURI, Director of International Organizations

Mr. Armando DURÁN MIRANDA, Member of the Nuclear Energy Commission

Mr. José Antonio de ARTIGAS SANZ, Director of the Institute for Advanced Studies

Mr. José Manuel ANIEL QUIROGA Y REDONDO, Director for European Political Affairs

Mr. Victoriano MUÑOZOMS, Managing Director of the Ribagorzans National Hydro-Electric Undertaking

Mr. Gabriel TORRES COST, Managing Director of the National Electricity Undertaking

Mr. Carlos SÁNCHEZ DEL RÍO Y SIERRA, Chief of the Experimental Physics Department, Nuclear Energy Commission

Mr. Ricardo FERNÁNDEZ CELLINI, Chief of the Analytical Chemistry Section, Nuclear Energy Commission

Mr. Eduardo RAMOS RODRIGUEZ, Chief of the Medical Department, Nuclear Energy Commission

Mr. Joaquín CATALÁ DE ALEMANY, Chief of the Physics Department of the Nuclear Energy Commission in Valencia

Mr. Miguel Angel GAMBOA LOYARTE, Secretary of the Biology Division, Nuclear Energy Commission

Mr. Rogelio SEGOVIA TORRES, Member of the Physics Department, Nuclear Energy Commission

Mr. José de TORRÓNTEGUI, Director of the Bilbao Engineering School and Managing Director of the Sociedad de Construcciones Babcock Wilcox

Mr. Alberto CASO MONTANER, Technical Adviser and Engineer, Sociedad Hidronitro Española

Mr. Federico GODED ECHEVARRÍA, Engineer, Sociedad General Eléctrica Española

Mr. Angel GARCÍA DE VINUESA, Engineer, Member of the Board of Management of the Seville Electricity Company

Mr. Luis GARCÍA DE LLERA, Minister Plenipotentiary

Mr. Luis de VILLEGAS Y URZAIZ, Embassy Secretary

SWEDEN

Mr. R. SANDLER, Ex-Prime Minister, Ex-Minister for Foreign Affairs, Member of the Foreign Ministry's Advisory Committee on Atomic Questions

Professor T. SVEDBERG, Dr. Phil. Med. and Techn., Member of the Foreign Ministry's Advisory Committee on Atomic Questions, Member of the Atomic Energy Commission

Professor G. de HEVESY, Dr. Phil.

Mr. H. BRYNIELSSON, Managing Director, Atomic Energy Company, Member of the Foreign Ministry's Advisory Committee on Atomic Questions, Associated Member of the Atomic Energy Commission

Dr. G. FUNKE, Member of the Foreign Ministry's Advisory Committee on Atomic Questions, Associated Member and Secretary General of the Atomic Energy Commission

Mr. A. BERGSTEDT, Engineer, Department of Physics, Atomic Energy Company

Mr. G. von DARDEL, Assistant Professor of University

Mr. L. EHRENBERG, Assistant Professor of University

Mr. S. EKLUND, Assistant Professor of University, Director, Department of Physics, Atomic Energy Company; Associated Member of the Atomic Energy Commission

Mr. A. GUSTAFSSON, Professor of University

Mr. E. HAEFFNER, Licentiate of Technology, Atomic Energy Company

Mr. E. HELLSTRAND, Licentiate of Technology, Department of Physics, Atomic Energy Company

Mr. A. KIESSLING, Assistant Professor of University, Head of the Section of Physical Metallurgy, Atomic Energy Company

Mr. R. LILJEBLAD, Managing Director

Mr. R. PERSSON, Licentiate of Technology, Atomic Energy Company

Mr. G. RATHSMAN, Assistant Director General, Deputy Chief of the State Power Board

Mr. R. SIEVERT, Professor of University, Institute of Radiophysics, Karlinska-Sjukhuset Hospital, Stockholm

Mr. G. SJÖSTRAND, Licentiate of Technology, Atomic Energy Company

Mr. E. SVENKE, Director, Department of Chemistry, Atomic Energy Company

Mr. S. RYNELL, Chief of Section of the Ministry for Foreign Affairs, Member and Secretary of the Foreign Ministry's Advisory Committee on Atomic Questions, Secretary of the Delegation

SWITZERLAND

M. Paul SCHERRER, Professeur à l'Institut de physique de l'Ecole polytechnique fédérale, Zürich

M. Paul HUBER, Professeur, Institut de physique de l'Université de Bâle

M. Richard-C. EXTERMANN, Professeur, Institut de physique, Genève

M. H. STAUB, Professeur, Institut de physique de l'Université de Zürich

M. J. ROSSEL, Professeur, Institut de physique, Neuchâtel

M. le Ministre Pierre MICHELI, Chef de la Division des organisations internationales du Département politique

M. P. de HALLER, Directeur, Maison Sulzer et frères, Winterthour

M. J. SEITZ, Maison Emil Haefely & Cie S.A., Bâle

M. ARNET, Ing. dipl., Maison Escher Wyss, Zürich

M. W. DUBS, Maison Escher Wyss, Zürich

M. G. GIANELLA, Ing. dipl., Motor Columbus, Baden

M. Peter SULZER, Maison Sulzer et frères, Winterthour

M. STRUB, Ing. dipl., Maison Sulzer et frères, Winterthour

M. A. STEBLER, Maison Landis & Gyr, Zoug

M. BLOCH, Aluminium-Industrie A. G., Neuhausen

M. W. BOVERI, Zürich

M. WIDEROE, BBC, Baden

M. W. HÄLG, BBC, Baden

M. J. LALIVE D'EPINAY, Ing. dipl., BBC, Baden

M. E. ROMETSCH, Ciba, Bâle

M. C. SEIPPEL, BBC, Baden

M. R. SONTHEIM, Zürich

M. A. WINIGER, Directeur, Elektro-Watt, Zürich

M. R. NEESER, Professeur, Administrateur-délégué des Ateliers des Charmilles, Genève

Dr. K. BERNHARD, Professeur, Institut physiologique, Bâle

Dr. Hedi FRITZ-NIGGLI, Institut de radiothérapie de l'Université de Zürich

Dr. A. JENTZER, Professeur, Institut du radium de l'Université de Genève

Dr. G. JOYET, Hôpital cantonal, Zürich

Dr. J. H. MULLER, Professeur, Maternité, Zürich

Dr. A. VANNOTTI, Professeur, Hôpital Nestlé, Lausanne

Dr. P. WENGER, Directeur de l'Institut du Radium du Centre Anticancéreux de Genève

Dr. A. ZUPPINGER, Professeur, Institut de radiothérapie de l'Hôpital de l'Ile, Berne

M. Marc GRÜNENFELDER, Institut de physique, Bâle

M. F. ALDER, Institut de physique, Bâle

M. P. SCHMID, c/o J.E.N.E.R. Lillestrøm (Norvège)

M. W. ZÜNTI, Institut de physique de l'Ecole polytechnique fédérale, Zürich

M. P. BAERTSCHI, Institut de physicochimie, Bâle

M. Ch. HAENNY, Professeur, Institut de physique de l'Université de Berne

M. F. HOUTERMANS, Professeur, Institut de physique de l'Université de Berne

M. P. E. WENGER, Professeur, Vice-Président de la Faculté des Sciences de l'Université de Genève

Dr. Max AUWÄRTER, Gerätebau-Anstalt Balzers

SYRIA

M. Kazem JAZZAR, Secrétaire Général du Ministère des Travaux Publics

M. Wajih SAMMAN, Directeur Général de l'Electricité de Damas

M. Toufik MOUNAJED, Professeur de Physique à la Faculté des Sciences de l'Université Syrienne

Dr. Antoine GENNAOUI, Professeur de Physique à la Faculté des Sciences de l'Université Syrienne

M. Michel NAHAS, Professeur à la Faculté des Sciences de l'Université Syrienne

THAILAND

Air Marshal Muni M. Veiyant RANGSRISHT, Deputy Prime-Minister, Chairman, Civil Service Commission, Chairman, Thai Technical Economic Committee, Rector, Chulalongkorn University

Professor Dr. Tab NILANIDHI, Dean, Faculty of Science, Chulalongkorn University

Professor Dr. Amnuey SMERASUTA, Head, Department of Radiology Siriraj Hospital

Mr. Vija SETHAPUT, Acting Director-General, Department of Mines

Dr. Boonrod BINSON, Secretary-General, National Energy Commission

Professor Yen SUNDARA-VICHARANA, Head, Department of Physics, Chulalongkorn University

Group-Captain Dr. Svasti SRISUKH, Head of Technical Division, Ordnance Department, Royal Thai Air Force

Dr. Pradist CHEOSKUL, Associate Professor, Albany Medical College, New York

Mr. Obeboon VANIKKUL

TURKEY

Ambassador Faik Zihni AKDUR, Ambassador of Turkey in Switzerland

Professor Dr. Fahir YENICAG, Professor of Physics at the University of Istanbul

Professor Dr. Besim TANYEL, Professor of Physics at the University of Ankara

Professor Dr. Muhterem GÖKMEN, Professor of Radiology at the University of Istanbul

Professor Dr. Perihan CAMBEL, Director of Cancer Research Institute

Dr. Refet KORUR, Head of the Department of Atom, Biology and Chemistry of the Ministry of Defence

Professor Dr. Muvaffak SEYHAN, Professor of Chemistry at the University of Istanbul

Engineer Dr. Cavit ERGINSOY

Engineer Dr. Rasit TOLUN

Engineer Halim DOGRUSÖZ

UKRAINIAN SSR

Mr. A. V. PALLADIN, President of the Ukrainian SSR Academy of Sciences

Mr. M. V. PASECHNIK, Professor, Institute of Physics, Academy of Sciences, Ukrainian SSR

Mr. J. K. DELIMARSKI, Professor, Institute of Chemistry, Academy of Sciences, USSR

Mr. R. E. KAVETSKY, Professor

Mr. G. V. KARPENKO, Institute of Machines and Automatics, Academy of Sciences, USSR

Mr. S. P. DEMTCHENKO, Secretary

Mr. V. M. KOUZNETSOV, Secretary

UNION OF SOUTH AFRICA

Dr. S. M. NAUDE, President, Council for Scientific and Industrial Research

Dr. J. T. HATTINGH, Chairman, Electricity Supply Commission

Mr. T. K. PRENTICE, Uranium Consultant, Central Mining Investment Corporation

Dr. H. J. VAN ECK, Chairman, Industrial Development Corporation

Mr. G. HARDING, General Manager, Electricity Supply Commission

Mr. A. M. SCHADY, Chief Scientific Liaison Officer to the South African High Commissioner, London

UNION OF SOVIET SOCIALIST REPUBLICS

Professor D. V. SKOBELTZIN, Member of the USSR Academy of Sciences

Professor D. I. BLOKHINTSEV

Dr. A. N. LAVRISHCHEV

Professor A. P. VINOGRADOV, Member of the USSR Academy of Sciences

Professor V. I. VEKSLER, Corresponding Member of the USSR Academy of Sciences

Professor V. S. EMELYANOV, Corresponding Member of the USSR Academy of Sciences

Professor I. I. NOVIKOV

Mr. A. A. SOLDATOV

Professor A. V. TOPCHYEV, Member of the USSR Academy of Sciences

Mr. S. K. TSARAPKIN

Engineer E. K. AVERIN

Mr. B. P. ADYASSEVICH, Graduate in Science

Professor M. N. ALTHAUSEN

Engineer L. M. BARKOV

Dr. V. A. BAUM

Engineer V. V. BOCHKAREV

Dr. V. V. VLADIMIRSKI

Mr. K. V. VLADIMIRSKI, Graduate in Science

Engineer S. M. VLADIMIRSKI

Mr. K. D. VOSKRESENSKI, Graduate in Science

Engineer V. F. ERASIMOV

Dr. N. I. GLAGOLEV

Mr. V. M. GRYAZNOV, Graduate in Science

Engineer I. A. DMITRYEV

Mr. M. P. DOMSHLAK, Graduate in Science

Engineer K. P. DUBROVIN

Professor G. S. ZHDANOV

Engineer G. N. ZHEMCHUZHNIKOV

Engineer T. N. ZUBAREV

Mr. O. D. KAZACHKOVSKI, Graduate in Science

Professor V. M. KLECHKOVSKI

Engineer A. I. KOVALEV

Dr. M. S. KOZODAYEV

Professor V. N. KONDRATYEV, Member of the USSR Academy of Sciences

Engineer V. N. KOSSYAKOV

Professor F. G. KROTKOV, Member of the USSR Academy of Medical Sciences

Dr. G. N. KRUZHILIN, Corresponding Member of the USSR Academy of Sciences

Professor A. M. KUZIN

Professor G. V. KURDYUMOV, Member of the USSR Academy of Sciences

Professor A. L. KURSANOV, Member of the USSR Academy of Sciences

Professor A. V. LEBEDINSKI, Corresponding Member of the USSR Academy of Medical Sciences

Engineer V. A. MALYKH

Professor M. A. MARKOV, Corresponding Member of the USSR Academy of Sciences

Professor G. A. MEYERSON

Professor V. G. MELKOV

Engineer I. G. MOROZOV

Mr. V. I. MOSTOVOI, Graduate in Science

Mr. S. T. NAZAROV, Graduate in Science

Engineer U. G. NIKOLAYEV

Engineer S. E. PAVLOV

Mr. M. K. ROMANOVSKI, Graduate in Science

Mr. A. P. RUDIK, Graduate in Science

Professor D. I. RYABCHIKOV

Professor A. M. SAMARIN, Corresponding Member of the USSR Academy of Sciences

Professor N. M. SISSAKIAN, Corresponding Member of the USSR Academy of Sciences

Professor B. S. SOTSKOV

Engineer L. Y. SUVOROV

Engineer S. I. SUKHORUCHKIN

Professor B. N. TARUSSOV

Engineer V. P. TERENTYEV

Mr. V. G. TIMOSHEV, Graduate in Science

Professor V. L. TROITSKI

Professor M. N. FATEYEVA

Engineer V. G. KHRUSHCHEV

Engineer G. M. CHUIKOV

Mr. F. L. SHAPIRO, Graduate in Science

Professor V. V. SHCHERBINA

Delegation Secretariat

Mr. M. M. GOLIKOV, Secretary-General

Mr. I. I. LEITAN, Deputy Secretary-General

Mr. N. T. RATNIKOV, Deputy Secretary-General

Mr. M. M. YUNIN, Deputy Secretary-General

UNITED KINGDOM

Sir John COCKCROFT, K.C.B., C.B.E., F.R.S., Director, Atomic Energy Research Establishment, Harwell

Sir Christopher HINTON, F. R. S., Managing Director, U.K.A.E.A. Industrial Group, Risley

Sir George THOMSON, F.R.S., Master of Corpus Christi College, Cambridge and Member of the Scientific Advisory Panel of D.S.I.R.

Dr. J. F. LOUTIT, M.R.C. Radiobiological Research Unit, A.E.R.E., Harwell

Dr. Willis JACKSON, Director of Research and Education, Metropolitan Vickers Electrical Co. Ltd.

Sir Edwin PLOWDEN, United Kingdom Atomic Energy Authority

Sir Ivan STEDEFORD, United Kingdom Atomic Energy Authority

Sir Harold HARTLEY, United Kingdom Atomic Energy Authority

Mr. J. A. JUKES, United Kingdom Atomic Energy Authority

Mr. J. H. AWBERY, United Kingdom Atomic Energy Authority

Dr. B. F. J. SHONLAND, Deputy Director, Atomic Energy Research Establishment, Harwell

Dr. H. SELIGMAN, Isotope Division, Atomic Energy Research Establishment, Harwell

Mr. W. S. EASTWOOD, Isotope Division, Atomic Energy Research Establishment, Harwell

Dr. G. B. COOK, Isotope Division, Atomic Energy Research Establishment, Harwell

Mr. J. L. PUTMAN, Isotope Division, Atomic Energy Research Establishment, Harwell

Dr. R. ROBERTS, Isotope Division, Atomic Energy Research Establishment, Harwell

Dr. W. G. MARLEY, Health Physics Division, Atomic Energy Research Establishment, Harwell

Mr. N. G. STEWART, Health Physics Division, Atomic Energy Research Establishment, Harwell

Mr. L. S. SMITH, Health Physics Division, Atomic Energy Research Establishment, Harwell

Mr. H. J. DUNSTER, Health Physics Division, Atomic Energy Research Establishment, Harwell

Mr. A. C. CHAMBERLAIN, Health Physics Division, Atomic Energy Research Establishment, Harwell

Mr. H. J. GROUT, Reactor Engineering Division, Atomic Energy Research Establishment, Harwell

Mr. R. F. JACKSON, Reactor Engineering Division, Atomic Energy Research Establishment, Harwell

Dr. J. V. DUNWORTH, Reactor Physics Division, Atomic Energy Research Establishment, Harwell

Mr. F. W. FENNING, Reactor Physics Division, Atomic Energy Research Establishment, Harwell

Dr. L. R. SHEPHERD, Reactor Physics Division, Atomic Energy Research Establishment, Harwell

Mr. T. M. FRY, Reactor Physics Division, Atomic Energy Research Establishment, Harwell

Mr. P. W. MUMMERY, Reactor Physics Division, Atomic Energy Research Establishment, Harwell

Mr. J. CODD, Reactor Physics Division, Atomic Energy Research Establishment, Harwell

Mr. C. H. KINCHIN, Reactor Physics Division, Atomic Energy Research Establishment, Harwell

Dr. J. E. SANDERS, Reactor Physics Division, Atomic Energy Research Establishment, Harwell

Mr. B. T. PRICE, Reactor Physics Division, Atomic Energy Research Establishment, Harwell

Dr. R. SPENCE, Chemistry Division, Atomic Energy Research Establishment, Harwell

Dr. R. HURST, Chemistry Division, Atomic Energy Research Establishment, Harwell

Mr. J. WRIGHT, Chemistry Division, Atomic Energy Research Establishment, Harwell

Dr. J. M. FLETCHER, Chemistry Division, Atomic Energy Research Establishment, Harwell

Dr. E. GLUECKAUF, Chemistry Division, Atomic Energy Research Establishment, Harwell

Mr. A. A. SMALES, Chemistry Division, Atomic Energy Research Establishment, Harwell

Mr. G. N. WALTON, Chemistry Division, Atomic Energy Research Establishment, Harwell

Mr. H. A. C. McKAY, Chemistry Division, Atomic Energy Research Establishment, Harwell

Dr. W. WILD, Chemistry Division, Atomic Energy Research Establishment, Harwell

Dr. K. W. BAGNALL, Chemistry Division, Atomic Energy Research Establishment, Harwell

Dr. J. K. DAWSON, Chemistry Division, Atomic Energy Research Establishment, Harwell

Mr. F. HUDSWELL, Chemistry Division, Atomic Energy Research Establishment, Harwell

Mr. C. M. NICHOLLS, Chemical Engineering Division, Atomic Energy Research Establishment, Harwell

Dr. H. R. C. PRATT, Chemical Engineering Division, Atomic Energy Research Establishment, Harwell

Mr. J. M. HUTCHEON, Chemical Engineering Division, Atomic Energy Research Establishment, Harwell

Mr. B. L. GOODLET, Engineering Research and Development Division, Atomic Energy Research Establishment, Harwell

Mr. G. W. K. FORD, Engineering Research and Development Division, Atomic Energy Research Establishment, Harwell

Dr. P. FORTESCUE, Engineering Research and Development Division, Atomic Energy Research Establishment, Harwell

Dr. B. H. FLOWERS, Theoretical Physics Division, Atomic Energy Research Establishment, Harwell

Dr. J. H. TAIT, Theoretical Physics Division, Atomic Energy Research Establishment, Harwell

Mr. R. J. COX, Electronics Division, Atomic Energy Research Establishment, Harwell

Mr. H. BISBY, Electronics Division, Atomic Energy Research Establishment, Harwell

Dr. H. M. FINNISTON, Metallurgy Division, Atomic Energy Research Establishment, Harwell

Mr. S. F. PUGH, Metallurgy Division, Atomic Energy Research Establishment, Harwell

Dr. E. BRETSCHER, Nuclear Physics Division, Atomic Energy Research Establishment, Harwell

Dr. E. R. WIBLIN, Nuclear Physics Division, Atomic Energy Research Establishment, Harwell

Dr. P. A. EGELSTAFF, Nuclear Physics Division, Atomic Energy Research Establishment, Harwell

Dr. D. W. FRY, General Physics Division, Atomic Energy Research Establishment, Harwell

Dr. K. WILLIAMS, Medical Division, Atomic Energy Research Establishment, Harwell

Dr. C. R. HAMAND, Medical Division, Atomic Energy Research Establishment, Harwell

Dr. N. G. DOUGLAS, Medical Division, Atomic Energy Research Establishment, Harwell

Mr. D. R. WILLSON, Atomic Energy Research Establishment, Harwell

Mr. P. BOWLES, Engineering Services Division, Atomic Energy Research Establishment, Harwell

Mr. W. B. HALL, U.K.A.E.A. Industrial Group

Dr. A. S. McLEAN, U.K.A.E.A. Industrial Group

Dr. F. R. FARMER, U.K.A.E.A. Industrial Group

Dr. J. M. HILL, U.K.A.E.A. Industrial Group

Mr. D. R. FAIR, U.K.A.E.A. Industrial Group

Maj. Gen. S. W. JOSLIN, U.K.A.E.A. Industrial Group

Mr. R. V. MOORE, U.K.A.E.A. Industrial Group

Mr. L. ROTHERHAM, U.K.A.E.A. Industrial Group

Mr. P. DANCKWERTS, U.K.A.E.A. Industrial Group

Mr. J. C. C. STEWART, U.K.A.E.A. Industrial Group

Mr. H. N. BASSETT, U.K.A.E.A. Industrial Group

Dr. H. KRONBERGER, U.K.A.E.A. Industrial Group

Mr. H. H. GOTT, U.K.A.E.A. Industrial Group

Mr. G. R. H. GEOGHEGAN, U.K.A.E.A. Industrial Group

Dr. T. E. GRAHAM, U.K.A.E.A. Industrial Group

Dr S. C. CURRAN, U.K.A.E.A. Industrial Group

Dr. F. MORGAN, U.K.A.E.A. Industrial Group

Mr. R. R. GALLIE, U.K.A.E.A. Industrial Group

Mr. K. R. SANDEFORD, U.K.A.E.A. Industrial Group

Dr. J. P. CATCH, Radio-Chemical Centre, Amersham

Dr. P. E. CARTER, Radio-Chemical Centre, Amersham

Dr. W. P. GROVE, Radio-Chemical Centre, Amersham

Mr. C. JOLLIFFE, Department of Scientific and Industrial Research

Mr. J. KNOX, Department of Scientific and Industrial Research

Dr. R. M. S. SMELLIE, Department of Biochemistry, The University, Glasgow

Dr. L. H. GRAY, Radiobiological Research Department, Mount Vernon Hospital and the Radium Institute, Northwood, Middlesex

Dr. R. SCOTT RUSSELL, Department of Agriculture, University of Oxford, Oxford

Mr. W. BINKS, Radiobiological Protection Service, Downs Nursery Hospital, Sutton, Surrey

Professor W. V. MAYNEORD, Institute of Cancer Research, Royal Marsden Hospital, Fulham Road, London

Professor J. S. MITCHELL, Department of Radiotherapeutics, Downing Street, Cambridge

Dr. E. E. POCHIN, Medical Research Council, Department of Clinical Research, University College Hospital Medical School, London

Dr. R. F. GLASCOCK, National Institute for Research in Dairying, Shinfield, Reading, Berks

Dr. T. C. CARTER, M.R.C., Radiobiological Research Unit, A.E.R.E., Harwell

Dr. Helen K. PORTER, Research Institute of Plant Physiology, Imperial College of Science and Technology, Royal College of Science

Sir Ernest ROCK-CARLING, Home Office, Whitehall, London

Professor A. HADDOW, Chester Beatty Research Institute, Royal Marsden Hospital, London

Dr. H. F. FREUNDLICH, Medical Research Council

Dr. N. G. TROTT, Department of Physics, Institute of Cancer Research, Royal Marsden Hospital, London

Dr. E. H. BELCHER, Institute of Cancer Research, Royal Marsden Hospital, London

Dr. J. R. CLARKSON, Radiobiology Unit, Royal Southants Hospital, Southampton

Dr. E. LESTER-SMITH, Glaxo Laboratories Ltd., Greenford, Middlesex

Dr. A. S. McFARLANE, National Institute for Medical Research, The Ridgeway, Mill Hill, London

Mr. A. C. COPISAROW, British Embassy, Paris

Professor E. A. G. ROBINSON

Professor Sir Francis SIMON

Professor J. DIAMOND

Professor H. SKINNER

Professor R. E. PEIERLS

Professor H. J. EMELEUS

Mr. S. H. U. BOWIE, Geological Survey and Museum

Mr. A. McDONALD, Institute of Civil Engineers

Dr. R. A. WELLS, Chemical Research Laboratories

Dr. G. H. DANIEL, Ministry Fuel and Power

Mr. H. S. ARMS, English Electric Co., Ltd.

Mr. A. T. BOWDEN, C. A. Parsons Ltd.

Mr. S. A. GHALIB, Associated Electric Industries

Mr. R. M. MILLAR, General Electric Co.

Mr. A. CHARLESBY, Tube Investments, Ltd.

Mr. S. BAUER, Rolls Royce Ltd.

Mr. J. C. DUCKWORTH, Central Electricity Authority

Mr. G. E. PREECE, De Havilland Engine Co.

Mr. E. P. HAWTHORNE, Hawker Siddeley

Mr. G. A. PLUMMER, John Thompson Water Tube Boilers

Mr. W. R. WOOTTON, Babcock and Wilcox, Ltd.

Mr. J. M. KAY, Kennedy and Donkin

Mr. J. P. MIDDLETON, Bristol Aircraft

Mr. M. REJZEK, Head, Wrightson Processes, Ltd.

Mr. A. M. ROBERTS, Imperial Chemical Industries Ltd.

Mr. N. S. FORWARD

UK Technical Secretariat

Mr. J. G. CUNINGHAME

Mr. D. D. McVICAR

UNITED STATES OF AMERICA

Lewis L. STRAUSS, Chairman, Atomic Energy Commission, Washington, D. C.

Willard F. LIBBY, Commissioner, Atomic Energy Commission, Washington, D. C.

Isidor I. RABI, Chairman, General Advisory Committee, Atomic Energy Commission; Higgins Professor of Physics, Columbia University, New York

Detlev W. BRONK, President, National Academy of Sciences; President, Rockefeller Institute for Medical Research, New York

Shields WARREN, Scientific Director, Cancer Research Institute New England Deaconess Hospital, Boston, Mass.

Clinton P. ANDERSON, United States Senate

John O. PASTORE, United States Senate

Bourke B. HICKENLOOPER, United States Senate

John W. BRICKER, United States Senate

Carl T. DURHAM, United States House of Representatives

Chet HOLIFIELD, United States House of Representatives

W. Sterling COLE, United States House of Representatives

Carl HINSHAW, United States House of Representatives

Paul C. AEBERSOLD, Director, Isotopes Division, U. S. Atomic Energy Commission, Oak Ridge, Tennessee

Augustine Oliver ALLEN, Brookhaven National Laboratory, Upton, New York

William Freer BALE, Professor of Radiation Biology, University of Rochester School of Medicine, University of Rochester, Rochester, New York

Bernard G. BECHHOEFER, Special Assistant to the U. S. Representative for International Atomic Energy Agency Negotiations, Department of State

Clifford Keith BECK, Head, Department of Physics, North Carolina State College, Raleigh, North Carolina

Manson BENEDICT, Massachusetts Institute of Technology, Cambridge, Massachusetts

Seymour S. BERNSTEIN, Oak Ridge National Laboratory, Oak Ridge, Tennessee

Hans A. BETHE, Nuclear Studies Laboratory, Cornell University, Ithaca, New York

Douglas Sheldon BILLINGTON, Oak Ridge National Laboratory, Oak Ridge, Tennessee

Clifton R. BLINCOE, University of Missouri, Columbia, Missouri

Lowell Moyer BOLLINGER, Argonne National Laboratory, Lemont, Illinois

Harvey BROOKS, Professor of Applied Physics, Harvard University, Cambridge, Massachusetts

George Bosworth BROWN, Sloan-Kettering Institute for Cancer Research, New York, New York

Harrison Scott BROWN, Division of Geological Sciences, California Institute of Technology, Pasadena, California

Weldon Grant BROWN, Argonne National Laboratory, Lemont, Illinois

Lloyd Earl BROWNELL, Fission Products Laboratory, University of Michigan, Ann Arbor, Michigan

F. R. BRUCE, Associate Director, Chemical Technology Division, Oak Ridge National Laboratory, Oak Ridge, Tennessee

Marshall Herbert BRUCER, Oak Ridge Institute of Nuclear Studies, Oak Ridge, Tennessee

Austin Moore BRUES, Argonne National Laboratory, Lemont, Illinois

John C. BUGHER, Director, Division of Biology and Medicine, U. S. Atomic Energy Commission, Washington, D. C.

George O. BURR, Department of Physiology and Biochemistry, Experiment Station of Hawaiian Sugar Plantation, Honolulu, Hawaii

Richard S. CALDECOTT, Geneticist, Agricultural Research Service, Field Crops Research Branch, University of Minnesota, St. Paul, Minnesota

Alfred Dixon CALLIHAN, Oak Ridge National Laboratory, Oak Ridge, Tennessee

Melvin CALVIN, University of California Radiation Laboratory, Berkeley, California

George W. CASARETT, Department of Radiation Biology, University of Rochester, Rochester, New York

Benedict CASSEN, Chief, Medical Physics Section, University of California, Los Angeles, California

Walker L. CISLER, Detroit Edison Company, Detroit, Michigan

Dwight Edwin CLARK, Professor of Surgery, University of Chicago, Chicago, Illinois

Walter D. CLAUS, Chief, Biophysics Branch, Division of Biology and Medicine, U. S. Atomic Energy Commission, Washington, D. C.

Emanuel Richard COHEN, Theoretical Physics, North American Aviation, Downey, California

Karl Paley COHEN, Vice President, Walter Kidde Nuclear Laboratories, Garden City, New York

Cyril Lewis COMAR, Principal Scientist, Oak Ridge Institute of Nuclear Studies, Oak Ridge, Tennessee

Frederick P. COWAN, Brookhaven National Laboratory, Upton, New York

Lawrence CRANBERG, Los Alamos Scientific Laboratory, Los Alamos, New Mexico

James Homer CRAWFORD, Jr., Oak Ridge National Laboratory, Oak Ridge, Tennessee

Floyd Leroy CULLER, Jr., Director, Chemical Technology Division, Oak Ridge National Laboratory, Oak Ridge, Tennessee

Burris Bell CUNNINGHAM, University of California Radiation Laboratory, Berkeley, California

John Edward CUNNINGHAM, Head Metallurgist, Oak Ridge National Laboratory, Oak Ridge, Tennessee

Laughlin MacLaurin CURRIE, National Carbon Company, Cleveland, Ohio

Farrington DANIELS, University of Wisconsin, Madison, Wisconsin

Willard Kenneth DAVIS, Director, Division of Reactor Development, U. S. Atomic Energy Commission, Washington, D. C.

Robert Briggs DAY, Los Alamos Scientific Laboratory, Los Alamos, New Mexico

George Julian DIENES, Senior Physicist, Brookhaven National Laboratory, Upton, New York

Joseph Robert DIETRICH, Associate Director, Reactor Engineering Division, Argonne National Laboratory, Lemont, Illinois

Benjamin Clinton DIVEN, University of California, Los Alamos Scientific Laboratory, Los Alamos, New Mexico

Frank J. DIXON, Jr., University of Pittsburgh, Pittsburgh, Pennsylvania

Richard Lloyd DOAN, Phillips Petroleum Company, Idaho Falls, Idaho

Richard Wolford DODSON, Chairman, Chemistry Department, Brookhaven National Laboratory, Upton, New York

Joseph Edward DRALEY, Argonne National Laboratory, Lemont, Illinois

Samuel Edward EATON, Head of Radiochemistry Group, Arthur D. Little, Inc., Cambridge, Massachusetts

Merril EISENBUD, Manager, New York Operations Office, (Director, Health and Safety Laboratory), U. S. Atomic Energy Commission, New York, New York

Emanuel EPSTEIN, Agricultural Research Service, Department of Agriculture, Washington, D. C.

Leo Francis EPSTEIN, General Electric Company, Knolls Atomic Power Laboratory, Schenectady, New York

Gioacchino FAILLA, Director, Radiological Research Laboratory, Columbia University, New York, New York

Lee Edward FARR, Brookhaven National Laboratory, Upton, New York

Harold Morton FEDER, Argonne National Laboratory Lemont, Illinois

Don Ernest FERGUSON, Oak Ridge National Laboratory, Oak Ridge, Tennessee

Frank Gale FOOTE, Director, Metallurgy Division, Argonne National Laboratory, Lemont, Illinois

Richard F. FOSTER, General Electric Company, Richland, Washington

Marvin Fox, Chairman, Reactor Department, Brookhaven National Laboratory, Upton, New York

Paul F. GAST, General Electric Company, Richland, Washington

Albert GHIORSO, University of California, Radiation Laboratory, Berkeley, California

Lawrence Elgin GLENDENIN, Argonne National Laboratory, Lemont, Illinois

Raymond C. GOERTZ, Director, Remote Control Engineering Division, Argonne National Laboratory, Lemont, Illinois

Henri Jacob GOMBERG, Phoenix Project of University of Michigan, Ann Arbor, Michigan

David Harris GURINSKY, Head of Metallurgy Division, Brookhaven National Laboratory, Upton, New York

William O. HALL, United States Mission to the United Nations, New York, New York

R. Philip HAMMOND, Los Alamos Scientific Laboratory, University of California, Los Alamos, New Mexico

Joseph M. HARRER, Argonne National Laboratory, Lemont, Illinois

John Arthur HARVEY, Brookhaven National Laboratory, Upton, New York

Menelaus D. HASSIALIS, Project Director and Executive Officer, School of Mines, Columbia University, New York, New York

Robert J. HASTERLIK, Argonne Cancer Research Hospital, University of Chicago, Chicago, Illinois

Albert Baird HASTINGS, Professor of Biological Chemistry, Harvard Medical School, Boston, Massachusetts

William Westerfield HAVENS, Jr., Professor of Physics, Columbia University, New York, New York

Leland J. HAWORTH, Director, Brookhaven National Laboratory, Upton, New York

Gerhart Richard HENNIG, Argonne National Laboratory, Lemont, Illinois

William Alfred HIGINBOTHAM, Instrumentation Division, Brookhaven National Laboratory, Associated Universities, Inc., Upton, New York

James Clark HINDMAN, Argonne National Laboratory, Lemont, Illinois

Clarence Joseph HOCHANADEL, Oak Ridge National Laboratory, Oak Ridge, Tennessee

Frank Edward HOECKER, Radiation, Biophysics Program, University of Kansas, Lawrence, Kansas

Alexander HOLLAENDER, Oak Ridge National Laboratory, Oak Ridge, Tennessee

John P. HOWE, Nuclear Engineering and Manufacturing, North American Aviation, Inc., Downey, California

John Randolph HUFFMAN, Phillips Petroleum Company, Research and Development, U. S. Atomic Energy Commission, Idaho Falls, Idaho

Donald James HUGHES, Brookhaven National Laboratory, Upton, New York

Henry HURWITZ, Jr., General Electric Company—KAPL, Schenectady, New York

Earle Kenneth HYDE, University of California, Radiation Laboratory, Berkeley, California

Mark Gordon INGHRAM, Argonne National Laboratory, Lemont, Illinois

Dale W. JENKINS, Chairman, Institute of Animal Resources, National Research Council, Washington, D. C.

Jesse C. JOHNSON, Director, Division of Raw Materials, U. S. Atomic Energy Commission, Washington, D. C.

Thomas Hope JOHNSON, Director, Division of Research, U. S. Atomic Energy Commission, Washington, D. C.

Warren C. JOHNSON, Department of Chemistry, University of Chicago, Chicago, Illinois

William Harper JOHNSTON, Purdue University, Lafayette, Indiana

William Rudolph KANNE, General Electric Company—KAPL, Schenectady, New York

Irving KAPLAN, Head, Reactor Physics Division, Nuclear Engineering Department, Brookhaven National Laboratory, Upton, New York

Joseph J. KATZ, Senior Chemist, Argonne National Laboratory, Lemont, Illinois

Albert Rudolph KAUFMANN, Vice President, Nuclear Metals, Inc., Cambridge, Massachusetts

George Robert KEEPIN, Jr., Los Alamos Scientific Laboratory, Los Alamos, New Mexico

L. D. Percival KING, University of California, Los Alamos Scientific Laboratory, Los Alamos, New Mexico

Leonard John KOCH, Argonne National Laboratory, Lemont, Illinois

Daniel Edward KOSHLAND, Brookhaven National Laboratory, Upton, New York

Sidney KRASIK, Manager, PWY Physics Department, Westinghouse Atomic Power Division, Pittsburgh, Pennsylvania

Kurt A. KRAUS, Senior Chemist, Oak Ridge National Laboratory, Oak Ridge, Tennessee

James Arthur LANE, Oak Ridge National Laboratory, Oak Ridge, Tennessee

Clarence LARSON, Director, Oak Ridge National Laboratory Oak Ridge, Tennessee

John Seth LAUGHLIN, Department of Physics, Sloan-Kettering Institute for Cancer Research, New York, New York

Ernest O. LAWRENCE, University of California Radiation Laboratory, Berkeley, California

John Hundale LAWRENCE, Director, Donner Laboratory, University of California, Berkeley, California

Stephen LAWROSKI, Director of Chemical Engineering Division, Argonne National Laboratory, Lemont, Illinois

Robert Briggs LEACHMAN, Los Alamos, Scientific Laboratory, Los Alamos, New Mexico

Jan Felix LIBICH, American Embassy, Paris

Harold V. LICHTENBERGER, Director, Idaho Division, Argonne National Laboratory, Lemont, Illinois

Ernest Gustaf LINDER, Radio Corporation of America Laboratories, Princeton, New Jersey

Blake Marshall LORING, Department of Chemical Engineering, University of Maryland, College Park, Maryland

Richard Norton LYON, Oak Ridge National Laboratory, Oak Ridge, Tennessee

Winston Marvel MANNING, Director, Chemistry Division, Argonne National Laboratory, Lemont, Illinois

Bernard MANOWITZ, Fission Product Utilization Project, Brookhaven National Laboratory, Upton, New York

Joseph J. MARTIN, Associate Professor of Chemical and Metallurgical Engineering, Engineering Research Institute, Ann Arbor, Michigan

George G. MARVIN, Division of Raw Materials, U. S. Atomic Energy Commission, Washington, D. C.

Edward S. MASON, Dean, Graduate School of Public Administration, Harvard University, Cambridge, Massachusetts

Karl M. MAYER, Production Economist, U. S. Atomic Energy Commission, Washington, D. C.

C. Rogers McCULLOUGH, Research and Engineering Division, Monsanto Chemical Company, St. Louis, Missouri

William MITCHELL, General Counsel, U. S. Atomic Energy Commission, Washington, D. C.

Karl Ziegler MORGAN, Director, Health Physics Division, Oak Ridge National Laboratory, Oak Ridge, Tennessee

Samuel Brooks MORRIS, Department of Water and Power, Los Angeles, California

George Ashmun MORTON, Associate Director, Chemical-Physical Laboratory, RCA Laboratories, Princeton, New Jersey

Robert S. MULLIKEN, Science Attaché, American Embassy, London

William Frederick NEUMAN, Associate Professor of Pharmacology, University of Rochester, Rochester, New York

Robert D. NININGER, Division of Raw Materials, U. S. Atomic Energy Commission, Washington, D. C.

Eugene Pleasants ODUM, Professor of Zoology, University of Georgia, Athens, Georgia

David OKRENT, Argonne National Laboratory, Lemont, Illinois

Lincoln Ridler PAGE, Geological Survey, Department of the Interior, Washington, D. C.

Harry PALEVSKY, Brookhaven National Laboratory, Upton, New York

Herbert Myers PARKER, Hanford Atomic Products Operation, Radiological Sciences Department, Richland, Washington

William Edwards PARKINS, North American Aviation, Inc., Nuclear Engineering and Manufacturing, Downey, California

Morehead PATTERSON, U. S. Representative for International Atomic Energy Agency Negotiations, Department of State

Robert Allen PENNEMAN, Los Alamos Scientific Laboratory, Los Alamos, New Mexico

Bernard Emerson PROCTOR, Professor of Food Technology, Massachusetts Institute of Technology, Cambridge, Massachusetts

Roger R. D. REVELLE, Scripps Institute of Oceanography, University of California, La Jolla, California

Albert J. RIKER, University of Wisconsin, Madison, Wisconsin

Howard A. ROBINSON, Special Assistant to the Ambassador, American Embassy, Paris

Clement James RODDEN, New Brunswick Area Office, U. S. Atomic Energy Commission, New Brunswick, New Jersey

Joseph Foster Ross, University of California Medical Center, Los Angeles, California

Arthur Frederick RUPP, Superintendent, Operations Division, Oak Ridge National Laboratory, Oak Ridge, Tennessee

Liane Brauch RUSSELL, Oak Ridge National Laboratory, Oak Ridge, Tennessee

William Lawson RUSSELL, Principal Geneticist, Biology Division, Oak Ridge National Laboratory, Oak Ridge, Tennessee

Vance Lewis SAILOR, Brookhaven National Laboratory, Upton, New York

Jack SCHUBERT, Argonne National Laboratory, Lemont, Illinois

Glenn Theodore SEABORG, University of California, Radiation Laboratory, Chemical Division, Berkeley, California

Charles Harold SECOY, Oak Ridge National Laboratory, Oak Ridge, Tennessee

Frederick SEITZ, Department of Physics, University of Illinois, Urbana, Illinois

Stephen Matheson SHELTON, Bureau of Mines, U. S. Department of the Interior, Albany, Oregon

Sidney SIEGEL, North American Aviation, Inc., Downey, California

Leslie SILVERMAN, Associate Professor of Industrial Hygiene Engineering, Harvard University School of Public Health, Boston, Massachusetts

John Wistar SIMPSON, Westinghouse Atomic Power Division, Pittsburgh, Pennsylvania

Oliver Cecil SIMPSON, Associate Director of Chemistry, Argonne National Laboratory, Lemont, Illinois

Willard Ralph SINGLETON, Brookhaven National Laboratory, Upton, New York

Cyril Stanley SMITH, Director, Institute for the Study of Metals, University of Chicago, Chicago, Illinois

Gerard C. SMITH, Special Assistant to the Secretary of State on Atomic Energy Affairs, Department of State

Arthur Hawley SNELL, Oak Ridge National Laboratory, Oak Ridge, Tennessee

Thomas M. SNYDER, General Electric Company—KAPL, Schenectady, New York

Frank Harold SPEDDING, Ames Laboratory, Iowa State College, Ames, Iowa

George C. SPIEGEL, Office of the Special Assistant to the Secretary of State on Atomic Energy Affairs, Department of State

Bernard Israel SPINRAD, Senior Physicist, Reactor Engineering Division, Argonne National Laboratory, Lemont, Illinois

Philip SPORN, President, American Gas and Electric, Service Corporation, New York, New York

Chauncey STARR, North American Aviation, Inc., Downey, California

Eric STEIN, Office of United Nations Political Affairs, Department of State

Ellis Philip STEINBERG, Argonne National Laboratory, Lemont, Illinois

Robert Spences STONE, Radiological Laboratory, University of California Medical Center, San Francisco, California

John Arthur SWARTOUT, Deputy Research Director, Oak Ridge National Laboratory, Oak Ridge, Tennessee

William Herbert SWEET, Associate Clinical Professor of Surgery, Massachusetts General Hospital, Boston, Massachusetts

Richard Ferdinand TASCHEK, Los Alamos Scientific Laboratory, Los Alamos, New Mexico

Lauriston S. TAYLOR, Atomic and Radiation Physics Division, National Bureau of Standards, Washington, D. C.

Donald Earl THOMAS, LSR Metallurgy Section, Westinghouse Atomic Power Division, Westinghouse Electric Corporation, Bettis Field, Pittsburgh, Pennsylvania

Ray Elliott TOMLINSON, Hanford Atomic Products Operations General Electric Company, Richland, Washington

Thomas TROCKI, Knolls Atomic Power Laboratory, General Electric Company, Schenectady, New York

Harold Bradford TUKEY, Head, Department of Horticulture, Michigan State University, East Lansing, Michigan

John TURKEVICH, Princeton University, Frick Chemical Laboratory, Princeton, New Jersey

Bruce WALLACE, Geneticist, Long Island Biological Laboratory, Cold Spring Harbor, New York

Martin WALT, IV, Los Alamos Scientific Laboratory, Los Alamos, New Mexico

Joel WARREN, Science Attaché, American Embassy, Stockholm

Clifford Edward WEBER, Knolls Atomic Power Laboratory, General Electric Company, Schenectady, New York

Alvin M. WEINBERG, Oak Ridge National Laboratory, Oak Ridge, Tennessee

Victor F. WEISSKOPF, Massachusetts Institute of Technology, Cambridge, Massachusetts

Theodore Allen WELTON, Physicist, Oak Ridge National Laboratory, Oak Ridge, Tennessee

Harry WEXLER, Weather Bureau, Department of Commerce, Washington, D. C.

John Archibald WHEELER, Professor, Palmer Physical Laboratory, Princeton University, Princeton, New Jersey

Eugene Paul WIGNER, Professor of Mathematical Physics, Institute for Advanced Study, Princeton University, Princeton, New Jersey

Harley Almey WILHELM, Iowa State College of Agriculture and Mechanical Arts, Ames, Iowa

J. Ernest WILKINS, Jr., Nuclear Development Associates, Inc., White Plains, New York

Clarke WILLIAMS, Chairman, Nuclear Engineering Department, Brookhaven National Laboratory, Upton, New York

Abel WOLMAN, Professor of Sanitary Engineering, Johns Hopkins University, Baltimore, Maryland

Wallace Kelly WOODS, General Electric Company, Richland, Washington

Walter Henry ZINN, Director, Argonne National Laboratory, Lemont, Illinois

Assistants to the United States Representatives

Charles BATES, Assistant to the Chairman, United States Atomic Energy Commission, Washington, D. C.

Everett R. HOLLES, Assistant to the Chairman, United States Atomic Energy Commission, Washington, D. C.

William C. WAMPLER, Assistant to the Chairman, United States Atomic Energy Commission, Washington, D. C.

Executive Officer

Harry S. TRAYNOR, Assistant General Manager, United States Atomic Energy Commission

Assistant Executive Officer

George M. FENNEMORE, Office of International Conferences, Department of State

Special Assistant

Christopher L. HENDERSON, United States Atomic Energy Commission

Director, Office of Technical Programs and Exhibits

George L. WEIL, United States Atomic Energy Commission

Administrative Officer

Thomas O. JONES, United States Atomic Energy Commission

Historian

Laura FERMI, United States Atomic Energy Commission

Technical Writers

Norvell W. PAGE, United States Atomic Energy Commission

Roland SAWYER, United States Atomic Energy Commission

Stephen WHITE, United States Atomic Energy Commission

Technical Papers Officer

Paul W. McDANIEL, United States Atomic Energy Commission

Assistants

Stephen P. COBB, Jr., United States Atomic Energy Commission

Paul G. LEFEVRE, United States Atomic Energy Commission

Andrew W. McREYNOLDS, Brookhaven National Laboratory, Upton, New York

Scientific Secretaries

Robert Carson DALZELL, United States Atomic Energy Commission

Edward EPREMIAN, United States Atomic Energy Commission

George Andrew KOLSTAD, United States Atomic Energy Commission

Paul B. PEARSON, United States Atomic Energy Commission

Alvin RADKOWSKY, United States Atomic Energy Commission

Ulysses M. STAEBLER, United States Atomic Energy Commission

Reactor Officer

George G. MANOV, United States Atomic Energy Commission

Assistant

David F. COPE, United States Atomic Energy Commission

Exhibits Officer

Alberto F. THOMSON, United States Atomic Energy Commission

Assistant

Richard L. BRECKER, United States Information Agency

Director, Information Office

John P. McKNIGHT, United States Atomic Energy Commission

Deputies

Morse SALISBURY, United States Atomic Energy Commission

Joseph O. HANSON, United States Information Agency

Richard FRIEDMAN, Department of State

Media Service Officers

Charter HESLEP, United States Atomic Energy Commission

Albin E. JOHNSON, United States Atomic Energy Commission

Session Reporters

John F. HOGERTON, United States Atomic Energy Commission

Robert C. TUMBLESON, Oberlin School of Commerce, Oberlin, Ohio

Gordon M. DUNNING, United States Atomic Energy Commission

Director, Office of Liaison and Protocol

John A. HALL, United States Atomic Energy Commission

Director, Classification Office

Charles D. LUKE, United States Atomic Energy Commission

Deputy

Charles L. MARSHALL, United States Atomic Energy Commission

Co-Directors, Special Services Office

Daniel H. CLARE, Jr., Department of State

Bryan F. LAPLANTE, United States Atomic Energy Commission

Deputies

Richard G. CAVANAUGH, United States Atomic Energy Commission

Keith O. LYNCH, Department of State

Director, Administrative Office

Albert J. CIAFFONE, Department of State

URUGUAY

Dr. Felix LEBORGNE

Eng. German VILLAR

Eng. Walter HILL

VENEZUELA

Dr. Francisco J. DUARTE

Dr. Humberto FERNÁNDEZ MORÁN

Dr. Carlos Luis CARMONA

Dr. Marcel GRANIER

Dr. Marcel ROCHE

VIET NAM

M. NGUYEN QUANG TRINH, Recteur de l'Université Nationale du Viet Nam, Professeur à la Faculté des Sciences (chimie)

M. Pham Bieu Tam, Doyen des Facultés de Médecine et Pharmacie à Saïgon, Directeur technique de l'Institut du Cancer du Viet Nam

M. Pham Tinh Quat, Professeur de la Faculté des Sciences à Saïgon (Mathématiques)

YUGOSLAVIA

Professeur Pavle Savić, Membre de l'Académie, Vice-président de la Commission fédérale de l'Energie Nucléaire, Président du Conseil scientifique de l'Institut des Sciences Nucléaires "Boris Kidric"

Dr. Franc Kos, Ministre plénipotentiaire au Secrétariat d'Etat des Affaires Etrangères

Dr. Slobodan Nakićenović, Secrétaire de la Commission fédérale de l'énergie nucléaire

Dr. Ivan Supek, Professeur de l'Université, Membre de la Commission fédérale de l'énergie nucléaire

Dr. Stojan Pavlović, Membre de l'Académie

Mr. Miladin Radulović, Chef de la Direction pour les matières premières et membre de la Commission fédéralé de l'énergie nucléaire

Mr. Vojko Pavičić, Directeur de l'Institut des sciences nucléaires "Boris Kidric" et membre de la Commission fédérale de l'énergie nucléaire

Mr. Čedo Milićević, Directeur de la Commission de l'économie électrique yougoslave et membre de la Commission fédérale de l'énergie nucléaire

Dr. Dragoslav Popović, Collaborateur de l'Institut des sciences nucléaires "Boris Kidric"

Mr. Vjekoslav Mikinčić, Géologue, Président du Conseil d'administration de l'Institut fédéral de géologie

Mr. Milorad Ristić, Ing., membre de la Commission fédérale de l'énergié nucléaire

Dr. Bozo Težak, Professeur d'Université

Mr. Lado Kosta, Ing., collaborateur de l'Institut "Jozef Stefan"

Dr. Drago Grdenić, Membre de la Commission fédérale de l'énergie nucléaire

Mr. Janez Dekleva, Ing., collaborateur de l'Institut "Jozef Stefan"

Mr. Tomo Bosanac, Ing., collaborateur de l'Institut "Rudjer Boskovic", Ingénieur en chef de "Rade Koncar"

Dr. Dina Keglević, Collaborateur de l'Institut "Rudjer Boskovic"

Mr. Bela Bunji, Ing., directeur de l'Institut fédéral de technologie

Dr. Borivoje Damjanović, Collaborateur de l'Institut des sciences nucléaires "Boris Kidric"

Mr. Miodrag Petrovic, Ing. d'électricité, collaborateur de l'Institut des sciences nucléaires "Boris Kidric"

Mr. Slobodan Ribnikar, Chimiste, collaborateur de l'Institut des sciences nucléaries "Boris Kidric"

Mr. Bogoljub Jovanović, Secrétaire au Secrétariat d'Etat des Affaires étrangères

Mr. Milenko Šušić, Chimiste, collaborateur de l'Institut des sciences nucléaires "Boris Kidric"

Delegations of Specialized Agencies of the United Nations

INTERNATIONAL LABOUR OFFICE

Mr. David A. Morse, Director-General

Mr. C. W. Jenks, Assistant Director-General

Mr. J. L. Mowat, Chief, Special Research and Reports Division

Mr. M. Robert, Chief, Occupational Safety and Health Division

Mr. K. L. Goodall, H. M. Chemical Inspector of Factories, Factory Department, Ministry of Labour and National Service, London

FOOD AND AGRICULTURE ORGANIZATION OF THE UNITED NATIONS

Dr. F. T. Wahlen, Director of the Agriculture Division

Dr. R. A. Silow, Agriculture Division

UNITED NATIONS EDUCATIONAL SCIENTIFIC AND CULTURAL ORGANIZATION

Professor P. Auger, Director, Department of Natural Sciences

Professor N. B. Cacciapuoti, Deputy Director, Department of Natural Sciences

Dr. L. Kowarski

WORLD HEALTH ORGANIZATION

Dr. Pierre Dorolle, Deputy Director-General

Dr. V. A. Sutter, Assistant Director-General, Department of Advisory Services

Dr. A. L. Bravo, Chief, Section of Social and Occupational Health

Dr. G. Löfström, Chief, Section of Health Laboratory Methods

Dr. I. S. Eve, Medical Officer in charge of questions dealing with atomic energy and health

INTERNATIONAL CIVIL AVIATION ORGANIZATION

Mr. E. R. Marlin, Director of Technical Assistance and External Relations Officer

Mr. A. Munch, Technical Officer, Bureau of Air Navigation

INTERNATIONAL TELECOMMUNICATION UNION

Dr. Marco Aurelio Andrada, Secretary-General

Mr. Alfonso Catá, President of the International Frequency Registration Board

Mr. Georges Valensi, Director, International Telephone Consultative Committee

Professor Dr. Balth. van der Pol, Director, International Radio Consultative Committee

INTERNATIONAL BANK FOR RECONSTRUCTION AND DEVELOPMENT

Mr. Brian H. Colquhoun, Chief Engineering Adviser

Dr. Wayne Rembert

Mr. Corbin Allardice, Adviser on Atomic Energy

WORLD METEOROLOGICAL ORGANIZATION

Mr. D. A. Davies, Secretary-General

Dr. G. Swoboda, Acting Secretary-General

Mr. G. R. Rivet, Assisting Secretary-General

Dr. K. Langlo, Chief of Technical Division

Conference Secretariat

UNITED NATIONS SECRETARIAT

Under-Secretaries of the United Nations:
Dr. Ralph J. Bunche
Mr. Ilya S. Tchernychev
Special Adviser to the Secretary-General of the United Nations:
Dr. Gunnar Randers
Director of the European Office:
Mr. Adrian Pelt
Deputy-Director, European Office:
M. Georges Palthey

CONFERENCE SECRETARIAT

Conference Secretary-General:
Professor Walter G. Whitman
Deputy Conference Secretary-General:
Dr. Viktor S. Vavilov
Executive Assistant to the Conference
Secretary-General:
Mr. Brian E. Urquhart
Executive Officer to the Conference
Secretary-General:
Mr. Donald G. Sullivan
Administrative Officers:
Mr. Granville Fletcher
Miss Dagmar Schlesinger

Interpreting Service
G. S. Rabinovitch

Verbatim Reporting Service
G. R. Read

Meeting Services
G. J. Mathieu

Documents Control
S. Feiffer

Public Information
P. Aylen

Scientific Secretaries:
Dr. Robert A. Charpie
Dr. Frederic de Hoffmann
Dr. Donald J. Dewar
Dr. Nikolai A. Dobrotin

Dr. André Finkelstein
Dr. John Gaunt
Dr. Jakob Goedkoop
Dr. Reinosuke Hara
Dr. Elwyn O. Hughes
Dr. Leonard F. Lamerton
Dr. Jose Leite Lopes
Dr. Derrik J. Littler
Dr. Aleksander Milojevic
Dr. Carlo Polvani
Dr. Brahm Prakash
Dr. Ivan D. Rojanski
Dr. Abdus Salam
Dr. César A. Sastre
Dr. Michael Trocheris
Dr. Ivan Ulehla
Moderator of the Panel on Uranium and Thorium Occurrences:
Prof. P. Kerr
United Nations:
Mr. N. B. Guyol
Father E. S. de Breuvery
Mr. Pierre Sevette

EUROPEAN OFFICE CONFERENCE SECRETARIAT

Finance and Administrative Services
P. Coïdan

Languages Division
F. Veillet-Lavallée

Rooms and Technical Services
A. Renn

Customs, Transport and Restaurant Services
F. S. Roulet

Distribution of Documents
F. R. Hapgood

Printing of Documents
E. E. Butterworth

Assistants to the Deputy Director
R. Bernard
A. Bovay

Journal of the Conference
P. Garaud

Office of Conference Services and Liaison
Miss J. L. Day

Outside the meeting halls. *Left:* Delegates discussing problems between sessions. *Right:* Mr. D. Mauricio Buhlar (Argentina) and Mr. D. Arturo Cairo (Argentina) sorting slides for one of the sessions

ANNEX II

RULES OF PROCEDURE

Rules of Procedure of the International Conference on the Peaceful Uses of Atomic Energy

Convened in Geneva on 8 August 1955, in Pursuance of Resolution
810 (IX) of the General Assembly of the United Nations of 4
December 1954

CHAPTER I. AGENDA, PARTICIPATION AND CREDENTIALS

Rule 1

The Conference shall consider items included in the detailed Agenda and Programme prepared by the Secretary-General of the United Nations with the advice of the Advisory Committee in accordance with paragraph 5 of resolution 810 (IX) of the General Assembly of 4 December 1954, and circulated to the invitees to the Conference on 1 February.

Rule 2

Each State invited to the Conference in accordance with paragraph 3 of resolution 810 (IX) of the General Assembly may be represented at the Conference by not more than five representatives, including, to the extent possible, individual experts competent in the atomic energy field. The representatives may be accompanied by such number of advisers as may be required, in the general interest of the Conference, to ensure adequate presentation and discussion of technical papers.

Rule 3

The representation of each interested specialized agency, invited to the Conference in accordance with paragraph 7 of resolution 810 (IX) of the General Assembly, should be on the basis of an agreement with the Secretary-General of the United Nations, bearing in mind that such representation shall not exceed five for any specialized agency.

Rule 4

The list of representatives of each participating State shall be issued either by the Head of the State, or Government, or by the Minister of Foreign Affairs or his nominee and communicated to the Conference Secretary-General in good time and in any case not less than fourteen days before the convening of the Conference. Lists of proposed advisers shall be sent to the Conference Secretary General not less than fourteen days in advance of the opening of the Conference

Rule 5

The Conference Secretary General, in consultation with the representatives designated by the Secretary-General of the United Nations as President and Vice-Presidents of the Conference, shall examine the lists of representatives, which shall constitute the credentials of the representatives to the Conference, and shall circulate to the Conference for its information a report on this examination.

CHAPTER II. OFFICERS OF CONFERENCE

Rule 6

The officers of the Conference shall comprise the following: The President, the Vice-Presidents, the Chairmen and Vice-Chairmen of sessions. They shall be appointed by the Secretary-General of the United Nations in advance of the Conference from among representatives eminent in the fields of concern to the Conference, and in their selection regard shall be had to an equitable geographical distribution of posts.

The Conference Secretary General shall also be an officer of it.

The Secretary-General of the United Nations shall place the list of officers before the Conference at its first plenary session for affirmation.*

Rule 7

The Secretariat of the Conference shall comprise a Conference Secretary General, his Deputy and such other staff provided by the Secretary-General of the United Nations as may be required by the Conference.

Rule 8

The Conference Secretary General, acting under the authority of the Secretary-General of the United Nations, and in accordance with the rules and obligations applying to members of the United Nations Secretariat, shall be primarily responsible for the preparation of the Conference and for making all necessary arrangements for meetings, and shall direct all other work connected with the Conference. He may designate another member of the Conference Secretariat to take his place at any meeting of the Conference.

Rule 9

The Conference Secretary General and his Deputy may, subject to the provisions of rule 11, make oral as well as written statements to the Conference concerning any matter relating to it.

CHAPTER III. ORGANIZATION OF THE WORK OF THE CONFERENCE

Rule 10

The work of the Conference shall be conducted in plenary meetings and in meetings of sessions, in accordance with a programme prepared and distributed to participants in advance of the Conference by the Secretary-General of the United Nations in consultation with the Advisory Committee.

---

* It is the view of the Advisory Committee and the Secretary-General that, it being desirable to avoid nominations of and debate on officers in a Conference of this nature and size, and since there is important work to be done by the Officers of the Conference during its preparatory stage, the sense of this Rule is that the Conference would approve the list of officers by acclamation.

Rule 11

The President shall declare the opening and closing of each plenary meeting of the Conference, accord the right to speak and, subject to these rules of procedure, shall have complete control of the proceedings in the meeting and the maintenance of order therein. The President may call a speaker to order if his remarks are not relevant to the subject under discussion. He may limit the time to be allowed to speakers, limit the number of times each participant may speak on any question, close the list of speakers or close the discussions. He may suspend or adjourn a meeting or adjourn the discussion on the item under consideration.

Rule 12

Participants may address meetings of the Conference only through recognition by the presiding officer. The presiding officer shall call upon speakers in the order in which they express their desire to speak

Rule 13

No proposals requiring adoption by voting shall be submitted or entertained by the Conference. The presiding officer of any meeting may, however, ascertain the sense of the meeting on matters not relating to the substance of an item on the agenda.

Rule 14

At the request of the President, one of the Vice-Presidents designated by the President may preside over any plenary meeting of the Conference. A Vice-President acting as President shall have the same powers and duties as the President.

Rule 15

The meetings of each session of the Conference shall be presided over by the Chairman of the session, whose powers and functions shall be similar to those of the President of the Conference at plenary meetings as provided in rules 11 and 12.

Rule 16

The Vice-Chairman of each session shall keep the President and the Conference Secretary General informed of the progress, trends and major points emerging in the discussions of the session.

CHAPTER IV. LANGUAGES

Rule 17

English, French, Russian and Spanish shall be the languages of the Conference.

Rule 18

Speeches made in one of the languages of the Conference shall be interpreted into its other languages.

Rule 19

A participant may employ a language other than one of the four languages of the Conference subject to the condition that he shall himself provide for interpretation into one of the four languages. Interpretation into the other languages by an interpreter of the Secretariat may be based on the interpretation given in the first language.

CHAPTER V. RECORDS

Rule 20

Verbatim records of all plenary and session meetings shall be established by the Secretariat in the four languages. These records shall be for inclusion in the Proceedings of the Conference. They shall be available in provisional form to participants in the Conference as soon as possible.

CHAPTER VI. PUBLICITY OF MEETINGS

Rule 21

All plenary and session meetings of the Conference shall be held in public.

CHAPTER VII. PUBLICATION OF PROCEEDINGS

Rule 22

The Proceedings of the Conference, which shall be compiled by the Conference Secretary General, shall be published by the Secretary-General of the United Nations in the languages of the Conference and shall include, in addition to introductory material relating to the convening of the Conference, its organization and composition, the records of plenary and session meetings and all Conference papers, as provided in Rule C of the Annex to these Rules, together with the abstracts referred to in Rule B of the Annex.

Rule 23

In addition to the distribution of the Proceedings of the Conference to the participating Governments and specialized agencies, each officer of the Conference and each author of a paper accepted for the Conference shall be entitled to one copy without cost.

CHAPTER VIII. EXPENSES

Rule 24

Expenses of whatever nature incurred by participants in the Conference shall not be an obligation of the United Nations. All other costs involved in holding the Conference shall be defrayed by the United Nations.

ANNEX

Rule A

The subjects of all papers shall be in conformity with the purpose of the Conference as defined in resolution 810 (IX) of the General Assembly and accordingly shall be dealt with and presented only from the scientific and technical points of view.

Rule B

Papers for presentation at the Conference shall be submitted to the Secretary-General of the United Nations in original and three copies, in one of the languages of the Conference. An abstract of each paper in original and three copies, not exceeding 500 words, shall also be submitted. In order to facilitate the preparations for the Conference, abstracts and full texts of papers should be submitted at the earliest possible date. In any case, the full texts of the papers themselves shall be submitted to the Secretary-General of the United Nations not later than 1 July, while the titles and abstracts shall be submitted, if possible, not later than 15 May. Supplements to papers, where necessary to bring them up to date, may be submitted up to 1 August.

Rule C

All papers submitted by participants in the Conference, if they conform to Rule A, shall be considered as Conference papers and, whether or not presented orally at a session of the Conference in full or in part, shall be included in the Proceedings of the Conference. Since, owing to limitations of time, all papers submitted cannot be presented orally at the Conference, a selection of those papers to be presented orally in full or in part shall be made by a panel (or panels) of qualified scientists, designated by the Secretary-General of the United Nations on the advice of the Advisory Committee, and serving for this purpose as members of the United Nations Secretariat. The Secretary-General shall consult with the Advisory Committee on the results of such review.

Rule D

Assignments by Governments for the preparation of papers for the Conference should be offered only to their own nationals.

Rule E

All papers prepared and submitted in advance in accordance with Rule B shall be distributed without delay to all States participating in the Conference for their confidential information before the opening of the Conference. With regard to communications which may not have been submitted in advance of the opening of the Conference, such communications shall be distributed to the participants as soon as possible after their submission to the Secretary-General of the United Nations or their delivery before the Conference.

The press being briefed by the chairman, vice-chairman and scientific secretaries of a session

ANNEX III

NUMERICAL INDEX OF PAPERS

Paper	Title	Author or Authors	Session	Volume
P/68	Liquid scintillation counting of natural radiocarbon	F. N. Hayes et al.	20C.1	XIV
P/69	Mechanical arms incorporating a sense of feel for conducting experiments with radioactive materials	J. R. Burnett et al.	19C.3	XIV
P/70	Absolute dosimetry of cobalt-60 gamma rays	J. S. Laughlin et al.	20C.2	XIV
P/71	Dosimetry of ionizing particles	G. Failla	20C.4	XIV
P/72	Irreversibility of damage produced by alpha emitters	J. N. Stannard et al.	11C	XI
P/73	Mechanism of uranium poisoning	H. C. Hodge	17C.2	XIII
P/74	Experimental data useful in establishing maximum permissible single and multiple exposures to polonium	D. S. Anthony et al.	17C.1	XIII
P/75	Potentiated lethal action of radioisotopes used in combination	H. L. Friedell and P. R. Salerno	11C	XI
P/76	Radiation dosage to lungs from radon and its daughter products	W. F. Bale and J. Shapiro	17C.2	XIII
P/77	Hazards to the embryo and fetus from ionizing radiation	L. B. Russell and W. L. Russell	11C	XI
P/78	Studies on protection by treatment before and after exposure to X and gamma radiation	A. Hollaender and G. E. Stapleton	12C	XI
P/79	Maximum permissible concentration of radioisotopes in air and water for short periods of exposure	K. Z. Morgan et al.	17C.1	XIII
P/80	Internal emitters and tumor induction	M. P. Finkel	11C	XI
P/81	Biological effects of fast neutrons and gamma rays	J. W. Clark et al.	11C	XI
P/82	Commentary on the modes of radiation injury	A. M. Brues	11C	XI
P/83	Studies on the biological basis of radiosensitivity	T. N. Tahmisian	12C	XI
P/84	Medical care of wounds contaminated with radioactive materials	A. J. Finkel and E. A. Hathaway	12C	XI
P/85	Industrial hygiene of uranium processing	M. Eisenbud and J. A. Quigley	17C.2	XI
P/86	Transportation of large quantities of radioactive materials	H. Blatz	19C	XIV
P/87	Relative biological effectiveness	G. D. Adams et al.	12C	XI
P/88	The deposition of radioactive substances in bone	F. E. Hoecker	11C	XI
P/89	Maximum permissible exposure standards	R. S. Stone	17C.1	XIII
P/90	Radioisotopes in animal physiology and nutrition-mineral metabolism	C. L. Comar	15C.1	XII
P/91	The mechanism of gastric acid secretion as revealed by radioisotopes	C. A. M. Hogben	15C.1	XII
P/92	Time relation between potassium K^{42} outflux, action potential and contraction phase of heart muscle as revealed by the effluogram	W. S. Wilde et al.	15C.1	XII
P/93	Isotopes in research on animal nutrition and metabolism	M. Kleiber et al.	15C.1	XII
P/94	Use of partial-cell irradiation in studies of cell division	R. E. Zirkle et al.	12C	XI
P/95	Use of radioactive iodine (I^{131}) and thyroxine to determine the thyroid hormone secretion of intact animals	E. P. Reineke and H. A. Henneman	15C.1	XII
P/96	Respiratory carbon-14 patterns and physiological state	B. M. Tolbert et al.	15C.1	XII
P/97	Studies on the mechanism of phytohormone damage by ionizing radiations	S. A. Gordon	12C	XI
P/98	Metabolism of radioisotope-labelled drugs	P. K. Smith	16C	XII
P/99	Studies of brain potassium in relation to the adrenal cortex	J. R. Bergen et al.	15C.1	XII
P/100	Use of radioisotopes in tracing fungicidal action	L. P. Miller and S. E. A. McCallan	14C	XII
P/101	Ionizing radiations as tool for plant breeders	R. S. Caldecott	13C.2	XII
P/102	Withdrawn			
P/103	Resistance to rust induced by ionizing radiations in wheat and oats	W. M. Myers et al.	13C.2	XII
P/104	Applications of radioisotopes to the study of soils and fertilizers: A review	L. A. Dean	14C	XII
P/105	The use of radioactive isotopes to ascertain the role of root-grafting in the translocation of water, nutrients, and disease-inducing organisms among forest trees	J. E. Kuntz and A. J. Riker	14C	XII
P/106	Utilization of radioactive isotopes in resolving the effectiveness of foliar absorption of plant nutrients	H. B. Tukey et al.	14C	XII
P/107	The comparative effect of radiation and hybridization in plant breeding	W. C. Gregory	13C.2	XII
P/108	Absorption of radioactive sulphur by the fruit system in comparison to the roots of peanuts	H. C. Harris	14C	XII

Paper	Title	Author or Authors	Session	Volume
	USA			
P/467	Alternate energy sources (unconventional types)	F. Daniels	2.1	I
P/468	The role of energy and the role of nuclear energy in the United States	P. Sporn	5	I
P/469	A century of growth of electric power requirements in the United States	E. T. Hughes and N. C. Nelson	2.2	I
P/470	Nuclear fuel for the world power program	J. C. Johnson	6B	VI
P/471	Natural occurrence of uranium in the United States	United States Geological Survey and the United States Atomic Energy Commission	6B	VI
P/472	Uranium in terrestrial sedimentary rocks in the United States exclusive of the Colorado Plateau	W. I. Finch	6B	VI
P/473	Uranium-vanadium-copper deposits on the Colorado Plateau	R. P. Fischer	6B	VI
P/474	Examples of uranium deposits in the Upper Jurassic Morrison Formation on the Colorado Plateau	P. H. Dodd	6B	VI
P/475	A study of the economic potential of nuclear energy	K. M. Mayer	5	I
P/476	Economics of nuclear power	J. A. Lane	4.1	I
P/477	Capital investment required for nuclear energy	W. K. Davis	3.2	I
P/478	Physical dosimetry and clinical observances on four human beings involved in an accidental critical assembly excursion	R. J. Hasterlik and L. D. Marinelli	6.1	XI
P/479	Radium inhalation accident—radium excretion study	W. B. Looney *et al.*	6.1	XI
P/480	Consideration of the total environment in power reactor waste disposal	E. P. Odum	18C.2	XIII
P/481	Experimental determinations of the self-regulation and safety of operating water-moderated reactors	J. R. Dietrich	6.2	XIII
P/482	Environmental effects of a major reactor disaster	H. M. Parker and J. W. Healy	6.2	XIII
P/483	Radiological monitoring of a nuclear release	C. W. Sill *et al.*	6.2	XIII
P/484	The nuclear reactor in basic science	A. H. Snell	8A.1	II
P/485	The materials testing reactor—experimental program and reactor operation	R. L. Doan and J. R. Huffman	8A.2	II
P/486	Research program and operating experience on ORNL reactors	M. E. Ramsey and C. D. Cagle	8A.2	II
P/487	Operation, training and research experiences with the Raleigh Research Reactor	C. Beck	8A.2	II
P/488	Design and description of water boiler reactors	L. D. P. King	9A	II
P/489	The "Swimming Pool"—a low cost reactor for research and medicine	W. M. Breazeale *et al.*	9A	II
P/490	The materials testing reactor and related research reactors	A. M. Weinberg *et al.*	9A	II
P/491	A developmental fast neutron breeder reactor	A. Amorosi *et al.*	12A	III
P/492	A graphite-moderated nuclear power plant design	R. K. Anderson *et al.*	11A	III
P/493	A sodium graphite reactor 75,000 electrical kilowatt power plant	C. Starr	11A	III
P/494	Liquid metal fuel reactor	F. T. Miles and C. Williams	11A	III
P/495	Heavy water reactors for industrial power including boiling reactors	H. P. Iskenderian *et al.*	12A	III
P/496	Aqueous homogeneous power reactors	R. B. Briggs and J. A. Swartout	12A	III
P/497	The engineering design of a prototype boiling water reactor power plant	J. M. Harrer *et al.*	13A	III
P/498	The homogeneous reactor test	S. E. Beall and J. A. Swartout	13A	III
P/499	The sodium reactor experiment	W. E. Parkins	14A	III
P/500	Los Alamos power reactor experiments	D. Froman *et al.*	13A	III
P/501	The engineering design of a prototype fast neutron reactor power plant	A. H. Barnes *et al.*	14A	III
P/502	Rock alteration criteria in the search for uranium	P. F. Kerr	7B	VI
P/503	Techniques for prospecting for uranium and thorium	Staffs of the United States Geological Survey and the United States Atomic Energy Commission	7B	VI
P/504	Geologic prospecting for uranium and thorium	L. R. Page	7B	VI
P/505	Heavy-mineral prospecting	W. C. Overstreet *et al.*	7B	VI

Paper	Title	Author or Authors	Session	Volume
P/546	Decontamination of irradiated reactor fuels by fractional distillation processes using uranium hexafluoride	H. H. Hyman *et al.*	22B.1	IX
P/547	Nuclear reactor fuel dissolution	D. L. Foster *et al.*	21B	IX
P/548	The removal of fission products from stainless steel	D. O. Campbell	21B	IX
P/549	High level sampling devices for radiochemical plants	J. W. Landry	21B	IX
P/550	High temperature processing systems for liquid-metal fuels and breeder blankets	O. E. Dwyer *et al.*	22B.1	IX
P/551	The chemical processing of aqueous homogeneous reactor fuel	D. E. Ferguson	21B	IX
P/552	The design and operation of high level waste storage facilities	C. R. Anderson and C. A. Rohrmann	22B.2	IX
P/553	Processes for high level waste disposal	L. P. Hatch *et al.*	22B.2	IX
P/554	Disposal of high level radioactive liquid wastes in terrestrial pits	E. G. Struxness *et al.*	23B.1	IX
P/555	Physical metallurgy of uranium	F. G. Foote	18B.1	IX
P/556	The metallurgy of thorium and its alloys	O. N. Carlson *et al.*	18B.1	IX
P/557	Thermal cycling effects in uranium	H. H. Chiswik and L. R. Kelman	18B.1	IX
P/558	The alloys of uranium	H. A. Saller and F. A. Rough	18B.1	IX
P/559	The technology of UO_2 and ThO_2	J. R. Johnson and C. E. Curtis	18B.2	IX
P/560	*Withdrawn*			
P/561	Dispersion type fuel elements	C. E. Weber and H. H. Hirsch	18B.2	IX
P/562	Preparation, properties, and cladding of aluminium-uranium alloys	H. A. Saller	18B.2	IX
P/563	*Withdrawn*			
P/564	Problems of ground disposal of nuclear wastes	C. V. Theis	23B.1	IX
P/565	Disposal of liquid wastes to the ground	R. E. Brown *et al.*	23B.1	IX
P/566	*Withdrawn*			
P/567	The variation of effluent concentrations from an elevated point source	M. E. Smith	23B.3	IX
P/568	*Withdrawn*			
P/569	Disposal of radioactive wastes at sea	C. E. Renn	23B.2	IX
P/570	*Withdrawn*			
P/571	Air and gas cleaning for nuclear energy processes	L. Silverman	23B.3	IX
P/572	Radiation from clouds of reactor debris	J. Z. Holland	6.2	XIII
P/573	Techniques for measuring elastic, non-elastic and transport neutron cross sections	R. F. Taschek	15A	IV
P/574	Pulsed accelerator slow neutron velocity spectrometers	W. W. Havens, Jr.	15A	IV
P/575	*Withdrawn*			
P/576	Neutron velocity selectors used at reactors	D. J. Hughes	15A	IV
P/577	Time-of-flight techniques applied to fast neutron measurements	L. Cranberg	15A	IV
P/578	Van de Graaff and Cockcroft-Walton accelerators for fast neutron cross-section measurements	T. W. Bonner	16A.1	IV
P/579	Neutron diffraction research in the United States	E. O. Wollen and C. G. Shull	6A	II
P/580	Recent advances in neutron detection	L. M. Bollinger	15A	IV
P/581	Gamma rays from inelastic neutron scattering	R. B. Day	6A	II
P/582	Techniques for measurement of neutron cross-sections and energy spectra for sources which are continuous in energy and time	L. Rosen	15A	IV
P/583	Analysis of low energy neutron resonances	E. Melkonian	18A	IV
P/584	Cyclotrons designed for precision fast neutron cross-section measurements	R. L. Thornton *et al.*	15A	IV
P/585	Theoretical analysis of neutron resonances in fissile materials	H. A. Bethe	18A	IV
P/586	The low energy cross-section of U^{235}	V. L. Sailor	17A	IV
P/587	Measurement of capture to fission ratio of U^{235}, U^{233} and Pu^{239} by a new method	H. Pavelsky	18A	IV
P/588	Angular distributions and non-elastic neutron scattering	M. Walt *et al.*	6A	II
P/589	The total and fission cross-section of plutonium	B. R. Leonard, Jr.	17A	IV
P/590	Status of information on reactor material cross-sections	H. Hurwitz, Jr.	18A	IV
P/591	Summary of cross-section measurements of the fission product poison, Xe^{135}, as a function of energy	S. Bernstein and E. C. Smith	16A.2	IV

USSR

Paper	Title	Author or Authors	Session	Volume
P/673	Metal research "hot" laboratory	N. F. Pravdjuk	8B.2	VII
P/674	On methods of separation of neptunium from plutonium	I. K. Shvetsov and A. M. Vorobyev	10B.2	VII
P/675	Electrodeposition of plutonium, americium and curium	V. B. Dedov and V. N. Kosyakov	10B.3	VII
P/676	Spectrophotometric studies of the behaviour of americium ions in solutions	G. N. Yakovlev and V. N. Kosyakov	10B.3	VII
P/677	Coprecipitation of americium(V) with double carbonates of uranium(VI) or plutonium(VI) with potassium	G. N. Yakovlev and S. S. Gorbenko-Germanov	10B.2	VII
P/678	The sulphate method of separating plutonium and neptunium	B. V. Kurchatov et al.	10B.2	VII
P/679	Radiolysis of water in the presence of H_2 and O_2 under the action of reactor irradiations, fission fragments and X-rays	P. I. Dolin and B. W. Ershler	12B	VII
P/680	The effect of irradiation on the structure and properties of structural materials	S. T. Konobeevsky et al.	11B	VII
P/681	Effect of irradiation on structure and properties of fissionable materials	S. T. Konobeevsky et al.	11B	VII
P/682	Radiation chemical processes in inorganic systems	V. I. Veselovsky	12B	VII
P/683	Radiolytic oxidation of organic compounds	N. A. Bach	12B	VII
P/684	Experience in clinical and diagnostic application of some radioactive isotopes in the USSR	M. N. Fateyeva	9C	X
P/685	Medical application of some radioactive isotopes	A. V. Kozlova	8C	X
P/686	Investigation of the incorporation of amino acids into proteins *in vivo* and *in vitro*	V. N. Orekhovich	16C	XII
P/687	The application of radioactive phosphorus in investigating the processes of phosphorylation	S. E. Severin	16C	XII
P/688	The role of radioactive isotopes in investigating the physiology and biochemistry of digestion	K. S. Zamychkina and D. E. Grodzensky	15C.1	XII
P/689	Health protection of workers exposed to ionizing radiations	A. A. Letavet	17C.1	XIII
P/690	The biological effect of ionizing radiation on microorganisms	M. N. Meissel	12C	XI
P/691	On the nature of changes in metabolism under irradiation effects	N. M. Sissakian	12C	XI
P/692	Some aspects of the immunity of the organism exposed to ionizing radiation	I. A. Pigalyev	11C	XI
P/693	On the early reactions of the organism to irradiation depending on the site of application	G. M. Frank	11C	XI
P/694	The use of tracer atoms in studying the application of fertilizers	V. M. Klechkovski	14C	XII
P/695	Determination of the availability of soil phosphates and fertilizers with the aid of radioactive isotopes of phosphorus	A. V. Sokolov	14C	XII
P/696	Analysis of the movement of substances in plants by means of radioactive isotopes	A. L. Kursanov	14C	XII
P/697	Tracer atoms used to study the products of photosynthesis depending on the conditions under which the process takes place	A. A. Nichiporovich	15C.2	XII
P/698	Application of the isotope method to the study of absorption of electrolytes by soils in connection with land improvement	I. N. Antipov-Karatayev	14C	XII
P/699	Utilization of ionizing radiations in agriculture	A. M. Kuzin	14C	XII
P/700	Application of radioactive isotopes to the study of processes of photosynthesis and chemosynthesis in lakes	S. I. Kuznetsov	15C.2	XII
P/701	Research by means of radioactive isotopes concerning penetration into and residues of phosphoorganic insecticides in plants	K. A. Gar and R. Y. Kipiani	14C	XII
P/702	Investigation of diffusion and atomic interaction in alloys with the aid of radioactive isotopes	G. V. Kurdiumov	21C.3	XV
P/703	Distribution and diffusion of components in metal alloys studied by the autoradiographic method	S. T. Kishkin and S. Z. Bokstein	21C.3	XV
P/704	Application of radioisotopes to control technological processes	B. S. Sotskov et al.	22C	XV
P/705	The application of radioactive isotopes in gamma-ray radiography	S. T. Nazarov	22C	XV
P/706	Application of radioactive isotopes in chemical analysis	I. P. Alimarin	21C.2	XV
P/707	The use of artificially radioactive isotopes in the study of the processes of the production of steel and iron	A. M. Samarin	22C	XV
P/708	Application of tracer atoms in the study of the mechanism of chemical reactions	V. N. Kondratyev	21C.1	XV

Paper	Title	Author or Authors	Session	Volume

UKRAINIAN SSR

P/709	The use of radioactive isotopes in the study of the analytical chemistry of zirconium and hafnium	N. S. Poluectov	17B.1	VIII
P/710	The use of radioactive isotopes in the study of the functional biochemistry of the brain	A. V. Palladin and G. E. Vladimirov	16C	XII
P/711	The application of radioactive isotopes to the study of the biochemistry of muscles	D. L. Ferdman	10C	X
P/712	An investigation of cobalt diffusion in cobalt-aluminium and cobalt-nickel-manganese alloys with the aid of the radioactive isotope, cobalt-60	S. D. Gertsricken and I. Y. Dekhtyar	21C.3	XV
P/713	The use of radioactive isotopes in the study of wear of machine parts	D. B. Grozin	22C	XV
P/714	Inelastic scattering of fast neutrons by atomic nuclei	M. V. Pasechnik	6A	II

BYELORUSSIAN SSR

P/715	C^{14} in the study of the biosynthesis of chlorophyll	T. N. Godnev and A. A. Shlik	15C.2	XII
P/716	Co^{60} in the study of the role of cobalt as a microelement in the nutrition of plants	O. K. Kedrov-Zikhman	14C	XII

USA

P/717	*Withdrawn*			
P/718	Spontaneous fission correlations	A. Ghiorso	8B.1	VII
P/719	Solvent extraction chemistry of fission products	F. R. Bruce	9B.1	VII
P/720	*Withdrawn*			
P/721	Determination of pile constants by chemical methods	C. E. Crouthamel and E. Turk	8B.1	VII
P/722	Laboratory handling of radioactive materials	N. B. Garden	8B.2	VII
P/723	Hot laboratory facilities and techniques for handling radioactive material	S. E. Dismuke *et al.*	8B.2	VII
P/724	Chemical processing in intense radiation fields	R. P. Hammond	9B.1	VII
P/725	Hot laboratory facilities for a wide variety of radiochemical problems	P. R. Fields and H. Youngquist	8B.2	VII
P/726	Thermodynamics of the heavy elements	B. B. Cunningham	10B.1	VII
P/727	*Withdrawn*			
P/728	Radiochemical separations methods for the actinide elements	E. K. Hyde	10B.2	VII
P/729	Rare earth and transplutonium element separations by ion exchange methods	D. C. Stewart	10B.2	VII
P/730	The chemistry and crystal chemistry of heavy element compounds	S. Fried and W. H. Zachariasen	10B.1	VII
P/731	Hydrolytic behaviour of the heavy elements	K. A. Kraus	10B.1	VII
P/732	Effective capture cross-sections of Pa^{233} and Np^{239} for thermal reactor neutrons	J. Halperin *et al.*	10B.1	VII
P/733	The properties of plutonium hexafluoride	J. G. Malm and B. Weinstock	10B.3	VII
P/734	Recent developments in the chemistry of thorium	L. I. Katzin	10B.3	VII
P/735	Vapor pressure of liquid plutonium	T. E. Phipps *et al.*	10B.3	VII
P/736	Some recent developments in the chemistry of neptunium	D. Cohen *et al.*	10B.3	VII
P/737	Recent developments in the chemistry of uranium oxygen system	H. R. Hoekstra and S. Siegel	10B.3	VII
P/738	A survey of recent American research in the radiation of aqueous solutions	A. O. Allen	12B	VII
P/739	The radiation-induced reaction of hydrogen and oxygen in water at 25°C to 250°C	C. J. Hochanadel	12B	VII
P/740	The effects of reactor radiation upon high temperature static water systems	J. R. Humphreys	12B	VII
P/741	The decomposition of water by fission recoil particles	J. W. Boyle *et al.*	12B	VII
P/742	Organics as reactor moderator-coolants: some aspects of their thermal and radiation stabilities	R. O. Bolt and J. G. Carroll	12B	VII
P/743	Radiation damage to radiochemical processing reagents	G. I. Cathers	11B	VII
P/744	Radiation damage in reactor materials	D. S. Billington	11B	VII
P/745	Irradiation effects in uranium and its alloys	S. H. Paine and J. H. Kittel	11B	VII
P/746	Irradiation damage to artificial graphite	W. K. Woods *et al.*	11B	VII
P/747	The effects of irradiation on structural materials	F. E. Faris	11B	VII

Paper	Title	Author or Authors	Session	Volume
P/783	Swedish Atomic Energy Company—a co-operation between Government and private industry	H. Brynielsson	4.3	XIII
P/784	Recovery of uranium from uranium-bearing alum shale	E. Svenke	14B	VIII
P/785	The extraction of uranium and plutonium with tetrabutylammonium nitrate, cupferron and neocupferron as complexing agents	E. Haeffner *et al.*	21B	IX
P/786	The solid state reaction between uranium and aluminium	R. Kiessling	18B.1	IX
P/787	Observations on the corrosion of uranium in liquid sodium	H. Mogard	19B.3	IX
P/788	Properties of electrostatic precipitators for the measurement of radioactive aerosols	A. Bergstedt	23B.3	IX
P/789	Measurements on a subcritical reactor with a pulsed neutron source	N. G. Sjöstrand	19A	V
P/790	Some experiences from measurements on an exponential pile of uranium and heavy water	R. Persson *et al.*	21A	V
P/791	Characteristics of the Swedish heavy water reactor	E. Hellstrand *et al.*	21A	V
P/792	Measurements of low-level radioactivity particularly the gamma-radiation from living subjects	R. M. Sievert	17C.1	XIII
P/793	The production of beneficial new hereditary traits by means of ionizing radiation	L. Ehrenberg *et al.*	13C.2	XII
P/794	Study on the properties of an electrolytic cell consisting of an electrode system in a chloroform alcohol solution under gamma-irradiation	C. G. Osterlundh and E. Haeffner	23C.3	XV

CZECHOSLOVAKIA

Paper	Title	Author or Authors	Session	Volume
P/795	Neutron counter for moisture content of soil	J. Urbanec	20C.3	XIV
P/796	Remarks about the Milne's problem with cylindrical symmetry	L. Trlifaj	23A	V
P/797	Prospective uses of atomic energy from the viewpoint of radiology	F. Herchik	6.2	XIII
P/798	The significance for the economic utilization of nuclear energy of factors arising from the thermal and electrical parts of the process	I. Vechvarzhy and A. Shevchik	4.1	I
P/799	Prospects of power development in Czechoslovakia and the part to be played by nuclear energy for peaceful purposes	A. Shevchik	2.2	I
P/800	The peaceful uses of atomic energy in the Czechoslovak Republic	F. Shorm	24.1	XVI
P/801	The use of radioisotopes in Czechoslovakia	C. Shimane	19C.1	XIV

USA

Paper	Title	Author or Authors	Session	Volume
P/802	Energy requirements and economic growth	E. S. Mason	2.1	I
P/803	Biological effects of radiation	J. C. Bugher	6.1	XI
P/804	The need for basic research in an atomic energy program	T. H. Johnson	8A.1	II
P/805	International co-operation in atomic energy developments	W. F. Libby	24.1	XVI
P/806	Time-of-flight instrumentation for neutron spectrometers	W. A. Higinbotham	15A	IV
P/807	Physics research with reactors	A. W. McReynolds	6A	II
P/808	*Withdrawn*			
P/809	The formation of higher isotopes and higher elements by reactor irradiation of Pu^{239}; some nuclear properties of the heavier isotopes	W. C. Bentley *et al.*	10B.1	VII
P/810	The outlook for nuclear power in Puerto Rico	P. Mullenbach	5	I
P/811	Aqueous uranium and thorium slurries	A. S. Kitzes and R. N. Lyon	20B	IX
P/812	The use of high temperature sodium in manufacture of Na-K alloy	C. B. Jackson and R. C. Werner	19B.1	IX
P/813	Operating experience and experimental results obtained from a NaK cooled fast reactor	H. V. Lichtenberger *et al.*	14A	III
P/814	Review of fast power reactors	W. H. Zinn	12A	III
P/815	Description of the pressurized water reactor (PWR) power plant at Shippingport, Pa.	J. W. Simpson *et al.*	13A	III
P/816	Objectives and summary of USAEC civilian power reactor program	U. M. Staebler	13A	III
P/817	The preparation of uranium metal by the reduction of uranium tetrafluoride with magnesium	H. A. Wilhelm	15B.2	VIII
P/818	The use of ion exchange resins for the determination of uranium in ore sand solutions	S. Fisher and R. Kunin	15B.2	VIII
P/819	Survey of heavy water processes	M. Benedict	16B.1	VIII

Paper	Title	Author or Authors	Session	Volume
P/820	Status of beryllium technology in the USA	A. R. Kaufmann and B. R. F. Kjellgren	17B.2	VIII
P/821	Survey of homogeneous reactor chemical problems	C. H. Secoy	20B	IX
P/822	Reprocessing of reactor fuel and blanket materials by solvent extraction	F. L. Culler	21B	IX
P/823	Survey of separations processes	S. Lawroski	22B.1	IX
P/824	Practical limitations of solvent extraction processes	R. E. Tomlinson	21B	IX
P/825	The metallurgy of reactor fuels	J. P. Howe	18B.2	IX
P/826	The intermetallic compounds of plutonium	A. S. Coffinberry and F. H. Ellinger	18B.1	IX
P/827	Fabrication of alloyed uranium	A. R. Kaufmann	18B.2	IX
P/828	The fabrication of the fuel elements of the Brookhaven reactor	D. H. Gurinsky et al.	18B.2	IX
P/829	Basic technology of the sodium graphite reactor	S. Siegel et al.	19B.3	IX
P/830	The theoretical prediction of neutron cross-sections of non-fissionable elements for energies up to 10 Mev	V. F. Weisskopf	6A	II
P/831	Delayed neutrons	G. R. Keepin et al.	16A.3	IV
P/832	The determination and evaluation of fundamental thermal neutron cross-sections	J. A. Harvey	16A.2	IV
P/833	Resonance capture integrals	R. L. Macklin and H. S. Pomerance	20A.1	V
P/834	Small thermal homogeneous critical assemblies	A. D. Callihan et al.	20A.3	V
P/835	Reactivity changes and reactivity lifetimes of fixed fuel elements in thermal reactors	B. I. Spinrad et al.	20A.2	V
P/836	The nuclear fission process	J. R. Huizenga	7A	II
P/837	Anion exchange studies of the fission products	K. A. Kraus and F. Nelson	9B.1	VII
P/838	A review of americium and curium chemistry	R. A. Penneman and L. B. Asprey	10B.3	VII
P/839	The decomposition of light and heavy water boric acid solutions by nuclear reactor radiations	E. J. Hart et al.	12B	VII
P/840	The use of isotopes in analysis of metabolic disorders	D. Stetten, Jr.	10C	X
P/841	Isotopes in the study of red cell volume, production and destruction	N. I. Berlin and J. H. Lawrence	9C	X
P/842	Isotopic studies of steroid metabolism in man	L. Hellman et al.	16C	XI
P/843	Steroid metabolism studies with the aid of C^{14}-labelled compounds	G. J. Alexander et al.	16C	XII
P/844	Studies of the use of Rb^{86} as a tracer of potassium in man	G. E. Burch et al.	10C	X
P/845	Approaches to treatment of poisoning by both radioactive and non-radioactive elements encountered in atomic energy operations.	J. Schubert	18C.1	XIII
P/846	The biosynthesis of porphyrins	D. Shemin	16C	XII
P/847	The use of isotopes in study of skeletal physiology and metabolism	W. F. Neuman	11C	XI
P/848	Fundamental considerations in the release of large quantities of radioactive wastes to land and sea	W. D. Claus	7.3	IX
P/849	Need in the United States for small power reactors	S. B. Morris	5	I
P/850	The possibilities of securing long-range supplies of uranium, thorium and other substances from igneous rocks	H. Brown and L. T. Silver	14B	VIII
P/851	Design and operating experience of a prototype boiling water power reactor	J. R. Dietrich et al.	3.1	III
P/852	Studies on the radium content of humans arising from the natural radium of their environment	A. F. Stehny and H. F. Lucas, Jr.	6.1	XI
P/853	The safety of nuclear reactors	E. Teller et al.	6.2	XIII
P/854	Some administrative and legal problems related to the widespread use of high-level radiation sources	W. Mitchell	4.3	XIII
P/855	Problems in the legal and administrative control of a program for distribution of radioisotopes	S. P. Cobb, Jr.	4.3	XIII
P/856	Boiler safety codes for power reactors	E. C. Miller	4.3	XIII
P/857	Administrative problems in the industrial utilization of atomic energy	G. G. Manov	4.3	XIII
P/858	*Withdrawn*			
P/859	Research program and operating experience on ANL reactors	W. H. McCorkle and W. H. Zinn	8A.2	II
P/860	The Brookhaven reactor	M. Fox	9A	II

Paper	Title	Author or Authors	Session	Volume
P/861	Design and description of Argonne National Laboratory's Research Reactors (CP-3, CP-3′, CP-5)	W. H. Zinn	10A.1	II
P/862	Survey of fuel cycles and reactor types	A. M. Weinberg	10A.2	III
P/863	The role which nuclear energy can play as an energy source during the next 25 to 50 years	W. Cisler	5	I

CHINA

P/864	The role of nuclear power in China's power development program in the next fifty years	Yun-Suan Sun	2.2	I
P/865	Exploration of monazite and associated minerals in the province of Taiwan, China	Jin-Tai Shen	6B	VI

UNITED KINGDOM

P/866	Liquid metal handling	S. G. Bauer	19B.1	IX
P/867	The possible role of thorium in nuclear energy	J. V. Dunworth	4.2	I

INDIA

P/868	The role of atomic power in India and its immediate possibilities	H. J. Bhabha	2.2	I
P/869	Remote location of uranium and thorium deposits	K. G. Vohra	7B	VI
P/870	Thermal inelastic scattering of cold neutrons in polycrystalline solids	K. S. Singwi and L. S. Kothari	6A	II
P/871	An ion exchange process for the recovery of uranium from carbonate leach solutions	J. Shankar *et al.*	14B	VIII
P/872	On the determination of diffusion and slowing down constants of ordinary water and beryllium oxide using a pulsed neutron source	R. Ramanna *et al.*	19A	V
P/873	Beneficiation characteristics of uraniferous ores in India	R. Krishnaswamy *et al.*	14B	VIII
P/874	A method of recording the pulmonary circulation times in the cat	A. S. Paintal	15C.1	XII
P/875	Natural occurrences of uranium and thorium in India	D. N. Wadia	6B	VI
P/876	Separation of hafnium from zirconium by vapour phase dechlorination	B. Prakash and C. V. Sundaram	17B.1	VIII

NORWAY

P/877	Energy consumption in Norway	F. Vogt	2.2	I
P/878	Cysteamine-cystamine: On the mechanism for the protective action against ionizing radiation	L. Eldjarn *et al.*	12C	XI
P/879	Preliminary study of an experimental pressurized heavy water reactor	O. Dahl	13A	III
P/880	Corrosion of aluminium and aluminium alloys in aqueous solutions at high temperatures	K. Carlsen	20B	IX
P/881	The distribution of nuclear charge in low and high energy fission	A. C. Pappas	8B.1	VII
P/882	Some industrial uses of radioisotopes in Norway	U. Been and E. Saeland	22C	XV
P/883	Measurements of the effective resonance integral of uranium with the pile-oscillator	V. O. Eriksen *et al.*	20A.1	V
P/884	Angular correlation of fission neutrons	K. Skarsvåg	7A	II
P/885	*Withdrawn*			
P/886	Separation of carrier-free isotopes by diffusion methods	K. Samsahl and K. Taugböl	19C.2	XIV
P/887	On the occurrence of uranium and thorium in Norway	T. Siggerud	6B	VI
P/888	Practical experiences with the J.E.E.P. Reactor	T. J. Barendregt *et al.*	8A.2	II
P/889	Effects of gamma-rays on sprouting and growth during storage in carrots and potatoes	N. Mikaelsen *et al.*	14.C	XII
P/890	Studies on genetic effects of chronic gamma-radiation on plants	K. Mikaelsen	13C.2	XII
P/891	High energy gamma-rays from short-lived fission products	A. Lundby *et al.*	7A	II

UNITED NATIONS

P/892	*Withdrawn*			
P/893	Some economic implications of nuclear power for underdeveloped countries	E. S. de Breuvery *et al.*	5	I

BRAZIL

P/894	*Withdrawn*			
P/895	*Withdrawn*			

Paper	Title	Author or Authors	Session	Volume
P/896	*Withdrawn*			
P/897	Studies on the nuclear photoeffect	M. D. de Souza Santos *et al.*	7A	II

UNITED KINGDOM

P/898	Comparative studies of the biological effects of radiation and of radiomimetic chemical agents	A. Haddow	12C	XI
P/899	Biological damage resulting from exposure to ionizing radiations	L. H. Gray	12C	XI
P/900	Chemical problems of power reactors	R. Hurst and J. Wright	20B	IX

ARGENTINA

P/901	*Withdrawn*			

UNITED NATIONS

P/902	World requirements of energy, 1975-2000	N. B. Guyol *et al.*	2.1	I

INDIA

P/903	*Withdrawn*			
P/904	Cytological and cytochemical effects of radiation (and radiomimetic substances) in actively proliferating biological systems	A. R. Gopal-Ayengar	12C	XI
P/905	Chemical effects of beta-gamma radiations on solutions of nucleic acid, purines and pyrimidines	N. S. Ranadive *et al.*	12C	XI
P/906	Biological effects of 220kvp roentgen rays and 1000 Mevp protons	K. C. Bora	12C	XI

ILO

P/907	The protection of workers against ionizing radiations		17C	XIII

DENMARK

P/908	Isotopes in permeability studies	H. H. Ussing	15C.1	XII
P/909	Expected consumption of energy in Denmark *Abstract only received*			

BELGIUM

P/910	Treatment of 400 cases of thyreotoxocosis with I^{181}	L. Brull	8C	X

DENMARK

P/911	On the theory of nuclear fission	A. Bohr	7A	II
P/912	An electromagnetic isotope separator and its application in laboratories for nuclear research	J. Koch and K. O. Nielsen	7.1	XIV
P/913	Energy loss and total charges of fission fragments passing through matter	N. O. Lassen	7A	II

AUSTRIA

P/914	Use of isotopes in Austria	B. Karlik	7.1	XIV

SWITZERLAND

P/915	Description of the Swiss research reactor	F. Alder *et al.*	9A	II
P/916	Matrix formulation of the two group diffusion theory for a multiple reflector spherical reactor	P. Schmid	23A	V
P/917	Radioiodine dynamics in normal and pathological thyroid functions	G. Joyet	9C	X

ITALY

P/918	Present state of uranium surveys in Italy	F. Ippolito	6B	VI
P/919	Italian power requirements in 1975 and 2000. Role which nuclear energy can play in Italy as an energy source during the next fifty years	F. Giordani	2.2	I
P/920	Calculations for heavy water and natural uranium 10 MW reactor	C. Salvetti and S. Gallone	21A	V

INDIA

P/921	Synthesis of 4:4'—diaminodiphenylsulphone—S^{85} (DDS) and its uses in leprosy research	V. R. Khanolkar *et al.*	10C	X

SWITZERLAND

P/922	Determination of phosphoryl oxydation in the hepatic cell using P^{32}	J. Frei *et al.*	16C	XII

Paper	Title	Author or Authors	Session	Volume
	NORWAY			
P/954	*Withdrawn*			
	THAILAND			
P/955	Thailand's needs and possibilities for power and heat	B. Binson	2.2	I
P/956	Survey paper on the natural occurrences of uranium and thorium in Thailand	Delegation of Thailand	6B	VI
	YUGOSLAVIA			
P/957	Extraction of uranium from low-grade Yugoslav ores, by chlorination	O. S. Gal	14B	VIII
P/958	Efficiency of some catalysts in the exchange reaction between heavy water and hydrogen	P. Savic *et al.*	16B.1	VIII
P/959	Paper chromatography separation of uranium in natural resources	D. Cvjeticanin and N. Belegisanin	15B.2	VIII
P/960	Temperature dependence of the deuterium distribution in the reaction $LiA1H4 + 4HDO$	P. Savic *et al.*	16B.1	VIII
P/961	Thermal strains and deformations of the rod and the protective canning in the heterogeneous high flux reactor	M. Ristic *et al.*	18B.2	IX
P/962	Requirements and possibilities of production of energy in Yugoslavia	I. Kovacevic *et al.*	2.2	I
P/963	Deposits of uranium and thorium in Yugoslavia	M. Ristic	6B	VI
P/964	Polarography of uranium. Polarographic determination of uranium in ores without preliminary chemical separation	M. V. Susic	15B.2	VIII
P/965	Extraction of uranium from low-grade uranium ores	B. Bunji	14B	VIII
P/966	Complex formation between uranyl ion and 1-ascorbic acid	I. J. Gal	15B.2	VIII
P/967	The synthesis of beta-amino-gamma-methyl-^{14}C-thiobutyric acid/beta-methionine-methyl-^{14}C	D. Keglevic-Brovet	16C	XII
	PORTUGAL			
P/968	Uranium prospection in Portugal	R. Cavaca	6B	VI
P/969	Performance of several radiation applications in the National Laboratory for Civilian Engineering	A. Gibert	7.1	XIV
P/970	An accurate method for treatment of hyperthyroidism with I^{131}	V. H. Franco *et al.*	8C	X
P/971	A theory of the thyroid function and its diagnosis with tagged iodine	J. Palacios	9C	X
P/972	Diagnosis of the thyroid function in 520 patients with I^{131}	V. H. Franco *et al.*	9C	X
P/973	New technique for the therapeutic application of radioisotopes	V. H. Franco *et al.*	8C	X
P/974	The association of a spark counter or a Geiger-Müller counter with a photomultiplier as nuclear radiation detectors	A. M. Baptista and A. J. G. Ramalho	20C.4	XIV
P/975	Determination of atmospheric radioactivity	F. Barreira and M. Laranjeira	23B.3	IX
P/976	Analysis of uranium and thorium complex ores by measurements of their gamma activity	A. M. Baptista *et al.*	15B.2	VIII
P/977	Some aspects of the chemical treatment of Portuguese uranium ores	F. Videira *et al.*	14B	VIII
P/978	Analytical chemistry of the study and enrichment of uranium ores	A. H. de Carvalho	15B.2	VIII
P/979	Notes on the half-life of I^{131}	F. Barreira and M. Laranjeira	9B.2	VII
	PHILIPPINES			
P/980	Uranium deposits in the Philippines	A. Clemente and E. Reyes	6B	VI
P/981	Power and fuel resources of the Philippines	F. C. Rodriguez and C. S. Ramirez	2.2	I
	NETHERLANDS			
P/982	*Withdrawn*			
	UNESCO			
P/983	Training of research staff in the field of peaceful uses of atomic energy		24.2	I
	AUSTRALIA			
P/984	An account of atomic energy developments in Australia		4	XIII

Paper	Title	Author or Authors	Session	Volume
P/1057	On the distribution of radioactivity in the North Pacific Ocean in 1954-1955	Y. Miyake	18C.2	XIII
P/1058	Radiochemical analysis of radioactive dusts	K. Kimura	9B	VII
P/1059	Radiochemical interpretation of the radioactive fallout	K. Kimura *et al.*	9B	VII
P/1060	Japan's energy utilization, the present and the future	K. Aki	2.2	I
P/1061	Applications of radioisotopes to research and industrial problems in Japan	K. Kimura	22C	XV
P/1062	Importance of isotopes in medicine	M. Nakaidzumi	7.2	X
P/1063	Administrative and legal problems in the use of radioisotopes in Japan	K. Suzue	4.3	XIII
P/1064	*Withdrawn*			
P/1065	Application of nuclear energy in the solution of special problems in biomedical research	M. Nakaidzumi	9C	X
P/1066	Biological cycles of fission products in agriculture in Japan	R. Sasaki	18C.2	XIII
P/1067	Some observations on the biological influences of radioactive isotopes upon the physiological functions	R. Sasaki	15C.1	XII
P/1068	Industrial utilization of fission products; radiation sterilization of foods	M. Nakaidzumi	23C.2	XV
P/1069	A brief review of the radiation instruments in Japan	F. Yamasaki	20C.4	XIV

SWITZERLAND

P/1070	Dominant lethal factors and embryonic mortality after irradiation at 180 kev and 31 Mev	H. Fritz-Niggli *et al.*	11C	XI

AUSTRALIA

P/1071	Natural occurrence of U and Th	Dept. of National Development, Australia	6B	VI

AUSTRIA

P/1072	Research reactor planning	B. Karlik	4.3	XIII
P/1073	Natural occurrence of uranium and thorium		6B	VI
P/1074	Austria's needs and possibilities for power and heat during the next fifty years		2.2	I

ARGENTINA

P/1075	Spectrographic determination of microquantities of beryllium and its application to the determination in air and in biological tissues	A. G. Taudien	17B.2	VIII
P/1076	Neutron spectrum determination by means of nuclear plates and its application to the measurement of Be^8 excitation levels	P. J. Waloschek and E. Pérez Ferreira	6A	II

UNITED KINGDOM

P/1077	*Withdrawn*			

UNION OF SOUTH AFRICA

P/1078	Nuclear energy and Southern Africa	B. F. J. Schonland	5	I

UNITED KINGDOM

P/1079	Labelling locusts with radioactive isotopes	H. B. D. Kettlewell	14C	XII
P/1080	Co-operation by the United Kingdom in the use of atomic energy for peaceful purposes	Sir John Cockcroft	24.1	XVI

PORTUGAL

P/1081	A short account of the use of radiation in the National Laboratory of Civil Engineering *Abstract only received*	A. Gibert		

NEW ZEALAND

P/1082	Note on the supply and demand for electric power in New Zealand	State Hydro Electric Department, New Zealand	2.2	I

PORTUGAL

P/1083	Power sources and requirements in Portugal	A. A. Manzanares	2.2	I

EGYPT

P/1084	*Withdrawn*			

Paper	Title	Author or Authors	Session	Volume
	URUGUAY			
P/1085	Estimates of the energy requirements of Uruguay in the periods 1955-1975 and 1975-2000	W. S. Hill and G. E. Villar	2.2	I
P/1086	Usable energy sources to meet the energy needs of Uruguay in 1955-1975 and 1975-2000 and possibilities for the use of nuclear power energy in this country	W. S. Hill and G. E. Villar	2.2	I
P/1087	Influence of intermediate capacity nuclear power stations on future civilization and their possible use in Uruguay	W. S. Hill and G. E. Villar	5	I
P/1088	Radioisotope uses in Uruguay and their possible production in this country	W. S. Hill and G. E. Villar	19C	XIV
	ROMANIA			
P/1089	Statistics of photographic fission tracks and range estimate of fragments	J. S. Ausländer and T. Visky	7A	II
P/1090	On the vapour pressure of polonium at room temperature	J. S. Ausländer and J. I. Georgescu	10B.3	VII
P/1091	On the mass estimation of non-relativistic charged particles in nuclear emulsions	J. S. Ausländer *et al.*	6A	II
P/1092	*Withdrawn*			
P/1093	Prospects of pure and applied research in the nuclear field *Abstract only received*			
P/1094	On multipolar electromagnetic radiation, application to nuclear physics	S. Titeica and C. Iusim	6A	II
P/1095	A method for the determination of uranium and thorium using nuclear emulsions	M. Petrascou and G. Besliu	15B.2	VIII
P/1096	A natural isotope of element 84 with a very long half-life	R. Ripan *et al.*	10B.3	VII
P/1097	Influence of central nervous system dynamics on iodine fixation in the thyroid	St. Milcou *et al.*	9C	X
P/1098	Action of chlorephenothyasine on I^{131} concentration in the thyroid of the albino guinea pig	St. Milcou *et al.*	9C	X
P/1099	The effect of oestradiole-iodine fixation in the thyroid	St. Milcou *et al.*	9C	X
P/1100	*Withdrawn*			
	GREECE			
P/1101	Uranium and thorium occurrence in Greece	The Atomic Energy Commission, Greece	6B	VI
P/1102	Energy needs and sources in Greece. Heat and power requirements during the next forty years	The Atomic Energy Commission, Greece	2.2	I
	BELGIUM			
P/1103	A simple method for the comparison of reactor coolant efficiency	M. Hoyaux	19B.2	IX
P/1104	Uranium metallurgy in Belgium		15B.1	VIII
P/1105	Shinkolobwe uranium deposit	J. J. Derriks and J. F. Vaes	6B	VI
	FINLAND			
P/1106	Finland's future needs and possibilities for power and heat	B. Nordqvist	2.2	I
	EGYPT			
P/1107	Strychnine uranyl fluoride, a new compound suitable for the determination of fluorine and uranium in presence of some other metals	A. R. Tourky and A. M. Amin	15B.2	VIII
P/1108	Power and heat requirements of the Republic of Egypt	M. A. B. Elkoshairy and I. H. Abdel Rahman	2.2	I
P/1109	Chemical radiation protection *Abstract only received*	M. S. M. Awad		
	UNITED KINGDOM			
P/1110	Plutonium hexafluoride. Preparation and some physical and chemical properties	C. J. Mandleberg *et al.*	10B.3	VII
	USA			
P/1111	*Withdrawn*			
	AUSTRIA			
P/1112	Foliar fertilization with phosphatic nutrient labelled with P^{32} *Abstract only received*	K. Kaindl		

AUTHOR INDEX

Name	Paper Number	Session and Volume	Name	Paper Number	Session and Volume
ABDEL-RAHMAN, I. H. *et al.*	P/1108	2.2, I	ATHERTON, J. E. *et al.*	P/828	18B.2, IX
ABECASIS MANZANNARES, A.	P/1083	2.2, I	ATTIX, F. H. *et al.*	P/62	20C.1, XIV
ABSON, W. *et al.*	P/434	22A.2, V	AUBERT, J. P. *et al.*	P/373	15C.2, XII
ACKROYD, R. T.	P/431	23A, V	AUCLAIR, J. M. *et al.*	P/354	17A, IV
ADAMCHUK, Y. B. *et al.*	P/645	17A, IV	AUSEMUS, E. R. *et al.*	P/103	13C.2, XII
ADAMS, G. D. *et al.*	P/87	12C, XI	AUSLÄNDER, J. S. *et al.*	P/1089	7A, II
	P/197	8C, X		P/1090	10B.3, VII
ADAMS, W. A. *et al.*	P/24	6B, VI		P/1091	6A, II
ADYASEVICH, B. P. *et al.*	P/651	6A, II			
AEBERHART, A. *et al.*	P/374	10C, X	AUSTRALIA, Commonwealth Dept. of National Development		
AEBERSOLD, P. C.	P/308	7.1, XIV		P/987	2.2, I
AGUILO, A. *et al.*	P/1012	15B.2, VIII		P/1071	6B, VI
AHMAD, B.	P/1127	16C, XII	AVERY, R. *et al.*	P/609	22A.1, V
AILLERET, P.	P/326	2.1, I			
AILLERET, P. *et al.*	P/327	5, I	BACH, N.	P/683	12B, VII
	P/337	11A, III	BACQ, Z. M.	P/939	12C, XI
AKI, K.	P/1060	2.2, I	BAERTSCHI, P. *et al.*	P/927	16B.1, VIII
ALDER, F. *et al.*	P/915	9A, II	BAGNALL, K. W.	P/439	10B.3, VII
ALEXANDER, G. J. *et al.*	P/843	16C, XII	BA HLI, F.	P/324	2.1, I
ALIA, M.	P/1122	6B, VI		P/325	2.2, I
ALICHANOW, A. I. *et al.*	P/623	9A, II	BAILES, R. H. *et al.*	P/524	14B, VIII
	P/624	12A, III	BAIR, W. J. *et al.*	P/253	12C, XI
	P/658	18A, IV	BAISOGOLOV, G. D. *et al.*	P/617	6.1, XI
ALIMARIN, I. P.	P/706	21C.2, XV	BALE, W. F. *et al.*	P/76	17C.2, XIII
ALLEN, A. A.	P/738	12B, VII		P/199	9C, X
ALLEN, A. O. *et al.*	P/154	20C.3, XIV	BAPTISTA, A. M. *et al.*	P/970	8C, X
	P/155	20C.2, XIV		P/972	9C, X
ALMEIDA, J. D. *et al.*	P/977	14B, VIII		P/973	8C, X
ALSINA, F. *et al.*	P/1003	23A, V		P/974	20C.4, XIV
ALTSCHULER, Z. S. *et al.*	P/292	6B, VI		P/976	15B.2, VIII
AMIEL, S. *et al.*	P/773	7B, VI	BARANOV, V. I.	P/625	7B, VI
AMIN, A. M. *et al.*	P/1107	15B.2, VIII	BARBIER, G. *et al.*	P/380	14C, XII
AMOROSI, A. *et al.*	P/491	12A, III	BARCLAY, W. R. *et al.*	P/229	10C, X
ANASTASIJEVIC, P. *et al.*	P/961	18B.2, IX	BARENDREGT, T. J. *et al.*	P/888	8A.2, II
ANDERSEN, E. *et al.*	P/891	7A, II		P/933	19A, V
ANDERSEN, R. K. *et al.*	P/492	11A, III	BARNEA, J. *et al.*	P/121	5, I
ANDERSON, C. *et al.*	P/168	23C.1, XV	BARNES, A. H.	P/501	19B.1, IX
ANDERSON, C. R. *et al.*	P/552	22B.2, IX		P/455	14A, III
ANDERSON, E. C. *et al.*	P/67	20C.4, XIV	BARNES, D. W. H. *et al.*	P/1019	12C, XI
	P/68	20C.1, XIV	BARO, G. B. *et al.*	P/1022	9B.2, VII
ANDERSON, E. E. *et al.*	P/755	24.2, I			9B.2, VII
ANDREWS, G. A. *et al.*	P/184	8C, X	BARREIRA, F. *et al.*	P/975	23B.3, IX
ANDREWS, H. L. *et al.*	P/251	11C, XI		P/979	9B.2, VII
ANGELELLI, V.	P/999	6B, VI	BASSHAM, J. A. *et al.*	P/259	15C.2, XII
ANGER, H. O. *et al.*	P/158	20C.2, XIV	BAT, G. A. *et al.*	P/655	23A, V
	P/201	8C, X	BAT, G. A.	P/665	23A, V
ANIKINA, M. P. *et al.*	P/644	17A, IV	BATES, T. H. *et al.*	P/445	12B, VII
ANTHONY, D. S. *et al.*	P/74	17C.1, XIII	BATUECAS RODRIGUEZ, T. *et al.*	P/1121	6B, VI
ANTIPOV-KARATAYEV, I. N.	P/698	14C, XII	BAUER, F. *et al.*	P/198	9C, X
ANTON, N.	P/152	20C.4, XIV	BAUER, S. G.	P/866	19B.1, IX
ANTONOV, A. V. *et al.*	P/661	19A, V	BAUM, V. A. *et al.*	P/639	19B.2, IX
APT, L. *et al.*	P/227	9C, X	BAUS, R. A. *et al.*	P/124	19B.3, IX
ARAGAO, M. B., *et al.*	P/140	10C, X	BAXTER, R. C. *et al.*	P/72	11C, XI
ARCHER, V. E. *et al.*	P/479	6.1, XI	BAY, I. *et al.*	P/92	15C.1, XII
ARNOLD, J. R. *et al.*	P/68	20C.1, XIV	BEALL, S. E. *et al.*	P/498	13A, III
ARRAGON, Ph. *et al.*	P/343	16B.2, VIII	BEATTY, K. O. *et al.*	P/148	22C, XV
ARTOM, C.	P/261	16C.2, XII	BECK, C.	P/487	8A.2, II
ASHTON, F. M. *et al.*	P/115	14C, XII	BECRAFT, G. E.	P/22	6B, VI
ASLING, C. W. *et al.*	P/206	8C, X	BEEN, U. *et al.*	P/882	22C, XV
ASPREY, L. B. *et al.*	P/838	10B.3, VII	BEKHUM, D. W. Van *et al.*	P/932	12C, XI

Name	Paper Number	Session and Volume	Name	Paper Number	Session and Volume
Fox, M.	P/860	9A, II	Ghiorso, A.	P/718	8B.1, VII
Fraenz, I. G. de *et al.*	P/1008	15B.2, VIII	Ghormley, J. A. *et al.*	P/741	12B, VII
	P/1020	9B.2, VII	Gibert, A.	P/969	7.1, XIV
Francis, J. E. *et al.*	P/157	20C.4, XIV	Gigon, J. *et al.*	P/362	12B, VII
Francis, K. E. *et al.*	P/1110	10B.3, VII	Gill, J. R. *et al.*	P/57	6B, VI
Franco, V. H. *et al.*	P/970	8C, X	Gillespie, A. B. *et al.*	P/434	22A.2, V
	P/972	9C, X	Gindler, J. E. *et al.*	P/809	10B.1, VII
	P/973	8C, X	Ginocchio, A.	P/340	14B, VIII
Frank, G. M.	P/693	11C, XI	Giordani, F.	P/919	2.2, I
Frank, I. M. *et al.*	P/661	19A, V	Girshfeld, S. V.	P/648	16A.3, IV
Franklin, E. *et al.*	P/763	7B, VI	Gispert, M. *et al.*	P/1120	16B.1, VIII
Frederick, E. J. *et al.*	P/316	19C.3, XIV	Glascock, R. F.	P/456	16C, XII
Freedberg, A. S. *et al.*	P/185	8C, X	Glatfeld, J. N. *et al.*	P/274	15C.2, XII
	P/189	9C, X	Glendenin, L. E. *et al.*	P/614	8B.1, VII
Freeman, V. L. *et al.*	P/38	6B, VI	Glueckauf, E.	P/398	7.3, IX
Frei, J. *et al.*	P/922	16C, XII	Glueckauf, E. *et al.*	P/415	22B.2, IX
Fried, S. *et al.*	P/730	10B.1, VII	Godnev, T. N. *et al.*	P/715	15C.2, XII
Friedberg, W. *et al.*	P/222	16C, XII	Goeller, H. E. *et al.*	P/316	19C.3, XIV
Friedell, H. L. *et al.*	P/75	11C, XI	Goertz, R. C. *et al.*	P/69	19C.3, XIV
	P/191	9C, X	Goertzel, G.	P/613	23A, V
	P/193	9C, X	Golbeck, G. R. *et al.*	P/630	15B.2, VIII
	P/203	8C, X	Goldberg, E. D. *et al.*	P/277	18C.2, XIII
Friedlander, E. *et al.*	P/1091	6A, II	Goldblith, S. A. *et al.*	P/172	23C.2, XV
Friedman, A. M. *et al.*	P/809	10B.1, VII	Goldemberg, J. *et al.*	P/897	7A, II
Fries, B. A. *et al.*	P/166	22C, XV	Goldin, A. S. *et al.*	P/232	21C.1, XV
Fritz-Niggli, H. *et al.*	P/1070	11C, XI	Goldin, L. L. *et al.*	P/644	17A, IV
Fromageot, P. *et al.*	P/377	16C, XII	Goldschmidt, B. *et al.*	P/341	15.1, VIII
Froman, D. *et al.*	P/500	13A, III		P/349	21B, IX
Frondel, C.	P/302	6B, VI	Goldwasser, E. *et al.*	P/249	12C, XI
Frota-Pessoa, E. *et al.*	P/136	15B.2, VIII	Gomberg, H. J. *et al.*	P/159	20C.4, XIV
	P/140	10C, X		P/225	23C.2, XV
Fry, T. M. *et al.*	P/394	6.2, XIII	Goodlet, B. L. *et al.*	P/466	24.2, I
	P/405	12A, III	Gopal-Ayengar, A. R.	P/904	12C, XI
Fukushima, D. K. *et al.*	P/842	16C, XI	Gopal-Ayengar, A. R. *et al.*	P/921	10C, X
			Gorbenko-Germanov, D. S.	P/677	10B.2, VII
Gabelman, J. W.	P/37	6B, VI	Gordon, S. *et al.*	P/839	13B, VII
	P/50	6B, VI	Gordon, S. A.	P/97	12C, XI
Gal, I. J.	P/966	15B.2, VIII	Gori, A. *et al.*	P/1004	15B.2, VIII
Gal, O. S.	P/957	14B, VIII		P/1005	15B.2, VIII
Galanin, A. D. *et al.*	P/623	9A, II	Gorman, A. E.	P/283	18C.2, XIII
Galanin, A. D.	P/647	23A, V	Gorman, A. E. *et al.*	P/310	7.3, IX
	P/663	23A, V	Gott, G. B. *et al.*	P/47	6B, VI
	P/664	23A, V		P/289	6B, VI
	P/666	23A, V	Gottdenker, F. *et al.*	P/133	14B, VIII
	P/668	23A, V	Gottfried, D. *et al.*	P/17	6B, VI
Galananina, N. D. *et al.*	P/646	17A, IV	Gould, R. G. *et al.*	P/842	16C, XI
Gallagher, T. F. *et al.*	P/842	16C, XI	Gould, S. E. *et al.*	P/225	23C.2, XV
Gallimore, J. C. *et al.*	P/213	8C, X	Gowen, J. W.	P/236	11C, XI
Gallone, S. *et al.*	P/920	21A, V		P/256	11C, XI
Galper, M. J. *et al.*	P/604	21A, V	Grainger, L.	P/407	15B.1, VIII
Galula, M. *et al.*	P/354	17A, IV	Grand, J. A. *et al.*	P/124	19B.3, IX
	P/357	19A, V	Granhall, I. *et al.*	P/793	17C.1, XIII
Gamba, O. *et al.*	P/1003	23A, V	Gray, L. H.	P/899	12C, XI
Gar, K. A. *et al.*	P/701	14C, XII	Gray, P. M. J.	P/986	14B, VIII
Garden, N. B.	P/722	8B.2, VII	Grebenshikova, V. I. *et al.*	P/678	10B.2, VII
Garrels, R. M. *et al.*	P/300	6B, VI	Greece—Atomic Energy	P/1101	6B, VI
Gary-Bobo, J. *et al.*	P/372	12C, XI	Commission	P/1102	2.2, I
Gasco Sánchez, L. *et al.*	P/1123	15B.2, VIII	Green, A. E. S. *et al.*	P/950	6A, II
Gast, P. F.	P/607	21A, V		P/951	6A, II
	P/612	22A.2, V	Greenberg, J. *et al.*	P/212	8C, X
Gaude, G. *et al.*	P/375	11C, XI	Greene, B. A.	P/323	4.3, XIII
Gaudin, A. M.	P/529	14B, VIII	Greenleaf, E. *et al.*	P/519	14B, VIII
Gaunt, J.	P/410	16B.1, VIII	Gregory, W. C.	P/107	13C.2, XII
Gawrillow, S. A. *et al.*	P/623	9A, II	Gresky, H. T.	P/540	21B, IX
Geilikman, B. T.	P/652	7A, II	Griffiths, P. *et al.*	P/483	6.2, XIII
Genna, S. *et al.*	P/70	20C.2, XIV	Grinstead, R. R. *et al.*	P/522	14B, VIII
Georgescu, I. I. *et al.*	P/1090	10B.3, VII		P/523	14B, VIII
Gerraseva, L. A. *et al.*	P/662	19A, V	Grodsensky, D. E. *et al.*	P/688	15C.1, XII
Gerasimov, V. F. *et al.*	P/645	17A, IV	Groshev, L. V. *et al.*	P/651	6A, II
Gerchik, F.	P/797	6.1, XI	Gross, E. B. *et al.*	P/297	6B, VI
Gerlit, J. B.	P/671	9B.2, VII	Grout, H. J. *et al.*	P/401	8A.1, II
Gertsricken, S. D. *et al.*	P/712	21C.3, XV		P/402	10A.1, II
Geyer, J. C. *et al.*	P/312	7.3, IX			

Name	Paper Number	Session and Volume
GROZIN, B. D.	P/713	22C, XV
GRUNDY, W. D. *et al.*	P/517	7B, VI
GRUNER, J. W.	P/296	6B, VI
GRUTT, E. W. Jr.	P/45	6B, VI
GUEDES, S. V. *et al.*	P/132	7B, VI
GUÉRON, J.	P/331	7.1, XIV
GUÉRON, J. *et al.*	P/343	16B.2, VIII
GUIMARAES, D.	P/126	6B, VI
GUIMARAES, D. *et al.*	P/131	6B, VI
GUNCKEL, J. E. *et al.*	P/266	13C.2, XII
GUREVICH, I. I. *et al.*	P/649	23A, V
GURINSKY, D. H. *et al.*	P/118	19B.3, IX
	P/828	18B.2, IX
GUSKOVA, A. K. *et al.*	P/617	6.1, XI
GUSTAFSSON, A. *et al.*	P/793	17C.1, XIII
GUYOL, N. B. *et al.*	P/902	2.1, I
HADDOW, A.	P/898	12C, XI
HAEFFNER, E. *et al.*	P/785	21B, IX
	P/794	23C.3, XV
HAHN, P. F.	P/202	8C, X
HAIL, W. J., Jr. *et al.*	P/288	6B, VI
HALEY, T. J. *et al.*	P/255	12C, XI
HALG, W. *et al.*	P/915	9A, II
HALKETT, J. *et al.*	P/227	9C, X
HALL, G. R. *et al.*	P/440	10B.1, VII
HALL, W. B.	P/417	19B.2, IX
HALPERIN, J. *et al.*	P/732	10B.1, VII
HAMILTON, J. G. *et al.*	P/206	8C, X
HAMISTER, V. C. *et al.*	P/534	16B.2, VIII
HAMMOND, R. P. *et al.*	P/318	19C.2, XIV
	P/500	13A, III
HAMMOND, R. P.	P/724	9B.1, VII
HANKS, L. V. *et al.*	P/228	10C, X
HANSEN, R. A. *et al.*	P/190	9C, X
HANSON, W. C. *et al.*	P/281	18C.2, XIII
HARPER, P. V. *et al.*	P/200	8C, X
	P/208	8C, X
HARRER, J. M. *et al.*	P/497	13A, III
HARRIS, H. C.	P/108	14C, XII
HARRISON, G. E. *et al.*	P/448	11C, XI
HART, E. J. *et al.*	P/839	12B, VII
HART, H. E. *et al.*	P/212	8C, X
HARTMAN, L. *et al.*	P/368	8C, X
HARTT, C. E. *et al.*	P/115	14C, XII
HARVEY, J. A.	P/832	16A.2, IV
HASSIALIS, M. D. *et al.*	P/116	15B.2, VIII
	P/521	14B, VIII
HASTERLICK, R. J.	P/243	11C, XI
HASTERLICK, R. J. *et al.*	P/478	6.1, XI
HASTINGS, A. B.	P/178	10C, X
HATCH, L. P. *et al.*	P/553	22B.2, IX
HATHAWAY, E. A. *et al.*	P/84	12C, XI
HAUROWITZ, F. *et al.*	P/222	16C, XII
HAVENS, W. W., Jr.	P/574	15A, IV
HAYDEN, R. J. *et al.*	P/596	16A.1, IV
HAYES, F. N. *et al.*	P/67	20C.4, XIV
	P/68	20C.1, XIV
HAYWARD, B. R. *et al.*	P/829	19B.2, IX
HEALY, J. W. *et al.*	P/482	6.2, XIII
HEALY, T. V. *et al.*	P/415	22B.2, IX
HECHTER, O. *et al.*	P/843	16C, XII
HEIDELBERGER, C.	P/220	10C, X
HELD, E. F. M. van der	P/948	20A.1, V
HELLENS, R. L. *et al.*	P/597	19A, V
	P/604	21A, V
HELLMAN, L. *et al.*	P/842	16C, XI
HELLSTRAND, E. *et al.*	P/791	21A, V
HENDERSON, H. J. *et al.*	P/214	10C, X
HENDRICKS, S. B. *et al.*	P/112	14C, XII
HENNEMAN, H. A. *et al.*	P/95	12C, XI
HENNIG, G. R. *et al.*	P/751	13B, VII

Name	Paper Number	Session and Volume
HENSCHKE, U. K.	P/209	8C, X
HERING, H. *et al.*	P/343	16B.2, VIII
	P/386	20C.2, XIV
HERMANS, M. E. A. *et al.*	P/936	11A, III
HERMSEN, J. *et al.*	P/930	20C.4, XIV
HESS, D. C. *et al.*	P/596	18A, IV
	P/809	10B.1, VII
HETLAND, D. L. *et al.*	P/44	6B, VI
HEVESY, G. de		*Evening lecture XVI*
HIDLE, N. *et al.*	P/888	8A.2, II
HIGINBOTHAM, W. A.	P/806	15A, IV
HILL, J. M. *et al.*	P/391	3.2, I
HILL, W. S. *et al.*	P/1085	2.2, I
	P/1086	2.2, I
	P/1087	5, I
	P/1088	19C, XIV
HILPERT, L. S. *et al.*	P/38	6B, VI
HINDMAN, J. C. *et al.*	P/736	10B.3, VII
HINTON, C.	P/406	14A, III
HIRSCH, H. H. *et al.*	P/561	18B.2, IX
HITTMAN, F. *et al.*	P/553	22B.2, IX
HIYAMA, Y.	P/1052	18C.2, XIII
HOAGLAND, H. *et al.*	P/99	15C.1, XII
HOAGLAND, M. B. *et al.*	P/265	16C, XII
HOCHANADEL, C. J.	P/739	12B, VII
HOCHANADEL, C. J. *et al.*	P/741	12B, VII
HOCHMAN, A. *et al.*	P/777	9C, X
HOCHSTEIN, F. A. *et al.*	P/273	16C, XII
HODGE, H. C.	P/73	17C.2, XIII
HOECKER, F. E.	P/88	11C, XI
HOEKSTRA, H. R. *et al.*	P/299	6B, VI
	P/737	12B, VII
HOGBEN, C. A. M.	P/91	15C.1 XII
HOLADAY, D. A. *et al.*	P/258	17C.2, XIII
HOLBAN, R. *et al.*	P/1097	9C, X
HOLLAENDER, A. *et al.*	P/78	12C, XI
HOLLAENDER, A.		*Evening lecture XVI*
HOLLAND, J. Z.	P/572	6.2, XIII
HOLLIS, R. F. *et al.*	P/526	14B, VIII
HOREKER, B. L. *et al.*	P/268	16C, XII
HOROWITZ, J. *et al.*	P/360	19A, V
HOROWITZ, J.	P/361	21A, V
HORR, C. A. *et al.*	P/288	6B, VI
HORTON, C. L. *et al.*	P/428	20A.3, V
HOVE, J. E. *et al.*	P/751	13B, VII
HOWE, J. P.	P/825	18B.2, IX
HOWLETT, J. *et al.*	P/430	23A, V
HOYAUX, M.	P/1103	15B.2, IX
HSU, K. J. *et al.*	P/103	13C.2, XII
HUBER, P. *et al.*	P/1033	6A, II
HUBER, P.	P/1035	6B, VI
HUBER, T. E. *et al.*	P/176	23C.2, XV
HUBERT, P. *et al.*	P/354	17A, IV
HUDDLE, R. A. U.	P/411	20B, IX
HUDSON, G. W. *et al.*	P/252	12C, XI
HUDSWELL, F. *et al.*	P/409	17B.1, VIII
HUFF, R. L. *et al.*	P/207	9C, X
HUFFMAN, J. R. *et al.*	P/485	8A.2, II
HUGGINS, C. *et al.*	P/201	8C, X
HUGGINS, J. C. *et al.*	P/525	14B, VIII
HUGHES, D. J.	P/576	15A, IV
HUGHES, E. T. *et al.*	P/469	2.2, I
HUGUET, J. L. *et al.*	P/1012	15B.2, VIII
HUIZENGA, J. R. *et al.*	P/809	10B.1, VII
HUIZENGA, J. R.	P/836	7A, II
HULL, D. E. *et al.*	P/166	22C, XV
HULTGREN, A. *et al.*	P/785	21B, IX
HULUBEI, H. *et al.*	P/1096	10B.3, VII
HUMMEL, H. H. *et al.*	P/598	22A.1, V
	P/609	22A.1, V
HUMPHREYS, J. R.	P/740	12B, VII
HUMPHREYS, R. F. *et al.*	P/156	23C, XV

Name	Paper Number	Session and Volume	Name	Paper Number	Session and Volume
HUNGATE, F. P. *et al.*	P/278	18C.2, XIII	JORDAN, G. G. *et al.*	P/704	22C, XV
HURE, J. *et al.*	P/344	16B.2, VIII	JOSHI, B. V. *et al.*	P/872	19A, V
	P/347	17B.1, VIII	JOSLIN, S. W. *et al.*	P/391	3.2, I
HURSH, J. B. *et al.*	P/257	11C, XI	JOYET, G.	P/917	9C, X
	P/479	6.1, XI	JUKES, J. A.	P/390	4.1, I
HURST, D. G.	P/5	20A.2, V			
HURST, G. S. *et al.*	P/65	20C.3, XIV	KADE, H. *et al.*	P/190	9C, X
HURST, R. *et al.*	P/900	20B, IX	KAMAYEV, A. V. *et al.*	P/662	19A, V
	P/1110	10B.3, VII	KANNE, W. R. *et al.*	P/595	18A, IV
HURWITZ, H., Jr.	P/590	18A, IV	KAPLAN, G. E.	P/636	15B.1, VIII
HURWITZ, H., Jr. *et al.*	P/608	23A, V	KAPLAN, I. *et al.*	P/606	21A, V
HUTCHEON, J. M. *et al.*	P/409	17B.1, VIII	KAPLAN, L. *et al.*	P/149	21C.1, XV
HUTTER, J. C. *et al.*	P/346	17B.2, VIII	KARLIK, B.	P/914	7.1, XIV
HYDE, E. K.	P/728	10B.2, VII		P/1072	4.3, XIII
HYMANN, H. H. *et al.*	P/546	22B.1, IX	KARNOVSKY, M. L. *et al.*	P/214	10C, X
IGNATIEW, K. J. *et al.*	P/646	17A, IV	KATO, M. *et al.*	P/1053	22C, XV
INGRAM, M.	P/241	17C.1, XIII	KATO, M.	P/1054	22C, XV
INGHRAM, M. G. *et al.*	P/596	18A, IV	KATO, W. Y. *et al.*	P/813	14A, III
	P/809	10B.1, VII	KATZ, J. J. (A.E.C.) *et al.*	P/299	6B, VI
INTERNATIONAL LABOUR OFFICE	P/907	4.3, XIII	KATZ, J. J. *et al.*	P/546	22B.1, IX
INOSE, S. *et al.*	P/1053	22C, XV	KATZ, M. Y. *et al.*	P/631	16B.1, VIII
IONESCU, V. *et al.*	P/1125	9C, X	KATZIN, L. I.	P/734	10B.3, VIII
IPPOLITO, F.	P/918	6B, VI	KAUFMANN, A. R. *et al.*	P/820	17B.2, VIII
IRAOLAGOITIA, P. E.	P/1002	5, I	KAUFMANN, A. R.	P/827	18B.2, IX
ISAACS, J. D. *et al.*	P/277	18C.2, XIII	KAY, J. M.	P/758	5, I
ISACHSEN, Y. W.	P/39	6B, VI	KEDROV-ZIKMAN, O. K.	P/716	14C, XII
ISACOFF, A. I. *et al.*	P/642	16A.1, IV	KEEPIN, G. R. *et al.*	P/831	16A,3, IV
	P/661	19A, V	KEGLEVIC-BROVET, D.	P/967	16C, XII
ISBIN, H. S.		III	KELLER, E. B. *et al.*	P/265	16C, XII
Nuclear reactor catalogue			KELLER, R. *et al.*	P/1131	23C, XV
ISHII, C.	P/1056	23B, IX	KELLERSHORN, C. *et al.*	P/376	9C, X
ISKENDERIAN, H. P. *et al.*	P/495	12A, III	KELLEY, G. G.	P/66	20C.4, XIV
ISRAEL (Atomic Energy Commission of)	P/772	2.2, I	KELLEY, V. C.	P/29	6B, VI
			KELMAN, L. R. *et al.*	P/557	18B.1, IX
IUSIM, C. H. *et al.*	P/1094	6A, II	KENDALL, J. W. *et al.*	P/405	12A, III
IYENGAR, P. K. *et al.*	P/872	19A, V	KERR, P. F.	P/502	7B, VI
IYENGAR, S. B. D. *et al.*	P/872	19A, V		P/1114	6B, VI
JACKSON, C. B. *et al.*	P/812	19B.1, IX	KETTELWELL, H. B.	P/1079	14C, XII
JACKSON, R. F.	P/762	8A.2, II	KEYS, W. S.	P/41	6B, VI
JACROT, B. *et al.*	P/354	17A, IV	KHANOLKAR, V. R.	P/921	10.C, X
	P/357	19A, V	KIEFFER, W. F. *et al.*	P/741	12B, VII
JAFFE, E. B. *et al.*	P/292	6B, VI	KIESSLING, R.	P/786	18B.1, IX
JAFFEY, A. H. *et al.*	P/809	10B.1, VII	KIMURA, K.	P/1058	9B, VII
JAIMET, C. H. *et al.*	P/9	9C, X	KIMURA, K. *et al.*	P/1059	9B, VII
JAKOVLEV, J. V.	P/632	21C.2, XV	KIMURA, K.	P/1061	2.2, VII
JAMESON, A. S. *et al.*	P/497	13A, XIII	KINCHIN, G. H.	P/442	11B, VII
JAMMET, H. *et al.*	P/369	18C.1, XIII	KING, J. W.	P/286	6B, VI
	P/370	17C.2, XIII	KING, L. D. P.	P/488	9A, II
JANIK, J. A.	P/941	6A, II	KING, L. D. P. *et al.*	P/500	13A, III
JAPAN			KIPIANI, R. Y. *et al.*	P/701	14C, XII
Ministry of International Trade and Industry	P/1036	6B, VI	KISHKIN, S. T. *et al.*	P/703	21C.3, XV
			KITTEL, J. H. *et al.*	P/745	11B, VII
Central Meteorological Laboratory (Tokyo)	P/1051	23B, IX	KITZES, A. S. *et al.*	P/811	20B, IX
			KJELLGREN, B. R. F. *et al.*	P/820	17B.2, VIII
JASINSKI, W. *et al.*	P/944	17C.1, XIII	KLAMUT, C. J. *et al.*	P/118	19B.3, IX
JASPERS, A. M. J. *et al.*	P/930	20C.4, XIV	KLECHKOVSKI, V. M.	P/694	14C, XII
JEFFERSON, S. *et al.*	P/462	22C, XV	KLEIBER, M.	P/93	15C.1, XII
JENKINS, D. W.	P/224	10C, X	KLEINFELD, M. *et al.*	P/321	4.3, XIII
JENTZER, A.	P/1119	9C, X	KLEINHAMPL, F. J. *et al.*	P/509	7B, VI
JOBIN, D. A.	P/32	6B, VI	KLEPPER, M. R. *et al.*	P/14	6B, VI
JOCKEY, P. *et al.*	P/366	8C, X	KNIPLING, E. F. *et al.*	P/114	14C, XII
JOFFRE, H. *et al.*	P/369	18C.1, XIII	KNISELY, R. M. *et al.*	P/184	8C, X
JOHNSON, J. C.	P/470	6B, VI	KNOP, L.	P/988	16B.1, VIII
JOHNSON, J. R. *et al.*	P/559	18B.2, IX	KOCH, J. *et al.*	P/912	7.1, XIV
JOHNSON, T. H.	P/804	8A.1, II	KOCH, L. J. *et al.*	P/501	14A, III
JOHNSTON, M. E. *et al.*	P/206	8C, X	KOCH-WESER, D. *et al.*	P/229	10C, X
JOHNSTON, W. H.	P/150	20C.1, XIV	KOECHLIN, J. C. *et al.*	P/359	19A, V
JOLLEY, W. P. *et al.*	P/74	17C.1, XIII	KOEHLER, J. S. *et al.*	P/749	13B, VII
JOLY, R. *et al.*	P/354	17A, IV	KOHN, H. I. *et al.*	P/87	12C, XI
JONSSON, G. *et al.*	P/791	21A, V	KOKUBU, N. *et al.*	P/1059	9B, VII
JORDAN, D. L. *et al.*	P/81	11C, XI	KOLGANOW, W. Z. *et al.*	P/643	16A.1, IV
			KONDIC, N. *et al.*	P/961	18B.2, IX

Name	Paper Number	Session and Volume
KONDRATYEV, V. N.	P/708	21C.1, XV
KONOBEEVSKY, S. T. et al.	P/680	11B, VII
	P/681	11B, VII
KONZAK, C. F. et al.	P/110	13C, XII
KOO, F. K. S. et al.	P/103	13C.2, XII
KOOI, J.	P/929	10B.2, VII
KOPELMAN, B.	P/531	15B.1, VIII
KORGAONKAR, K. S. et al.	P/905	12C, XI
KORNBERG, H. A. et al.	P/245	17C.1, XIII
	P/281	18C.2, XIII
KOSHLAND, D. E.	P/262	16C, XII
KOSTA, L.	P/989	15B.2, VIII
KOSTAL, G. et al.	P/274	15C.2, XII
KOSTIC, V. et al.	P/994	7B, VI
KOSYAKOV, V. N. et al.	P/675	10B.3, VII
	P/676	10B.3, VII
KOTHARI, L. S. et al.	P/870	6A, II
KOUTS, H. et al.	P/600	21A, V
KOVACEVIC, I. et al.	P/962	2.2, I
KOWARSKI, L.	P/946	8A.1, II
KOZLOVA, A. V.	P/685	8C, X
KRAAYEVELD, P. et al.	P/930	20C.4, XIV
KRASIK, S. et al.	P/601	21A, V
	P/604	21A, V
KRASIN, A. K. et al.	P/662	19A, V
KRASSOIEVITCH, A. et al.	P/1131	23C, XV
KRAUS, K. A.	P/731	10B.1, VII
KRAUS, K. A. et al.	P/837	9B.1, VII
KRAYBILL, H. F. et al.	P/176	23C.2, XV
KRAYBILL, H. R. et al.	P/173	23C.2, XV
KRETCHMAR, A. L. et al.	P/184	8C, X
KRIEGER, H. et al.	P/193	9C, X
KRISHNASWAMY, R. et al.	P/873	14B, VIII
KROHMER, J. S. et al.	P/191	9C, X
	P/203	8C, X
KRONER, R. C. et al.	P/232	21C.1, XV
KRUMHOLZ, P. et al.	P/133	14B, VIII
KRUZHILIN, G. N.	P/620	10A.1, II
KUHN, W. et al.	P/927	16B.1, VIII
KUKAVADSE, G. M. et al.	P/644	17A, IV
KUNIN, R. et al.	P/527	14B, VIII
	P/818	15B.2, VIII
KUNTZ, J. E. et al.	P/105	14C, XII
KURCHATOV, B. V. et al.	P/678	10B.2, VII
KURDIUMOV, G. V.	P/702	21C.3, XV
KURLAND, G. S. et al.	P/185	8C, X
	P/189	9C, X
KURSANOV, A. L.	P/618	7.2, XII
	P/696	14C, XII
		Evening lecture XVI
KUTAITSEV, V. I. et al.	P/680	11B, VII
	P/681	11B, VII
KUZIN, A. M.	P/699	14C, XII
KUZNETSOV, S. I.	P/700	15C.2, XII
LABEYRIE, J. et al.	P/336	11A, III
	P/353	23B.2, IX
LACY, W. J. et al.	P/311	7.3, IX
LAGOS, A. E.	P/1011	15B.2, VIII
LAKIN, H. W. et al.	P/508	7B, VI
LAMARQUE, P. et al.	P/372	12C, XI
LANDRY, J. W.	P/549	21B, IX
LANE, J. A.	P/476	4.1, I
LANG, A. H.	P/1	7B, VI
LANGMAN, W. H. et al.	P/67	20C.4, XIV
LANTZ, P. M. et al.	P/313	19C.2, XIV
LANZL, L. H. et al.	P/210	8C, X
LARANJEIRA, M. et al.	P/975	23B.3, IX
	P/979	9B.2, VII
LARSEN, E. S., Jr. et al.	P/17	6B, VI
LARSON, K. E. et al.	P/791	21A, V
LASSEN, N. O.	P/913	7A, II

Name	Paper Number	Session and Volume
LATHROP, K. A. et al.	P/200	8C, X
LAUGHLIN, J. S. et al.	P/70	20C.2, XIV
LAVERTY, R. A. et al.	P/297	6B, VI
LAVRENCHYK, V. I. et al.	P/659	20A.1, V
LAVRISHCHEV, A. N.	P/619	24.1, XVI
LAWRENCE, E. O.		Evening lecture XVI
LAWRENCE, J. H. et al.	P/96	15C.1, XII
LAWRENCE, J. H.	P/183	8C, X
LAWRENCE, J. H. et al.	P/201	8C, X
	P/841	9C, X
LAWROSKI, S.	P/823	22B.1, IX
LAZZLO, D. et al.	P/212	8C, X
LEACHMAN, R. B.	P /592	7A, II
LEBEDEW, A. W. et al.	P/643	16A.1, IV
LEBEDINSKY, A. V.	P/616	6.1, XI
LEBEZ, D. et al.	P/990	15B.2, VIII
LEDDICOTTE, G. W. et al.	P/117	15B.2, VIII
LEE, K. et al.	P/950	6A, II
	P/951	6A, II
LEGENDRE, P. et al.	P/343	16B.2, VIII
LEHMANN, J. et al.	P/352	18B.1, IX
LEHRER, Y. et al.	P/774	16B.1, VIII
LEITE LOPES, J. et al.	P/897	7A, II
LEMON, R. B. et al.	P/543	21B.1, IX
LENNOX, D. H. et al.	P/598	22A.1, V
LENOBLE, A.	P/338	7B, VI
LEONARD, B. R., Jr.	P/589	17A, IV
LEONARD, C. D. et al.	P/109	14C, XII
LEPRINCE-RINGUET, L.		Evening lecture XVI
LERCH, P. et al.	P/922	16C, XII
LEROY, G. V. et al.	P/842	16C, XI
LESTER SMITH, E. et al.	P/447	10C, X
LETAVET, A. A.	P/689	17C.1, XIII
LEVEQUE, P.	P/342	21C.2, XV
LEVEQUE, P. et al.	P/383	22C, XV
LEWIS, L. et al.	P/64	20C.1, XIV
LEWIS, W. B.	P/4	10A.2, III
LEWIS, W. B. et al.	P/11	5. I
LIBBY, W. F.	P/805	24.1, XVI
		Evening lecture XVI
LICHTENBERGER, H. V. et al.	P/813	14A, III
	P/851	3.1, III
LILLIE, A. B.	P/13	19C.3, XIV
LINACRE, J. K. et al.	P/445	12B, VII
LINARES, E.	P/1000	6B, VI
LINDER, E. G. et al.	P/169	23C.3, XV
LINDQUIST, A. W. et al.	P/114	14C, XII
LINK, L. E. et al.	P/495	12A, III
LIPKIN, H. J. et al.	P/775	22A.2, V
LITTLEFIELD, J. W. et al.	P/265	16C, XII
LITTLER, D. J.	P/432	20A.2, V
LOCKEY, D. J. et al.	P/424	17A, IV
LOCKHART, L. B., Jr. et al.	P/124	19B.3, IX
LOFERSKI, J. J. et al.	P/169	23C.3, XV
LOFGREEN, G. P. et al.	P/93	15C.1, XII
LOFTFIELD, K. B. et al.	P/265	16C, XII
LOMKAZY, G. S. et al.	P/643	16A.1, IV
LONG, E. R. et al.	P/214	10C, X
LONG, G. et al.	P/1110	10B,3, VII
LONG, R. S. et al.	P/523	14B, VIII
	P/524	14B, VIII
LONG, W. G. et al.	P/106	14C, XII
LOONEY, W. B. et al.	P/479	6.1, XI
LOUTIT, J. F.	P/392	6.1, XI
LOUTIT, J. F. et al.	P/393	18C.2, XIII
	P/455	12C, XI
LOVE, J. E. et al.	P/492	11A, III
LOVERDO, A. et al.	P/368	8C, X
LOVERING, T. S. et al.	P/508	7B, VI
LOW-BEER, B. V. A. et al.	P/201	8C, X
LUCAS, H. F. et al.	P/852	6.1, XI
LUESSENHOP, A. J. et al.	P/213	8C, X

Name	Paper Number	Session and Volume	Name	Paper Number	Session and Volume
Luick, J. R. *et al.*	P/93	15C.1, XII	Marley, W. G. *et al.*	P/394	6.2, XIII
Lundby, A. *et al.*	P/888	8A.2, II		P/452	18C.1, XIII
	P/891	7A, II	Marrecas Ferreira, P. *et al.*	P/977	14B, VIII
Lupulescou, A. *et al.*	P/1099	9C, X	Marsh, W. R. *et al.*	P/445	12B, VIII
Lyman, W. J. *et al.*	P/815	13A, III	Martelly, J. *et al.*	P/358	19A, V
Lynn, J. E. *et al.*	P/423	17A, IV		P/359	19A, V
Lyon, R. N.	P/120	19B.2, IX	Martens, F. H. *et al.*	P/598	22A.1, V
Lyon, R. N. *et al.*	P/811	20B, IX	Martin, F. S. *et al.*	P/437	9B.2, VII
			Martin, J. J. *et al.*	P/168	23C.1, XV
Macdonald, R. D. *et al.*	P/520	14B, VIII	Martin, R. P. *et al.*	P/393	18C.2, XIII
MacFadyen, D. A. *et al.*	P/132	7B, VI	Martin, W. J. *et al.*	P/313	19C.2, XIV
MacIntyre, W. J. *et al.*	P/193	9C, X	Martinelli, P. *et al.*	P/383	22C, XV
MacMurray, L. C. *et al.*	P/312	7.3, IX	Martins, M. C. *et al.*	P/970	8C, X
MacPherson, H. G. *et al.*	P/534	16B.2, VIII		P/972	9C, X
McArthur, C. K. *et al.*	P/526	14B, VIII	Marvin, G. *et al.*	P/519	14B, VIII
McCallan, S. E. A. *et al.*	P/100	14C, XII	Mas, F. R. *et al.*	P/1024	9B.2, VII
McClain, J. H. *et al.*	P/533	17B.1, VIII	Mason, E. S. *et al.*	P/802	2.1, I
McClaine, L. A. *et al.*	P/525	14B, VIII	Masurky, H.	P/56	6B, VI
McClean, A. S. *et al.*	P/420	23B.2, IX	De Mattos, B. C. *et al.*	P/145	5, I
McCombs, R. *et al.*	P/201	8C, X	Matvejev, V. V. *et al.*	P/630	15B.2, VIII
McCorkle, W. H. *et al.*	P/859	8A.2, II	Mawson, C. A.	P/12	23B.1, IX
McCormick, D. B. *et al.*	P/252	12C, XI	Mayer, G. *et al.*	P/362	12B, VII
McCormick, W. G. *et al.*	P/255	12C, XI	Mayer, K. M.	P/475	5, I
McCullen, J. D. *et al.*	P/428	20A.3, V	Maynard, L. S. *et al.*	P/270	16C, XII
McCulloh, E. F. *et al.*	P/255	12C, XI	Mayneord, W. V.	P/768	9C, X
McCullough, C. R. *et al.*	P/853	6.2, XIII	Mech, J. F. *et al.*	P/809	10B.1, VII
McDonell, W. R. *et al.*	P/839	12B, VII	Meier, R. W. *et al.*	P/883	20A.1, V
McFarlane, A. S.	P/397	7.2, X	Meissel, M. N.	P/690	12C, XI
McKay, E. J. *et al.*	P/46	6B, VI	Mele, R. Van	P/949	2.2, I
McKay, H. A. C.	P/441	10B.2, VII	Melkonian, E.	P/583	18A, IV
McKay, H. A. C. *et al.*	P/454	18C.1, XIII	Mendivelzua, G.	P/998	2.2, I
McKelvey, V. E.	P/290	6B, VI	Meredith, O. M., Jr. *et al.*	P/190	9C, X
McKelvey, V. E. *et al.*	P/291	6B, VI	Mesquita, M. P. de *et al.*	P/144	8C, X
	P/300	6B, VI	Meyerson, G. A.	P/633	17B.2, VIII
McKeown, F. A. *et al.*	P/46	6B, VI		P/635	15B.1, VIII
McLean, A. S. *et al.*	P/771	18C.2, XIII	Michaelis, M.	P/167	23C.2, XV
McLean, C. S. *et al.*	P/997	14B, VIII	Migirdicyan, E. *et al.*	P/363	12B, VII
McLean, L. *et al.*	P/828	18B.2, IX	Mikaelsen, K. *et al.*	P/889	14C, XII
McMillan, J. A.	P/1017	17B, VIII	Mikaelsen, K.	P/890	13C.2, XII
McReynolds, A. W.	P/807	6A, II	Mikheyev, M. A. *et al.*	P/639	19B.2, IX
Machta, L. *et al.*	P/276	18C.2, XIII	Milcou, St. *et al.*	P/1097	9C, X
Mackin, J. H. *et al.*	P/305	6B, VI		P/1098	9C, X
Macklin, R. L. *et al.*	P/833	20A.1, V		P/1099	9C, X
Maffei, F. J. *et al.*	P/134	14B, VIII	Miles, F. T. *et al.*	P/494	11A, III
Magat, M. *et al.*	P/363	12B, VII	Milhaud, G. *et al.*	P/373	15C.2, XII
Magnusson, L. B. *et al.*	P/809	10B.1, VII	Miller, A. *et al.*	P/754	9C, X
Mahlman, H. A. *et al.*	P/117	15B.2, VIII	Miller, E. C.	P/856	4.3, XIII
Maisin, H. *et al.*	P/940	12C, XI	Miller, L. L. *et al.*	P/219	10C, X
Maisin, J. *et al.*	P/940	12C, XI	Miller, L. P. *et al.*	P/100	14C, XII
Maldague, P. *et al.*	P/940	12C, XI	Miller, R. R. *et al.*	P/124	19B.3, IX
Malm, J. G. *et al.*	P/733	10B.3, VII	Miller, S. E. *et al.*	P/258	17C.2, XIII
Malvicini, A. *et al.*	P/995	23B.3, IX	Miller, W. E. *et al.*	P/118	19B.3, IX
Mancini, R. E. *et al.*	P/1031	16C, XII	Mills, M. M. *et al.*	P/853	6.2, XIII
	P/1032	16C, XII	Mills, W. A. *et al.*	P/65	20C.3, XIV
Mandel, H. G. *et al.*	P/98	16C, XII	Milner, G. W. C.	P/412	20B, IX
Mandil, I. H. *et al.*	P/815	13A, III	Milojevic, A. *et al.*	P/994	7B, VI
Mandl, M. E. *et al.*	P/430	23A, V	Minami, E. *et al.*	P/1059	9B, VII
Mandleberg, C. J. *et al.*	P/1110	10B.3, VII	Mirkov, M. *et al.*	P/962	2.2, I
Mani, G. S. *et al.*	P/872	19A, V	Mitchell, J. S.	P/446	8C, X
Mann, M. M. *et al.*	P/490	9A, II	Mitchell, W.	P/854	4.3, XIII
Manning, W. M. *et al.*	P/809	10B.1, VII	Mitsui, S.	P/1040	14C, XII
Manov, G. G.	P/857	4.3, XIII		P/1049	14C, XII
Manowitz, B. *et al.*	P/553	22B.2, IX	Miyake, Y.	P/1055	18C.2, XIII
Mapel, W. J.	P/54	6B, VI		P/1057	18C.2, XIII
Marais, P. G. *et al.*	P/460	14C, XII	Moeller, D. W. *et al.*	P/233	21C.1, XV
Marcovich, H.	P/371	12, XI	Mogard, H.	P/787	19B.3, IX
Margem, N. *et al.*	P/136	15B.2, VIII	Mollin, D. L. *et al.*	P/447	10C, X
	P/140	10C, X	Mondet, L. *et al.*	P/343	16B.2, VIII
Maricic, S. *et al.*	P/992	16B.2, VIII	Monson, H. O. *et al.*	P/501	14A, III
Marinelli, L. D. *et al.*	P/478	6.1, XI	Mooney, R. T. *et al.*	P/211	8C, X
Marks, P. A. *et al.*	P/268	16C, XII	Morales, L. J. de	P/127	6B, VI

Name	Paper Number	Session and Volume
MOREL, F. *et al.*	P/379	15C.1, XII
MORFITT, J. W. *et al.*	P/834	20A.3, V
MORGAN, B. *et al.*	P/174	23C.2, XV
MORGAN, K. Z. *et al.*	P/79	17C.1, XIII
MORIWAKI, D. *et al.*	P/1042	13C.2, XII
MOROSOV, I. G. *et al.*	P/662	19A, V
MORPHEW, A. *et al.*	P/519	14B, VIII
MORRIS, S. B.	P/849	5, I
MORTIMER, R. K. *et al.*	P/158	20C.2, XIV
MORTON, G. A.	P/61	20C.4, XIV
MORTON, M. E. *et al.*	P/217	10C, X
MORTON, R. J. *et al.*	P/311	7.3, IX
	P/554	23B.1, IX
MOSTOVOI, V. I. *et al.*	P/640	15A, IV
	P/645	17A, IV
MOTTA, E. E.	P/542	22B.1, IX
MOTTA REZENDE, E.	P/125	2.2, I
MOURET, P. *et al.*	P/339	14B, VIII
MULLENBACH, P.	P/810	5, I
MULLER, H. J.	P/234	13C.1, XI
MULLER, J. H.	P/925	8C, X
MULLER, W. E. *et al.*	P/118	19B.3, IX
MULNER, C. W. C. *et al.*	P/412	20B, IX
MUMMERY, P. W.	P/429	21A, V
MURATI, K. *et al.*	P/1042	13C.2, XII
MURIN, I. D. *et al.*	P/642	16A.1, IV
	P/661	19A, V
MURPHY, G. *et al.*	P/556	18B.1, IX
MURTHY, T. K. S. *et al.*	P/871	14B, VIII
MUSA, R. C. *et al.*	P/116	15B.2, VIII
	P/521	14B, VIII
MYERS, A. T. *et al.*	P/288	6B, VI
MYERS, W. M. *et al.*	P/103	13C.2, XII
MYERSCOUGH, L. C. *et al.*	P/461	19C.2, XIV
MYTTON, J. W. *et al.*	P/289	6B, VI
NAGGIAR, V. *et al.*	P/355	17A, IV
NAKAIDZUMI, M.	P/1041	17C.1, XIII
	P/1062	7.2, X
	P/1065	9C, X
	P/1068	23C.2, XV
NASSIFF, S. J.	P/1027	9B.2, VII
NAZAROV, S. T.	P/705	22C, XV
NEARY, G. J. *et al.*	P/401	8A.1, II
NEGOESCOU, I. *et al.*	P/1098	9C, X
NELSON, F. *et al.*	P/837	9B.1, VII
NELSON, N. C. *et al.*	P/469	2.2, I
NEMIROVSKI, P. E.	P/654	6A, II
NETTER, F. *et al.*	P/354	17A, IV
	P/355	17A, IV
	P/357	19A, V
NEUERBURG, G. J.	P/16	6B, VI
NEUMAN, W. F.	P/847	11C, XI
NEUPOCOYEV, B. A. *et al.*	P/661	19A, V
NEW ZEALAND — STATE HYDRO ELECTRIC DEPARTMENT	P/1082	2.2, I
NICHIPOROVICH, A. A.	P/697	15C.2, XII
NICHOLS, C. M.	P/414	21B, IX
NICHOLS, C. M. *et al.*	P/454	18C.1, XIII
NIELSEN, K. O. *et al.*	P/912	7.1, XIV
NIETZEL, O. A. *et al.*	P/532	15B.2, VIII
NIKITIN, S. J. *et al.*	P/623	9A, II
	P/643	6A, II
	P/646	17A, IV
	P/658	18A, IV
NIKOLAYEV, N. A. *et al.*	P/615	3.1, III
NIKOLAEV, Y. G.	P/621	9A, II
	P/622	9A, II
NILSSON, G. *et al.*	P/785	21B, IX
NIVEN, C. F. Jr. *et al.*	P/173	23C.2, XV
NORDQVIST, B.	P/1106	2.2, I
NOSSOFF, V. G.	P/653	7A, II

Name	Paper Number	Session and Volume
NOVAKOVIC, M. *et al.*	P/960	16B.1, VIII
	P/961	18B.2, IX
NOVICK, M. *et al.*	P/813	14A, III
NÚÑEZ, C.	P/1029	9C, X
	P/1030	16C, XII
NÚÑEZ, C. *et al.*	P/1031	16C, XII
	P/1032	16C, XII
NUSSIS, N. *et al.*	P/1018	9B.2, VII
	P/1021	9B.2, VII
O'BRIEN, J. F. *et al.*	P/63	20C.3, XIV
O'BRIEN, J. M. *et al.*	P/92	15C.1, XII
ODUM, E. P.	P/480	18C.2, XIII
OKADA, Y. *et al.*	P/1048	15C.1, XII
OKOROKOW, W. W. *et al.*	P/646	17A, IV
OKRENT, D. *et al.*	P/609	22A.1, V
OLESON, F. B. *et al.*	P/64	20C.1, XIV
OLSON, J. C. *et al.*	P/304	6B, VI
OLSON, R. S. *et al.*	P/522	14B, VIII
OREKHOVISH, V. N.	P/686	16C, XII
ORTAVANT, R.	P/381	14C, XII
OSTANEK, M. *et al.*	P/990	15B.2, VIII
OSTERLUNDH, C. G. *et al.*	P/794	23C.3, XV
OSTERWALD, F. W. *et al.*	P/23	6B, VI
	P/25	6B, VI
OSTERWALD, F. W.	P/28	6B, VI
OTERO, J. C. *et al.*	P/1120	16B.1, VIII
OVERHOLT, D. C. *et al.*	P/732	10B.1, VII
OVERMAN, R. T.	P/755	24.2, I
OVERSTREET, W. C. *et al.*	P/306	6B, VI
	P/505	7B, VI
PACK, D. H. *et al.*	P/276	18C.2, XIII
PAGE, L. R.	P/504	7B, VI
PAGNY, P. *et al.*	P/339	14B, VIII
PAHISSA CAMPA, J. *et al.*	P/1018	9B.2, VII
	P/1021	9B.2, VII
PAINE, S. H. *et al.*	P/745	11B, VII
PAINTAL, A. S.	P/874	15C.1, XII
PALACIOS, J. *et al.*	P/970	8C, X
PALACIOS, J.	P/971	9C, X
PALACIOS, J. *et al.*	P/976	15B.2, VIII
PALADI, R. *et al.*	P/1096	10B.3, VII
PALEVSKY, H.	P/587	18A, IV
PALEY, P. N.	P/629	15B.2, VIII
PALLADIN, A. V. *et al.*	P/710	16C, XII
PALLADINO, N. J. *et al.*	P/815	13A, III
PALMER, E. L. *et al.*	P/184	8C, X
PAPPAS, A. C.	P/881	8B.1, VII
PARHON, C. I. *et al.*	P/1125	9C, X
PARK, C.	P/1115	2.2, I
PARKER, G. W. *et al.*	P/313	19C.2, XIV
	P/723	8B.2, VII
PARKER, H. M.	P/240	18C.1, XIII
PARKER, H. M. *et al.*	P/245	17C.1, XIII
	P/248	18C.1, XIII
PARKER, H. M.	P/279	18C.2, XIII
PARKER, H. M. *et al.*	P/482	6.2, XIII
	P/565	23B.1, IX
PARKINS, W. E.	P/499	14A, III
PARRISH, D. *et al.*	P/207	9C, X
PASCAL, M. *et al.*	P/333	11A, III
PASECHNIK, M. V.	P/714	6A, II
PATTENDEN, N. J. *et al.*	P/423	17A, IV
PAVLOVIC, B. *et al.*	P/958	16B.1, VIII
PAYNE, J. H. *et al.*	P/115	14C, XII
PELLERIN, P. *et al.*	P/376	9C, X
PELSER, J.	P/934	22A.2, V
PENNEMAN, R. A. *et al.*	P/838	10B.3, VII
PEPELYAEVA, E. A. *et al.*	P/634	17B.1, IX
PEREZ, W. *et al.*	P/136	15B.2, VIII
PEREZ-FERNANDES, M. A. *et al.*	P/970	8C, X
	P/972	9C, X

Name	Paper Number	Session and Volume
Rossi, H. H. *et al.*	P/59	20C.1, XIV
Roth, E. *et al.*	P/348	20B, IX
Rothstein, A.	P/267	16C, XII
Roubault, M.	P/328	6B, VI
Rough, F. A. *et al.*	P/558	18B.1, IX
Rouguin, A. *et al.*	P/336	11A, III
Rule, J. H. *et al.*	P/194	8C, X
Rupp, A. F.	P/314	19C.2, XIV
	P/315	19C.3, XIV
Russell, E. W. *et al.*	P/460	14C, XII
Russell, L. B, *et al.*	P/77	11C, XI
Russell, W. L. *et al.*	P/77	11C, XI
Russell, W. L.	P/235	13C.1, XI
Ruther, W. E. *et al.*	P/535	20B, IX
Ryabchikov, D. I. *et al.*	P/628	15B.2, VIII
Saba, N. *et al.*	P/843	16C XII
Sadaoka, G. *et al.*	P/115	14C, XII
Saeland, E. *et al.*	P/882	22C, XV
	P/888	8A.2, II
Sahasrabudhe, M. B. *et al.*	P/905	12C, XI
Sahleanu, V. *et al.*	P/1097	9C, X
Sailor, V. L.	P/586	17A, IV
Saint-James, R. *et al.*	P/347	17B.1, VIII
Saito, N. *et al.*	P/1059	9B, VII
Sajin, N. P. *et al.*	P/634	17B.1, VIII
	P/637	19B, IX
Sakakura, A. Y.	P/518	7B, VI
Salerno, P. R. *et al.*	P/75	11C, XI
Saller, H. A. *et al.*	P/558	18B.1, IX
Saller, H. A.	P/562	18B.2, IX
Salles Fonseca, A. de *et al.*	P/144	8C, X
Salvetti, C. *et al.*	P/920	21A, V
Samarin, A. M.	P/707	22C, XV
Sambucetti, C. *et al.*	P/1004	15B.2, VIII
	P/1005	15B.2, VIII
Samsahl, K. *et al*	P/886	19C.2, XIV
Sanders, J. E. *et al.*	P/425	18A, IV
Santalo, L. A. *et al.*	P/1003	23A, V
Saraiya, P. R. *et al.*	P/921	10C, X
Sasaki, R.	P/1046	15C.1, XII
	P/1047	15C.1, XII
	P/1066	18C.2, XIII
	P/1067	15C.1, XII
Sasaki, Y. *et al.*	P/1059	9B, VII
Sato, S. *et al.*	P/1053	22C, XV
Saukoff, A. A.	P/626	7B, VI
Savard, K. *et al.*	P/843	16C, XII
Savic, P. *et al.*	P/958	16B.1, VIII
	P/960	16B.1, VIII
Savolainen, J. E. *et al.*	P/547	21B, IX
Scazziga, B. R. *et al.*	P/924	9C, X
Schee, B. L. A. van der *et al.*	P/936	11A, III
	P/938	11A, III
Schiller, S. *et al.*	P/271	15C.2, XII
Schlesinger, M. J., Jr. *et al.*	P/159	20C.4, XIV
Schmid, P. *et al.*	P/883	20A.1, V
	P/916	23A, V
Schmidt, D. L. *et al.*	P/305	6B, VI
Schnabel, R. W. *et al.*	P/15	6B, VI
	P/47	6B, VI
Schonland, B. F. J.	P/1078	5, I
Schubert, J.	P/845	18C.1, XIII
Schulte, J. W. *et al.*	P/318	19C.2, XIV
Schwarz, H. A. *et al.*	P/155	20C.4, XIV
Schweigert, B. S. *et al.*	P/173	23C.2, XV
Schwenk, E. *et al.*	P/843	16C, XII
Scott Keys, W.	P/41	6B, VI
Scott Russell, R. *et al.*	P/393	18C.2, XIII
	P/460	14C, XII
Scully, N. J. *et al.*	P/274	15C.2, XII
Seal, M. S. *et al.*	P/233	21C.1, XV
Sears, G. W. *et al.*	P/735	10B.3, VII

Name	Paper Number	Session and Volume
Secoy, C. H.	P/821	20B, IX
Seelman-Eggebert, W. *et al.*	P/1008	15B.2, VIII
	P/1019	9B.2, VII
	P/1022	9B.2, VII
	P/1023	9B.2, VII
	P/1026	9B.2, VII
	P/1027	9B.2, VII
Segal, S. *et al.*	P/1125	9C, X
Seiffert, R. L. *et al.*	P/735	10B.3, VII
Seitz, F. *et al.*	P/749	13B, VII
Seitz, J. *et al.*	P/1033	6A, II
Seligman, H.	P/395	7.1, XIV
	P/418	23B.2, IX
Senyavin, M. M. *et al.*	P/628	15B.2, VIII
Serban, J. *et al.*	P/363	12B, VII
Serduk, R. L. *et al.*	P/624	12A, III
Sesa, M. A. de *et al.*	P/532	15B.2, VIII
Severin, S. E.	P/687	16C, XII
Sevette, P. *et al.*	P/1116	2.2, I
Shankar, J. *et al.*	P/871	14B, VIII
Shapiro, B. *et al.*	P/776	16C, XII
	P/878	12C, XI
Shapiro, F. L. *et al.*	P/642	16A.1, IV
	P/661	19A, V
Shapiro, J. *et al.*	P/76	17C.2, XIII
Shapiro, S. *et al.*	P/110	13C, XII
Sharp, B. J.	P/19	6B, VI
Sharp, W. N. *et al.*	P/46	6B, VI
Shaw, K. G. *et al.*	P/523	14B, VIII
Shaw, M. *et al.*	P/815	13A, III
Shawe, D. R.	P/36	6B, VI
Shelton, S. M. *et al.*	P/533	17B.1, VIII
Shemin, D.	P/846	16C, XII
Shen, J. T.	P/865	6B, VI
Shepherd, L. R.	P/404	22A.1, V
Sher, R. *et al.*	P/600	21A, V
Shevchik, A. *et al.*	P/798	4.1, I
Shevchik, A.	P/799	2.2, I
Shimane, C.	P/801	19C.1, XIV
Shiraishi, N. *et al.*	P/1053	22C, XV
Shliapnikov, R. S. *et al.*	P/630	15B.2, VIII
Shlik, A. A. *et al.*	P/715	15C.2, XII
Shoemaker, E. M.	P/48	6B, VI
Shorm, F.	P/800	24.1, XVI
Shorr, W.	P/171	23C.3, XV
Shtranikh, I. V. *et al.*	P/642	16A.1, IV
	P/661	19A, V
Shull, C. G. *et al.*	P/579	6A, II
Shvetsov, I. K. *et al.*	P/674	10B.2, VII
Siegel, E. *et al.*	P/212	8C, X
Siegel, J. M.	P/269	15C.2, XII
Siegel, S. *et al.*	P/829	19B.3, IX
Siegel, S. *et al.*	P/737	12B, VII
Sievert, R. M.	P/792	17C.1, XIII
Siggerud, T.	P/887	6B, VI
Silberberg, M. *et al.*	P/118	19B.3, IX
Silberman, E.	P/1010	16B.1, VIII
Sill, C. W. *et al.*	P/483	6.2, XIII
Silva, E. *et al.*	P/897	7A, II
Silva, J. A. *et al.*	P/115	14C, XII
Silver, L. T. *et al.*	P/850	14B, VIII
Silverman, L.	P/571	23B.3, IX
Simon, R. H. *et al.*	P/317	19C.2, XIV
Simpson, J. W. *et al.*	P/815	13A, III
Simpson, O. C. *et al.*	P/735	10B.3, VII
Sims, P. K. *et al.*	P/21	6B, VI
Singewald, Q. D. *et al.*	P/303	6B, VI
Singleton, W. R. *et al.*	P/110	13C, XII
Singwi, K. S. *et al.*	P/870	14B, VIII
Sissakian, N. M.	P/691	12C, XI
Siu, R. G. H. *et al.*	P/174	23C.2, XV
Sjoblom, R. *et al.*	P/809	10B.1, VII

Name	Paper Number	Session and Volume
THADEN, R. E. et al.	P/42	6B, VI
THAILAND, DELEGATION OF	P/956	6B, VI
THALCOTT, F. W. et al.	P/813	14A, III
THEIS, C. V.	P/564	23B.1, IX
THEOBOLD, P. K. et al.	P/505	7B, VI
THIEBERGER, R. et al.	P/775	22A.2, V
THODE, H. G. et al.	P/9	9C, X
THOMAS, C. I. et al.	P/191	9C, X
	P/203	8C, X
THOMAS, D. E.	P/537	20B, IX
THOMAS, H. A. JR.	P/226	21C.1, XV
THOMAS, J. T. et al	P/834	20A.3, V
THOMPSON R, C. et al.	P/245	17C.1, XIII
THOMPSON. W. M. et al.	P/69	19C.3, XIV
THORNTON, R. L. et al.	P/584	15A, IV
THREEFOOT, S. A. et al.	P/844	10C, X
THUNAES, A.	P/2	14B, VIII
THURLOW, E. E.	P/27	6B, VI
TISCHER, R. G. et al.	P/174	23C.2, XV
TITEICA, S. et al.	P/1094	6A, II
TOBIAS, C. A. et al.	P/158	20C.2, XIV
	P/201	8C, X
TOLBERT, B. M. et al.	P/96	15C.1, XII
TOM, C. W. et al.	P/516	7B, VI
TOMLINSON, R. E.	P/824	21B, IX
TOOKER, E. W. et al.	P/21	6B, VI
TOURKY, A. R.	P/1107	15B, VIII
TOURNARIE, M. et al.	P/362	12B, VII
TRESHOW, M. et al.	P/495	12A, III
TRETHEWAY, H. C. et al.	P/448	11C, XI
TRICOU, B. J. et al.	P/229	10C, X
TRITES, A. F. et al.	P/42	6B, VI
TRLIFAJ, L.	P/796	23A, V
TROCKI, T. et al.	P/123	19B.1, IX
TROMBKA, J. et al.	P/196	9C, X
TRUMPY, G. et al.	P/888	8A.2, II
TSITOVICH, A. P. et al.	P/640	15A, IV
	P/645	17A, IV
TSIVOGLOU, E. C.	P/230	17C.2, XIII
TSUJII, T. et al.	P/1048	15C.1, XII
TSUPRUN, L. I. et al.	P/638	19B.3, IX
TSUZUKI, M.	P/1037	6.1, XI
	P/1043	11C, XI
	P/1044	11C, XI
	P/1045	11C, XI
TUBIANA, M. et al.	P/366	8C, X
TUKEY, H. B. et al.	P/106	14C, XII
TURK, E. et al.	P/721	8B.1, VII
TURKEVICH, J.	P/163	21C.1, XV
TUROVLIN, B. et al.	P/828	18B.2, IX
TWENHOFEL, W. S. et al.	P/301	6B, VI
UNGAR, F. et al.	P/843	16C, XII
UNITED NATIONS	P/893	5, I
	P/902	2.1, I
	P/1116	2.2, I
UNITED NATIONS EDUCATIONAL, SCIENTIFIC AND CULTURAL ORGANIZATION	P/946	8A.1, II
	P/983	24.2, I
UNITED STATES ATOMIC ENERGY COMMISSION et al.	P/471	6B, VI
	P/503	7B, VI
UNITED STATES GEOLOGICAL SURVEY STAFF et al.	P/471	6B, VI
	P/503	7B, VI
UPCHURCH, T. et al.	P/519	14B, VIII
URBANEC, J.	P/795	20C.3, XIV
URETZ, R. B. et al.	P/94	12C, XI
USSACHOFF, L. N.	P/656	23A, 5
USSING, H. H.	P/908	15C.1, XII
UZAN, R. et al.	P/365	9C, X

Name	Paper Number	Session and Volume
VACIRCA, S. J. et al.	P/70	20C.2, XIV
VAES, J. F. et al.	P/1105	6B, VI
VANBLARCOM, E. et al.	P/519	14B, VIII
VAN DILLA, M. et al.	P/189	9C, X
VAN DYKEN, A. R. et al.	P/149	21C.1, XV
VANOTTI, A. et al.	P/922	16C, XII
	P/924	9C, X
VARLEY, J. H. O.	P/444	13B, VII
VEKSLER, V. I.	Evening Lecture XVI	
VECHVARZHY, I. et al.	P/798	4.1, I
VENDRYES, G. et al.	P/354	17A, IV
VERA PALOMINO, J. et al.	P/1121	6B, VI
VERGNE, J. et al.	P/329	4.3, XIII
VERTES, P. et al.	P/341	15B.1, VIII
VESELOVSKY, V. I.	P/682	12B, VII
VICKERS, R. C.	P/307	6B, VI
VIDEIRA, F. et al.	P/977	14B, VIII
VIDELA, G. J. et al.	P/1016	17B, VIII
VILLAGA, S. S. et al.	P/897	7A, II
VILLAR, G. E. et al.	P/1085	2.2, I
	P/1086	2.2, I
	P/1087	5, I
	P/1088	19C, XIV
VINE, J. D.	P/55	6B, VI
VINOGRADOV, A. P.	P/627	15B.2, VIII
VISKY, T. et al.	P/1089	7A, II
VLADIMIROV, G. E. et al.	P/710	16C, XII
VLADIMIRSKI, K. V. et al.	P/631	16B.1, VIII
VLADIMIRSKI, V. V. et al.	P/623	9A, II
	P/641	17A, IV
	P/658	18A, IV
VOGEL, H. H. et al.	P/81	11C, XI
VOGEL, R. C. et al.	P/546	22B.1, IX
VOGT, F.	P/877	2.2, I
VOHRA, K. G.	P/869	7B, VI
VOIGT, A. F.	P/545	22B.1, IX
VOMOCIL, J. A.	P/113	14C, XII
VONDERLAGE, F. C. et al.	P/755	24.2, I
VOROBYEV, A. M. et al.	P/674	10B.2, VII
VOSKERENSKY, K. D. et al.	P/639	19B.2, IX
VOSS, M. et al.	P/556	18B.1, IX
WADIA, D. N.	P/875	6B, VI
WAGNER, H. A. et al	P/491	12A, III
WAGNER, R. L. JR. et al.	P/273	16C, XII
WAINWRIGHT, W. W.	P/188	10C, X
WALKER, G. W. et al.	P/25	6B, VI
WALLACE, B.	P/238	13C.1, XI
WALLACE, S. R. et al.	P/304	6B, VI
WALLHAUSEN, C. W.	P/170	23C.1, XV
WALOSCHEK, P. J. et al.	P/1076	6A, II
WALSH. V. et al.	P/600	21A, V
WALT, M.	P/588	6A, II
WALTER, H. et al.	P/222	16C, XII
WALTON, G. N. et al.	P/435	9B.2, VII
	P/436	9B.2, VII
WARD, A. G.	P/6	20A.2, V
WARD, F. N. et al.	P/508	7B, VI
WARNER, W. T. et al.	P/828	18B.2, IX
WARREN, S.	P/309	7.2, X
WATABE, N. et al.	P/1048	15C.1, XII
WATANABE, R. et al.	P/274	15C.2, XII
WATKINS, J. W. et al.	P/161	21C.1, XV
WEBER, C. E. et al.	P/561	18B.2, IX
WEEKS, A. D.	P/295	6B, VI
WEEKS, J. R. et al.	P/118	19B.3, IX
WEIL, J.	P/335	12A, III
WEIL, J. et al.	P/353	23B.2, IX
WEINBERG, A. M. et al.	P/490	9A, II
	P/862	10A.2, III
WEINSTOCK, B. et al.	P/733	10B.3, VII
WEISS, J. et al.	P/155	20C.2, XIV

Name	Paper Number	Session and Volume	Name	Paper Number	Session and Volume
WEISSKOPF, V. F.	P/830	6A, II	WOOD, H. B.	P/30	6B, VI
WELTON, T. A.	P/610	22A.2, V	WOOD, H. B. et al.	P/517	7B, VI
WENT, J. J. et al.	P/936	11A, III	WOODS, W. R. et al.	P/746	11B, VII
	P/938	11A, III	WORLD HEALTH ORGANIZATION	P/778	4.3, XIII
WERNER, C. B. et al.	P/812	19B.1, IX		P/779	24.2, I
WEST, J. M. et al.	P/495	12A, III	WRIGHT, J. et al.	P/401	8A, II
	P/497	13A, III		P/445	12B, VII
WESTOVER, J. L. et al.	P/190	9C, X		P/900	20B, IX
WEXLER, H. et al.	P/276	18C.2, XIII	WYANT, D. G. et al.	P/14	6B, VI
WHEAT, J. D. et al.	P/264	16C, XII	WYMER, R. G. et al.	P/547	21B, IX
WHEELER, J. A.	P/593	7A, II			
WHITE, A. M. et al.	P/46	6B, VI	YAKOVLEV, G. N. et al.	P/672	8B.2, VII
	P/306	6B, VI		P/676	10B.3, VII
WHITE, A. S. et al.	P/466	24.2, I		P/677	10B.2, VII
WHITE, F. A. et al.	P/595	18A, IV		P/678	10B.2, VII
WHITE, F. D. et al.	P/276	18C.2, XIII	YAMASAKI, F.	P/1069	20C.4, XIV
WHITE, H. J. JR.	P/160	21C, XV	YEFIMOV, B. V. et al.	P/645	17A, IV
WHITE, M. G.	P/130	6B, VI	YENSON, M. et al.	P/222	16C, XII
WHITE, W. F. et al.	P/249	12C, XI	YEROZOLIMSKY, B. G. et al.	P/657	18A, IV
WHITLOW, J. W. et al.	P/505	7B, VI	YOSHI, G. et al.	P/1048	15C.1, XII
WIBLIN, E. R.	P/421	15A, IV	YOUNGQUIST, C. H. et al.	P/725	10B.1, VII
WILDE, W. S. et al.	P/92	15C.1, XII	YUHL, E. T. et al.	P/208	8C, X
WILHELM, H. A. et al.	P/556	18B.1, IX	YUN, T. S.	P/1118	6B, VI
WILHELM, H. A.	P/817	15B.2, VIII	YVON, J. et al.	P/337	11A, III
WILHELMI, Z.	P/945	6A, II	YVON, J.	P/387	9A, II
WILHELMSEN, M. et al.	P/483	6.2, XIII			
WILKINS, J. E. JR. et al	P/597	19A, V	ZABALA, I. et al.	P/1019	9B.2, VII
WILLARD, J. E.	P/147	21C.2, XV	ZACHARIASEN, W. H. et al.	P/730	10B.1, VII
WILLIAMS, C. et al.	P/494	11A, III	ZAMECNIK, P. C. et al.	P/265	16C, XII
WILLIAMS, C. R.	P/320	19C.2, XIV	ZAMYCHKINA, K. S. et al.	P/688	15C.1, XII
WILLIAMS, D. D. et al.	P/124	19B.3, IX	ZARETZKY, D. F. et al.	P/655	23A, V
WILLIAMS, G. A. et al.	P/34	6B, VI	ZARETZKY, D. F.	P/667	23A, V
WILZBACH, K. E. et al.	P/149	21C.1, XV	ZAVOISKY, W. H. et al.	P/624	12A, III
WIMETT, T. F. et al.	P/831	16A.3, II	ZELLER, H. D. et al.	P/507	7B, VI
WINSBERG, L. et al.	P/773	7B, VI	ZENKEVICH, V. S. et al.	P/645	17A, IV
WINTHER, B. et al.	P/891	7A, II	ZIMMER, E. L.	P/996	14B, VIII
WIRTZ, K.	P/1132	16B.2, VIII	ZINN, W. H.	P/814	12A, III
WISWALL, R. H. JR. et al.	P/550	22B.1, IX	ZINN, W. H. et al.	P/851	3.1, III
WITKIND, I. J.	P/40	6B, VI		P/859	8A.2, II
WITT, E. et al.	P/1004	15B.2, VIII	ZINN, W. H.	P/861	10A.1, II
	P/1005	15B.2, VIII	ZIRKLE, R. E. et al.	P/94	12C, XI
WITTELS, M. C. et al.	P/753	13B, VII	ZLOTOWSKI, I. et al.	P/944	17C.1, XIII
WITTWER, S. H. et al.	P/106	14C, XII	ZUNTI, W. et al.	P/915	9A, II
WOLDRINGH, H. H.	P/937	23A, V	ZUPPINGER, A.	P/926	11C, XI
WOLLAN, E. O. et al.	P/579	6A, II	ZVYAGINTSEV, O. F.	P/670	9B.2, VII
WOLMAN, A. et al.	P/310	7.3, IX	ZWIFEL, P. F. et al.	P/597	19A, V

PEACEFUL USES OF ATOMIC ENERGY:

Proceedings of the International Conference in Geneva, August 1955.

The following is a complete listing of the sixteen volumes which comprise this publication, together with the main subjects covered by each volume.

SALES AGENTS FOR UNITED NATIONS PUBLICATIONS

Editorial Sudamericana S.A., Alsina 500, Buenos Aires.

AUSTRALIA
ARGENTINA
H. A. Goddard, 255a George St., Sydney; 90 Queen St., Melbourne.
Melbourne University Press, Carlton N.3, Victoria.

AUSTRIA
B. Wüllerstorff, Markus Sittikusstrasse 10, Salzburg.
Gerold & Co., Graben 31, Wien.

BELGIUM
Agence et Messageries de la Presse S.A., 14-22 rue du Persil, Bruxelles.
W. H. Smith & Son, 71-75, boulevard Adolphe-Max, Bruxelles.

BOLIVIA
Librería Selecciones, Casilla 972, La Paz.

BRAZIL
Livraria Agir, Río de Janeiro, Sao Paulo and Belo Horizonte.

CAMBODIA
Papeterie-Librairie Nouvelle, Albert Portail, 14 Avenue Boulloche, Pnom-Penh.

CANADA
Ryerson Press, 299 Queen St. West, Toronto.
Periodica, Inc., 5112 Ave. Papineau, Montreal.

CEYLON
Lake House Bookshop, The Associated Newspapers of Ceylon, Ltd., P. O. Box 244, Colombo.

CHILE
Librería Ivens, Casilla 205, Santiago.
Editorial del Pacífico, Ahumada 57, Santiago.

CHINA
The World Book Co., Ltd., 99 Chungking Road, 1st Section, Taipeh, Taiwan.
Commercial Press, 211 Honan Rd., Shanghai.

COLOMBIA
Librería América, Medellín.
Librería Nacional Ltda., Barranquilla.
Librería Buchholz Galería, Bogotá.

COSTA RICA
Trejos Hermanos, Apartado 1313, San José.

CUBA
La Casa Belga, O'Reilly 455, La Habana.

CZECHOSLOVAKIA
Ceskoslovensky Spisovatel, Národní Trída 9, Praha 1.

DENMARK
Einar Munksqaard, Ltd., Norregade 6, Kobenhavn, K.

DOMINICAN REPUBLIC
Librería Dominicana, Mercedes 49, Ciudad Trujillo.

ECUADOR
Librería Científica, Guayaquil and Quito.

EGYPT
Librarie "La Renaissance d'Egypte," 9 Sh. Adly Pasha, Cairo.

EL SALVADOR
Manuel Navas y Cía., 1a. Avenida sur 37, San Salvador.

FINLAND
Akateeminen Kirjakauppa, 2 Keskuskatu, Helsinki.

FRANCE
Editons A. Pedone, 13, rue Soufflot, Paris V.

GERMANY
Elwert & Meurer, Hauptstrasse 101, Berlin-Schoneberg.
W. E. Saarbach, Gereonstrasse 25-29, Köln (22c).
Alexander Horn, Spiegelgasse 9, Wiesbaden.

GREECE
Kauffmann Bookshop, 28 Stadion Street, Athens.

HAITI
Librairie "A la Caravelle," Boîte postale 111-B, Port-au-Prince.

HONDURAS
Librería Panamericana, Tegucigalpa.

HONG KONG
The Swindon Book Co., 25 Nathan Road, Kowloon.

ICELAND
Bokaverzlun Sigfusar Eymundssonar H. F., Austurstraeti 18, Reykjavik.

INDIA
Orient Longmans, Calcutta, Bombay, and Madras.
Oxford Book & Stationery Co., New Delhi and Calcutta.
P. Varadachary & Co., Madras.

INDONESIA
Pembangunan, Ltd., Gunung Sahari 84, Djakarta.

IRAN
"Guity", 482 Avenue Ferdowsi, Teheran.

IRAQ
Mackenzie's Bookshop, Baghdad.

ISRAEL
Blumstein's Bookstores Ltd., 35 Allenby Road, Tel-Aviv.

ITALY
Librería Commissionaria Sansoni, Via Gina Capponi 26, Firenze.

JAPAN
Maruzen Company, Ltd., 6 Tori-Nichome, Nihonbashi, Tokyo.

LEBANON
Librairie Universelle, Beyrouth.

LIBERIA
J. Momolu Kamara, Monrovia.

LUXEMBOURG
Librairie J. Schummer, Luxembourg.

MEXICO
Editorial Hermes S.A., Ignacio Mariscal 41, México, D.F.

NETHERLANDS
N.V. Martinus Nijhoff, Lange Voorhout 9, 's-Gravenhage.

NEW ZEALAND
United Nations Association of New Zealand, C.P.O. 1011, Wellington.

NORWAY
Johan Grundt Tanum Forlag, Kr. Augustsgt. 7A, Oslo.

PAKISTAN
Thomas & Thomas, Karachi.
Publishers United Ltd., Lahore.
The Pakistan Cooperative Book Society, Dacca and Chittagong (East Pak.).

PANAMA
José Menéndez, Plaza de Arango, Panamá.

PARAGUAY
Agencia de Librerías de Salvador Nizza, Calle Pte. Franco No. 39-43, Asunción.

PERU
Librería Internacional del Peru, S. A., Lima and Arequipa.

PHILIPPINES
Alemar's Book Store, 749 Rizal Avenue, Manila.

PORTUGAL
Livraria Rodrigues, 186 Rua Aurea, Lisboa.

SINGAPORE
The City Book Store, Ltd., Winchester House, Collyer Quay.

SPAIN
Librería Bosch, 11 Ronda Universidad, Barcelona.
Librería Mundi-Prensa, Lagasca 38, Madrid.

SWEDEN
C. E. Fritze's Kungl. Hovbokhandel A-B, Fredsgatan 2, Stockholm.

SWITZERLAND
Librairie Payot S.A., Lausanne, Genève.
Hans Raunhardt, Kirchgasse 17, Zurich 1.

SYRIA
Librairie Universelle, Damas.

THAILAND
Pramuan Mit Ltd., 55 Chakrawat Road, Wat Tuk, Bangkok.

TURKEY
Librairie Hachette, 469 Istiklal Caddesi, Beyoglu, Istanbul.

UNION OF SOUTH AFRICA
Van Schaik's Bookstore (Pty.), Ltd., Box 724, Pretoria.

UNITED KINGDOM
H.M. Stationery Office, P. O. Box 569, London, S.E. 1 (and at H.M.S.O. Shops).

UNITED STATES OF AMERICA
International Documents Service, Columbia University Press, 2960 Broadway, New York 27, N. Y.

URUGUAY
Representación de Editoriales, Prof. H. D'Elía, Av. 18 de Julio 1333, Montevideo.

VENEZUELA
Librería del Este, Av. Miranda No. 52, Edf. Galipan, Caracas.

VIET-NAM
Papeterie-Librairie Nouvelle, Albert Portail, Boîte Postale 283, Saigon.

YUGOSLAVIA
Drzavno Preduzece, Jugoslovenska Knjiga, Terazije 27/11, Beograd.
Cankarjeva Zalozba, Ljubljana, Slovenia.

Orders and inquiries from countries where sales agents have not yet been appointed may be sent to: Sales and Circulation Section, United Nations, New York, U.S.A.; or Sales Section, United Nations, Palais des Nations, Geneva, Switzerland.

U·BOATS

U·BOATS

ANTONY PRESTON

EXCALIBUR BOOKS

A BISON BOOK

Published by E. P. Dutton,
A Division of Sequoia-Elsevier, Inc.

Copyright © 1978 Bison
Books Limited

Produced by Bison Books
Limited, 4 Cromwell Place,
London SW7, England

All rights reserved

Library of Congress Catalog
Card Number: 78 58551

ISBN 0 525 70499

Printed in Hong Kong

CONTENTS

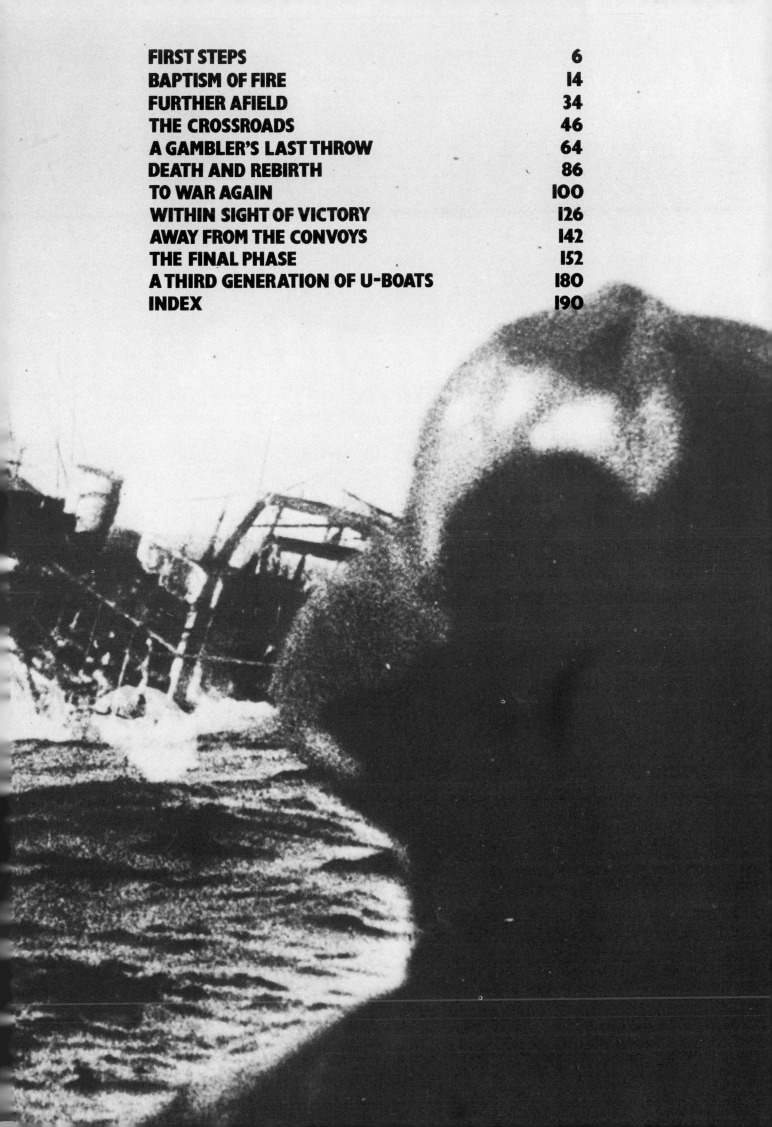

FIRST STEPS

U.1 was the first U-Boat to be built for the German Navy in 1905–06. She was only a moderate success, but she paved the way for better designs. Based on the successful French *Narval*, she was only useful for coastal operations and took no active part in World War I.

Many nations have contributed to the development of the submarine, but Germany seemed predestined to make more of its potential than any other country. As early as 1850 a non-commissioned army officer from Bavaria called Wilhelm Bauer produced his *Seetaucher* or Sea Diver, as an answer to the blockade by Danish men-o'-war. He succeeded in his purpose, and the Danes kept a more respectful distance, just as the British had been forced to do after David Bushnell's *Turtle* had attacked Lord Howe's flagship off New York in 1776.

Bauer persevered with his experiments, but in February 1851 the *Seetaucher*'s iron hull buckled, and she plunged to the bottom of Kiel Harbour. His Bavarian sense of discipline prevailed and he persuaded his two panic-stricken seamen to do the one thing that would save their lives. They allowed more water to enter, until the pressure was sufficient to burst the hatches open and let all three men swim to the surface. It is only a coincidence that the rusting hull of the *Seetaucher* was found in 1887 during dredging in Kiel, but the discovery came at a time when German interest in submarines had revived, and she was subsequently exhibited outside the Naval School.

The disaster marked the beginning of a decline in Bauer's fortunes, and his backers must have withdrawn their support. For lack of funds he was forced to offer his ideas abroad, first to Austria and then to Great Britain, involved at the time in the Crimean War. But little came of these enquiries, and finally Bauer turned to the Russians, who provided him with funds to build his second submarine, called the *Seeteufel* or Sea Devil. But again, Bauer's luck ran out, and when the *Seeteufel* sank the Russians refused to sanction any further expenditure, leaving Bauer to drift into obscurity.

Another 30 years passed before German inventors turned their minds to submarines, but in 1890 two boats were built to the designs of the Swedish Nordenfelt company at Kiel and Danzig. Just what happened to these boats, *W.1* and *W.2*, is not known, but they were not bought by the German Navy, which maintained

as sceptical an attitude as any. Indeed, Admiral Tirpitz defended his conservatism stoutly, saying that he would never adopt any new weapon until its military usefulness had been clearly demonstrated even if it meant hardship to inventors. If the performance of Turkey's two Nordenfelts is any yardstick, the German Navy had lost little ground by refusing to buy *W.1* and *W.2*, and it must be assumed that they remained in their builders' hands until sold for scrap.

The Tirpitz 'ban' on submarines meant that the next German submarine also had to be built as a private venture. In February 1902 Krupp's new Germania shipyard at Kiel began work on a small submarine, designed to enable the company to keep abreast of developments in Britain, France and the United States. There was little originality in the design, and she was like the French *Gymnote*, designed by Gustave Zédé nearly 15 years earlier. She displaced only 15.5 tons, and her electric motor gave her a radius of action of only 4.5 miles. The boat was laid down in July 1902 and launched on 8 June 1903; she attracted a lot of attention from the Imperial Navy, but no offers were made to buy her. The Emperor watched a demonstration, and his brother Prince Henry of Prussia even went to sea in her. Had it not been for the Russo-Japanese War the Navy Office might have relented and bought her for evaluation, but as things turned out, the Russians were only too glad to buy her. Under the name of *Forel* (Trout) she ran trials off St Petersburg in the summer of 1904 and was then loaded onto a railway truck for shipment to Vladivostok via the Trans-Siberian Railway.

It would be nice to say that the first successful German submarine covered herself with honours, but nothing more was heard of the *Forel*. She probably reached Vladivostok safely, but there is no record of her operations, and she is believed to have been scrapped about 1911. But the Russians did not give up easily, and in June 1904 they ordered three more submarines from Krupp, the *Karp*, *Karas* and *Kambala*. These followed a much more ambitious design, intended to be 'autonomous', unlike the little *Forel*, which had to recharge her batteries before each run from a mother-ship or a shore-based generator. Krupp was confident that he could produce a much bigger boat, for he had recently recruited the Frenchman, d'Equevilley, who based his designs on the ideas of the leading French submarine designer, Maxime Laubeuf, but without the cumbersome steam engine used in French *submersibles* for surface-running. Another improvement by d'Equevilley was to stow fuel in the external ballast tanks, but whereas he proposed the use of a benzol or gasoline motor for surface-running, Krupp would not allow the use of such volatile fuels,

and insisted on a 'heavy' oil with a lower flash-point. The American Holland design, which was adopted by the Royal Navy as well as the US Navy, was already notorious for the explosions of petrol fumes, which rapidly concentrated in the confined space of a submarine.

There was not yet sufficient faith in the new Diesel engine which worked on compression-ignition, although the French Navy had ordered its first Diesel-driven submarine, the *Aigrette*, in May 1902. But the firm of Körting Brothers was making 'heavy oil' engines driven by kerosene for use in motor launches and heavy trucks,

(l to r) *U.1*, *U.2*, *U.3* and *U.4* nestle alongside their tender *Kiel*. The limited accommodation and poor endurance of the early U-Boats made them heavily reliant on base facilities. Seagoing tenders, often old cruisers, carried out running repairs and could provide the accommodation which the U-Boats lacked.

and although its most powerful unit only developed 8hp, the company was willing to develop a 200 brake horsepower (bhp) unit to Krupp's specification. And so the *Karp* Class were promised a much safer propulsion system, although it must be said that the dense clouds of white kerosene fumes emitted by the Körting engines were not ideal for a craft which relied on secrecy and stealth. To make matters worse, a tall exhaust-funnel had to be provided to carry the choking fumes clear of the conning tower, and this had to be lowered and stowed before the boat could dive, adding to the time taken to submerge.

The Russian boats left for Libau in 1906–7 but not before they were examined by the Navy, and as a result the *Marineamt* finally decided to order the first *unterseeboot* ('undersea boat'). A total of 1.5 million marks (approximately

The hull of *U. I* was saved by Krupp's Germania shipyard as a memorial, and after surviving bomb damage in World War II it was restored by the *Deutschesmuseum* in München. This view of the after section shows the Körting kerosene motor and the accumulator batteries which drove the electric motors.

£73,000 or $292,000 at pre-1914 prices) was allocated in the 1905–6 Navy Estimates. Her keel was laid on 30 August 1905 and her launching took place at the Germania Yard on 4 August 1906. She was handed over at the end of that year, and spent the next 18 months on trials to evaluate her performance. She was very similar to the Russian boats, displacing 238 tonnes on the surface, and 283 tonnes submerged; her armament was only a single bow torpedo-tube, and three 45cm torpedoes. She was good for 10.8 knots on the surface and could make 8.7 knots underwater in short bursts, but her surface endurance proved in practice to be a good deal less than the 1500 miles promised by the designers.

In short, *U.1* was only moderately successful. The official report on her trials under Leutnant Bartenbach, later to command the Flanders

(l to r) *U.22*, *U.20*, *U.19* and *U.21*, **the first truly seagoing U-Boats. With their eight-cylinder diesel motors they had greater endurance and speed. They drew heavily on experience from the earlier prototypes and were to bear the brunt of early patrols in World War I.**

submarines, stated that she was unfit for operations at any distance from the coast, as her employment on the high seas was dangerous. But she had proved that the concept was basically sound, and in March 1906, a month before *U.1* took the water, an improved type was laid down at the Imperial Dockyard, Danzig. This was *U.2*, ten feet longer and over 100 tons heavier. She had more powerful machinery, 600bhp (brake horsepower) Daimler engines and 630shp (shaft horsepower) electric motors, and carried two 45cm torpedo-tubes at the bow and another two in the stern. Like *U.1*, she was largely experimental, not reliable enough for operations far from base, and her endurance was no higher.

To those officers dedicated to developing the new weapon, the official policy was far too cautious. In 1908 when *U.2* entered service, the US Navy had a dozen submarines, the French had 60 and Great Britain had 68; Germany had only two small prototypes and another two building. But the foreign submarines were also, for the most part, small coastal types. While the older French types were quite useless for com-

bat, the *Marineamt* was trying to ensure that each successive design was a major improvement. The pair ordered in August 1907, *U.3* and *U.4*, were nearly 200 tons heavier than *U.1* and had better endurance. By the end of 1907 it was possible to assess the experience so far and this was embodied in four 'desiderata':

1. 15 knots' surface speed, and 10.5 knots submerged.
2. 2000 miles endurance on the surface.
3. A complement of 20 officers and men, with 72 hours' air-supply.
4. Four torpedo-tubes, with reloads for the two bow-tubes.

These qualities forced a further rise in displacement to provide both habitability and power, and in all 14 boats were built to develop the characteristics. The stumbling block was the Körting engine which could only produce about 300 to 350 brake horsepower, whereas 15 knots required a minimum of 500hp per shaft and ideally 600hp. The answer was to couple two different types of Körting engine to each shaft, an eight-cylinder 350bhp unit and a six-cylinder 225 or 250bhp unit. Even so, few of the so-called 'desiderata-boats', *U.5* to *U.18*, could make the desired speed, and it varied from about 13.5 in *U.5–8* to 14.5 in *U.9–12* in ideal conditions. (*U.16* did manage 15.5 knots on trials.) To remedy this failing *U.17* and *U.18* were given two of the bigger eight-cylinder Körtings coupled to each shaft, pushing the horsepower up to a total of 1400.

Nobody was happy with the four-engine drive, and it was at last recognised that the Körting engine had reached its limit of development. In November 1910 orders were placed for four more boats, *U.19–22*, but this time they were to be driven by two MAN eight-cylinder diesel engines, each developing 850bhp. Krupp had also been investigating the possibility of diesels for U-Boats and had developed both two-cycle and four-cycle versions, but in the end it was the MAN design which won the competition. Even so, the first diesel-engined submarine built in Germany was not for the Imperial Navy but for the Italians; the *Atropo* (1911–13) was given two 350bhp Krupp diesels but in other ways resembled *U.2*. Not until July 1913 when *U.19* commissioned, did the German Navy possess a diesel-driven submarine, by which time the French, Russians, British and Americans had all adopted this excellent (German) invention for their submarines.

Time was running out for the German Navy, for the Agadir Crisis in 1911 revealed that her diplomats had not only failed to lull British suspicions about the expansion of the Imperial

A U-Boat's engine-room was cramped and densely packed with machinery and control gear. The engineer officer and his crew wore leather clothing to protect them from the grease and the clammy condensation.

Navy, but had so alienated British opinion as to make them likely allies of the French against Germany. There was nothing inevitable about war, but the growing ambitions and fears of the Germans were reflected in the stepped-up building programme for U-Boats. In March 1911 four more, *U.23–26* were ordered, then *U.27–30* in February 1912, followed by 11 more, *U.31–41*, three months later. Only three more could be ordered before the outbreak of war, and out of these, *U.42* would never fly the German ensign as she was building in an Italian yard when Italy declared war on Germany.

It has often been asked why Germany did not order more U-Boats before World War I, and the usual answer given is that Admiral Tirpitz and the other senior admirals were conservative and too obstinate to appreciate the tremendous potential of the new weapon. Unfortunately this view relies on hindsight, and ignores two incontrovertible facts. First, if the decision to expand the U-Boat strength had been made too early, say in 1909 or 1910 or even earlier, the design chosen would have been the unsuccessful *U.3* or one of the 'desiderata' types, and the

Fleet would then have been burdened with large numbers of boats incapable of operating in the Atlantic. Second, the concentration of U-Boats' building on the Germania Yard and the use of only two diesel-producers, Krupp and MAN, meant that the capacity to build U-Boats was very limited. Only three of the 18 U-Boats ordered between February 1912 and July 1913 were completed by the outbreak of war, and these were not ready to put to sea for another two months. The remainder would complete between the end of August 1914 and October 1915, which gives some idea of the time which had to elapse.

Strenuous efforts were made to provide more U-Boats, first by hurriedly placing orders for the remaining five of the U.43 Class, U.46–50, and then ordering the very similar U.51–56. But for the moment there were only 20 U-Boats available for war-service. U.1 and U.2 were suitable only for training as were U.3 and U.4; the latter were assigned to coast defence in 1914–15 but later returned to training. The later boats, U.5–18, were not suitable for extended patrols, and only six of the big diesel-engined boats, U.19–24, were commissioned and fully operational, with U.25 and U.26 working up to full operational efficiency. It was a small enough force with which to start a war against the world's largest maritime power, but they were to bring about a startling change in naval thinking.

Above: U.4 and her sister U.3 ordered in 1907, were bigger and better but were still crude prototypes. The raised exhaust pipe for the Körting oil-engines can be seen abaft the open after hatch. This was necessary to ventilate the interior of the hull.

Top left: U.6, second of the series of 'desiderata' boats ordered between 1908 and 1910 as prototypes. The plume of white smoke from her Körting oil-engine partially obscures the dreadnought behind her, demonstrating the drawback to this form of propulsion.

One of the most famous
U-Boats of World War I
is photographed against
the setting sun. In the
days before aircraft
became dangerous, this
was a favourite moment
for a respite and
permission was often
given to smoke a quick
cigarette.

BAPTISM OF FIRE

For two days after the outbreak of war on 4 August 1914, the U-Boats remained in port, but by 6 August it had dawned on the High Command that something was wrong with its predictions. It had been assumed that the Royal Navy would institute a close blockade, and so offer fairly easy targets to both torpedo boats and destroyers, but, unknown to the Germans, the British had long since abandoned the idea of a close blockade in favour of a distant blockade; thus the expected British ships were not encountered. To try and find them Korvettenkapitän Herman Bauer (by a strange coincidence the future Commodore in charge of U-Boats bore the same surname as the submarine pioneer who built the *Seetaucher* 60 years before) took *U.5, U.7, U.8, U.9, U.13, U.14, U.15, U.16, U.17* and *U.18* to sea in the early hours of 6 August. Their objective was to reach the limit of a line between the Shetlands and Bergen, and then they would return to base.

Things soon went wrong. Two days later, when the first half-flotilla was 225 miles from Heligoland, *U.9*'s engines broke down, and she was sent home. Off Fair Isle they sighted a British battle squadron, but a torpedo fired by *U.13* or *U.15* missed HMS *Monarch* and alerted the enemy. Next morning at 0227 hours Kapitän-Leutnant Pohle of *U.15* radioed to *U.18* that she was going to operate in the middle of the North Sea between the Moray Firth and Stavanger, and by dawn she must have reached her destination, for the British light cruiser *Birmingham* spotted her. Evidently she was having engine trouble, because the British lookouts could hear hammering from inside the hull, but one will never know as the cruiser opened fire and increased speed to ram the luckless U-Boat. Her forged steel stem sliced through *U.15* at over 20 knots, and for a moment the two cylindrical parts of the hull reared out of the water before disappearing, taking all 29 of her crew with them.

On 12 August the flotilla returned to Heligoland, to discover that another of their number had gone, *U.13*, under K/Lt von Schweinitz. Her loss is a mystery and for some time the Germans believed that she was rammed by one of the

battleships which had been sighted on 8 August, but as none of the British ships reported even the slightest jar or traces of a collision, it is now thought that she was lost by straying into a German minefield or by accident. The loss of two submarines was a heavy price to pay for the reconnaissance, but far from depressing the German submariners, the trip enhanced their confidence in their boats, and particularly in the newer type. The enemy, on the other hand, was lulled into a false sense of security, believing that warships had little to fear from U-Boat attack.

A second patrol was sent out on 8 August while the first was still at sea, to reconnoitre the area southwest of the line between Ter-schelling and Flamborough Head and to attack the British Expeditionary Force, which was believed by the High Command to be crossing in that area. The patrol consisted of four of the diesel-engined boats, U.19, U.21, U.22 and U.24 of the second half-flotilla, but even these new boats had their teething troubles, and all but U.21 had to turn back. K/Lt Hersing in U.21 found nothing, which is not surprising because the BEF did not cross until a week later, and then by a more westerly route.

These early war cruises were beneficial, no matter how poor the results, for they showed up many minor defects in design, as well as giving officers and men invaluable experience.

The first sinking of a merchant ship in October 1914 was carried out under the strict provisions of international law. Under the unrestricted campaigns, however, ships like these were sunk by gunfire or torpedo without warning. One torpedo was usually enough to sink a tramp steamer, and even the giant liner *Lusitania* succumbed to a single 'fish'.

For example the telephone buoy, which was designed to float clear in case of accident, was found to be floating clear on diving, and was likely to give the U-Boat's position away. There was a need for a klaxon alarm, to give warning throughout the boat when she started an emergency dive; it was easy to miss a shouted order in the forward torpedo-room, for example, or in the engine-room when the diesels were running. Another recommendation was for future U-Boats to be given a larger navigating platform, better protected against wind and spray.

It was Hersing in U.21 that scored the first success. On 2 September he managed to penetrate the Firth of Forth to see if he could attack any warships, and although spotted, made his escape. Three days later, on the afternoon of 5 May, he found the small cruiser HMS *Pathfinder* off St Abb's Head with her flotilla of destroyers. It was typical of Hersing that he should ignore the fact that the rough sea was making U.21 plunge wildly and likely to reveal her presence by 'porpoising' to the surface. The torpedo ran true and four minutes after being hit under the forward funnel, the little cruiser sank with 259 of her crew. The rough seas actually prevented the torpedo from being spotted, and for some days the Royal Navy was in some doubt as to the true cause.

The next blow struck by the U-Boats left no doubt at all about their capabilities. On 22 September at about 06 30 hours the three elderly British armoured cruisers, *Aboukir*, *Cressy* and *Hogue*, were patrolling in line abreast, about two miles apart, when they were sighted by *U.9*. Her commander, K/Lt Otto Weddigen, was confused by the distortion of the lens of his periscope and mistook them for light cruisers of the *Birmingham* Class. 'Revenge for *U.15*,' he said to his second-in-command, and it was not until he could study the stricken *Aboukir* as she slowly capsized, that he realised that his victim was in fact a 12,000-ton armoured cruiser, almost as

In 1916 the famous *U.9* was relegated to training. After being surrendered in November 1918 she was condemned to be scrapped. While in tow from Harwich to Morecambe she broke adrift and grounded in shallow water at Dover, but was later refloated to continue her last voyage.

big as a battleship. To his joy he now realised that the other two cruisers were stopping to lower boats, being under the impression that their sister-ship had struck a mine. This gave Weddigen the chance for a feat which is rarely permitted to a submariner, the consecutive bow- and stern-shot. Reloading the bow-tube which had been fired, he manoeuvred between the *Hogue* and the *Cressy*, and sank first one and

Below: An artist's impression of the triumphant return of Otto Weddigen's *U.9* to Wilhelmshaven on 23 September 1914. The sinking of the three British armoured cruisers showed how vulnerable surface ships were to the U-Boat, and Weddigen's feat marks the beginning of a revolution in naval warfare which is still under way.

then the other in the space of five minutes. The *Hogue* went down in five minutes, and the *Cressy* in 15 taking with them 62 officers and 1073 men.

The loss stunned the Royal Navy for it had been thought that the short, steep seas running would prevent a U-Boat from using her periscope. On 15 October Weddigen and *U.9* were to deal one more blow to the complacency of the British when he encountered three old cruisers of the Northern Patrol east of Aberdeen. The cruisers did not make the mistake of the *Aboukir*, *Cressy* and *Hogue*, and were altering their course and speed, and for some hours Weddigen was unable to work *U.9* into a firing position. But suddenly and inexplicably, he saw that one of them was stopping to lower a boat, and seized his chance to fire a torpedo. His victim was the old cruiser *Hawke*, which had imprudently hove-to to pick up mail from her sister *Endymion*; she sank in eight minutes with the loss of 500 men.

Two days earlier *U.17* under K/Lt Feldkirchner had achieved a less glamorous but much more significant success off the Norwegian coast near Stavanger. Her victim was the small merchant steamer *Glitra* (866 tons), which was stopped and searched under the provisions of International Law and then sunk. So far was this against German policy that Feldkirchner expected to be censured on his return, but his superiors read his report and approved the use of submarines for the destruction of commerce. Suddenly the light dawned, and in November 1914 the leading officers of the High Seas Fleet drafted a memorandum to the Chief of the Naval Staff, Admiral von Pohl.

'As England completely disregards International Law there is not the least reason why we should exercise any restraint in our conduct of the war.... We must make use of this weapon, and do so in the way most suitable to its peculiarities. Consequently a U-Boat cannot spare the crews of steamers, but must send them to the bottom with their ships. The shipping world can be warned ... and all shipping trade with England should cease within a short time.'

The reference to British breaches of International Law was to the British enforcement of the blockade. The many well-meaning attempts to abolish war on commerce since the Crimean War culminated in the Declaration of London in 1911 which declared that 'private property' at sea must be immune from capture. The British government of the day, at the insistence of the Admiralty had refused to ratify this denial of the Navy's 'right of search'. It was felt that such a rule would lead to flagrant evasion of the laws of contraband, and virtually all munitions and the sinews of war would be listed as the property of, say, an American export company. Great Britain had even gone to war with the United States in 1812 over the right to examine

The gun proved a useful weapon against solitary unarmed steamers, and in 1915 all operational U-Boats were given a gun varying from 88mm (3.5 inch) to 105mm (4.1 inch). Here a gun-crew fires the short-barrelled 88mm gun at sea; with no fire-control the shooting was usually poor, but at short range it was impossible to miss.

neutral ships for contraband, and as blockade offered a sea power the only certain method of attacking a major land power, it was unthinkable that such a well-proven form of attack should be made illegal. But the British had taken their stand on the blockade even further. In the hysteria of August 1914 over 'gallant little Belgium' it had been reported erroneously that the German government had commandeered all food imports, and so by Order-in-Council the British government announced that even food imports via neutral Holland and Denmark, in greater amounts than usual, would be assumed to have Germany as their 'final destination', and would therefore be declared contraband.

The fact was that both sides had drifted into total war without realising it. The Germans for their part, had treated the civilian population of Belgium with unbelievable harshness in full view of horrified foreign journalists, particu-

larly American. The British, on the other hand, knew that their small army could do little to help, whereas their vast merchant fleet and the might of the Royal Navy could supply the French armies and deny supplies to the Germans.

The argument suited the British, for they were not only the owners of by far the largest number of merchant ships, but also had the geographical advantage of being astride the exit-routes for German shipping from the North Sea into the Atlantic. Their only real weakness was that one-third of their imports were carried in ships owned by neutrals, and it was this weak point that the Germans intended to attack. Just as the Army had hoped to frighten Belgium into allowing them to pass through to attack France, so the Navy now hoped that its U-Boats could frighten the neutrals away from trading with Britain. Then it would be a simple matter to strangle British sea-communications and force the islanders to sue for peace or abandon the French.

Admiral von Pohl was convinced, and he and his staff overcame the diplomatists' misgivings about the effect of 'unrestricted' submarine warfare against shipping. In fact Tirpitz had already tested the temperature of American opinion by giving an interview to an American journalist, in which he hinted that all-out war against shipping was planned despite the protests of the Chancellor, Bethmann-Hollweg, about the effect on neutral opinion and the doubts of Tirpitz himself who felt that the 29 U-Boats available at the end of December 1914 were too few to sustain widespread operations. But nothing could restrain the hotheads, and the appointment of von Pohl as Commander-in-

Left: In all but the calmest weather, spray would sweep the narrow deck and conning tower of a U-Boat running on the surface. These four, including two lookouts with their Zeiss binoculars, look cold and damp despite their oilskins and warm clothing, but the fresh air was a welcome change after the fetid atmosphere below.

Right: The earliest photo of a U-Boat sinking, with the boats of the British destroyer *Maori* picking up survivors from *U.8*, blown up by an explosive sweep on 4 March 1915. She was a victim of one of the first weapons effective against submerged U-Boats.

Chief of the High Seas Fleet gave them their head. On 4 February 1915 the Kaiser inspected the U-Boats at Wilhelmshaven and later that day an order was promulgated declaring the waters around the British Isles to be a War Zone. From 18 February any merchantman carrying cargoes to a British port and found in this zone would be sunk, and it 'would not always be possible to obviate the danger with which the crews and passengers are thereby threatened'. Neutrals were warned that they would run the risk of being taken for hostile traders, and in fact the orders to the U-Boats were quite explicit:

'The first consideration is the safety of the U-Boat. Rising to the surface to examine a ship must be avoided for the boat's safety, because, apart from the danger of a possible surprise attack by the enemy surface ships, there is no guarantee that one is not dealing with an enemy ship even if she bears the distinguishing marks of a neutral. The fact that a steamer flies a neutral flag is no guarantee that it is a neutral vessel. Its destruction will therefore be justified unless other attendant circumstances indicate its neutrality.'

The German government was shocked to find neutral opinion, particularly American, extremely hostile, just as the Chancellor had predicted. As a compromise it was agreed four days before the start of the unrestricted campaign that ships flying neutral flags must be granted immunity unless definitely identified as operating under false colours. A day later, on 15 February, the Kaiser had second thoughts and tried to postpone the operation, but it was too late as *U.20* had already left harbour.

Much detailed planning was needed before even 30 U-Boats could begin extended operations. First they had to be provided with 88mm guns bolted to the deck-casing. The guns were not too difficult to provide as they could be spared from the battleships, but the submarines' decks had to be stiffened and ammunition lockers had to be installed. Officers and men had to be trained to identify the different types of merchantmen and their house-flags. There was soon a shortage of qualified radio-operators, as extended operations needed much more communication between the U-Boats and their bases, exchanging intelligence about shipping movements, reporting sinkings, etc. Submarines are complex machines, and the large number of new boats building in the shipyards would need trained officers and men to man them. The manufacture of torpedoes would have to be stepped up, although it was hoped that the use of gunfire would save torpedoes. Whenever possible a 'war pilot' had to be provided, an experienced man from the mercantile marine who could advise the commanding officer about shipping routes and help to identify targets.

Gebt für die U·Boot·Spende

Above: The hard life did little to hinder recruiting, for the U-Boats offered a more exciting life than the inactive battle fleet. Increasingly the cream of naval officers and ratings transferred to the U-Boats and torpedo boats, leading to a corresponding drop in the efficiency and morale of the surface fleet.

Left: A seaman flanked by lookouts in sou'westers and oilskins, exemplifies the dirt and misery of prolonged operations in bad weather. Although a U-Boat could escape the worst weather by diving, her cramped hull soon became a damp and smelly prison for her crew.

When *Der Tag* arrived, 20 U-Boats were available to go to sea, but even after a week only *U.8*, *U.20*, *U.27* and *U.30* had reached their operational areas. Nevertheless these four attacked 11 ships and sank seven without loss to themselves, a good return for the effort. As the weeks passed the losses mounted but on 4 March the old *U.8* was passing westward through the Dover Straits. A British drifter spotted the movement of the indicator buoys and called the patrolling destroyers which were equipped with a new anti-submarine device known as the explosive sweep. As soon as the sweep snagged against the U-Boat's hull it was fired electrically, with disastrous results. All lights in *U.8* were smashed by the explosion and water began to pour in through holes in the casing; then sea-water made the switchboard short-circuit, and within minutes the submarine was filled with chlorine and smoke. There was nothing to do but blow tanks and come to the surface, and so the captain and crew filed up through the conning hatch, raised their hands above their heads and waited to be rescued.

Six days later *U.12* came to grief at the hands

of two destroyers off Fife Ness. One destroyer was able to damage her conning tower by ramming, while the other destroyer pumped shells into it; when K/Lt Krazatch tried to reach the conning tower to signal his surrender, he was killed by a bursting shell. In the confusion *U.12* sank rapidly and only two officers and eight men survived. On 26 March Otto Weddigen overreached himself when he tried to attack a squadron of battleships exercising in the northern North Sea. A torpedo missed HMS *Neptune*, and before the U-boat could dive deeper she was spotted by an alert lookout aboard HMS *Dreadnought*. With remarkable agility the 18,000-ton ship wheeled out of line and steered for the 'feather' of the periscope; seconds later she slid over *U.29* with nothing more than a slight shudder but the U-Boat's bow reared up for a moment and then plunged to the bottom. The battleships then withdrew quickly, leaving a cruiser to identify the mass of wreckage and oil that marked the graves of Weddigen and his crew.

On the credit side, the statistics of shipping lost to submarines were rising steadily. From August 1914 to the end of December 1915 the British had lost an average of about 48,000 tons of shipping per month and other countries had lost a further 14,000 tons to all forms of German attack (mines, submarines and cruisers). Taking the average tonnage of a freighter as 5000 tons,

this was the equivalent of 13 ships a month, a minute percentage of the world's shipping. In January 1915, however, the figures began to climb:

	British	France, Belgium and neutrals
January	32,000 tons	15,900 tons
February	36,300	23,600
March	71,400	9,300
April	22,400	33,300
May	84,300	35,700
June	83,100	48,300
July	52,800	56,800
August	148,400	37,400
September	101,600	50,200
October	54,100	34,400
November	94,400	58,600
December	74,400	48,700

These figures were not unbearable, but they represented an enormous loss of cargoes to the Allied war-effort. Each ship sunk was another hull which could not carry troops, food or war material to Europe. What made them worse was the short-sighted policy of the British in stopping the construction of new merchant ships from the outbreak of war. It was to be a short war and, so the argument ran, resources should be devoted to building warships. Nor was there any worthwhile salvage or repair service, and numbers of hapless vessels were sunk by Allied

Below: Horseplay on a U-Boat's deck. In calm weather there was no danger of being washed overboard, and the tell-tale plume of smoke on the horizon would give ample warning of an approaching ship.

warships while limping into port, to remove a hazard to navigation. There were no rescue tugs, and hardly any repair organisations, which meant that the Allies' pool of tonnage was shrinking as each month went by.

The anti-submarine measures were vigorous but on the whole ineffective. The Royal Navy had enjoyed a century of peace, and had lost sight of its prime function of protecting trade. In fruitless attempts to 'take the offensive' against the U-Boats the Royal Navy formed an Auxiliary Patrol of about 500 yachts and trawlers, and deployed them in 21 areas around the British Isles. The other countermeasure was the laying of mine-barriers and nets in the Channel to prevent the U-Boats from passing through to the Western Approaches, but these proved of limited use. The patrols were easily evaded and had very little chance of sighting the small target presented by

Right: A classic scene of a U-Boat in rough seas with the cliffs of Heligoland visible on the horizon. She is a UB III type, but this shot has often been wrongly identified as a World War II U-Boat.

Below: A somewhat idealised picture of a U-Boat giving the crew of a merchantman time to escape before sinking her. The harsh reality was that U-Boats were more and more vulnerable to counterattack and had to sink their targets as quickly as possible. This meant that the survivors had to look after themselves.

German U Boat breaking surface in a rough sea off Heligoland.

a U-Boat at any distance. In contrast, the U-Boat could lie near any known point where shipping was concentrated, such as the St George's Channel, and wait until a victim arrived; if it turned out to be a patrol vessel she submerged before being spotted and waited until a more promising target arrived. Through the whole of 1915 the random patrols sank only two U-Boats; the other 17 were sunk by a variety of causes including accidents.

The most effective countermeasure was that adopted by merchantmen: turn towards the U-Boat in the hope that she would submerge, and then escape at high speed. It worked surprisingly well, and 38 out of 43 ships which tried this tactic succeeded in getting away. The mines and nets were only partially effective; the British mines were rightly regarded with derision by the U-Boats as so many failed to explode, and a hardened steel net-cutter on the bows would enable a U-Boat to 'saw' her way through a net unless the wires became entangled around her propellers. But the loss of *U.8* led Captain Bauer, the *Führer der U-Boats*, to believe that an effective barrier existed across the Straits, and when *U.37* failed to return on 7 April he ordered the U-Boats to avoid the Channel route. This meant that his boats had to make a journey around Scotland, adding 1400 miles to each cruise and reducing the time they could spend on patrol. What Bauer did not know was that the indicator-buoys at this date were so ineffective that they did not even betray the passage of a submarine through the nets below; German historians since have been very critical of his over-cautious response. However it is interesting that Bartenbach, commanding the Flanders U-Boats, gave similar orders on 27 April.

The Flanders flotilla was the result of some remarkable improvisation. In October 1914 it was realised that a supply of 60hp four-cylinder diesels made by Daimler and Körting was available. To take advantage of this, a new class of coastal submarines was hurriedly designed and ordered in November 1914. A total of 17 of these tiny craft, known affectionately to their crews as 'tin tadpoles', were built and the first came into service in January 1915. They were slow and carried only two 45cm torpedo-tubes in the bow, but they achieved remarkable feats in the fierce currents and tidal rips in the Channel. At the same time a slightly larger type of submarine was ordered, a class of 15 mine-layers, capable of laying 12 mines from six vertical tubes in the forward part of the hull. The 'tin tadpoles' were given UB-numbers to distinguish them from the seagoing U-Boats, and the minlayers were given UC-numbers. Both classes were so small that they could be sent by rail in sections from Bremen to Antwerp, and as soon as *UB.10* was ready, on 29 March, the Flanders flotilla was formed under Captain

Bartenbach, the one-time commander of *U.I*.

The Flanders flotilla was separate from the High Seas Fleet and had the task of harassing the cross-Channel traffic and East Coast shipping. The first UC-Boat did not begin to operate until June 1915, but by the autumn there were no fewer than nine UB-Boats and eight UC-Boats based on Bruges. Their lack of size was offset to a great degree by their closeness to the

The diminutive *UB.3* is loaded by crane for shipment to the Mediterranean. These 28-metre 'tin tadpoles' could be built faster than the big U-Boats, and they were developed into a useful utility type for service in shallower waters such as the North Sea and the Channel.

shipping routes, and the Flanders flotilla became more and more effective. The secret of the UC-Boats was well kept, and the first mines laid off the East Coast were a mystery to the British. It was believed that they were being laid by fishing craft disguised as neutrals until early in July 1915 when a steamer struck a submerged object off Yarmouth. The same night there was an explosion under water and divers found the wreck of UC.2. She had apparently gone to the bottom with severe damage from the collision, and then been blown up by the detonation of one of her own mines.

By far the most spectacular success of the unrestricted campaign was the sinking of the Cunard liner *Lusitania* in April 1915, but in the long run it did the U-Boats little good. The boat involved was Schwieger's *U.20*, which, under

her previous commander, K/Lt Droescher, had achieved the first trip around the British Isles as early as October 1914. So many stories, claims and counter-claims have been made about the *Lusitania* that it will do no harm to sketch the outlines of Schwieger's patrol in *U.20*: he sailed from Wilhelmshaven on 30 April 1915, negotiated the swept channels in the Heligoland Bight and ran on the surface through the North Sea to the Orkneys. North of these islands some Auxiliary Patrol craft were sighted and avoided, and on 4 May, four days after leaving harbour, *U.20* reached her patrol area south of Ireland. Schwieger had been told to look out for troopships arriving from Canada, but apart from that warning, had only routine orders to attack shipping; on 4 May he fired a torpedo at a steamer but missed and next day sank a sailing vessel with gunfire. On 6 May he sank two steamers, one by gunfire and the other by torpedo, but on the following day he decided to head for home as he was running low on fuel and had only two torpedoes left. He was off the Old Head of Kinsale that afternoon when he sighted smoke and funnels. At first he assumed that a flotilla of destroyers was passing and was prepared to lie low until they were clear, but an alteration of course revealed that the forest of funnels was really a big four-funnelled ship. It did not take much to persuade the keen U-Boat

these photographs show various stages in her docking and repair. One of her mines was extracted from the launching tube and put on the dockside. When she was repaired she was exhibited in various English ports.
UC.5 carried 12 mines six vertical tubes, and they were dropped through the keel. Water ballast was admitted automatically to compensate for the loss of weight, or else the UC-Boat would rise to the surface. Like the UB-Boats the UC-series were steadily improved until the later classes were as big as prewar U-Boats.

On 27 April 1916 the small minelayer *UC.5* ran aground on a shoal off the English coast. The hull was raised and towed into port, and captain that the large ship was probably one of the troopships he had been warned to expect, and if not, an armed merchant cruiser, for most of the big prewar liners had been requisitioned for one or the other of these duties. The *Lusitania* was, however, one of the very few British liners still running a scheduled transatlantic passenger service.

The argument that Schwieger should automatically have recognised the *Lusitania* is hardly valid, and the claim that the German High Command knew that she was carrying ammunition, and had given permission to Schwieger to sink her is ludicrous. The field of vision from the

merchant cruiser in wartime. However in August 1914 she, her sister *Mauretania* and the *Aquitania* were found to consume too much coal, and were returned to their owners after a month. As an armed merchant cruiser she would have worn the White Ensign and would not have carried passengers as all the accommodation would have been stripped; the nature of naval guns makes the theory that they could have been kept on board and only mounted when clear of American territorial waters impossible. Nor would she have been permitted to carry passengers while carrying large quantities of explosives. What she was carrying was

bridge of a U-Boat is very limited and the vision through a periscope even more restricted. Schwieger's report makes it clear that he had no idea of the name of the ship he was attacking and had very little time to make up his mind about attacking her. The claim that the ship was armed is so ridiculous that it cannot be seriously maintained, and in any case, for the reason already given, Schwieger could never have seen and counted guns unless he had been alongside the ship. The *Lusitania* had been given strengthened decks when built in 1907 for the purpose of mounting six-inch guns, as it was assumed that she would be required to serve as an armed

A UB III type boat, probably *UB.7*. She has a 105mm deck gun and a prominent net-cutter on the bow. This type proved so useful that it was chosen 20 years later as the basis for the Type VII boat.

a relatively small cargo (37 tons) of munitions, mostly nose-caps for shells and rifle ammunition, neither of them the sort of ordnance to cause a gigantic explosion. Much has been made of the speed with which the *Lusitania* sank after a single hit from a torpedo, and of a reported second explosion, but Schwieger himself thought that it was caused by the boilers, coal or ammunition. A single torpedo would be highly destructive to a liner with her numerous boiler-rooms, and cold seawater entering the red-hot boilers would cause a tremendous 'implosion', much more destructive than anything resulting from fuzes and rifle cartridges.

for the monthly sinkings show, and in August they reached the staggering total of 185,800 tons. The richest pickings were in the south-western approaches to the British Isles, and by August there were no fewer than three U-Boats stationed in that area, out of 13 at sea.

The British answer to the growing number of attacks with gunfire was to arm merchantmen with light guns, and as a development of this idea they introduced the decoy ship, known as the Q-Ship. This was a harmless-looking vessel, sometimes even a sailing ship, with a naval crew and hidden armament; if attacked, her role was to lure the U-Boat within range and then sink

The giant liner sank within 20 minutes taking with her nearly 1200 passengers. Many of these were Americans, and although they were not the first US citizens to die in the unrestricted campaign, the magnitude of the tragedy roused American opinion. After a strongly worded protest from Washington, the Chancellor got a grudging promise from the Navy to spare passenger ships, and on 6 June orders to this effect were issued to the U-Boats. As a result of the intense diplomatic pressure, the number of ships torpedoed without warning dropped, and instead the U-Boats took to the gun. This proved to be much more effective as the figures

The little *UB.4* in Zeebrugge, with the Mole in the distance. She carried the only two 45cm torpedoes and with only 1600 miles' endurance she could only operate in coastal waters.

her. The most sophisticated form of trap was to use a trawler to tow a submerged submarine as a counter to U-Boats' attacks on fishing vessels off Aberdeen. However unlikely this ruse might sound, it caught *U.40* in June 1915, and less than a month later *U.23* was sunk the same way. In 1915 six U-Boats were sunk by decoys of one sort or another, and in many more actions the U-Boats only barely escaped. Not unnaturally, the use of decoys provided the U-Boats with justification for sinking ships on sight.

Faced by a mounting chorus of criticism from neutrals about inhuman methods of waging warfare, the German High Command was eager

to find corresponding evidence of British atrocities, and this was opportunely provided by the *Baralong* incident. On 19 August the liner *Nicosian* was stopped and shelled by *U.27* about 100 miles south of Queenstown (Cobh). But the *Nicosian*'s distress call had been picked up by the Q-Ship *Baralong*, which approached to within two-and-a-half miles before being sighted by *U.27*'s lookouts. The decoy was flying the American flag, a legitimate *ruse de guerre*, and pretended to stop to pick up the *Nicosian*'s boats. At this juncture K/Lt Wegener apparently decided to put *U.27* between the stranger and the *Nicosian*. Suddenly, as *U.27* came out from behind the *Nicosian*, the *Baralong* ran up the

Crew members of a big 'Mittel-U' watch as one of the small UB-boats passes by. This encounter is probably in the Mediterranean, as the big U-Boats did not normally operate in the North Sea and Channel.

White Ensign and opened fire from her concealed guns; at 600 yards 34 rounds were fired, and *U.27* was overwhelmed in a shower of shell-hits. As she sank, about a dozen survivors (including Wegener) were left in the water, and these men swam towards the nearby *Nicosian* and began to climb aboard. The captain of the *Baralong*, Lieutenant-Commander Herbert, assumed that their intention was to seize any arms they could find, and try to scuttle the prize, and so he gave the order for them to be shot with small-arms fire. Even so, four German sailors escaped and disappeared below, and a boarding party of Royal Marines was told to recapture the ship. The four unfortunates, who

probably had no intention but to surrender at the first opportunity, were shot in the engine-room.

The affair could not be hushed up for American sailors from the *Nicosian* were interviewed by US newspapers on their return to the United States later that month. Immediately the German government demanded that Godfrey and the crew of the *Baralong* should be indicted for the murder of Wegener and his men. The British reply was to suggest that the *Baralong* affair could be referred to an international tribunal along with three other incidents which had occurred during the same 48 hours: the sinking of the liner *Arabic* (by *U.24*), the killing of a man in an open boat from the collier *Ruel*, and the killing of 15 men from the British submarine *E.13* by gunfire from German torpedo-boats in Danish territorial waters. The offer was not taken up.

American anger over the loss of American lives in the *Arabic* carried more weight than German anger over *U.27*, and so many restrictions were imposed that on 27 August Captain Bauer ordered all his U-Boats to remain in harbour until clear-cut instructions were issued. Three days later an Imperial telegram arrived, instructing that U-Boats were not to be stationed to the west of the British Isles; passengers and crew of merchant vessels had to be given a chance to abandon ship; and neutrals could be sunk if they were carrying material to a British port. Taken literally, the new regula-

got off only one shot, which missed, but managed to submerge hurriedly. However, when she got down to a depth of 76 metres she continued to sink, and the only way to escape was to blow all tanks; this brought her to the surface once more, but only two officers were able to get out before she vanished again in a cloud of steam and smoke. Both survivors were picked up by the *Baralong*.

This disaster and other narrow escapes caused a deep and bitter political row in Germany. On the one hand there was Chancellor Bethmann-Hollweg and his ally, the Chief of the Kaiser's

tions were the end of the unrestricted campaign, and they also spelled increased danger to the U-Boats. Just how dangerous the new policy was, was demonstrated on 24 September, when *U.41* stopped the SS *Urbino* off the Scilly Isles. While engaged in sinking the ship, another ship hove in sight, and *U.41* prudently submerged. When he saw that the newcomer was flying the American flag, K/Lt Hansen surfaced and sent a boat away to examine her papers. But the stranger was not American; she was the *Baralong*, and suddenly the White Ensign replaced the Stars and Stripes and a murderous fire was opened at only 450 metres. The U-Boat

U.20 **conducted experiments with a Friedrichshafen seaplane, but the aircraft of the day were too frail to be of much use as scouts for U-Boats, and no further work was done in this area.**

Naval War Cabinet, von Müller, who were still trying to achieve a settlement of the *Lusitania* affair by means of arbitration. On the other side were Tirpitz and the new Chief of the Naval Staff, Bachmann, arguing for a continuation of unrestricted submarine warfare. Bethmann-Hollweg felt so strongly about the opinion of the United States that on his own authority he sent a note to Washington assuring the State Department that ships would not be sunk without warning and the German Ambassador in Washington, Bernstorff, went further by stating that the commander of *U.24* would be punished for exceeding his orders.

Before the depth-charge there were very few weapons capable of sinking a U-Boat. This lance bomb was intended for use against a U-Boat at very close quarters, but the only recorded case of its use resulted in the bomb bouncing off the casing.

Admiral Bachmann retired and was replaced by von Holtzendorf, but the friction between the naval chiefs and the supreme command continued, and it is this that led to the order of 27 August, confining U-Boats to harbour until further notice. Tirpitz was prepared to transfer the U-Boats to the Mediterranean rather than waste their potential. Both he and von Pohl offered their resignations when the Kaiser's order of 30 August was issued, but the offer was refused. As Tirpitz said much later, the campaign continued 'in a form in which it could not live and at the same time could not die'. To which Bethmann-Hollweg retorted that, as far as relations with the United States were concerned, he could not stay for ever on top of a volcano. The upshot of the *Arabic* sinking was an admission that *U.24*'s action had been illegal, and an offer to pay an indemnity.

For the U-Boats it was the end of the unre-stricted campaign, and on 18 September it was formally terminated by order of the Commander-in-Chief. Immediately the shipping losses fell, from 152,000 tons in September to 123,000 tons in December. The 'twilight phase' which followed was to last for a year, but, although the Allied High Command had been given a bad fright, the right lessons had not been learned. The exploits of the Q-Ships and the sheer scale of the Auxiliary Patrol operations concealed the fact that they had played no part in bringing the U-Boat campaign to an end. Rather the contrary, for the 'exchange rate', the number of merchant ships sunk for each U-Boat lost, had risen to 23 by the middle of September (in the first four years of World War II it was only 11 ships for every U-Boat sunk). In their hearts the U-Boat commanders knew that next time they would have more U-Boats and infinitely more experience.

FURTHER AFIELD

Although Admiral Tirpitz decided in August 1915 to divert U-Boats to the Mediterranean to avoid the chances of friction with the United States, there were also sound strategic reasons for so doing. There were French and British troops fighting the Turks in the Dardanelles and French troops crossing from North Africa, which meant ship-targets to be attacked. The Mediterranean was a vital shipping route for the British and the European neutrals, as well, and Germany's Austrian ally had too few submarines to mount a large-scale campaign.

The six small Austro-Hungarian submarines had too little range to allow them to be used outside the Adriatic, but this did not prevent them from striking some effective blows. On 17 October *IV* (all Austro-Hungarian submarines were known by roman numerals initially) attacked the big French armoured cruiser *Waldeck Rousseau* off Cattaro (Kotor), but her torpedo missed. On 21 December *XII* damaged the new dreadnought battleship *Jean Bart* in the Otranto Straits, but she managed to limp to Malta. These two incidents, following the British disasters in the North Sea, do not seem to have had any effect on French tactics, for when four months later on 26 April 1915, the submarine *V* encountered the armoured cruiser *Léon Gambetta* in the Straits of Otranto, the big ship was patrolling alone at 6.5 knots without any escorts. Two torpedoes tore into her hull and she sank in 10 minutes, taking Admiral Sénès and 650 officers and men with her. As a result the French Navy was forced to withdraw all heavy units from the blockade of the Otranto Straits, an important strategic victory for the Adriatic submarines. The entry of Italy into the war on 24 May opened a new chapter, but by as early as April it had been decided to despatch *U.21* (K/Lt Hersing) from the North Sea to the Mediterranean to bring support to the hard-pressed Turks. Hersing left Germany on 25 April and arrived at Cattaro on 13 May; after repairs at Pola (now Pula) he set out for the Dardanelles on 20 May and arrived five days later.

There was no shortage of targets off the Gallipoli peninsula, for the ANZAC and British troops were fighting desperately to hold on to their precarious lodgements. Troopships and transports lay off the beaches, and battleships and cruisers poured in supporting fire against the Turkish positions. After missing the Russian cruiser *Askold* and the British battleships *Swiftsure* and *Vengeance*, *U.20* moved on to Gaba Tepe where she found HMS *Triumph*. Even so, Hersing had to wait two hours before he could get a good shot at her; once that moment came one torpedo was enough, and the battleship heeled over and sank. In the confusion that followed, *U.20* had to escape by diving *under* the sinking *Triumph*, but she got away safely and lay on the bottom for the next 28 hours before rising under cover of darkness to recharge her batteries. To sink one capital ship would have been enough for most submariners, but next day Hersing took *U.20* back to Gaba Tepe to look for more targets. Finding none there, he headed for Cape Helles, and on 27 May found HMS

The Austro-Hungarian U-Boat *IV*, later renumbered *U.4*, was one of two boats built at Krupp's Germania yard in 1907–09. They were very similar to the early German boats and saw service in World War I. *U.3* was sunk by a French destroyer in 1915, but *U.4* survived.

Majestic, surrounded by anti-torpedo nets and patrol craft. But nothing could deter Hersing, and he waited patiently until a small gap appeared in the swarm of small ships around their charge; within seven minutes the 22-year-old battleship had capsized, the victim of a single torpedo which had gone through the nets as if they were made of tissue-paper. Like the French in the Otranto Straits, the British were now forced to withdraw all their big ships to Mudros, and leave bombardment work to the destroyers; the sinkings had taken place in full view of the troops fighting ashore, heartening the Turks and causing untold confusion to the naval forces. Although Hersing would have tried to

sink more battleships if he could have found them, he had to give up finally, and arrived at Constantinople on 1 June to be greeted with hysterical fervour by the Turks.

Long before Hersing left for the Mediterranean other reinforcements for the Austrians were in hand. Six of the small UB-Boats and UC minelayers had been earmarked for the Mediterranean, and were shipped by rail in sections from Germany to Pola where they were assembled and manned by their German crews. The boats involved were: *UB.1* (completed in January 1915), *UB.3* and *UB.14* (completed March), *UB.7* (completed May), *UB.8* and *UB.15* (completed April), *UC.12* and *UC.13* (completed

Top: The German *U.35* was one of ten U-Boats sent to the Mediterranean to reinforce the Austrians and to attack the Allies' lines of communication. Under her famous commander, de la Perière, she had a dazzling run of successes; between November 1914 and the Armistice she sank over half a million tons of shipping. She is seen here at Cattaro in April 1917, the Austrian base used by the U-Boats from 1915.

Bottom: A small UB-Boat comes alongside *U.35* in the Mediterranean. The officer in British uniform walking on the forward casing is the King's Messenger Captain Wilson, who was taken prisoner from a ship sunk by *U.35*. Lothar Arnauld de la Perière achieved his successes while maintaining the highest standards of chivalry.

May) and *UC.14* and *UC.15* (completed June). Three of them, *UB.3*, *UB.7* and *UB.8* were sent to the Dardanelles, carrying ammunition for the the Turks but also to harass Allied shipping off Gallipoli. One, *UB.3*, was lost in the Aegean near Smyrna on or after 23 May, either by accident or by striking a mine, but the other two arrived safely at Constantinople. Eventually a half-flotilla was formed under Hersing, based on Varna, with *U.21*, *UB.7*, *UB.8*, *UC.14* and *UC.15*. From here they were able to attack Russian shipping in the Black Sea, and also hit back at the British submarines in the Sea of Marmora.

More of the bigger U-Boats were sent out from Germany to Cattaro in August 1915, *U.33*, *U.34*, *U.35* and *U.39*, followed by *U.38* in November. In particular *U.35* was to distinguish herself under a commander appointed to her after her first commander, Kophamel, was appointed to run the new U-Boat base established at Cattaro. The officer was Lothar Arnauld de la Perière, a man who was to establish himself as the 'ace of aces'. He was to make *U.35* the most successful U-Boat ever, with 224 ships totalling 535,900 tons sunk between first commissioning in November 1914 and the Armistice (although he did not command her throughout the War). Her four sisters also totted up high scores:

U.33 – 76 ships totalling 193,558 tons
U.34 – 120 ships totalling 258,900 tons
U.38 – 136 ships totalling 292,977 tons
U.39 – 151 ships totalling 398,564 tons

The greatest cruise was made by Arnauld de la Perière in *U.35* between 26 July and 20 August 1916. With a new 10.5cm gun in place of the 8.8cm gun previously mounted, and a first-rate gunner borrowed from the High Seas Fleet, he was able to destroy 54 ships totalling 91,000 tons. To do this he expended 900 rounds of ammunition, but only four torpedoes for he scorned the use of such expensive weapons. De la Perière's favourite method was to open fire on his victim at a range of about 6000 yards, and then come in closer, to about 3000 yards. When the ship was abandoned he would administer the *coup de grâce* with two shells, one into the bow and the other into the stern. One of the four torpedoes which were fired missed the French cruiser *Waldeck Rousseau*, which had already escaped from the Austrian *IV* two years earlier, making her one of the luckiest warships in the Mediterranean.

During his time in *U.35* de la Perière sent two warships, an armed merchant cruiser, five troopships, 125 steamers and 62 sailing ships to the bottom. Nearly all of these were sunk by gunfire, clear evidence of how ineffectual the anti-submarine measures were in the Mediterranean. The agreed policy was to run ships on fixed routes, which were patrolled by warships of all sizes, in the fond hope that these patrols would frighten away the U-Boats. In fact the

U-Boats had little difficulty in spotting the patrols and diving before they had been spotted. There were usually some 350 merchantmen at sea at any one time in the Mediterranean, and as their routes were fixed there was no difficulty in finding targets.

The divided Allied commands in the Mediterranean made the U-Boats' task easier: although the French C-in-C was in overall command, his forces were divided into 18 commands with little or no co-ordination. As a result not a single U-Boat was lost in the Mediterranean in 1915 apart from the unexplained loss of *UB.3* in

Above: A torpedo is swung on *U.35* from a tender, before being 'struck down' through the open torpedo-hatch in the foreground. The number of torpedoes was as important as the fuel-supply in determining how long a U-Boat could spend at sea.

Top right: By spring of 1917 *U.35* was so famous that a special attempt was made to record one of her cruises in the Mediterranean by sending a photographer to sea with her. Here she is seen running on the surface, partially trimmed down.

Bottom: A merchant ship stopped by *U.35* blows off steam and lowers boats. The U-Boat could shell her or, if time allowed, a boarding party could set demolition charges on board. Use of the gun saved precious torpedoes but exposed the U-Boat to the danger of being caught by a patrolling warship.

May. The record in 1916 was little better, with *UC.12* blown up in Taranto by her own mines in January, *UB.44* by unknown cause in the Aegean in August, and *UB.46* by a Russian mine in the Bosphorus in December. The attempt to bottle up the U-Boats in the Adriatic by means of the Otranto Barrage was a costly failure as the Straits were too deep for effective mine-laying.

The problem was complicated for both sides because the Italians were only at war with Austria-Hungary from May 1915 to August 1916. As a result the UB-Boats and UC-Boats based on Cattaro were nominally transferred to the KuK Marine in June 1915, although still manned by German crews. Some U-Boat commanders took advantage of this camouflage to attack Italian warships such as the armoured cruiser *Amalfi*, sunk in July 1915 by *UB.14* and the submarine *Medusa* sunk in June 1915 by *UB.15*. Others sank passenger-ships under the Austrian flag and in answer to American protests, the Germans were able to reply that no German craft were involved. The worst example was *U.38*'s sinking of the Italian liner *Ancona* in November 1915; as a result of this venture the Austrians had to make their own protests in private to their overbearing allies. In June 1915 the first of the UB-Boats were formally handed over to the

KuK Marine as *X* and *XI*, followed by three more later that year; they replaced five larger boats taken over by Germany in August 1914 while building at Krupp's, and later completed as *U.66–70*. In October the roman numerals were discarded in favour of U-numbers, and the five UB-Boats became the Austro-Hungarian *U.10*, *U.11*, *U.15*, *U.16* and *U.17*, and although these numbers duplicated German U-Boat numbers they helped to confuse Allied intelligence even more.

The original Austro-Hungarian submarines were also active, and the armoured cruiser *Giuseppe Garibaldi* was sunk in July 1915. In August, however, *XII* was lost in an Italian mine-field near Venice and *III* was sunk by a French destroyer off the coast of Montenegro. The French *Curie*, which had been caught in the nets protecting Pola harbour in December 1914, had been raised and rebuilt, and when she recommissioned in August 1915 she was given to Leutnant von Trapp, the man who had sunk the *Leon Gambetta* in *V* in April. As *XIV* (soon to be renumbered *U.14*) she went on to become the most successful Austro-Hungarian U-Boat. She survived the war and was returned to the French Navy after the Armistice.

In April 1916 the first of a new wave of reinforcements left Germany for the Mediterranean.

Above: The French submarine *Curie* was sunk at Pola in 1914. After salvage and repair she became the Austrian *U.14*, and is seen here at Sebenico. After a successful career under the ace v on Trapp she was returned to the French Navy in 1919.

They were large minelayers of the *U.71* Class, 755-tonners capable of laying 36 mines. They were a great improvement over the UC-Boats, and unlike them they did not lay their mines vertically; instead they carried three horizontal tiers of mines, which were winched aft and laid through doors at the stern. Both *U.73* and *U.74* laid successful fields on their way out to the Mediterranean, and *U.73* laid another equally deadly field off Malta. A third minelayer, *U.72*

joined them later in the year, followed by seven smaller minelayers of the UC II type. Four more of the big U-Boats were detached from the North Sea as well, and while on passage *U.52* was able to sink the old French battleship *Suffren* off Lisbon.

The U-Boats scored many successes in the Mediterranean in 1914–16, for targets were plenty and the opposition badly organised. The end of the phase known as 'cruiser warfare' occurred in January 1917, for the change in policy in the Atlantic was reflected in a similar change of policy in the Mediterranean. As if to symbolise the end of this phase, Hersing was ordered to take *U.21* home in February, after nearly two years in the Mediterranean. The 'destroyer of battleships' made his escape through the Straits of Gibraltar without difficulty, and passed through the Channel without mishap, but his triumphal progress was marred by an unfortunate incident. Off Falmouth he sighted what he took to be a particularly tempting convoy of eight steamers. They were, in fact, unescorted Dutch steamers, proceeding under a 'safe conduct' issued by the German government, but Hersing ignored the Dutch flags and sank six of the steamers before British vessels arrived to escort the survivors to safety. It was a lapse in communications, but one more incident to outrage neutral opinion, and in this instance one of the few neutrals with any degree of sympathy towards Germany. The sympathy of

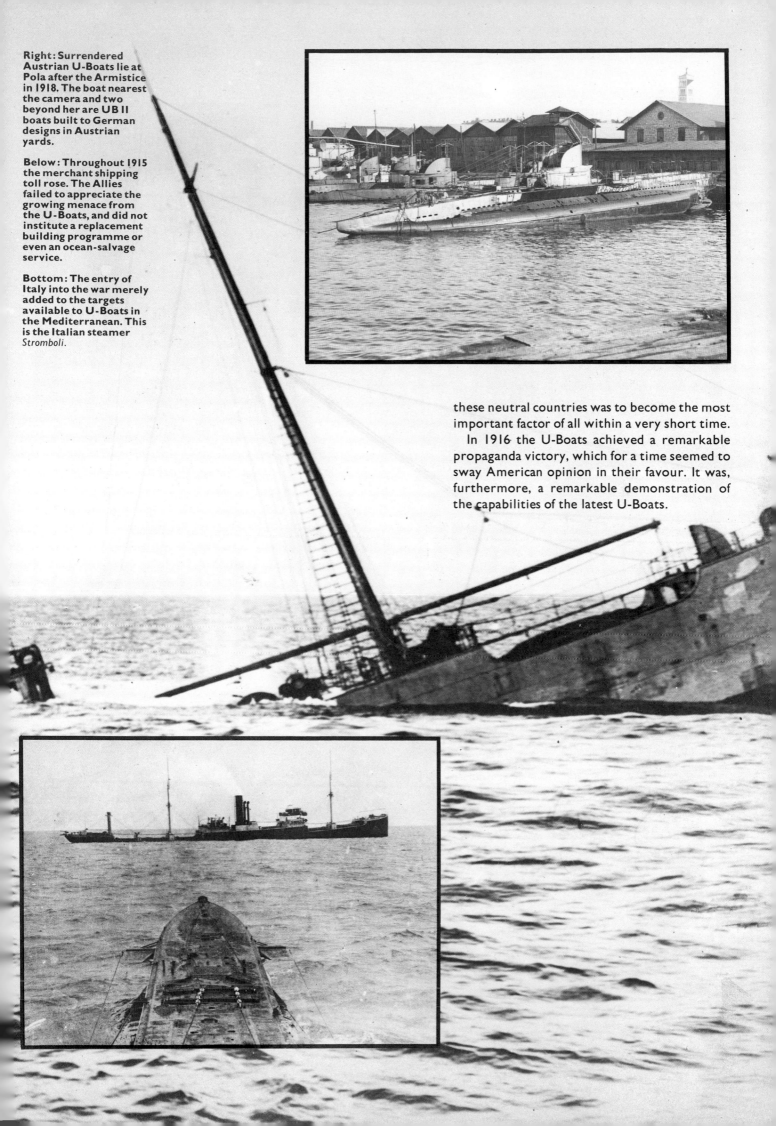

Right: Surrendered Austrian U-Boats lie at Pola after the Armistice in 1918. The boat nearest the camera and two beyond her are UB II boats built to German designs in Austrian yards.

Below: Throughout 1915 the merchant shipping toll rose. The Allies failed to appreciate the growing menace from the U-Boats, and did not institute a replacement building programme or even an ocean-salvage service.

Bottom: The entry of Italy into the war merely added to the targets available to U-Boats in the Mediterranean. This is the Italian steamer *Stromboli*.

these neutral countries was to become the most important factor of all within a very short time.

In 1916 the U-Boats achieved a remarkable propaganda victory, which for a time seemed to sway American opinion in their favour. It was, furthermore, a remarkable demonstration of the capabilities of the latest U-Boats.

Stern View of the "Deutschland"

Published by
The Fatherland Magazine

The Deutschland

Published by
The Fatherland Magazine

About an hour after midnight on the morning of Sunday 9 July 1916 a pilot boat off the Virginia Capes was hailed by a strange vessel. It was the submarine *Deutschland*, a 1500-ton craft built along the same lines as the normal U-Boats, but without torpedo-tubes or guns. Instead she had a beamier hull to accommodate a cargo-hold, for this was Germany's famous 'mercantile submarine', carrying a cargo of precious stones, dyes and chemicals to the United States, to show that the Allies' blockade could be defied with impunity.

The arrival of the *Deutschland* in Baltimore the following morning caused tremendous interest, for wild rumours had been circulating

Giant Supersubmarine ''Deutschland'' *Published by The Fatherland Ma*

DEUTSCHLAND

Published by The Fatherland Magazine   The Bow of the ''Deutschland''

The mercantile submarine *Deutschland* **sailed to the United States in mid-1916. The value of her cargo was nothing compared to the political value of her presence.**

for some time about a fleet of submarines about to run the blockade. The press was fascinated to meet K/Lt König and his men, and the captain lost no opportunity to embellish his account with stories of lying on the bottom of the English Channel listening to numerous cruisers searching for them. According to one account he and his men sipped champagne while listening to 'Peer Gynt' on a gramophone, but the influence of Jules Verne is more noticeable in the claim to have looked through 'portholes' at fish swimming in the blue sea. In fact the *Deutschland* had left Bremen on 14 June and had proceeded around the Orkneys rather than risk the nets and minefields of the Dover Barrage. Most of the journey she spent running on the surface, and her only submerged cruising was a run of about 90 miles across the North Sea, and a few miles off the Virginia Capes. Nor was it the first trip across the Atlantic for a submarine, for in 1915 ten much smaller submarines had crossed from Montreal to Great Britain under their own power.

The arrival of the *Deutschland* caused the State Department grave concern, but there was no doubt that the boat was what she claimed to be, a cargo-carrying craft with no provision for armament. There was even a company operating her, *Deutsche Ozean Reederei GmbH*, financed by Alfred Lohmann, who had persuaded the *Deutsche Bank* and *Norddeutscher Lloyd* to back his order for two cargo-carrying submarines from Krupp's in October 1915. Lohmann was hard-headed enough to realise that

the High Seas Fleet would not break the British blockade quickly, and he was convinced that a fleet of submarines, each carrying 750 tons of cargo, could bring in the rare metals and rubber which were cut off by the blockade. In fact a cargo-carrier had already been designed by one of the Krupp group, and this was adapted by the Germania Yard.

On 2 August the *Deutschland* put to sea again, escorted by a US Navy destroyer. In her hold she carried 802,000 lb of crude rubber, 752,000 lb of nickel and 181,000 lb of tin, all valued at over $1,000,000. But the value of the exercise in political terms was beyond price. The Allies had been outflanked and humiliated, and the US government had ignored their somewhat specious claims that the submarine was somehow 'inherently offensive in character'. The newspapers had done little but talk about the *Deutschland* for days on end, Captain König and his men were lionised, and the German Embassy took good care to invite as many dignitaries, including the distinguished submarine-designer Simon Lake, to visit the boat at Baltimore. Everybody was impressed, and there was even talk of an American businessman who was willing to pay $50,000 for a ticket to return to Germany on board.

Tugs warping the "Deutschland" to her dock in Baltimore
Published by The Fatherland Magazine

The Deutschland showing unique Construction of her Bow.
Published by The Fatherland Magazine

Tugs (above) took the *Deutschland* into Baltimore after US customs officials confirmed that she was not armed. The visit aroused enormous interest, particularly among the German community in the US. Most of these photographs and the ones on the preceding page were published by the *Fatherland Magazine*. In due course the *Deutschland* and her sisters were converted to U-Boats, with a heavy gun-armament and torpedo-tubes in place of the cargo-hold. In this role they were no more effective than they had been as commercial craft but they attracted undue respect on account of their great size.

The honeymoon did not last long. The second mercantile submarine, named *Bremen*, never arrived. Her fate is a mystery, and she was either rammed accidentally by one of the big armed liners of the Northern Patrol blockade squadron, north of the Orkneys, or she struck a mine. At the same time, September 1916, *U.53* under K/Lt Hans Rose was sent to 'blast a way through' the blockading ships for the *Bremen*, but in reality her purpose was to show that an ordinary U-Boat could equal the feats of the two mercantile boats by crossing the Atlantic. With every available inch of space crammed with stores, and some ballast tanks filled with oil, *U.53* set sail from Germany and arrived off Rhode Island on 7 October. Once again the American newspapers were captivated by Rose's audacity, although this time the State Department was more than perturbed at the infringement of neutrality, for Rose had taken his U-Boat into Newport, Rhode Island, with consummate

impudence to 'pay his respects to the US Navy'. However, he slipped out after 24 hours before Washington could make up its mind to intern him and his U-Boat. Rose was convinced that he had given the American government a salutary warning about the might of the U-Boat Arm, and proceeded to underline this message by sinking three British merchantmen, as well as a Dutch and a Norwegian ship within sight of the American warships which had just escorted him and his *U.53* out of US territorial waters. He returned to Germany on 28 October well pleased with his achievement, but his self-esteem might have been deflated if he had known how much damage he had done to the German cause. The US government had issued a stern warning to the British warships based in Halifax to avoid any possibility of attacking *U.53* in American waters, and so they had been kept out of the area, allowing *U.53* to sink two defenceless neutral ships.

Frachttauchboot "Deutschland" die Weser aufwärts nach Bremen

The American government did take heed, but not in the way intended, for the incident convinced the US Navy that it should prepare itself for a war against submarines, and strengthened the feeling that American interests were fundamentally closer to those of Great Britain and France, however exasperating the blockade might be. The changed climate was noticeable when the *Deutschland* paid a second visit to the USA, arriving in New London on 1 November 1916. As if to reinforce the impression of a cool reception, fate took a hand. As she left New London a tidal surge swept her against the tug which was escorting her out to sea, and the tug capsized and sank with the loss of five crewmen. After minor repairs the *Deutschland* left for Germany on 21 November, but it was her last commercial voyage. In February 1917 she was acquired by the Navy and given two torpedo-tubes and two 15cm guns, to become the 'U-cruiser' *U.155*. Six more had been ordered but the *Oldenburg* and her sisters were similarly converted on the stocks, and became *U.151–154* and *U.156–157*.

Count von Bernstorff had the last word on the episode: 'If we had sent 10 such merchant submarines to America and if the rest had carried on the submarine campaign according to the principles laid down for cruiser warfare, we should have attained far greater political results than has been the case.'

THE CROSSROADS

The High Command had not abandoned its hopes for a big U-Boat offensive, whatever the politicians had said. During 1915 a further 100 U-Boats were ordered, *U.63–65, U.71–104, UB.18–47* and *UC.16–48*. All were improved versions of the previous boats, and they incorporated a number of minor improvements suggested by war experience. They fell into the following classes:

U.63–65 ... basically similar to previous boats,
U.87–92 but with more powerful diesels.
U.99–104

U.71–80 ...large minelayers with 36 mines in horizontal tubes.

U.81–86 ...larger than the *U.63* type with two
U.93–98 more torpedo-tubes in the bow and a heavier gun-armament.

UB.18–47 ..UB II type, larger and armed with two 20-inch torpedo-tubes.

UC.16–48 ..UC II type, larger and armed with three 20-inch torpedo-tubes and 18 mines in six tubes.

The boats of this vast programme were to be completed from November 1915 (the UB-Boats), but the bigger boats and the mine-layers would take four to six months longer. For this reason none of the exponents of unrestricted warfare were unduly depressed by the virtual cessation of U-Boat activity during the winter of 1915–16. They were content to save their energies for the political struggle which began again in February; on 4 March the Kaiser reluctantly agreed to a renewal of unrestricted warfare, starting on 1 April. One of the arguments which swayed the Germans was the belief that American opinion was exasperated beyond endurance by British interpretations of the rules of blockade which prevented US traders from running supplies to the Central

UB III boats taking on torpedoes and preparing for a new patrol at Bruges. This inland port was used by the Flanders flotillas as their base, with exits to the North Sea through the canals of Zeebrugge and Ostend. In 1917 the Allies launched a disastrous land offensive to try to smoke out this hornets' nest, culminating in the Battle of Passchendaele.

Powers impartially. In January the United States government had also told the British that it would regard armed merchantmen as naval auxiliaries, a severe blow, and that it would not regard the sinking of merchant ships as illegal provided the crews were given time to abandon ship in safety.

It now seems clear that the U-Boats might have won the war if they had started a second unrestricted campaign at this moment. The United States was neutral, almost belligerently so, and there were more U-Boats at sea than before, and the Allies' countermeasures were no more effective. But the Kaiser and his advisers did not have the courage to go all the way, and on 13 March they modified the plans to permit the sinking of cargo vessels in the War Zone, but to exempt passenger ships. Then on 24 March *UB.29* torpedoed the cross-Channel steamer *Sussex*, which was carrying several American passengers. Fifty people were killed in the explosion, but as the ship was

towed into Boulogne it was possible to examine her, and fragments of the torpedo were found. The incident provoked a fresh protest from the US government, and on 18 April even a threat to break off diplomatic relations if the unrestricted campaign were not halted. Two days later the U-Boats were told that they were not to sink merchant ships without warning, unless their victim attempted to escape or offer resistance. A promise was also given that the captain of *UB.29*, K/Lt Pustkuchen, would be punished.

The new Commander-in-Chief, Admiral Scheer, was an advocate of unrestricted warfare, and in his view the restrictions made no sense as they exposed valuable and highly trained personnel to an unacceptable risk. Being a much firmer character than either Ingenohl or von Pohl, he recalled the U-Boats from the Western Approaches and redeployed them in the North Sea where they could at least support the High Seas Fleet by attacking

Bottom: Auxiliary patrol trawlers stand by a stricken ship. Note the floating barrels, carried by many ships to help them stay afloat after being torpedoed.

Below: One consequence of the unrestricted U-Boat offensives was the virtual extinction of the world's sailing ship fleet. Many hundreds of barques and schooners still traded in 1914, but they proved pitifully vulnerable to gunfire. Had the U-Boat war not taken the course it did, these graceful craft might have continued to trade for another 20 years.

British warships. The decision was ratified by the Kaiser at the end of the month, although he gave a guarded promise that unrestricted warfare would be permitted if the political and military situation changed. The Flanders U-Boats were also ordered to work with the Fleet, but in fact their main contribution was to lay minefields.

One of the Flanders minelayers, *UC.5*, became the first U-Boat to fall into British hands. On 27 April he ran aground off Shipwash Sand on the east coast of England and was unable to get off. Although K/Lt Mohrbutter destroyed his signal-books and charts, the demolition charges failed to go off, and so the cargo of mines was not detonated. The British destroyer *Firedrake* arrived in the afternoon, and rescued the crew, and shortly afterwards the luckless *UC.5* was in dock at Harwich, being examined by technical experts and intelligence officers. The information about *UC.5* was of great value to the Allies in their fight to contain the U-Boats, but it led

to dangerous over-confidence about the capabilities of the minelayers. In June 1916 the armoured cruiser *Hampshire* was sunk off the Orkneys after striking a mine laid by *U.75*; it had been correctly assumed by the Operations Staff that northern waters were beyond the radius of action of the UC-Boats, but the big *U.71* Class, already mentioned, were easily capable of extended cruising. [However, it is almost certain that British cryptanalysts had intercepted *U.75*'s signal giving the position of the minefield four days earlier. The Operations Division probably overlooked the information in the confusion following the Battle of Jutland.]

The intelligence game was one of constant bluff and counter-bluff. On 15 July 1916 a mine-net was being repaired by British drifters when

Two views of the sinking American steamer *Illinois*, stopped by a U-Boat on 18 March 1917. Neutrals tried to avoid destruction by painting their national colours, name and country on the side.

the corpse of a German telegraphist was found in the nets. The clothing of the corpse was examined, and a leave-pass for Bruges and an identity disc marked *U.10* were discovered. Three days later the telegraphist's name was published in a German casualty list, but *U.10* had not been in the North Sea since 1915, when all the surviving old U-Boats had been transferred to the Baltic. She had gone missing in June, and was almost certainly lost to a Russian mine late in May or early the following month; the motive for the 'plant' seems to have been merely to confuse British Intelligence, as there is no evidence of any other bogus information being planted on the body of the corpse.

The British were equally devious. Information on two U-Boat sinkings was released in March 1915, *U.8* and *U.29*, but the announcements were couched in deliberately misleading terms. The report of *U.8*'s loss hinted that she had been attacking shipping, whereas, as already stated, she had actually been sunk in the Dover

The human toll of U-Boat warfare was high. Even in summer and with adequate rations and drinking water survivors in open boats died of exposure if left adrift too long. In winter the chances of survival were drastically reduced.

in Belgium. In fact the Allies had been working away steadily at the U-Boat ciphers since the end of 1914, with increasing success.

One of the problems was that radio communication was so new that nobody was aware of the need for strict discipline. The campaign against shipping required a great number of messages to be passed, particularly from the shore-based command to the U-Boats at sea, giving them information about shipping movements, enemy warships, and many other details. Similarly the U-Boats had to report their positions, amount of fuel and number of torpedoes, so that they could be directed to the best positions for sinking ships. It was of paramount importance that this traffic was kept secure, and to maintain secrecy elaborate procedures were adopted. First the charts of the operational areas were divided into grid-patterns, each of which was allocated a coded reference, such as 068. Apart from abbreviating messages, it reduced the risk of giving away vital information to the enemy. However, obviously these grid-charts could be recovered from U-Boats sunk in coastal waters. As the war progressed messages were made shorter and shorter, partly to reduce the risk of decryption, and partly to speed up the flow of information. By 1918, a typical message sent by *U.53* would be '1–2–9–068–U53', which meant that *U.53* had sunk one ship of 2000 tons, had nine torpedoes left, and was in square 068 *alpha* (in the western

Straits by the explosive sweep of a destroyer. The sinking of *U.29* was said to have taken place in the Irish Sea, whereas it had occurred in the North Sea.

The interned lieutenant of *U.41* managed to get a letter through to Germany in December 1916, and it gave a revealing picture of British interrogation methods. The first point that struck him was the quality of the German spoken by his interrogator, and the second was the degree of knowledge in his interrogator's possession. When the prisoner refused to answer the questions, the correct answers were then given by the interrogator, with details about other U-Boats, nicknames of their commanders, and other snippets which gave the impression of omniscience. In fact much of this information was gained from letters and personal effects from sunken U-Boats, or from other prisoners already in captivity, but it produced a strong impression that the British had a widespread network of spies, particularly

The usefulness of the gun led to bigger guns being mounted in U-Boats. This 15cm gun on a 'U-cruiser' had an impressive range and punch, but the lighter 10.5cm gun was equally effective against thin-skinned merchantmen.

Channel). This message was then enciphered, and broadcast to Germany.

Although the Germans were aware that 'Room 40' of the Naval Intelligence Division in London was reading some radio messages, it was not known that the Russians had found a signal book in the arms of a dead signalman from the cruiser *Madeburg*, which was driven ashore in the Baltic after an action with the Baltic Fleet in October 1914. The code remained in force for a long time, the grid-charts were not changed until July 1918, but the cipher was changed every three months, and this was what British cryptanalysts worked on with conspicuous success. Even when it was changed once a week, and then once a day, Room 40 managed to keep abreast of the changes, as messages were frequently sent in both the old and the new ciphers, particularly when a U-Boat had been out on patrol at the time the cipher was changed, and had difficulty in reading the 'new' messages sent to her.

The U-Boat Arm might have lost the political battle in 1915–16 but it had not lost the material battle. By January 1916 a total of 186 U-Boats had been laid down, including the 45 ordered before the outbreak of war. Admiral von Tirpitz had ordered another 186, the last of which were laid down in February 1916. During the same period only 24 U-Boats had been sunk. Between August 1914 and December 1915 no fewer than 65 boats had joined the Fleet, and nearly a million tons of shipping had been sunk. If this ferocious exchange rate could be maintained there must come a point at which the British government could no longer prosecute the war. Even if the U-Boat could not win outright, it could easily force a negotiated peace which would force the British out of the war, thus isolating the French, and almost certainly leaving Germany in possession of most of her conquests.

Admiral von Capelle, the successor of Tirpitz, did not maintain the steady flow of orders month-by-month, and no orders were placed between February and the end of April 1916. The new Secretary for the Navy was later attacked for this apparent brake put on the programme, but the reason is simple: the existing programmes were outstripping the shipyards' capacity. U-Boats were relatively cheaper than large surface warships, but they required specialist skills to build and equip. The figures below give some idea of how the building programmes worked out in practice.

Nos.	Ordered	Building Time	Commissioned
		months	
U.46–50	Aug. 1914	14–24	Oct. 1915–July 1916
U.51–56	Aug.–Oct. 1914	18–22	Feb.–June 1916
U.57–62	Oct. 1914	21–26	July–Dec. 1916
U.66–70	Oct. 1914*	11–13	July–Sept. 1915
UA**	Oct. 1914	—	Oct. 1914
UB.1–17	Nov. 1914	3–7	Jan.–May 1915
UC.1–15	Nov. 1914	7–8	May–June 1915
U.71–80	Jan. 1915	11–17	Dec. 1915–June 1916
U.63–65	Mar. 1915	12–14	Mar.–May 1916
UB.18–47	Apr.–July 1915	8–15	Dec. 1915–July 1916
UB.81–92	June 1915	14–28	Aug. 1916–Oct. 1917
U.93–104	Aug. 1915	18–24	Feb.–Aug. 1917
UC.16–33	Aug. 1915	10–13	June–Sept. 1916
UC.34–48	Nov. 1915	10–12	Sept.–Nov. 1916
UC.49–79	Jan. 1916	11–12	Dec. 1916–Jan. 1917

* building for Austria in August 1914 and taken over.

** completed for Norway in August 1914 but not delivered.

These wild fluctuations in building time nevertheless show a consistent pattern. The smaller U-Boat, notably the original UB I type, could be built very quickly as long as the machinery was already in existence, but the building time more than doubled for the next batch as the rising demands for trucks for the Army soaked up the spare capacity of the manufacturers. The more complex UC I minelayers took longer to complete, and so did the larger UC II type (*UC.25* onwards), but the big 750–850-

tonners took up to two years or more, depending on a variety of circumstances. The most important cause of delays was the perennial shortage of diesel engines, but other items such as periscopes, batteries and air-compressors all had to be ordered in advance, and any sudden increase in submarine orders could cause dislocation in the supply of components. From June 1916 the Battle of the Skagerrak (Jutland) caused unexpected delay as the shipyards had to accept the huge work-load of ships which needed repairs to battle damage.

The original UB-Boats had been so small that the design was soon expanded to improve their fighting qualities. The UB II design (*UB.18* onwards) had the 50cm (19.7-inch) torpedo, and its beamier hull and bigger engines made it easier to handle. Thirty boats were built to this

U-Boats and crews are inspected at Kiel, 2 October 1918.

design between April 1915 and July 1916, but by
May 1916 a new UB III design was ready, and 24
were ordered. They embodied all the lessons
learned to date, and although nominally rated
as coastal boats, in many ways they were superior to the prewar seagoing U-Boats:

	U.19 Class	**UB.48 Class**
Displacement:	650/837 tons	516/651 tons
Dimensions:	210.5ft × 20ft ×	182ft × 19ft ×
	11.75ft	12ft
Machinery:	1700/1200hp	1100/788hp
Speed:	15½/9½ knots	13½/8 knots
Armament:	4 20-in TT	5 20-in TT
	(2 bow, 2 stern)	(4 bow, 1 stern)
	1 8.8cm gun	1 8.8cm gun
Crew:	35	34

Left: By 1917 aircraft, flying boats, seaplanes or 'blimps' were a growing threat to the U-Boat. The safest remedy was to dive, for the primitive bombs were of little use against a submerged U-Boat.

Below: Two big *U.81* Class boats exercise on the surface. These boats joined the fleet from the autumn of 1916 and incorporated many improvements suggested by war-experience.

The first UB III boats were not ready until the summer of 1917, and they proved to be the most successful design of all. By the Armistice nearly 90 were complete and many more were in various stages of building. They are a prime example of how a rational policy of simplifying design can speed up construction. The differences were kept to a minimum and the contracts were allocated to four firms: Krupp's Germania Yard, Blohm & Voss (Hamburg), AG Weser (Bremen) and AG Vulcan (Hamburg). A 10.5cm (4.1-in) gun replaced the 8.8cm in many units, and most had a saw-backed net-cutter over the distinctive raked bow.

The UC minelayers underwent a similar process of evolution, from the tiny UC I to the UC III type. The UC II type was some 50ft longer than the tiny UC I, with two shafts as opposed to one. It was soon recognised that a submarine-minelayer returning home after dropping her deadly 'eggs' might well encounter merchant ship targets (she would, of course, avoid action while her dangerous cargo was on board), and so the new class was given torpedo-tubes as well as more mine-stowage. As the *Marineamt* still preferred to have the mine-tubes inside the pressure hull, the forward torpedo-tubes had

GERMAN SUBMARINE "U C 39" SUNK BY H.M.S. "THRASHER"

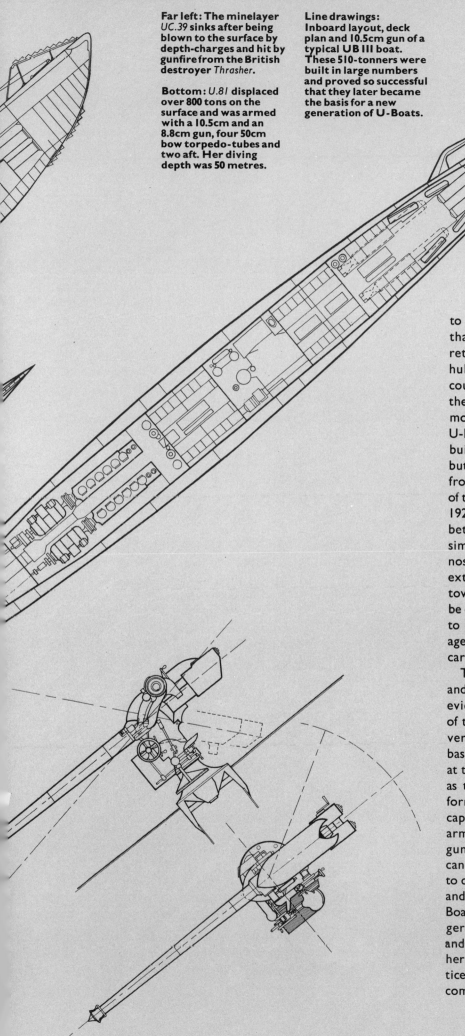

to be placed outside the casing, and this meant that they could not be reloaded until the boat returned to harbour. The greater depth of the hull meant that each of the six mine-tubes could now accommodate three mines bringing the total up to 18. The after torpedo-tube was mounted internally, just as in a conventional U-Boat. In all, 64 of these versatile craft were built between August 1915 and January 1917, but only 16 of a series of larger boats ordered from June 1917 onwards were ready by the end of the War. These were the UC III type (UC.80–192), of which UC.90 to UC.105 were completed between July and November 1918. They looked similar to the UB III type with a raked 'shark's nose' bow and net-cutter, a deck-gun and external torpedo-tubes abreast of the conning tower. As an added refinement, reloads could be carried externally as well, allowing the tubes to be reloaded on the surface. The mine-stowage was slightly decreased; six tubes were still carried but four of them carried only two mines.

The rational policy which produced the UB-and UC-Boats in such numbers was not so evident with the U-Boats. Up to U.104, the last of the 'Mittel-U' type ordered in August 1915, very few detailed changes had been made to the basic design. Six more were ordered in May, but at the same time ten ocean mine-layers, known as the UE II type, were ordered. These were formidable submarines, nearly 270ft long and capable of 6000 miles' endurance. They were armed with a 15cm (5.9-inch) gun and a 10.5cm gun, and carried extra torpedoes in external canisters in the deck-casing; their purpose was to destroy shipping off the American east coast, and they were by far the most formidable U-Boats yet built. The U.127 Class were even bigger, 1200 tons, with six 50cm torpedo-tubes and two 15cm guns but no mines. The U.117 and her sisters all entered service before the Armistice but only two of the U.127 Class were completed.

These 'U-cruisers' looked magnificent on paper, and the existence of U-Boats armed with 15cm guns certainly caused alarm and consternation to the Allies. For a while there was talk of having to provide guns of similar or even larger calibre for merchant ships, but nothing could be done about it. As things turned out the U-cruisers were too large and unwieldy, and the U-Boat commanders preferred the 'Mittel-U' and UB III types. The only advantages conferred by the extra size were the greater amount of fuel and, above all, the greater number of spare torpedoes which could be carried. The big U-Boats took longer to build and consumed more vital raw materials than the smaller types. What is more, the introduction of such a variety of new designs put even more strain on the shipyards and introduced further delays.

The Battle of the Skagerrak also had an important effect on the submarine war. As we have already seen, the need to repair the ships of the High Seas Fleet slowed down work on U-Boats, but there was no question of the Fleet returning to seek out the British Grand Fleet. Whatever losses the British might have sustained, and whatever the German press might claim, Admiral von Scheer was convinced that victory at sea could not be gained through another Skagerrak. On the other hand, he also felt that the good showing of the High Seas Fleet on 31 May 1916 had caused many influential neutral nations to modify their hostility to Germany. In short, he felt that a renewed campaign of unrestricted U-Boat warfare was the only way to win, and that it could achieve victory without bringing America into the war against Germany.

A conference was held at Pless on 30 August, with the military leaders, von Hindenburg and Ludendorff, the Chiefs of the Naval Staff and the *Marineamt*, and the principal government ministers. The Chief of the Naval Staff, Admiral von Hotzendorff, put forward the now familiar demand for unrestricted warfare, while von Jagow, the Foreign Minister, warned that the neutrals would be angered yet again. There was a difference, he warned, between the effect of the Allied blockade and the warfare waged by the U-Boats; one diverted German cargoes into their own ports without harming non-belligerent traders, but the other inevitably caused

heavy loss of innocent civilian lives. The Secretary of State, Helfferich, avoided the humanitarian issue, and took the line that the statistics cited to support the Naval Staff's views could be fallacious, and if they were, the U-Boat campaign would not only fail, but would precipitate a catastrophe.

The result was another victory for the Chancellor, but he compromised by leaving the final decision to Marshal von Hindenburg, pending the results of a campaign against Romania in the Carpathian Mountains. Permission was given to order 27 more U-Boats, but nine of these were 2100-ton cruisers, and only two 800-tonners and 16 UB IIIs were ordered. German historians all deplore the indecision and caution which prevailed. It was late in the day to be talking of waiting until the various types had 'proved themselves in action' before placing mass orders, especially with the prospect of a large-scale U-Boat campaign in the offing. It certainly appears odd that no attempt seems to have been made to convert some of the idle mercantile shipyards to U-Boat building, and it is on record that the Director of U-Boat Construction, Admiral Spindler, encountered considerable opposition to his efforts to speed up the ordering of new construction. Another authority, Captain Gayer, claimed that Admiral von Capelle did not want a large-scale building programme to start in 1916. The reason, claimed Gayer, was his fear that a huge fleet of submarines would be hard to administer and would hinder expansion of the surface fleet after Germany was victorious. A more generous, and indeed more likely view, is that von Capelle foresaw that the war would be over before a fraction of the new U-Boats were ready. In fact he maintained that no U-Boats should be ordered unless they could be completed within a year, a very sound decision. The situation was very much the same as it had been in 1910–14; unless the right type of U-Boat had been chosen, a large-scale programme would in all probability have tied up the shipyards in producing the wrong types. As it was, the programme was taken up with too many cruisers and not enough medium-sized boats.

U-Boats Built May 1916–November 1918

Numbers	Ordered	Building Time	Commissioned
U.105–114	May 1916	14–25 months	July 1917–June 1918
U.127–138	May 1916	25–27 months	completed June–August 1918
U.117–126	May 1916	22–29 months	9 completed March–October 1918
UB.48–71	May 1916	13–18 months	June–November 1917
U.139–141	August 1916	21–22 months	May–June 1918
U.115–116	September 1916	–	Not completed
UB.72–87	September 1916*	12–15 months	September–December 1917
U.142–150	November 1916*	24 months	1 completed November 1918
U.158–163	February 1917	–	Not completed
UB.88–132	February 1917	11–17 months	January–July 1918
U.151–157	February 1917**	–	July–December 1917
U.164–172	June 1917	16–17 months	2 completed October–November 1918
U.173–182	June 1917	–	Not completed
UB.133–169	June 1917	–	Not completed
UC.80–118	June 1917	11–14 months	16 completed July–October 1918
U.183–200	June–December 1917	–	Not completed
U.201–212	December 1917	–	Not completed
UB.170–205	December 1917	–	Not completed
UC.119–152	December 1917	–	Not completed
UF.1–20	December 1917	–	Not completed
U.213–228	May–June 1918	–	Not completed
U.229–276	June 1918	–	Not completed
UB.206–249	June 1918	–	Not completed
UC.153–192	June 1918	–	Not completed
UF.21–92	January–July 1918	–	Not completed

* the so-called 'Pless Programme'.

** ex-mercantile submarines; *Deutschland* became *U.155* and others converted during construction.

59

Above: *U.82*, lying alongside a UB III boat, shows the differing shapes of the hull, bow and conning tower.

Right: *U.80* was a large ocean-going minelayer, with a horizontal mine-deck aft instead of the vertical tubes in the UC-Boats.

The UF type was the last variant from the standard designs, and was intended as a coastal submarine for the Flanders coast. It was a single-hulled design, a little bigger than the UB II design of 1915, and was armed with four or five 50cm torpedo-tubes and an 8.8cm gun. Little else is known about the design as the drawings were destroyed in 1918, but it is notable as the first and only order to be given to non-specialist shipyards – a very belated recognition of a simple solution to the *Marineamt*'s problems.

On the tactical side the U-Boats' work with the High Seas Fleet during the 'twilight' period after the first unrestricted campaign had proved disappointing. The exaggerated respect for U-Boats shown by the British C-in-C, Sir John Jellicoe, throughout the Jutland battle (he was wary of being lured into a 'submarine trap') was wasted, for there were no U-Boats at sea with the Fleet on 31 May 1916. After the battle the German High Command assumed that the Grand Fleet would raid the Heligoland Bight, and 14 U-Boats were stationed off Borkum and the Horns Reef to give early warning of any incursion. British submarines were also on the *qui vive*, and U-Boats ran the risk of being

torpedoed while returning from a patrol.

The Flanders flotillas continued to harass shipping, and the British attempted to harass the U-Boats in turn, first by long-range bombardment of Ostend and Zeebrugge, and then, as aerial warfare developed, by bombing the U-Boat base at Bruges, about eight miles inland. Canals connected Bruges to Ostend and Zeebrugge, and at this inland port the Navy constructed a fully equipped repair base with machine shops, floating docks and accommodation for the crews of U-Boats under refit. The threat of bombing was met by the construction of shelters with reinforced concrete roofs, a foretaste of the giant 'pens' of World War II. On average, 18 U-Boats were to be found at Bruges at any time, repairing after a period at sea or getting ready to go out again. The casino at Ostend was a favourite haunt for the officers, and as the town had been a holiday resort before the War there was no great problem in providing rest and recreation for the crews.

The Flanders U-Boats had learned that the Dover Straits minefields were not as deadly as had been feared, and in 1916 first the UC-Boats and then the UB-Boats began to slip through.

The recommendations were passed back to the U-Boats based in Germany, and at the end of November Bauer finally rescinded his orders forbidding the use of the Straits. The only U-Boats which were required to use the northern route were those with inexperienced crews or damaged boats returning from a patrol.

Despite Admiral von Scheer's opposition to a half-hearted campaign, the High Command ordered a resumption of the war against shipping on 6 October but still subject to the hated Prize Regulations. Scheer complied with the order, but insisted that his U-Boats should have the right to torpedo armed merchantmen without warning. What persuaded him was the increased strength of the U-Boat force. There were now 119 U-Boats in service, and 87 were operational. The difference was made up of boats restricted to training or working up after completion. Eighty new boats had been delivered during the 'twilight' period, and only 17 had been sunk, and although only half the U-Boats had been operating against shipping, their number was in fact greater than the number in the first unrestricted campaign of 1915.

This, then, was the immutable factor in the

The large minelayer *U.78* shows off her unusual 'ripple' camouflage scheme.

arithmetic which had to be done by the Naval Staff. Whatever type of campaign that they fought they would have to make do with the U-Boats already built or completing, and the losses would have to justify themselves in terms of the number of enemy merchant ships sunk.

The third and final restricted U-Boat campaign ran for four months from 6 October 1916 to 31 January 1917. Despite the restrictions it was enormously successful, with 140 ships sunk in October, 113 in November, 128 in December, and 135 in January 1917, to say nothing of the many small sailing craft sunk. A sad by-product of this campaign was the virtual extinction of the small sail trading vessel, which might otherwise have lasted much longer. The previous worst figures had been in August 1914 when 185,800 tons of shipping had been sunk, but in

October 1916 the figure reached 353,600 tons of British and world shipping combined, nearly twice as much. November was nearly as bad, 311,500 tons; in December it topped 355,000 tons, and by the end of January the appalling figure of 368,500 tons. This brought the total of British ships sunk to 1942 (excluding those smaller than 100 tons BRT) since the outbreak of war. The 'exchange rate' was now 65 ships for each U-Boat sunk.

Hitherto the vast British mercantile marine had been able to sustain the losses, but the lack of any replacement building programme or of any workable defence against submarine attack was beginning to have a noticeable effect on the Allied war-effort. In December 1916 traffic to India, the Far East and Australasia had to be diverted around the Cape of Good Hope to avoid losses in the Mediterranean, and this automatically reduced the amount of cargo which could be imported in a given time. Total imports into British ports began to decline, and as Great Britain was making good the deficiencies of her Italian and French allies through imports, her partners also felt the effect. However it must be remembered that the British merchant fleet was enormous, and had only lost six per cent of its total strength at the end of 1916, and the shortages of war materials were relative; German civilians were feeling the shortages of food far more severely, and the factories were experiencing severe shortages.

The battle between the Naval Staff and the Chancellor continued all the while, for Scheer was determined to have the restrictions lifted as soon as possible. As early as 10 September 1916 Admiral von Holtzendorf had been secretly lobbying for General Ludendorff's support. An attempt to get prior agreement with the United States for a set of rules was upset because

President Wilson had to fight a presidential election early in November, but what the admirals wanted was the abandonment of what they contemptuously dismissed as the 'weapons of diplomacy'. This blunt proposal was actually put to the Kaiser in a memorandum in the hope that it would checkmate Bernstorff's overtures to the Americans. On 22 November Scheer won approval from Hindenburg and Ludendorff, now firmly entrenched as the saviours of Germany, and exactly a month later Imperial approval was given to begin U-Boat warfare without limitations. There was nothing for Bethmann-Hollweg but to accept the arguments of the hawks.

It must not be thought that the Navy's demands for an unrestricted campaign was a blind rush to discard moderation. It was the product of a carefully thought-out argument about tonnages, rates of sinkings, numbers of U-Boats and above all, time. In brief the Naval

Top left: U.93 at sea, showing the unusual grouping of the side-vents, through which seawater flooded to take her down. The vents were made larger in this class for faster diving.

shipping and just under a million tons of 'non-English' (that is Italian and French shipping). On the basis of these figures, the destruction of 600,000 tons a month and the frightening off of the 1,200,000 tons of neutral shipping would wreck the British supply-system within five months. The British mercantile marine would lose nearly 40 per cent of its strength, food-rationing would have to be imposed at a subsistence level, and the war-effort would be hamstrung by lack of raw materials. One example was the supply of pit-props from Scandinavia; if these were not imported the supply of coal would be cut back, and this would seriously harm the production of munitions and steel.

By comparison the periods of U-Boat warfare under the Prize Regulations had accounted for an average of only 80,000 tons per month, while the restricted campaigns had averaged 350,000 tons. The logic was irrefutable, or so it seemed. As before, there were men who raised a voice

U.91 returns to port.

Staff had taken into account certain indisputable facts. The British still had about 20 million gross tons of shipping, which was the Allies' biggest capital asset. It was reckoned that this figure was broken down as follows:

3.6 million tons requisitioned for military use;

.5 million tons of coastal traffic;

1.0 million tons under repair;

2.0 millions tons for supplying the other Allies;

12.9 million tons for British imports

_____

20.0

_____

According to German estimates only 6.75 million tons of British shipping had used British ports in 1916, with three million tons of neutral

of caution, questioning the time-scale and the validity of the statistics. One practical objection was the strain on the U-Boats and their crews. To maintain the pressure they would have to be overhauled and turned around as fast as possible, and it would be necessary to use even inexperienced crews. But so certain was everybody that five months of maximum effort would bring victory, that they convinced themselves that the problems would solve themselves.

There was one moment of final doubt when on 4 January 1917 the Kaiser seemed about to withdraw his approval on the advice of the Chancellor, but on 9 January Imperial assent was given to start the sinking of armed merchantmen without warning from 1 February. The fate of Germany and the outcome of the war were to be entrusted to the U-Boats.

A GAMBLER'S LAST THROW

The campaign which opened on 1 February 1917 was fought with unparalleled ferocity. Three days later the United States broke off diplomatic relations, but did nothing more; losses soared from 368,000 tons to 540,000 tons by the end of February. The following month they reached 594,000 tons, just short of the figure of 600,000 tons, the level at which it was calculated that victory would be won.

The distribution of U-Boats on 1 February concentrated nearly all of them in the North Sea, 43 operating from German ports, 23 in Flanders, 23 in the Adriatic, the three still left in the Black Sea, and ten operational boats kept in the Baltic to counter the British and Russian submarines. [Figures vary, but those compiled by Grant in 1914–1918 have been used.]

Eight of the Baltic U-Boats were earmarked

Top left: This purports to be a photograph of an Allied steamer being torpedoed by a U-Boat but on close examination the ship looks suspiciously like a model. It may well be a 'still' from a British propaganda film, superimposed on genuine film taken at sea.

Above: The SS *Clintonia* is hit by a torpedo from *U.28*, fired on the surface. On the same day, 8 August 1915, she sank two other ships.

Below: A UB-Boat in April 1917 tows a ship's life-boat. This demonstrates the futility of trying to wage war under the existing Prize Regulations.

for the North Sea, and soon joined their sisters; work on the UB-Boats and UC-Boats was pushed forward with utmost speed.

New orders for the campaign had been issued on 17 January. The most important change was the insistence on using the English Channel route to save time, although it was permitted to retain sufficient reserve of fuel to allow a return via Scotland if the boat was damaged. It was suggested too, that boats forced to use the northern route should let themselves be seen, to mislead the British patrols into believing that the Channel route was blocked. When passing through the Channel U-Boats were to travel on the surface at night, preferably when the weather was bad, and to assist them in choosing the best nights Radio Bruges would broadcast weather reports. If sighted by a patrol the U-Boat would dive immediately and go down to 40 metres to avoid nets. Information about Allied minefields was given, with the interesting observation that British mines were usually laid close to the surface, and rarely exploded because of a badly designed firing lever. Despite

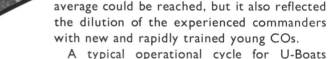

The gutted hulk of a Scandinavian sailing ship, photographed from an Allied cruiser.

this damning verdict 17 U-Boats were lost to British mines and mine-nets in 1917, and they were told to avoid minefields by diving to 20 or 30 metres. By this time it was known that Allied patrol craft were using directional hydrophones to track submerged U-Boats, and if any of these craft were encountered the U-Boat was to dive deep, stop all auxiliary machinery, and run quietly on one electric motor. To confuse the hydrophone operator the U-Boat would also stop from time to time to make a drastic change of course. It was also recommended that enemy submarines should be left alone, as torpedoes were needed to sink merchant ships.

An important innovation was the assignment of U-Boats to specific patrol areas whereas individual commanders had previously been given a free hand to choose areas likely to yield results. This was partly an inevitable tendency towards central direction, the only way in which the desired 600,000 tons per month

average could be reached, but it also reflected the dilution of the experienced commanders with new and rapidly trained young COs.

A typical operational cycle for U-Boats included five boats: one operating west of the English Channel ('on station'), one heading west to relieve her, a third returning home from a patrol, a fourth docked for repairs, and the fifth completing her refit. This explains why the whole strength could never be available at any one time; in theory the cycle could have been suspended to allow a massive concentration, but in practice the steady rotation of U-Boats maintained a relentless pressure which yielded far better results and kept the enemy's forces at full stretch. The biggest problem was the time spent in transit, and when the U-Boats began to seek targets 200 miles west of Fastnet it became necessary to extend the cycle to include seven boats. Each ocean patrol lasted an average of 25 days, and the Dover Straits route saved six days of the total for a U-Boat from Wilhelmshaven. The Flanders U-Boats, being smaller, carried out 14-day patrols, and using the Straits saved them eight days.

The U-Boats were pressing home the attack, and this led to a much higher loss-rate than before. Only 14 boats had been lost to anti-submarine measures and accidents in 1916, but no fewer than 11 were lost in the first four

months of 1917. Four were sunk by gunfire from Q-ships; two were UC-Boats blown up on their own mines; one was torpedoed by a British submarine and one was sunk by a mine. One, U.76, was rammed by a trawler and then foundered in a storm; UC.46 and UC.39 were both sunk by destroyers – one by ramming and the other by depth-charging.

For the Allies the losses were now horrifying. What had been an ulcer steadily draining their strength, had now become an open vein. Naturally the unrestricted campaign had not come as a surprise, and as early as October 1916 the Commander-in-Chief of the British Grand Fleet, Admiral Jellicoe, had warned the Admiralty that supplies of food and other necessities would be reduced to such a level that the British government could be forced to sue for peace by the summer of 1917. On 22 November Jellicoe relinquished command of the Grand Fleet to become First Sea Lord, and at the same time a

special Anti-Submarine Division of the Naval Staff was created. This division produced a paper on policy for 1917, but it simply reinforced the existing countermeasures: hunting groups of warships and auxiliary patrols, minefields across U-Boat routes, and submarines to lie in wait for U-Boats in transit or to escort shipping. Jellicoe's advice had included a warning that new methods had to be found, but the Admiralty seemed unable to think of any new measures, and told the government that no answer was likely to be found to the U-Boat menace.

There could be no doubt that the existing methods were not working. The hundreds of auxiliary patrol vessels and warships could do nothing but scurry from sinking to sinking, arriving in time to pick up survivors but never in time to even catch sight of the U-Boat. The only inconvenience caused to the U-Boats was to force them to operate further out in the

A camouflaged merchantman leaves a trail of oil as she sinks by the stern. 'Dazzle-painting' was introduced in 1917-18 to disguise a ship's course, speed and bearing, not to conceal her from a U-Boat. As all aiming of torpedoes had to be done by a visual estimate, this crude countermeasure often worked.

Atlantic, and as we have seen, this imposed a slight burden on the operating cycle, but did nothing to make U-Boats less effective. In fact the 'exchange rate' rose from 53 merchantmen to one U-Boat in February to 74 in March, and then to 167 in April.

The United States government had watched the slaughter of shipping with growing anger and finally on 3 April President Wilson told Congress:

'Civilisation itself seems in the balance, but right is more precious than peace, and we shall fight for the thing which we carry nearest to our hearts, for democracy, for the right of those who submit to authority to have a voice in their own government, for the rights and liberties of small nations, for the universal domination of right, for such a concert of free peoples as will bring peace and safety to all nations and make the world itself at least free. . . .'

There were many factors behind this decision – some selfish, some practical – but at the bottom of it was a final revulsion at the obtuseness of German diplomacy which had made very few concessions to neutral feelings. The mailed fist had been proclaimed too loud and too often as the arbiter of German claims, and British diplo-

Bottom left: The depth-charge and its thrower, the first weapon capable of sinking a U-Boat after she had dived. The hydrostatic valve could be set to the depth at which the U-Boat was likely to be, and even a near-miss usually caused sufficient damage to force the U-Boat to the surface.

Below: Another method of using depth-charges was to roll them off the stern of a destroyer.

macy had cunningly played on this insensitivity to libertarian sentiments. The use of Q-Ships, for example, had put the U-Boats in the position of having to attack without warning: the use of neutral flags, although historically regarded as a legitimate *ruse de guerre* for unarmed merchantmen, tempted U-Boat commanders to treat all neutral ships as Allied ships in disguise. But what could not be blamed on the Allies was the occasional example of the practice of *spurlos versenkt*, or 'sunk without trace'. One or two U-Boat commanders took the view that a sinking of an unauthorised category of merchantman could not be attributed to a U-Boat if there were no survivors. The most notorious instance of this was the sinking of the Hospital ship *Llandovery Castle*, which was returning empty from Halifax. On the night of 27 June 1917 she was hit by a torpedo fired by *U.86* (K/Lt Patzig) over 100 miles west of Fastnet, and sank within ten minutes. For some reason the U-Boat surfaced, and Patzig demanded to know if a party of American airmen had been on board. The master, Captain Sylvester, denied having US military personnel among his crew, and indicated that he had been carrying seven Canadian military doctors. The U-Boat then began to circle at speed, and fired 12 shells at some unseen target; only the master's boat was ever seen again and the evidence indicates that the remaining 234 survivors, including nurses, doctors and crew-members, were killed by gunfire from *U.86*, after which the boats were sunk. Patzig and his two lieutenants were listed by the Allies as war criminals, and the junior officers were indicted at Leipzig in 1921, but Patzig had to be tried in his absence. The evidence of the helmsman indicated that Patzig had been stalking the brightly-lit hospital ship for four hours, and had been begged to spare her; Lieutenants Boldt and Dittmar were sentenced to four years' imprisonment.

Genuine atrocities like this were fortunately rare, but the fact remains that unrestricted submarine warfare aroused deep repugnance in most people's minds. After all, for centuries sailors have regarded the sea as the ultimate enemy of all sailors, and by torpedoing a merchantman in the Atlantic a U-Boat captain handed his fellow-mariners over to the common enemy. The hallowed tradition of making every attempt to save life at sea, even that of your enemy, had to be disregarded for all the reasons already stated, although right to the end of the war there were chivalrous U-Boat captains who, if they were not at risk themselves, would provide survivors in open boats with a compass and provisions. The debris of U-Boat warfare was in its way as grisly as land-warfare on the Western Front, and accounts of the period speak of ships ploughing through waters strewn with corpses, dead mules and splintered boats.

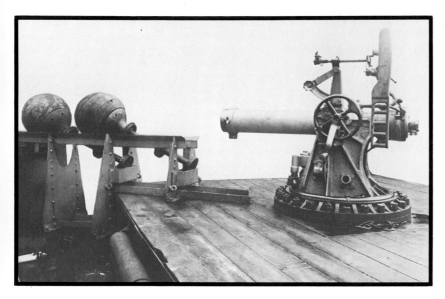

The furtive nature of submarine warfare made it seem underhand and unfair, and so the dangers and discomfort of the U-Boats crews were ignored. The U-Boats were uncomfortable at the best of times, and in winter the living conditions were barely tolerable. Condensation of moisture inside the pressure hull made tuberculosis an occupational hazard, but it also

On stereoscopic card:

190

Under the sea in a "U" boat! The torpedoes are released on their path of death through these tubes.

TRAVELS · REALISTIC · LONDON · CAPE TOWN · BOMBAY · MELBOURNE · TORONTO

BY ROYAL COMMAND TO THEIR IMPERIAL MAJESTIES KING GEORGE V AND QUEEN MARY

TORPEDO ROOM

Above: A stereoscopic view of the forward torpedo-tubes in a surrendered U-Boat.

Right: The two forward 50cm torpedo-tubes in the forward compartment of *U.155*. For their size this class of U-Boats was weakly armed.

made bread go mouldy and dry clothing was a rare luxury. Recently documentary film of an inspection of U-Boats in 1917 has been rediscovered, and the first impression on seeing a mechanic coming up through the after hatch of the U-Boat is of a Negro wearing a black uniform, but he is merely covered in grease from head to foot. The hysterical language of propaganda on both sides did nothing to help. To cite only one example: after the *Baralong* incident British newspapers tried to make out that the four German sailors from *U.27* had been lynched by

irate American sailors from the *Nicosian*, incensed at the sinking of their ship; the German press reported that the boarding party of Royal Marines had thrown the four men alive into the boilers. In recent years the uproar over a book on the *Lusitania* incident has been a convincing demonstration of how long-lived the lies of wartime propaganda can be.

America's declaration of war on 5 April, not as an ally of Great Britain and France, but as an 'associated power' had a tremendous effect on the U-Boat war, but not immediately. For one

Top right: Inside *U.155*'s conning tower, showing the voice pipe (left) and the counterweight for hoisting the periscope (right).

thing the German military chiefs had allowed for it in their calculations, although their misreading of the American President's motives led them to expect intervention to be deferred for much longer. The US Naval Mission sent to London under Admiral W S Sims was dismayed to be told by Jellicoe that the U-Boats were winning. The neutral shipowners had done what the U-Boats wanted them to do, by keeping their ships in port in the hope that American pressure would stop the campaign. Sims immediately responded by telling his superiors in Washington that massive assistance was needed, or there would be no war for the President to intervene in, and therefore no peace terms which he could dictate. As a stopgap six destroyers were sent over immediately to join the British escort forces in Queenstown (now Cobh) in the south of Ireland, but they could do little more than join the hunting groups which were frustrated participants in the deadly game of trying to catch U-Boats in the act of sinking ships.

189

BY ROYAL COMMAND TO THEIR IMPERIAL MAJESTIES KING GEORGE V AND QUEEN MARY

TRAVELS
REALISTIC TRADE MARK
LONDON · CAPE TOWN · BOMBAY · MELBOURNE · TORONTO

12-inch gun on a monster German submarine, ruthless pests that sank our shipping "without trace."

Centre right: A stereoscopic postcard of the 15cm gun on board *U.155* **– described for the British as a 12-inch (30.5cm) gun.**

Right: The control room of *U.155,* **(ex-***Deutschland***) as seen by British sightseers after the Armistice.**

were placed with American and Japanese shipyards. A proper salvage organisation was built up and much more economical use was made of shipping in a desperate attempt to cut the rate of attrition. Another long-overdue measure was to recall a number of good merchant ships which had been extravagantly requisitioned by the Royal Navy in 1914 as auxiliaries; they did little to reduce the efficiency of the Navy, and were far more use carrying cargoes. The introduction of the convoy was thus only the final keystone in a radical rethinking of Allied policy towards the U-Boats' war on commerce.

The Allies were taking desperate countermeasures to save themselves from defeat, but the U-Boats themselves had not achieved the victory that they had hoped for. The combined diplomatic efforts of the United States and Great Britain wooed the neutrals back to the lucrative trade in and out of British ports, and by July the total of voyages by neutral traders was only 20 per cent less than normal. This meant that far more of the ships sunk by the U-Boats were neutrals, and so only 400,000 tons out of the 600,000 tons average were British ships. This meant that the campaign had sunk only 2.25 million tons of British shipping against the 3.50 million allowed for in the Naval Staff's calculations. Another factor not taken into account was the very human tendency of U-Boat commanders to over-estimate their victims' tonnages. As a result, this inflation of the figures masked the shortfall in tonnage sunk, and the Allies proved somehow to be able to last much longer than expected. What had certainly not been foreseen by the admirals was the flexibility of the world's shipping, first in reorganising its entire trading pattern to meet the emergency, and second, in making the convoy organisation work remarkably well.

The first effect of convoy on the U-Boats was to scour the oceans clear of targets. All the reports of U-Boat commanders from May onwards tell the same tale; instead of lying in wait until a target arrived, a U-Boat might wait days, and then be confronted by as many as 20 ships surrounded by destroyers. Any attempt to attack would invariably bring down a shower of depth-charges the dreaded *wasserbomben*, whose reverberating explosions smashed electric light bulbs and damaged the boat. The first convoy from Gibraltar to England arrived on 20 May without sustaining a single loss, and another followed from Hampton Roads shortly afterwards. An immediate reaction by the U-Boats was to attack the outward-bound ships, which at this early stage could not be given full escort. Even so, by October, only 24 ships out of 1500 had been sunk, and of these 14 had been sunk after leaving their convoy or through failing to keep convoy-discipline. The effect of even this partial convoying was to put an end to operations far out into the Atlantic, and by

September very few ships were being sunk more than 50 miles away from Fastnet, whereas U-Boats had previously been able to pick off targets up to 300 miles out.

There were other problems in store for the U-Boats. From September the British began to lay a new and deadly mine, the H2, which was a copy of the efficient German mine. These were laid in increasing numbers off the Flanders coast and in the Heligoland Bight, and between July and December 18 U-Boats succumbed to these minefields. The Royal Naval Air Service was able to escort convoys with large flying boats in coastal waters, and provided numbers of small non-rigged airships, the famous 'blimps'.

The big minelayer *UC.92* and other boats lying alongside the Kaiser's yacht *Hohenzollern*. She had been hulked in 1914, but served as an accommodation ship at Wilhelmshaven.

These aircraft carried 100 lb and 250 lb bombs for use against surfaced U-Boats, and a 230 lb bomb with a delayed-action fuze to set it off 70 feet below the surface. The sight of a blimp or a 'Large America' flying boat over a convoy was usually enough to warn a U-Boat commander to keep out of the way, and so these air patrols achieved very few successes against the U-Boats in spite of their undoubted deterrent effect.

The convoy system has been blamed exclusively by German historians for the frustration of the unrestricted campaign, and has been equally praised by the other side as the only thing which saved the Allies. But during the crucial six months from February to the end of July only about 350 large merchantmen were convoyed out of a total of some 3000 voyages. On the existing loss ratio, this would have resulted in the loss of 35 if they had sailed independently, whereas only two of the 350 were sunk; this means that convoys only saved a possible 33 ships at a time when total casualties still approached 2000. Nevertheless in that time the exchange rate fell from 70 ships to 16 ships for each U-Boat sunk.

Another point which should not be forgotten is that 1917 saw the first serious casualties sustained by the U-Boats. In the first half of the year 20 were sunk, but in the second half this figure was more than doubled:

January .... 1 sunk by Q-Ship, 1 rammed.

February .. 1 rammed, 1 depth-charged, 2 sunk by Q-Ships, 1 sunk by her own mines.

March ..... 1 torpedoed by submarines, 1 sunk by Q-Ship, 1 sunk by her own mines.

April ...... 1 mined.

May .... 2 torpedoed by submarine, 2 rammed, 2 mined, 1 sunk by her own mines (?)

June ...... 1 sunk by Q-Ship, 1 depth-charged.

July .... 1 torpedoed by submarine, 2 mined, 1 wrecked, 1 rammed and depth-charged, 1 lost by accident.

August .... 2 mined, 1 sunk by Q-Ship and rammed, 1 sunk by Q-Ship, 1 sunk by her own mines.

September . 1 sunk by explosion of her victim, 4 mined, 1 sunk by her own mines, 2 rammed, 1 torpedoed by submarines, 1 bombed by seaplane (?), 1 by accident.

October ... 5 mined.

November . 2 torpedoed by submarines, 3 mined, 1 depth-charge, 1 rammed, 1 wrecked.

December . 4 mined, 1 lost by accident, 1 rammed, 2 depth-charged.

A U-Boat on its way to the scrap-yard finds itself on the beach of an English seaside resort after breaking her tow. She may be *U.122* or *U.123*, which ran aground on the East coast in 1921.

Efforts were made to devise new tactics to outwit the convoys. Commodore Bauer drew up a far-sighted plan to use the *U.151* Class (the former *Deutschland*-type mercantile submarines) as headquarters U-Boats in the Atlantic to the west of Ireland. If fitted with radio direction-finding equipment and given a team of cryptographers they would be able to decipher British messages to the convoys, convey up-to-date instructions to the U-Boats, and even refuel and supply ordinary U-Boats. Certainly the future Admiral Dönitz was impressed by the scheme, and it bears the germ of the ideas that were to become the 'milch cow' and the 'wolf pack' nearly 25 years later. The idea was tried in *U.66* early in June 1917 when she carried special radio equipment and trained personnel but she was not able to communicate with her base, and so there was no attempt to co-ordinate the work

in practice and as he later claimed, his ideas about finding an answer to convoys were never given a chance. Michelsen was not able to make any significant improvement, and even the ordering of another 100 U-Boats of various sizes came far too late to be of any use. In fact the Army commanders, who had given their approval to the unrestricted campaign as a way out of the deadlock on land, now changed their minds and went back to planning for a massive breakthrough on the Western Front. The Navy continued to hope for victory through the U-Boats but the Army Staff now made little secret of its conviction that the campaign would only be of use if it prevented American troops from reaching Europe in large numbers before the great spring offensive had reached the Channel. In other words the U-Boats were to harry the enemy, but there was no question of

of other U-Boats by the shore-based command. Later U-Boats tried working together, exchanging information about convoys sighted. There were even two observation points established west of the French coast with U-Boats assigned to do nothing but report on shipping movements so that their sisters could operate more effectively. The idea was sound and was to be developed to deadly effect in another war, but in 1917–18 the state of radio-communication was still crude and the equipment was too unreliable.

One of the lesser casualties of the period was Commodore Bauer who was replaced as Commander of U-Boats early in June by Andreas Michelsen. Bauer has rarely had full credit for what he had done to put U-Boat warfare on a sound footing. He was a clever and innovative submariner who from time to time went to sea in order to find out exactly how the ideas worked

any over-riding priority for raw materials and labour.

Despite the change in official attitudes, the U-Boat Arm continued to expand and from the beginning of 1918 was able to keep 36 U-Boats at sea, rising to 42 in July. The total of operational U-Boats averaged 120–130 during the last nine months rising to 179 in October, but the exchange rate was falling steadily, going down to 3–4 ships per U-Boat and plummeting to two ships by October. Even so the U-Boats were still inflicting losses on Allied shipping, and in 1918 a total of 1133 ships fell to them but only 134 of these were in convoy; the remainder were ships sailing independently. Fewer U-Boats were sunk in 1918 and deliveries of new boats exceeded the 61 lost.

A most serious setback was the final plugging of the Dover Straits in February, when the barriers of minefields and nets finally became too dangerous for the bigger U-Boats to attempt the passage under any circumstances. This forced a reversion to the route around Scotland, and cut the effective time they could spend on patrol. In January only five boats went through, and one of them was forced to dive into a minefield after sighting a patrol craft; two hours later a trawler saw a double explosion in the heart of the minefield where *U.109* had blown up. In the same week *U.95* had disappeared without trace, and on 8 February the Dover Barrage claimed *UB.38*. On 1 February Commodore Michelsen conferred with Captain Bartenbach of the Flanders flotilla, and they decided that the U-Boats operating from north Germany had to be allowed to avoid the Straits route; it is now known that even the gap which the two commanders recommended their U-Boats to use on the way home had been

operation at Ostend failed. Furthermore the UB III-type boats were able to squeeze past the obstructions at high water two weeks later; the Zeebrugge raid had not succeeded in bottling the Flanders flotillas in their lair. But the bases were under constant harassment from aerial bombing and gunfire from monitors of the Dover Patrol, firing heavy guns at ranges of 10 to 15 miles. In June a bombardment damaged the lock gates at Zeebrugge and put them out of action for five days.

The effectiveness of the Flanders flotillas began to decline noticeably after June. It is now known that regular deciphering of messages about swept channels enabled the British to lay mines in the exits to the routes used by the Flanders U-Boats. In some cases the minelayers would come over on the same night that the new route was announced, and losses soon

thickly sown with mines. Bartenbach was particularly keen to disrupt the Dover Barrage patrol line by means of a surface raid in order to make it easier for his U-Boats to get through, but bad weather forced the operation to be put off. When it finally got under way on the night of 14 February, six destroyers were able to roll up the patrol line, sinking eight of them and damaging seven more. The smaller UB-Boats and UC-Boats had less difficulty in avoiding detection but after 18 February no U-Boat from the north passed through.

The Flanders U-Boats had been such a thorn in the side of the Allies that plans had been under consideration for some time for an attack on Zeebrugge and Ostend, to block the canal-exits from Bruges. This finally took place on the night of 22–23 April, and three old cruisers filled with concrete were scuttled in the entrance to the Zeebrugge canal. A similar

became intolerably heavy. Every effort was made to keep the strength up by reinforcing the flotillas from Germany, but the loss of *UC.64, UB.57, UB.108, UC.77* and *UB.109*, and the return of *UC.71* badly damaged were heavy blows from which the hard-pressed flotillas could not recover. One flotilla had to be disbanded at the beginning of September, and Bartenbach gave orders that the Dover Straits route was no longer safe. It is hardly surprising, for between November 1917 and September 1918 the British had laid over 9000 mines in the Dover area. Then came the Allied military victories at the end of September, and when the British began to advance through Flanders it was clear that the game was up. On 4 October the U-Boats at sea were instructed by Radio Bruges to return to Germany at the end of their patrol. The ten U-Boats which had been refitting were patched up and sent back as well, leaving five elderly and damaged boats to be destroyed by demolition parties before the base was abandoned. With their small and inadequate UB I and UC I boats the Flander flotillas had achieved remarkable successes, and although their operations lacked the drama of the campaign waged by the 'Mittle-Us' on the high seas, they had exerted as much pressure on the Allies' jugular vein, and had required the maximum efforts to check their depredations.

Even at this late stage morale remained generally high, although it was clear that the U-Boats could not regain the initiative. Even when the crews of battleships of the High Seas Fleet became disaffected in May 1918 and later broke into open mutiny, the officers and men in the U-Boats remained steadfastly loyal. Indeed, when ordered to prepare to torpedo a mutinous battleship, a U-Boat crew was prepared to fire on their fellow sailors. True, the U-Boat personnel had longer leave allowed and were given better food at a time when the Allied blockade had reduced food supplies to subsistence level for German civilians and even soldiers and sailors had forgotten the taste of bread. But the terrifying strain of 1917–18 put them in a special position. Although there were cases of what was later known as 'battle fatigue' there were remarkably few instances of insanity, and as far as is known, no case of a U-Boat crew refusing to leave on patrol. Any deterioration in the vigour with which attacks were pressed home is attributable to the lack of

UC.91 **lies between a big U-cruiser and a UB-Boat.**

experience of the new officers and men who replaced the wily veterans of 1914–16.

The U-Boat Arm lost 515 officers and 4849 petty officers and seamen. The losses among officers were severe, and many historians now attribute the decay in the High Seas Fleet's *morale* to the steady drain of the officers and petty officers from the big ships to the U-Boats. Out of a total of about 113,000 men engaged in building, overhauling and manning the U-Boat fleet, Admiral Spindler estimated that actual U-Boat crews amounted to 13,000 men. On that basis the U-Boats suffered a loss of over 40 per cent of their front-line personnel. To many the U-Boat war was known as the 'war of the lieutenants' because of the swathe that it cut through the ranks of junior officers; about half the entire German Navy's strength of *kapitän-leutnants* and a third of the *leutnants* and *leutnants-zur-see* died in U-Boats.

The main efforts of the U-Boats in 1918 were directed to the sinking of troop-transports, in an attempt to halt the rising tide of American manpower which was reinforcing the battle-weary French and British Armies on the Western Front. This proved a failure, and an attempt in May to concentrate five U-Boats to catch a convoy of big troopships led to disaster: the giant liner *Olympic* rammed and sank *U.70*; a British submarine torpedoed *U.72* and *U.46*; *U.55*, *U.70* and *U.94* failed to make contact.

The long war against shipping finally drew to a close in the third week of October. On 15

October President Wilson had informed the German government that no armistice could be negotiated until the campaign against shipping was stopped. For three days the High Command debated the matter with the politicians, and finally the arguments of Hindenburg won; an armistice was the only way to preserve the myth that the German Armed Forces had not been defeated in open battle, so that they could continue to act as the guiding force of the nation. Accordingly while the German Army prepared for a ceasefire, Admiral Scheer sent a signal to all his U-Boats to return to harbour.

The U-Boats had also withdrawn from the Mediterranean. On 28 October, 15 U-Boats left Cattero for Germany, but first they had to pass through the heavily defended Straits of Gibraltar. Despite all the precautions only U.34 was sunk, and one of the fugitives found time to torpedo the elderly British battleship Britannia a fitting gesture of defiance to the Royal Navy.

But this was not to be a prelude to meek surrender. Scheer had one last grandiose plan to use the surface fleet to lure the British Grand Fleet into the classic 'U-Boat trap', with lines of U-Boats and minefields to decimate the over-eager British. Nobody thought that such a plan would win the war, but it was hoped that a last-minute victory would improve Germany's bargaining position at the conference table. In theory there were 23 U-Boats at sea and available for the last sortie, but in fact there were only 17 as four were returning to harbour and

Like UC.94, UC.98 was allocated to Italy under the terms of the Armistice in November 1918. Both boats were scrapped a year later.

two had already been sunk. But the sands had run out for Scheer, and the moment the news of the sortie leaked out the High Seas Fleet refused to sail, and the collapse of the German war-effort had started.

One last bizarre incident shows how dedicated the U-Boats still were, even at the end. On 25 October UB.116 sailed from Wilhelmshaven, with special orders for her captain, K/Lt Emsmann. He was to try to penetrate Scapa Flow to attack British battleships, as a prelude to the High Seas Fleet's sortie. Over the years a legend has persisted that UB.116 was manned by a crew composed entirely of fanatical officers bent on a kamikaze mission, but there is no evidence to support the story. What is true is that the U-Boat entered the Hoxa Sound entrance to the Flow at 23 30 hours on 28 October, where she was detected by a shore hydrophone station. As the operators listened to the noise of UB.116's electric motors she was moving closer and closer to a controlled minefield, and two minutes later, when the galvanometer needle dipped to indicate that a U-Boat was overhead, a row of mines was exploded.

As the roar of exploding mines subsided the operators listened intently for sounds of life, but there was nothing. At daybreak the patrol vessels found a huge oil slick and air bubbles; depth-charges were dropped, but they produced nothing but a huge bubble and a watch coat. Later a diver inspected the sunken hull and brought up UB.116's log.

UC.123 and other minelayers being scrapped in a British yard. Note the vertical mine-tubes revealed as the outer casing is stripped. [The large line running across the picture is caused by a crack in the original glass negative.]

390. Ex German Subv

Fleet of murderous "U" boats, the greatest menace that ever faced our Empire, surrender at Harwich.

Top left: Many of the surrendered U-Boats were paraded as prizes after the Armistice. *H.101* is seen here at Falmouth.

Left: The difference in size between the various types of U-Boats is well shown in this stereoscopic picture showing a UB III berthed between a U-cruiser and an older U-Boat.

The Armistice for which the German Army asked was granted, and took effect on 11 November; its conditions included the immediate surrender of all U-Boats, at ports designated by the victors. Within nine days the U-Boats were steaming across the North Sea in melancholy procession to the English port of Harwich, where they were inspected and interned. Work continued on some new boats to allow them to be made seaworthy for surrender, and by 1 December there were 122 boats lying in dejected rows. More followed, and it was not until the following February that the last U-Boats were delivered. Others surrendered to the neutral countries or to France and Italy, and finally 185 U-Boats passed into the hands of the victorious Allies, apart from seven which sank *en route* to surrender and one which was scuttled. Another 192 had been sunk or scuttled before passing into Allied hands.

The peace treaty was harsh. No U-Boats were to be designed, built or owned by Germany, and all U-Boat material, including drawings, engines and dockyard equipment such as salvage ships, was to be handed over. Under the supervision of an inter-Allied disarmament commission, all incomplete U-Boats were to be scrapped. Those U-Boats already in Allied hands were to be ignominiously parcelled out for experiments; 105 to Great Britain, 46 to France, ten to Italy, seven to Japan, six to the USA and two to Belgium. Only France was allowed to retain her ten boats for service in the French Navy as special compensation for the fact that she had been unable to build new submarines during the War. All the others had to be scrapped after a short period of trials and evaluation to allow the Navies concerned to learn all that they could about the U-Boat.

And so, within only four years of the end of World War I, the mighty armada of U-Boats built by Germany had virtually ceased to exist. What is more, the most powerful nations in the world had solemnly sworn that they would never allow another U-Boat fleet to be created.

DEATH AND REBIRTH

The U-Boat fleet may have perished in the catastrophe which engulfed Germany in 1918, but its spirit lived on. The truncated *Reichsmarine* might not be able to possess or even plan to possess U-Boats, but everyone connected with the Navy dreamed of the day when they could be built again, if only to provide the country with the best means of defence. In 1922 Dr Hans Techel and his talented team at Krupp's Germania Yard were told to hide all the

material they could from the prying eyes of the Inter-Allied Disarmament Commissioners. Shortly afterwards they moved with their priceless drawings, and above all their expertise and experience gathered during years of working on U-Boat designs, to Holland, where they joined the *Ingenieurskantoor voor Scheepsbouw* or shipbuilding bureau, an organisation which provided a 'front' for work to continue on U-Boat design. Money was provided from Ger-

many, and presumably the Dutch authorities turned a blind eye to what must have seemed to them a harmless activity. We know that the Dutch knew what was going on, because certain features designed by the Techel team found their way into new Dutch submarines during this period, but it must be remembered that the Dutch government had not signed the Treaty of Versailles.

The bureau did more than commit theoretical submarines to paper. With the backing of German diplomatic contacts it was able to procure contracts for the design of submarines for other navies; in 1927 two medium-sized submarines were built to their design in a Dutch shipyard; in 1930–33 three more and two small coastal types were built in Finland by the German-owned firm Crichton-Vulcan; and in 1932 a Spanish yard built a seagoing submarine for Turkey. It would be surprising if the *Reichsmarine* had not evaluated this series of submarines with a view to establishing its own requirements, and of course there was the vast body of experience gained in 1914–18.

The second of the new Type IIA U-Boats, *U.2*, at sea before World War II. This coastal design formed the backbone of the new U-Boat fleet, but they were mainly used for training. The design was based on the UF-Boats building in 1918.

The Naval Staff eventually decided that five types would suit German requirements:

1. a coastal U-Boat of about 250 tons
2. a seagoing craft of 500–750 tons
3. an ocean-going minelayer of about 1000 tons
4. a 1500-ton U-cruiser
5. a 500-ton coastal minelayer.

The 250-ton coastal boat was based on the original UF-Boats building in 1918, and developed in the Finnish *Vesikko*, and the seagoing type was based on the Turkish *Gür*. The design for the big minelayers was a development of the successful *U.81* type; the cruiser was a logical development of the big U-cruisers of 1917–18; and the small minelayer was based on the *UC.80* type. Apart from the U-cruiser, which had been developed by all the major navies in the 1920s from their ex-German prizes and then found to be too clumsy, the choice of designs was a balance of both offensive and defensive types.

One of the many promises made by Adolf Hitler to gain support for his bid to become Chancellor, was one to the senior officers of the Navy that they would be allowed to have U-Boats once again. At the end of January 1933, as soon as he had gained office, he called the heads of the Armed Forces together and told them to prepare for a massive expansion of military strength as soon as the 'shackles of Versailles' could be thrown off. With this welcome news Admiral Raeder, head of the Navy, gave permission for material to be ordered in advance from Spain, Holland and Finland, using the yards which had already built submarines under the direction of the *Ingenieurskantoor*. The material was delivered to Germany in secret, and was stored at Kiel; by the autumn of 1934 there were enough diesel engines, electric motors, periscopes, batteries and other items of major equipment to build ten U-Boats.

As a result of this meticulous planning, when in the early months of 1935 Hitler announced that Germany had unilaterally abrogated the Treaty of Versailles, it was possible for U-Boats to begin building immediately, as if the dragons' teeth had been sown to produce ships instead of armed men. The first boats ordered were two dozen of the 250-ton coastal type, known as Type II and numbered *U.1–24*; they were followed by *U.25* and *U.26*, seagoing Type I boats displacing a nominal 712 tons. Thus nearly 30 boats were under construction before the end

of 1935, and *U.1* was actually delivered in June the same year, a remarkable feat of shipbuilding, when one considers that it was 17 years since a German shipyard had launched a U-Boat. By the end of the year 13 more had joined her, and the bigger *U.25* and *U.26* were ready in the following spring.

The man chosen to head the new U-Boat Arm was a tough and experienced man who had been captured by the British in the Mediterranean in World War I. He was *Kapitän zur see* Karl Dönitz, a man who had devoted much time to studying the theory as well as the practice of U-Boat warfare. By reading the accounts of Spindler, Gayer, Spiess and Michelsen, and poring over the reports of every aspect of the great campaigns of 1914–18, he hoped to find a way of beating the convoy system. He had no doubt that given sufficient numbers and adequate communications, it would be possible to develop the ideas first put forward by Commodore Bauer in 1917. This was the starting point

Left: *U.18* was a unit of the Type IIB, an improved coastal design. She went to the Black Sea in 1943 and was sunk at Constanza in August 1944.

Below: Three variants of the Type II were built. *U.61* and her sisters of the Type IIC were armed with two bow tubes and one aft.

Above: The two Type I boats, *U.25* and *U.26* (seen here), were used for training, and were not repeated as they had a number of design-faults.

Centre: *U.26* prepares to dive during a prewar training exercise. The diesel exhaust can be seen in the after deck-casing.

of Dönitz's drive to develop what he called *rüdeltaktik*, or the tactics of the wolf-pack. This recommended, in essence, the use of numbers of U-Boats to smash through a convoy's defences, having first located the convoy and placed the U-Boats in the best attacking positions around it, to allow a simultaneous attack.

The use of pack-tactics had certain implications. First and foremost, it required large numbers of U-Boats to be at sea to allow a rapid concentration in any area selected. Second, but equally important, was the need for the highest-quality reconnaissance, and in this Dönitz had high hopes of long-range aircraft operating over the shipping-routes. The third requirement was a sophisticated communications network to allow U-Boats to have hour-by-hour reports on the whereabouts of their targets, and to allow U-Boats to pass similar information to one another.

There had been a significant improvement in aircraft and in radio communication since 1918, and so these points gave Dönitz few worries. But the modest building programme sanctioned by Hitler was not enough to operate even the smallest packs and so the designs chosen by the naval staff had to be looked at again. Nor did Dönitz's ideas on U-Boat warfare meet with universal approval in the Navy. There were two distinct lobbies in what had recently been renamed the *Kriegsmarine* which reflected the abolition of its purely coast-defence role: the senior officers wanted a balanced surface fleet, and many former U-Boat commanders favoured the construction of big ocean-going boats for operations in the distant oceans.

The admirals' obsession with battleships has been severely criticised, not only by Dönitz himself but by many naval historians, who claim that 'if only' priority had been given to U-Boat construction at the expense of battleships and heavy cruisers, there would have been three times as many U-Boats ready by 1939. But this argument is no more valid than the hindsight which was exercised in 1917, as it ignores the political realities of the 1930s. First and foremost, Admiral Raeder was no sentimental battleship-admiral; he was an extremely wily political administrator who worked long and hard to ensure that the German Navy received the support of Adolf Hitler, against the overriding claims of the Army and Air Force. The Army's prestige was very high, not least because of the carefully nurtured myth of being betrayed in 1918 but not beaten. In contrast the Navy had to live with the shame of having done little to save Germany, and then surrendering tamely and committing mass-suicide at Scapa Flow in 1919. Such accusations were grossly unfair, not only to the U-Boats but also to the ships of the High Seas Fleet which had given the British a run for their money at Jutland and, incidentally, had tied down enormous numbers of Allied warships for four years. But mythology plays an important part in the creation of the mystique and morale of a fighting service, and what is important is that the *Kriegsmarine* believed that it had to live down the memory of Scapa Flow and prove itself, and this meant a surface fleet as well as U-Boats.

Another point that is usually ignored is Hitler's need to avoid antagonising France and particularly Great Britain, if his plans to expand were not to be checked prematurely. Nobody knew in 1934 just how negative the reaction of the two Big Powers would be to Hitler's demands, and there were sound reasons for believing that a sudden burst of construction of large U-Boats would have produced an immediate and hostile reaction from the British. It was one thing to evade the provisions of the Washington and Versailles Treaties by building 'pocket-battleships', but it was quite another to lay down a hundred U-Boats; Hitler had no intention of provoking the British on the one sure point of sensitivity.

It was no part of Raeder's plan to build a 'showcase' fleet for prestige only, and he had a sound strategic plan to use the capital ships and cruisers in conjuction with the U-Boats. The heavy ships would operate against British shipping on the trade routes and would disrupt the convoys by sinking or driving off their escorts. The only reply to this would be for the convoy to scatter, which would give the U-Boats their chance to sink the ships one by one. This was the rationale for the creation of the *Scharnhorst* and *Gneisenau*, the *Bismarck* and *Tirpitz* and the *Admiral Hipper* Class heavy cruisers, and given the political climate both inside and outside Germany, it was more realistic than the idea of building a huge fleet of U-Boats. There was another risk, too, as there had been before World War I, that the wrong U-Boats would have been built. It is quite on the cards that a big U-Boat fleet could have compromised a

Below: The first of the Type VII boats, *U.27*, at sea after completion in 1936. Despite being based on the UB III type these boats were ideal for rapid construction and were developed into the standard U-Boat of World War II.

Left: Grand Admiral Erich Raeder was responsible for the rebirth of the U-Boat Arm in 1933 but he insisted on building a balanced surface fleet for a war against British commerce. Although this resulted in too few U-Boats for a large-scale campaign in 1939, Raeder had rather less freedom of action than his critics admitted.

Top right: U.27 seen from U.26 during training.

Below: In peacetime submarines often carried a small boat for getting libertymen ashore. Note the distress buoy in the foreground, which floated clear. The U-Boat suffered an accident while submerged.

collection of small coastal Type II boats and the large, unwieldy Type Is, or even bigger U-cruisers, none of which would have been useful for the operations envisaged by Dönitz.

Even the small programme announced in 1935 was sufficient to stir the British Admiralty to demand action by the Foreign Office to contain the German naval expansion. The solution was the Anglo-German Naval Agreement of June 1935, which allowed the standard tonnage of the *Kriegsmarine* to be one-third of the total of the Royal Navy, and gave Germany the right to parity in submarines. The agreement was denounced in many quarters in Britain, but in retrospect it appears to have been a reasonable compromise. Germany was rearming, and had no intention of going back to the humiliating position of 1918–34, so it made sense for the British to get agreement on the limits. In fact the German totals represented the peak of peacetime capacity for their shipyards, and at the time of signing Germany signified her intention of only building up to 45 per cent of the total of British submarine tonnage, and not to exceed this figure without further notice.

Above: the prewar years were devoted to intensive training of U-Boats and their crews.

The agreement also contained a clause which permitted either party to increase its tonnage in any category, but only at the expense of a corresponding reduction in other categories.

The situation after the signature of the Anglo-German agreement was that Germany was permitted to build 23,715 tons of U-Boats, assuming that 45 per cent of the British total was maintained. As a total of 12,425 tons had been announced for U-Boats already built or under construction, this left 11,290 tons for new construction. Immediately after the agreement was signed a further eight U-Boats, *U.37–44*, were announced, big ocean-going boats modelled on the original *U.81* of 1915. Their principal feature was a greatly enlarged capacity for reload-torpedoes and mines, 22 torpedoes or six torpedoes and 42 mines. For the purposes of complying with international agreements they were listed as having a standard displacement of 714 tons, but in fact displaced 1032 tons on the surface, and 1153 tons submerged. It was a type of U-Boat which met the requirements of the Naval Staff, and it was designated Type IX.

Dönitz was not to be outflanked by the non-submariners of the Naval Staff, and he prepared detailed arguments to show that it would be impossible to build up the strength of the U-Boat Arm to an effective level if the construction of big ocean-going U-Boats was continued. The Anglo-German agreement now limited the total tonnage, and if numbers were to be expanded a smaller general-purpose design of U-Boat would have to be built. This was all the more reason for moving away from the idea of attacking shipping on the high seas. Dönitz knew that the best place to beat the British convoy-system was in the Western Approaches, and that a concentration of U-Boats further afield would be countered by the introduction of convoys in whatever area the U-Boats showed themselves. If the convoys could be smashed in the crowded sea-routes converging in the Western Approaches the scale of losses would be much more decisive. Although operations

Foreground: Karl Dönitz was the German Navy's most senior submariner in 1939. His experience in World War I and his detailed studies convinced him that the U-Boat could win single-handed. Events nearly proved him right.

further afield would not be ignored, the Western Approaches would be the chosen battleground, and for this the U-Boats need not be too large.

Dönitz won the argument, and so the plans to build Types III, IV, V and VI were shelved. The first of these was an enlargement of the Type I design, and carried two small motor torpedo boats in cylindrical containers on deck. Very little is known of the other two designs as most of the records were lost. This cleared the way for evaluation of the next design, Type VII, which was a 500-ton (standard) seagoing boat. The basis for the design was the eminently successful UB III design of 1916, and the boat that resulted was about 25ft shorter than the Type I, carried less fuel and had five torpedo-tubes instead of six. The dimensions and equipment were carefully tailored to keep within the 500-ton limit, but in fact the surface displacement of the early Type VII was 626 tons. A maximum of 67 tons of fuel could be stowed, part of it in external tanks, and nine torpedoes were carried, five in the tubes and four reloads. The single stern tube was arranged in an unusual way, being a trainable mounting housed in the external casing; the idea was popular in French submarines but had never been used in a U-Boat before.

The trials of U.27, the first of the Type VII boats, took place in the autumn of 1936, and they showed that the new type answered all operational requirements. There were faults which needed correcting, but the decision was made to put the Type VII into mass production, with the Type II for coastal duties and training, and the Type IX for ocean work, but in much smaller numbers. Dönitz knew only too well that the U-Boat Arm could not afford the proliferation of types which had bedevilled production in 1914–1918, and the cancellation of the other types on the drawing board, although it prevented some interesting ideas from being developed, was undoubtedly the right decision. However on the debit side, it must be noted that the relatively small dimensions of the Type

Below: U.25 was the prototype for a class of oceangoing U-Boats. The armament was four bow tubes and two stern, and a 10.5cm gun.

VIII hull would inevitably militate against future expansion of the design, and this was to cause problems later. But at the time, and given the peculiar circumstances, it is hard to see what other course could have been followed if the U-Boat fleet was to be built up rapidly.

The improvements suggested for the Type VII resulted in the Type VIIB, with another 31 tons of fuel to push the surface endurance up to 6500 miles at 12 knots, nearly the same as the original Type I. A tendency in the Type VIIA to roll was cured by modifying the saddle-tanks, and more powerful diesels raised the speed to 17.25 knots. The electric motors and battery capacity were the same, giving a submerged maximum speed of eight knots and an endurance of 80 miles at four knots. The first of the Class, U.45 came into service in June 1938, and another ten followed. It was a Type VIIB boat, U.48, which scored the highest tonnage of enemy shipping sunk in World War II: 51 ships totalling 310,400 tons.

To match the capabilities of the new U-Boats, German scientists had produced a new torpedo to replace the standard compressed-air G7a 533mm (21-inch) type, which was very similar in performance to the British Mark VIII. Known as the G7e, it was slower and had less range than the G7a (see table below), but had the great advantage of leaving no wake, as well as being much cheaper to manufacture. Just as the design and testing of U-Boat hulls had been done outside Germany, so the initial testing of the electric torpedo was done with the connivance of Swedish companies as early as 1923, and the final successful trials had taken place in 1929. The design was then 'frozen' until needed for full-scale production, but during the intervening time the existence of the weapon remained a well-kept secret.

Type	Weight	Warhead	Speed	Range
G7a	3334 lbs	660 lbs	30kts	15,310 yards
			44kts	6560 yards
G7e	3545 lbs	655 lbs	30kts	5470 yards

Operating the G7e called for some changes in procedure. The batteries had to be at a temperature of 30° Centigrade for maximum range, and if run 'cold' the range dropped by as much as 1400 yards. Therefore the U-Boat's torpedo-officer had to ensure that the lead-acid batteries were kept heated while the boat was in the patrol area. For this reason the reliable G7a continued in service side by side with it, and about 25 per cent of all the German torpedoes fired at sea in the entire war were to be the old type.

There were soon enough U-Boats to form the 1st operational flotilla, and this was appropriately named the Weddigen Flotilla after the first 'ace' of World War I. It comprised the six

Type IIB boats, U.7–12, and was based at Kiel under the command of Captain Dönitz. Side by side was the Training Flotilla attached to the U-Boat School under Fregattenkapitän Slevogt, with U.1–6. Four old torpedo boats and the depot ship Saar were attached as seagoing tenders. The intention of the Naval Staff was to provide training as fast as possible, and at the same time to build a framework for expansion. Therefore a 2nd or Saltzwedel Flotilla was formed out of the new Type IIB boats and U.25 and U.26 as soon as they became available, followed by the 3rd or Lohs Flotilla, 5th or Emsmann Flotilla, 6th or Hundius Flotilla and 7th or Wegener Flotilla. The missing 4th Flotilla was not formed for some reason, and did not receive the name of a World War I 'ace', although plans existed for it on paper and several commanders had been appointed in the last months before the outbreak of war. The Saltzwedel and Hundius Flotillas were based at Wilhelmshaven and the others at Kiel.

Between 1935 and the outbreak of war 57 U-Boats were delivered but the list of commissionings stands at 58 boats, the total normally quoted by historians; the discrepancy is accounted for by the fact that U.18 sank on 22 November 1936 after colliding with the tender T.156, and was raised and recommissioned a second time. Incidentally the mishap does not appear to have given her any sort of jinx, for she survived until 1944, when she had to be scuttled in a Black Sea harbour to avoid capture. Some idea of the rapid expansion of the U-Boat Arm is given by this lineup in June 1939, only four years after the commissioning of U.1:

Weddigen Flotilla . U.9, U.13, U.15, U.17, U.19, U.21, U.23
Saltzwedel Flotilla . U.25, U.26, U.27, U.28, U.29, U.30, U.31, U.32, U.33, U.34, U.35
Lohs Flotilla U.12, U.14, U.16, U.18, U.20, U.22, U.24
Emsmann Flotilla . . U.56, U.57, U.58, U.59
Hundius Flotilla . . . U.37, U.38, U.39, U.40, U.41
Wegener Flotilla . . U.45, U.46, U.47, U.48, U.51, U.52, U.53
U-Boat School . . . . U.1, U.2, U.3, U.4, U.5, U.6, U.7, U.8, U.10, U.11, U.25 (to be transferred from 2nd Flotilla), U.36

As far as the training programme was concerned Dönitz was anxious to develop offensive tactics, and to train as many future commanding officers as possible, with the eventual aim of putting his rüdeltaktik into operation. The doctrine was tested successfully in the Baltic as early as 1937, so that all Dönitz's young captains knew what their chief had in mind; it was a principle of leadership which had gained superlative results for Nelson, and when the time came, Dönitz was not disappointed. There were other techniques to be developed, particularly the details of co-operation with aircraft. Here the problem was one of personalities, for the head of the Luftwaffe was Hermann Göring, and his boast was, 'Everything which flies belongs to me.' His answer to a request from Dönitz for a few long-range reconnaissance aircraft to be attached to the U-Boat Arm was greeted with an outright refusal. Even when war broke out, the desperate need of the U-Boats for accurate information about the convoys was met by obstruction, and only the intervention of Hitler enabled some improvement to be made.

Another technique which was developed during the last years of peace was the night attack on the surface. It was realised by one or two intrepid captains that there was little likelihood of a bridge lookout on board a merchantman spotting a low silhouette of a darkened U-Boat at night, and so it might be possible to penetrate *inside* the orderly ranks of a convoy. From here the U-Boat could fire her torpedoes with deadly effect, and use her high surface speed to avoid collision with the lumbering merchant ships; the Type VIIA could make 16 knots on diesels whereas the average convoy's speed might be as low as seven or eight knots.

It must be remembered that during all this time Dönitz was only *Führer der U-Boote*, and had no direct responsibility for high-level policy. His arguments had to be presented to the Naval High Command, *Oberkommando der Marine* (OKM) for approval, and as previously noted, their ideas were often at variance with his. Each victory that he won was a fight against the other two services as well as his superiors, but fortunately for Dönitz he was a wily political fighter, and as he was a loyal member of the Nazi Party he found no difficulty in joining the court circle which lobbied for the favours of Hitler. In 1938 when Hitler realised that the democracies were slowly summoning up their courage to curb his expansion in Europe, he invoked the clause in the Anglo-German Naval Agreement which permitted the same tonnage of submarines as the Royal Navy; in other words, the remaining 65 per cent was to be built. This was an open

To protect them from air attack during the Spanish Civil War neutral warships wore vertical stripes in the national colours. This photograph of *U.32*, an early Type VIIA, may have been taken in Spanish waters as the censor has very clumsily taken out the background.

endorsement of the policies put forward by Dönitz, and at the same time a clear warning to the British to prepare for a submarine onslaught on their shipping.

As a result of the revision of policy in 1938 the planned strength of the U-Boat Arm was enormously expanded to a total of 128 U-Boats by 1943, and 223 by 1947. This was part of the notorious 'Z-Plan', but it took little account of the German shipyards' capacities. In that year 35 U-Boats were ordered, but the following year only 11 could be ordered – proof of how misleading paper plans can be in assessing what might have happened if more U-Boats had been authorised earlier.

There was one problem which worried Dönitz and his technical advisers. Since 1918 the British had been working in utmost secrecy on a device to detect submerged submarines, using an ultra-sonic oscillator to bounce echoes off the hull. Known as ASDIC (from the original Anti-Submarine Devices Investigation Committee of 1918 which had initiated the research) it had developed into a formidable counter-measure, much more effective than the old passive hydrophones of World War I. Asdic could give a precise range and bearing even if the U-Boat stopped her motors, and if necessary could also function as a very sensitive hydrophone; as a result the British were confident that they could master the U-Boat threat. German Intelligence knew of its existence, but had no details of its performance or how it worked. Rumours about its effectiveness were rife, but no one knew for certain what was in store.

The U-Boats had one war-scare, in September 1938 at the time of the Munich Conference. They were sent to their war stations, and although soon told to return to harbour, the operation provided a useful dress-rehearsal. The only drawback was that no specific plans had been drawn up by OKM for using the U-Boats against Great Britain. Hitler had given repeated assurances to the Commander-in-Chief that there would be no war against the Royal Navy, and so until after Munich the war plans were vague about the overall strategic plan to be followed. Even as late as 22 July 1939 the senior officers of the U-Boat Arm were told by Admiral Raeder that war with Britain was 'unthinkable'. Four weeks later Captain Dönitz was recalled from leave to be told that the unthinkable had happened, and that he had two weeks to prepare his U-Boats for a campaign against the British. It is a remarkable tribute to his training and leadership that his command was able to respond so efficiently to this reversal of policy, but it also reflected his inner conviction that in the long run the U-Boats would only be used against the British.

The war plans drawn up by the *Kriegsmarine* provided for surface raiders and U-Boats to be at sea sometime before the outbreak of war, to avoid the inevitable British blockade. Accordingly in the third week of August 1939 two pocket-battleships and the first of 40 U-Boats headed for their war stations. To the U-Boats this meant a patrol line extending around the British Isles, but there was to be no unrestricted campaign. The *Führer* was well aware of the likely effect on American opinion, and as he still hoped to be able to bluff the British into withdrawing from what he saw as a quixotic gesture in coming to the aid of Poland, he instructed OKM to see that the U-Boats obeyed the Prize Regulations. These were basically the same as those of 1914–1918. Germany had signed an international protocol some years earlier forbidding the sinking of unarmed merchantmen, so there was a degree of commitment to exactly the same restrictions that had proved so unworkable in 1915. Yet Hitler's obsession with the need to win the support of neutrals and his hope that a quick victory on land would persuade the British to desert their allies, ensured that the U-Boats went to war under a great handicap.

TO WAR AGAIN

After all the trouble taken by Hitler to ensure that his U-Boats did nothing to offend neutral opinion, it is ironic that the very first day saw an accidental breach of the Prize Regulations by *U.30*. K/Lt Julius Lemp, on patrol in the Western Approaches, sighted the British liner *Athenia*, still painted in her peacetime house-colours but making for safety as fast as she could. Despite the colour-scheme Lemp decided that she was a troopship, possibly because the Donaldson Line funnel-markings resembled those of the well-known Bibby Line troopers; the liner sank quickly and *U.30* made her escape. When she returned to Wilhelmshaven, Lemp admitted to an irate Dönitz that he had realised too late that his victim was a liner, and after a few angry words Dönitz decided to accept his statement that he had

acted in good faith. But in the meantime the Propaganda Ministry under Dr Goebbels had taken a hand, and to rebut British charges of an illegal sinking of an unarmed passenger ship, had cooked up the unlikely story that the Royal Navy had torpedoed the *Athenia* to discredit the Germans. The upshot was that Dönitz was ordered to expunge the evidence from *U.30*'s log and to ensure that Lemp and his men were sworn to silence about the affair.

Despite this unpromising start Hitler was even more insistent that the U-Boats should obey the Prize Regulations, and some commanders like the irrepressible Herbert Schultze of *U.48* sent radio messages to the Admiralty in 'clear', asking Winston Churchill (then First Lord of the Admiralty) to come and pick up the survivors of the ship just sunk. On the British

side there was no faltering as there had been in 1914, and as soon as the *Athenia* sinking was reported, the convoy-system was introduced for shipping in home waters. As early as 1937 the Admiralty had drawn up plans on the assumption that the Germans would not obey the Prize Regulations for very long, and as they had no idea of the lengths to which Hitler would go to impress the United States, the *Athenia*'s sinking was thought to be the first shot in an unrestricted campaign. All merchant shipping was ordered not to obey any call to surrender, but to take evasive action and to send out an immediate distress signal, both measures which, under the Prize Regulations, entitled the U-Boat to open fire.

Against warships the U-Boats had no such problems, and on 17 September *U.29* scored a great success by sinking the aircraft carrier *Courageous*. Ironically the carrier was on anti-submarine duties at the time, and as the new *Ark Royal* had nearly been hit by a spread of four torpedoes from *U.39* three days earlier the Admiralty wisely decided that big fleet carriers were too valuable to risk in this way. To carry the offensive to the British, and more subtly, to impress those senior advisers close to Hitler who were still sceptical about the U-Boats'

ability to win the war by themselves, Dönitz planned a truly audacious raid on Scapa Flow, the same fleet base which had proved impregnable to U-Boats in the previous war.

The U-Boat chosen was *U.47*, commanded by K/Lt Günther Prien, and Dönitz briefed him in person, giving him the option of refusing to undertake the mission. Scapa Flow had several entrances, but all were guarded by nets, minefields and sunken ships, to say nothing of natural hazards in the form of fierce currents and tidal rips faster than the speed of a submerged U-Boat. But aerial reconnaissance had revealed a gap between the blockships in Kirk Sound, and Dönitz believed that a U-Boat might be able to get through the obstructions at slack water, despite the channel being little more than 15 yards wide and just over 20 feet deep.

Prien volunteered for the mission without hesitation, and by the night of 12/13 October *U.47* was lying off the Orkneys, resting on the

Above: Prien and his officers at Lorient in November 1940.

Right: Prien on the conning tower of *U.47*, with his 'laughing bull' insignia painted on the side.

Right: Günther Prien, captain of *U.47* and destroyer of the battleship *Royal Oak.*

Far right: After returning from his exploit, Prien receives the congratulations of Admiral Marschall and Admiral Raeder, the C-in-C. Apart from the sinking of an enemy battleship, it was also the first time a U-Boat had penetrated Scapa Flow and escaped.

seabed after charging her batteries. The following afternoon she began to prepare for the attack, and by 2200 hours she was on the surface, heading for Kirk Sound. After some minor hitches, including running aground for a short time, *U.47* inched her way through the channel with the chains of the blockships sunk there 24 years before scraping along her ballast tanks. Eventually Prien found himself inside the Flow, and eventually he came across the unmistakable silhouette of a big ship against the night sky. One of his forward torpedo-tubes was faulty, and so the salvo he fired was only three 'fish'. To his chagrin the entire salvo appeared to miss, although the British later revealed that one torpedo hit, but with such a mild detonation that nobody realised what it was. Prien had found the old battleship *Royal Oak*, and although he had only a hazy idea of the identity of his victim he was determined to sink her. After an hour's hard work reloading the three forward

Below: Insignia were more popular than they had been in World War I. This example of *graffiti* on the side of *U.48*'s conning tower is one of the more bizarre.

torpedo-tubes he returned to the attack, and fired a spread of three torpedoes set to explode under the battleship's keel. This time there was a tremendous explosion and HMS *Royal Oak* rolled over and blew up with the loss of 833 officers and men.

The sinking of a battleship, however elderly, inside Scapa Flow, was a tremendous blow to the British, and *U.47* and her crew were given a hero's welcome by Dönitz and the Fleet on their return to Kiel. Nor was the feat without its strategic consequences. The British Home Fleet was forced to abandon Scapa Flow temporarily until the defences of the anchorage could be overhauled and improved. While it used anchorages on the west coast of Scotland the ships were much more vulnerable to attack from U-Boats; in December the battleship *Barham* was damaged by a torpedo from *U.30*, and the *Nelson* touched off a magnetic mine laid by a U-Boat in the entrance to Loch Ewe. Had the German surface fleet been handled with as much dash as the U-Boats the temporary disarray of the Home Fleet might have been turned to advantage, but as things turned out, the chance was missed and the Home Fleet later returned to Scapa Flow without suffering further losses.

The U-Boats had not been able to operate with impunity, and they suffered more severely than they had in 1914. The British had worked hard at anti-submarine tactics, and in September 1939 destroyers sank *U.39* and *U.27*. In the following month three U-Boats succumbed to mines, and two more fell to destroyers. Only one, *U.36*, was lost in November to escorts, and a British submarine torpedoed *U.36* in December, making a total of nine U-Boats sunk in four months. But in the same period U-Boats had sunk 114 ships totalling 421,156 tons, and nine more U-Boats had been completed, so they were more than holding their own.

The Norwegian Campaign which started in April 1940 was the first chance the U-Boats had to attack concentrated warship-targets and, in all, 48 boats were withdrawn from Atlantic operations to support the surface forces. The British reacted quickly to the landing of six German divisions in Norway. Soon there were troopships, capital ships, carriers and cruisers operating in the North and Norwegian Seas.

Several attacks were carried out and, in all, about 42 sightings of British ships were reported of which 30 were followed by attacks. But throughout the entire time only one submarine was sunk, HMS Thistle, which was torpedoed by U.4 off Skudenes on 10 April. Puzzled and angry commanders reported that their torpedoes had apparently run true but had not exploded. At first Dönitz was sceptical because claims for ships sunk tend to be optimistic, but a growing volume of complaints, culminating in threats to refuse to go out on patrol until the torpedoes were checked for reliability, forced him to act. The result of the enquiry was horrifying for it was discovered that the magnetic-influence exploder for the torpedoes' warheads was faulty. As early as 1918 the Germans had been experimenting with what amounted to a proximity fuze which would detonate the warhead

Right: Admiral Dönitz with the ace Fritz-Julius Lemp (right).

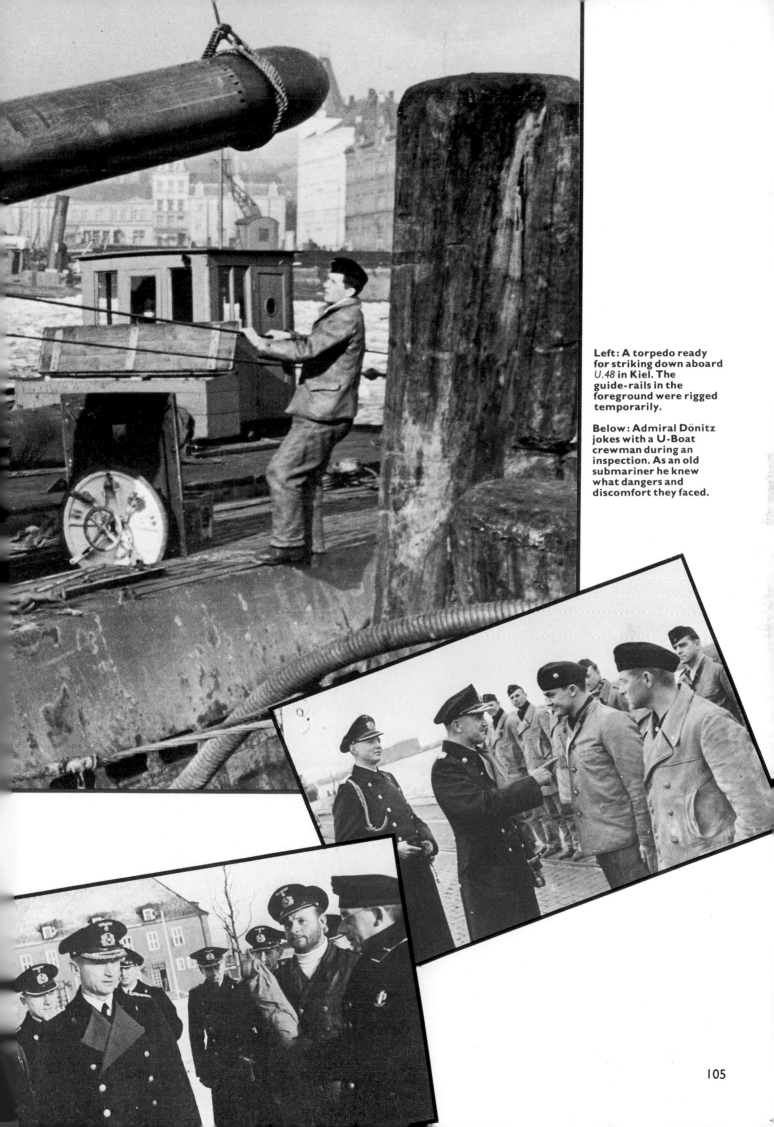

Left: A torpedo ready
for striking down aboard
U.48 in Kiel. The
guide-rails in the
foreground were rigged
temporarily.

Below: Admiral Dönitz
jokes with a U-Boat
crewman during an
inspection. As an old
submariner he knew
what dangers and
discomfort they faced.

of a torpedo as soon as it was close to the hull of the target. This enabled the torpedo to be set to run under the keel of a ship, where the explosion could inflict far more serious damage than it was likely to at a shallower depth against the ship's side. But the difficulty with a magnetic influence exploder was that it was very sensitive to variations in the earth's magnetic field, and these variations become more marked in high latitudes. What had happened was that the setting of the magnetic pistol which had been appropriate for the Atlantic was not appropriate for Norway.

There were other problems as well, concerning reliability and testing of torpedoes, and the ensuing witch-hunt revealed very bad co-ordination between the section of the Navy responsible for testing torpedoes and the inspectors who checked manufacture. The depth-setting mechanism proved faulty, and so many of the torpedoes had been running too deep for the magnetic exploder to function; the G7e electric torpedo had also been running erratically at times. These faults were experienced by other navies experimenting with new torpedoes, but the lack of liaison between the technicians and those who had to use their ideas was a serious fault in the German organisation which was to cause many problems later on.

The Norwegian campaign gave way to the invasion of France, and so the U-Boats and their problems were forgotten as the Panzer divisions rolled across the Low Countries. The collapse of the British and French Armies took place with such speed that within a month the northern half of France was in German hands, the British Expeditionary Force was back in England minus all transport, tanks and guns, and the invasion of the British Isles seemed imminent. But Dönitz showed little interest in the sudden enthusiasm for amphibious operations displayed by the General Staff; for him the occupation of France meant only the acquisition of bases for U-Boats. Without waiting to see if the Luftwaffe could make good its boast of defeating Britain by bombing or listening to the Army's plans for victory parades in London, he gave orders to establish forward bases in the Bay of Biscay and in Brittany. In 1914 the Flanders coast had provided a means of waging war against the British more effectively, but this time the U-Boats would be to the west of the English Channel, hundreds of miles closer to the Western Approaches. This was a strategic reversal of unexpected magnitude, and one which far outweighed the loss of the French Navy in its dangers for the British. Now the jugular vein of British shipping was exposed to constant attacks from U-Boats, with the added bonus of air cover from French airfields.

The changing strategic situation called for a massive reorganisation of the U-Boat Arm. Some changes had already taken place; for

Far left: *U.37* **off Lorient in August 1940. With the British licking their wounds after the fall of France and some convoys with only token escorts these were indeed the 'happy times'.**

example in October 1939 Dönitz had been promoted to Admiral under the new title of Commander-in-Chief U-Boats, or *Befehlshaber der Unterseeboote* (BdU). His former appointment as *Führer der Unterseeboote* (FdU) was now divided among three new FdUs, each responsible for an operational area: West with its HQ at Paris and Angers; Norway and Arctic with its HQ at Narvik; Italy and Mediterranean with its HQ at Rome, Toulon and Aix-en-Provence.

Much later (1944) a fourth FdU was appointed to Central Operational area with responsibility for anti-invasion measures. As the war developed and U-Boats operated in more distant oceans three additional areas were created, Black Sea, Baltic and Far East, but so few U-Boats were allocated to these commands that they were commanded by flotilla chiefs rather than FdUs.

The original flotillas were regrouped, with the Weddigen, Lohs and Emsmann Flotillas forming the new 1st Flotilla and Saltzwedel and Hundius Flotillas forming a new 2nd Flotilla, while the original Wegener Flotilla became the 3rd. A further ten flotillas were formed over a period of time, and they were distributed as follows: 6th, 7th, 9th, 10th and 12th U-Boat Flotillas under FdU West; 11th and 13th U-Boat Flotillas under FdU Norway and Arctic; 23rd and 29th U-Boat Flotillas under FdU Italy and Mediterranean; 30th U-Boat Flotilla in the Black Sea; and 22nd U-Boat Flotilla in the Baltic. The numbers of U-Boats varied within the flotillas, and there were frequent transfers. The flotillas in the Atlantic tended to be the largest as they were in the forefront of the battle. As in World War I, keeping up the pressure called for an operating cycle, with some U-Boats on station, and others proceeding to the patrol area, returning to port, preparing to leave, refitting and undergoing lengthy overhaul. To avoid congestion the Atlantic flotillas were spread out over a number of ports: Brest, Lorient, La Pallice, La Rochelle, St Nazaire and Bordeaux.

The introduction of convoy by the British immediately after the outbreak of war meant that there would be no easy task for the U-Boats. In addition their aircraft flew coastal patrols in large numbers, and this had the effect of forcing the U-Boats to operate further out to sea. For some months after the fall of France, the number of British destroyers retained to repel a possible invasion meant a severe reduction in the number of convoy escorts, and shipping losses rose alarmingly. In August 1940 Hitler ordered a 'general blockade' of the British Isles, after a series of progressive reductions of the Prize Regulations; unrestricted warfare was back in force, to compel the recalcitrant British to surrender. Once again American opinion was important, and Hitler refused to listen to his advisers who urged him to accept the inevitable

war with the USA for he hoped to knock out Britain before public opinion could swing round from its dominant attitude of isolation. Many of the German military leaders felt that America was so unprepared that a quick campaign now would probably have the desired effect, and that it would be folly to allow the United States to rearm. Hitler certainly underestimated the Americans as a nation, and he felt that the desire of John Doe to stay out of the war would outweigh President Roosevelt's known anti-Nazi convictions. For the moment the strict rules against attacking US shipping remained in force even after 50 old US destroyers were handed over to the British in September 1940.

For the U-Boats this was the 'Happy Time'. Their superbly trained crews had the measure of the convoy escorts to a large extent, having realised that Asdic had limitations. The saturation of coastal escorts and air patrols was

Far left: *U.101*, one of the last Type VIIBs to be built, comes alongside the depot ship on her return to port.

Above: For maximum strength the hatchways in U-Boats were circular. The control room below the conning tower contained the periscopes and all the principal controls for operating the U-Boat.

answered by moving further west, for even as late as the summer of 1940 there were not enough escorts to cover outward convoys beyond 15°W; at this point they took over the inward convoys as a desperate measure to compensate for the lack of numbers. With a convoy's escort consisting of a single destroyer and a trawler for example, it is not hard to see how a U-Boat could wreak havoc. In fact the main reason why the U-Boats did not cut British seaborne communications completely during this bleak time is the equally small number of U-Boats available. There were only 30 of them in the Atlantic, for the remaining 20 had to be retained at the new U-Boat school set up at Neustadt near Lübeck where they were out of reach of RAF bombers. With so many new U-Boats under construction the training programme had to be expanded well in advance.

It was the heyday of the 'aces', just as it had been in 1915–16. A galaxy of talented commanders amassed staggering totals of tonnage sunk: Otto Kretschmer in *U.99* was the leader, with 44 ships totalling 266,629 tons, followed by Lüth with 225,713 tons, Topp with 193,684 tons, Merten with 180,744 tons and the similarly named Schütze with 171,164 tons and Schultze with 171,122 tons. The highest scorers were awarded the Knight's Cross with Stars and Brilliants or the Knight's Cross with Oak Leaves and Stars, while those aces who sank more than 100,000 tons received the Knight's Cross with Oak Leaves. Admiral Dönitz operated a system of conspicuous rewards and exhortation, and a successful U-Boat returning from a patrol was given a rousing and flamboyant welcome. During a patrol too, there would be messages of encouragement from U-Boat Headquarters.

The prewar tactics were found to answer admirably. It was found that the Asdic beam could not detect a U-Boat on the surface, and so the idea of a surfaced attack at night was revived. Kretschmer was the greatest exponent of this technique, which involved the use of the U-Boat's hydrophone to detect the convoy's presence. At night the U-Boat was very hard to spot, even by the most alert lookouts, and she was rarely sighted by the escorts. At 15–16 knots she had little difficulty in manoeuvring into the best firing position; as soon as she fired her bow salvo she would disengage, still on the surface, and if sighted by an escort she would dive. This would entail depth-charging, but if the escort was not unduly proficient in making use of its Asdic, the U-Boat would escape, come to the surface again after a discreet interval, reload the torpedo tubes and try to get in contact with the convoy once more. The refinement perfected by Kretschmer was to move into the convoy itself where nobody would be looking for a U-Boat.

In October 1940 Dönitz decided to experiment with the long-planned pack-tactics, despite the shortage of U-Boats. The efficient communication system devised by Dönitz now

Top left: Wonders of culinary skill were achieved in the tiny galleys, but of necessity the food aboard U-Boats could not be as good as in surface ships.

Left: The two operators on the hydroplane controls were responsible for keeping the boat level at the required depth.

Below: Communications were vital to U-Boat operations, but despite the use of the Enigma coding machine (foreground) this was to prove the Achilles' heel of the wolf-packs.

Bottom right: In a U-Boat there was no space for a dining area, and so crewmen ate their meals sitting on their bunks.

persal point out, first to 17° and then 19°W.

The biggest headache now was to find the convoys, and during this time many convoys were not attacked at all. In August 1940 the first Luftwaffe aircraft were assigned to work with the U-Boats, but these were short-range types, and contributed little. The onset of winter made it even harder to find the quarry. Rough weather reduced the speed of a surfaced U-Boat and made it difficult to keep a good lookout; in addition torpedoes tended to run erratically. An expected reinforcement of 25 Italian submarines operating out of Bordeaux proved a mixed blessing for the Italians had little idea of aggressive tactics. They insisted on remaining submerged and would not hunt for targets on the surface; as a result they sank only one ship in two months. Later Dönitz tried to use them to scout for the U-Boats, but this was also beyond them.

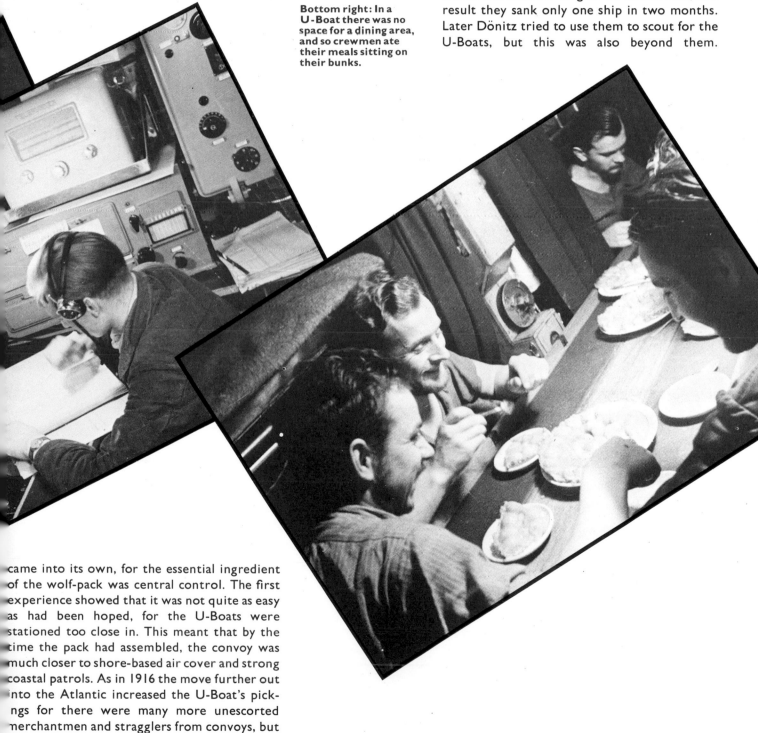

came into its own, for the essential ingredient of the wolf-pack was central control. The first experience showed that it was not quite as easy as had been hoped, for the U-Boats were stationed too close in. This meant that by the time the pack had assembled, the convoy was much closer to shore-based air cover and strong coastal patrols. As in 1916 the move further out into the Atlantic increased the U-Boat's pickings for there were many more unescorted merchantmen and stragglers from convoys, but in October the British moved the convoy dis-

Eventually they were allocated a patrol area near the Azores, well away from the U-Boats and left to get on as best they could against independently routed merchantmen.

Despite the problems the U-Boats did very well during this period, and between June 1940 and February 1941 they sank 400 ships, totalling two million tons, for a loss of only eight of their own number. Aircraft and surface craft accounted for another million tons, and in addition two million tons of shipping were damaged and out of action. The U-Boats had achieved an 'exchange rate' of 50 merchantmen sunk for every U-Boat during this period. This loss-rate was twice the rate at which British shipyards were building new hulls, but the collapse of Europe had produced one solitary benefit: the large mercantile fleets of Norway and the Netherlands and ships from other European countries had escaped to Britain, and this represented a gain of three million tons. Mass-production methods were beginning to produce results as well, and it was estimated that British and Canadian shipyards between them, with some help from the USA, could provide 2½ million tons of new ships a year.

The limited German shipbuilding resources were now beginning to show some signs of strain, and it was inevitable that the U-Boat programme would find itself competing for raw materials, particularly steel. It had been hoped to build 25 U-Boats a month, but in January 1941, although production had doubled, it was still only ten per month. However as losses totalled only 31 since the beginning of the war, even this reduced figure showed steady growth.

The British for their part were under no illusions about the significance of these figures. It was realised that too much faith had been placed in Asdic and so much more attention was paid to perfecting techniques, training and maintenance of the equipment. Escorts had to be increased, not only in numbers but in weaponry, and the convoy system had to be extended. On 6 March 1941 the Prime Minister, Winston Churchill, issued a famous directive identifying the fight against the U-Boats as the Battle of the Atlantic for the first time, and gave it the highest priority.

The new measures coincided with a remarkable run of bad luck for the U-Boats. In March five U-Boats were sunk in quick succession, including the three aces Prien (*U.47*), Kretschmer (*U.99*) and Schepke (*U.100*). Prien and K/Lt Matz (*U.70*) attacked convoy *OB.293* on the night of 7/8 March, and they had the misfortune to be picked up by well-trained escorts; *U.70* was sunk by the new corvettes, *Camellia* and *Arbutus*, and *U.47* was depth-charged to destruction by the old destroyer, *Wolverine*. On the night of 17 March *U.100* was caught by two destroyers, part of the escort of convoy *HX.112*. Her luck was out, for HMS *Walker* gained con-

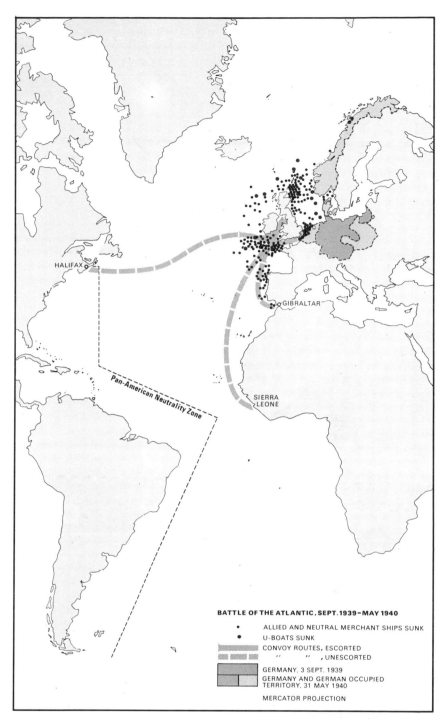

BATTLE OF THE ATLANTIC, SEPT. 1939 – MAY 1940

· ALLIED AND NEUTRAL MERCHANT SHIPS SUNK

• U-BOATS SUNK

CONVOY ROUTES, ESCORTED

'' '' , UNESCORTED

GERMANY, 3 SEPT. 1939
GERMANY AND GERMAN OCCUPIED TERRITORY, 31 MAY 1940

MERCATOR PROJECTION

tact using her Asdic, and the depth-charges caused sufficient damage to force the U-Boat to the surface. She might still have limped to safety but the other destroyer, HMS *Vanoc*, was equipped with one of the few surface-warning radar sets, a Type 286, which was capable of picking up the conning tower of a surfaced U-Boat. Alerted by the echo, the destroyer turned towards it and switched on her searchlights. Caught in the pale gleam, Schepke saw the destroyer increasing speed to ram, but he was misled by her vivid camouflage, and shouted down the voice-pipe that everything was OK, and the destroyer was going to miss. That was the last he knew, for HMS *Vanoc*'s bow sliced through the steel of *U.100*'s conning tower and crushed him against the periscope standard.

Far left: A British merchantman breaks in two and goes down after a hit amidships.

Far left: Victor and victim, view from the conning tower of *U.571*.

Left: Another merchantman sinks in a cloud of spray and steam.

Right: Survivors of a sunken ship seen from *U.571*. They are probably from the Norwegian tanker *Koll* or the British *Umtata*, sunk in mid-1942.

Far right: Survivors jump for safety to the steel deck of a U-Boat.

Below: This lone survivor seems oblivious to the U-Boat which has found him, surrounded by flotsam.

Right: A lookout wears sunglasses against the glare of the setting sun.

Far right: The hydrophone operator listens for the noise of propellers.

Bottom right: U-Boats were required to send signals about weather, convoys and sinkings, to help headquarters to assess progress in the Battle of the Atlantic.

Bottom Centre: Checking the torpedoes' running time against the chronometer.

Below: The navigator with his dividers and slide-rule had a most important job for a U-Boat on patrol had few chances to check her position. Radio-fixes had to be broadcast to help the U-Boats.

The two destroyers were busily fishing survivors out of the water when the *Walker*'s Asdic operator reported another contact. At first it was thought to be an echo from the merchant ship sunk by *U.100*, but when it was positively identified as a U-Boat, the *Walker* began to drop patterns of depth-charges. Suddenly *U.99* blew tanks and broke surface, and the delighted Commander McIntyre of HMS *Walker* learned that he had taken the redoubtable Otto Kretschmer prisoner.

On 9 May another loss of much greater significance occurred when *U.110* under Julius Lemp attacked a ship in convoy *OB.318*. First she was rocked by accurate patterns of depth-charges dropped by the corvette *Aubretia*, with the destroyers *Broadway* and *Bulldog* in support.

Given a certain degree of damage, there was little a U-Boat commander could do but blow tanks and surface, and so *U.110* came to the surface to find herself about a quarter of a mile away from the two destroyers. The *Bulldog* turned to ram, but her captain realised that he might be able to recover cipher material from the U-Boat instead. As the destroyer hove-to about 200 yards from the crippled U-Boat, guns firing at her, a boat with a boarding party went alongside smartly and boarded her. The first task was to bundle the prisoners into the whaler and get them back to the *Bulldog* so that they could be locked up without seeing anything of what followed. Then a specially briefed party went down the conning-tower hatch to find the radio-cabin, where ciphers and code-books would be found. This seemingly easy task was fraught with danger for it was likely that scuttling charges had been set to go off, and the atmosphere inside a damaged U-Boat was most unpleasant, with the probability of total darkness if the lights had been shattered by depth-charging, the smell of vomit, whiffs of chlorine gas if seawater had reached the batteries, and

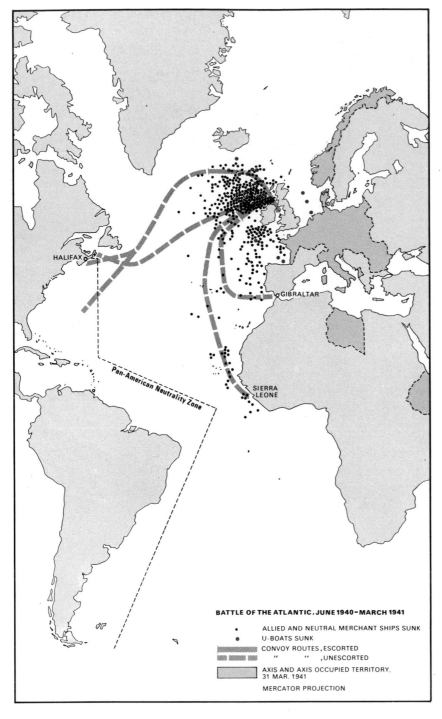

BATTLE OF THE ATLANTIC, JUNE 1940–MARCH 1941

· ALLIED AND NEUTRAL MERCHANT SHIPS SUNK
● U-BOATS SUNK
CONVOY ROUTES, ESCORTED
       "   "   , UNESCORTED
AXIS AND AXIS OCCUPIED TERRITORY,
31 MAR. 1941

MERCATOR PROJECTION

the knowledge that the U-Boat was slowly sinking from her damage. But *U.110*'s scuttling charges did not go off, and in the radio cabin the search-party found what it was looking for, not only cipher-books but a complete cipher-machine, the fabled Enigma, with a signal set up for transmission.

Just why the standing orders about destroying ciphers and the Enigma machine were not carried out is a mystery, and perhaps one can speculate that the suddenness of the attack by the *Bulldog* and the gunfire had combined to focus the attention of Lemp and his crew on the events around them. Or perhaps the man ordered to destroy the Enigma was killed before anyone realised that the order had not been carried out, but the result was the same – the

most valuable prize of the war had fallen into British hands. They had known of Enigma as early as July 1939 when the chief Polish cryptanalyst had given the British two of their Enigma machines, but this was not enough, as they did not know the key to the various changes of settings used.

The German Navy had a most advanced arrangement for enciphering its radio messages. The Enigma was appropriately known as the 'fruit machine', for it worked on similar principles, with random-spinning drums capable of producing an almost infinitely variable combination of characters. German cryptographers were convinced that the traditional methods of mathematical analysis and manual calculation would take literally years to provide solutions, but they failed to allow for the fact that the British would build the Colossus computer to process the material at undreamed-of speeds. To guard against a 'pinch' such as the boarding of *U.110* the setting instructions were printed on soluble paper, and it was assumed that any such capture would be checkmated by changing the settings, and thus putting the enemy cryptanalysts back where they had started. But the capture of *U.110* went unnoticed, for she sank in tow shortly afterwards, and the prisoners, like everyone else, were kept in the dark; in fact until 1958 the British listed *U.110* as sunk on 9 May. Her cipher-settings were valid until the end of June 1941, but what was even more valuable was the fact that British cryptanalysts were able to divine much more about the pattern of Enigma ciphers so that the new settings valid after June also became known, enabling a complete penetration of the Hydra cipher used by all operational U-Boats.

In passing, it would be appropriate to outline the method used by U-Boats in the receipt and transmission of messages at this time. A cruise did not normally exceed eight weeks, and so a U-Boat leaving on patrol would be issued with orders, instructions and cipher-settings valid for not more than three months. The settings for the Enigma machine were to be changed once a month, but in addition there were minor changes every 24 hours, at midnight at this time, but later at noon. By means of a double or treble encipherment it was possible to transmit messages for 'Officers Only' or even for 'Commanding Officer Only'. To avoid direction-finding fixes there were also 'Short' messages, used for standard instructions; these used simple code-words which were enciphered and prefaced by a Greek letter. Sighting reports were always prefaced Epsilon Epsilon, but weather reports had the roman WW.

The penetration of the Hydra cipher exposed the major weakness of the wolf-pack system: its excessive reliance on radio-traffic. Admiral Dönitz was aware of the risks, and issued a series of general instructions on the subject:

1. *In the actual operational area* radio was only to be used for sending tactically important information, or when ordered to do so by the U-Boat Command. It could also be used if the position of the U-Boat was already known to the enemy.

2. *In transit to or from the patrol area* the same conditions applied, but signals of lesser importance might be sent, but only occasionally. Care had to be taken to ensure that the transmission did not compromise the area for other U-Boats in the area, or those approaching it.

3. *Technical countermeasures* were to be used, in the form of frequent changes of wavelength and additional wavebands, as well as strict radio discipline, to confuse enemy direction-finding (DF).

Dönitz was basing his decision on two assumptions. The first was the one already discussed, that the ciphers were to all intents and purposes secure; the second was that Direction-Finding would never provide 'fixes' of sufficient accuracy to be of use in anti-submarine measures. This was true of shore-based medium-frequency DF stations, and the British had found this method of limited use. Even when an accurate fix had been obtained it was very difficult to identify it as coming from a single U-Boat or one of a pack, whether it was on patrol or in transit, or even if the message was a brief tactical one or a detailed operational transmission. But British scientists had been working on a high-frequency direction-finder (HF/DF) compact enough to be fitted in a small warship, and in July 1941, the ex-US coastguard-cutter *Culver* took the first HF/DF set to sea. Known as 'Huff-Duff' to the Royal Navy it soon proved its worth, and was able to 'home' onto the stream of signals sent out *before* a wolf-pack could attack. The routine of a wolf-pack was always the same: the sighting U-Boat would tail the convoy while sending out high-frequency radio messages to U-Boat HQ in France, and from there messages went to other U-Boats in the area, giving the last position, course and speed of the convoy; any alteration in these figures would have to be signalled again by the 'tail'. Then, as each U-Boat made contact, it had to report the fact to HQ, and only when the entire pack was in position would HQ give permission for the attack to begin. Even after this U-Boats would frequently report the results of their individual attacks.

Once the British realised how the wolf-packs were operating it was possible to use 'Huff-Duff' to full advantage. The first priority was to locate the U-Boat trailing the convoy, for if it could be forced to submerge the sighting signals would cease. Then a violent change of course would, it was hoped, take the convoy clear of the other U-Boats making for the area, and in this, of course, the Admiralty was able to assist with information from decrypted signals. As

operators gained experience with the equipment it became possible to distinguish between the sky-wave and the ground-wave, which gave a rough indication of how far away the U-Boat was, and it was even possible to distinguish between individual U-Boats by noting the radio-operators' individual 'signature'.

But without doubt the most important setback to the U-Boats at this time was the introduction of a 10cm wavelength radar set, specially designed to enable escorts to detect U-Boats. Designated Type 271, it was introduced in May 1941 and was in general use within five months; it could detect a surfaced U-Boat at 5000 yards, a conning-tower at 2800 yards, and gave good enough definition to detect a periscope at 1300 yards. This was the end of the surfaced attacks at night, and it had serious implications for the U-Boats. From this moment on, the Battle of the Atlantic would become as much a battle between rival scientists as a race between U-Boats and the enemy's shipyards.

A keen-eyed lookout sighting an aircraft could make the difference between life and death.

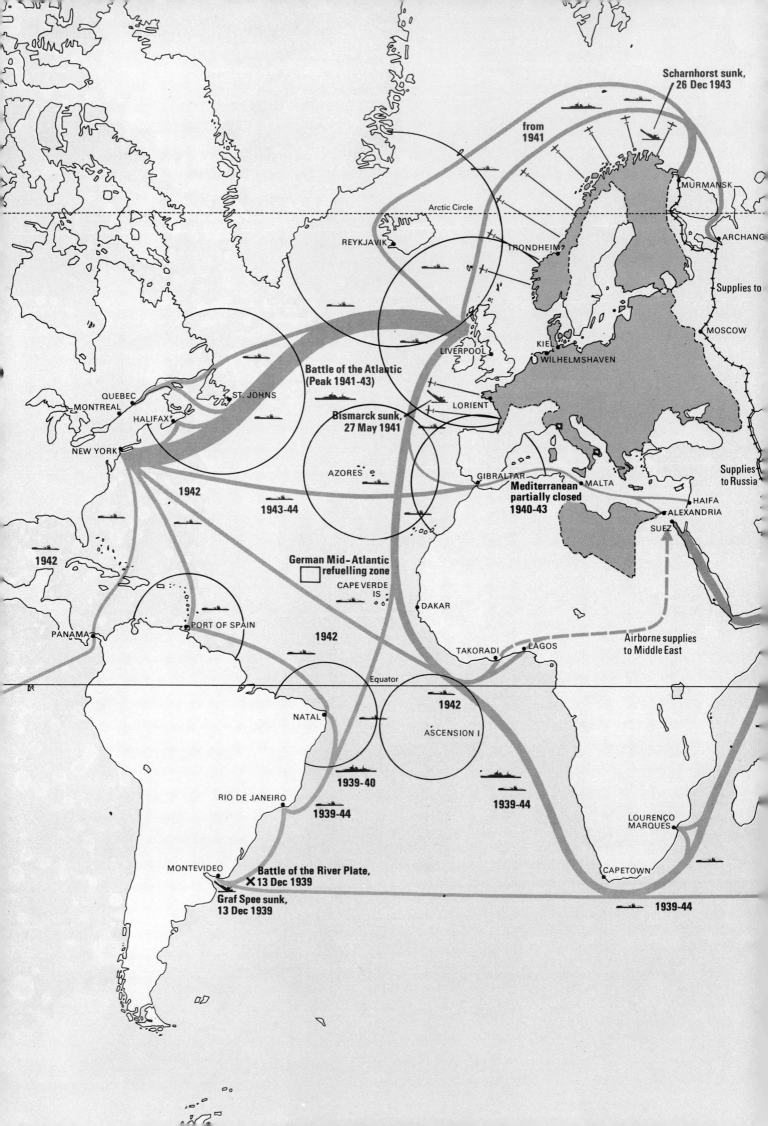

**Scharnhorst sunk,
26 Dec 1943**

from
1941

Arctic Circle

MURMANSK

ARCHANG

REYKJAVIK

TRONDHEIM?

Supplies to

MOSCOW

LIVERPOOL

KIEL

WILHELMSHAVEN

QUEBEC
MONTREAL

ST. JOHNS

HALIFAX

**Battle of the Atlantic
(Peak 1941-43)**

LORIENT

NEW YORK

**Bismarck sunk,
27 May 1941**

1942

AZORES

GIBRALTAR

MALTA

**Mediterranean
partially closed
1940-43**

Supplies
to Russia

HAIFA

ALEXANDRIA

1943-44

SUEZ

1942

German Mid–Atlantic
refuelling zone

CAPE VERDE
IS

DAKAR

PANAMA

PORT OF SPAIN

1942

TAKORADI

LAGOS

**Airborne supplies
to Middle East**

Equator

1942

NATAL

ASCENSION I

1939-40

RIO DE JANEIRO

1939-44

1939-44

LOURENÇO
MARQUES

MONTEVIDEO

**Battle of the River Plate,
✕ 13 Dec 1939**

CAPETOWN

**Graf Spee sunk,
13 Dec 1939**

1939-44

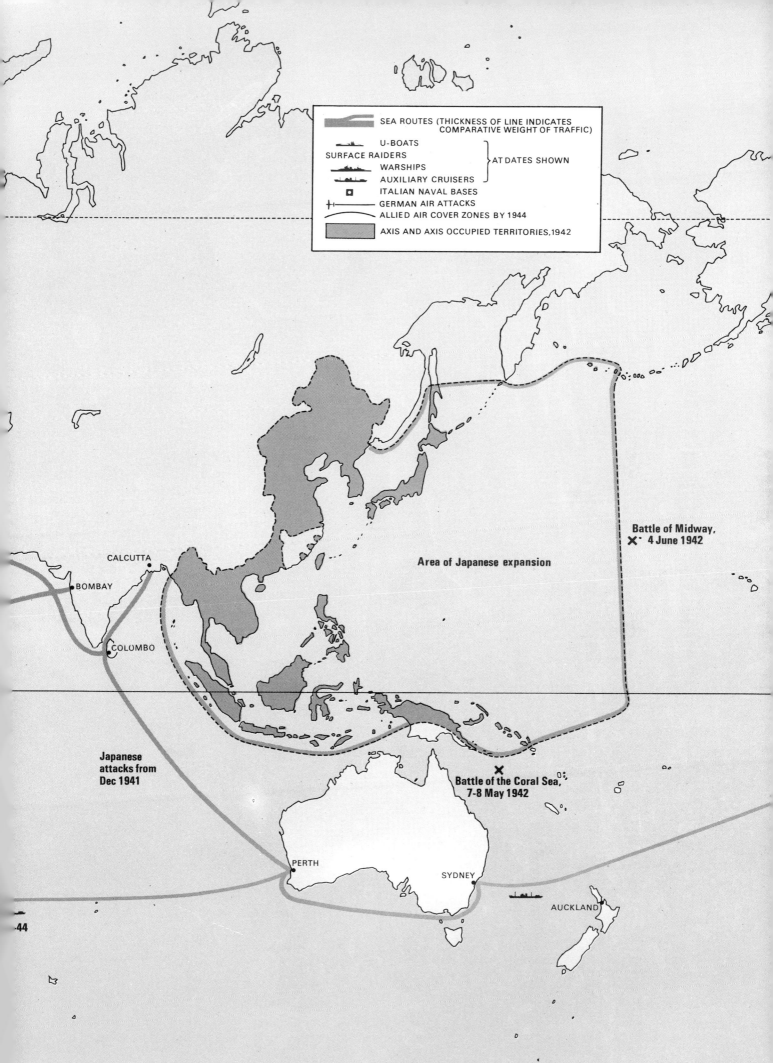

SEA ROUTES (THICKNESS OF LINE INDICATES COMPARATIVE WEIGHT OF TRAFFIC)

U-BOATS

SURFACE RAIDERS

WARSHIPS

AUXILIARY CRUISERS

} AT DATES SHOWN

ITALIAN NAVAL BASES

GERMAN AIR ATTACKS

ALLIED AIR COVER ZONES BY 1944

AXIS AND AXIS OCCUPIED TERRITORIES,1942

CALCUTTA

BOMBAY

COLOMBO

Area of Japanese expansion

Battle of Midway, 4 June 1942

Japanese attacks from Dec 1941

Battle of the Coral Sea, 7-8 May 1942

PERTH

SYDNEY

AUCKLAND

-44

MERCATOR PROJECTION

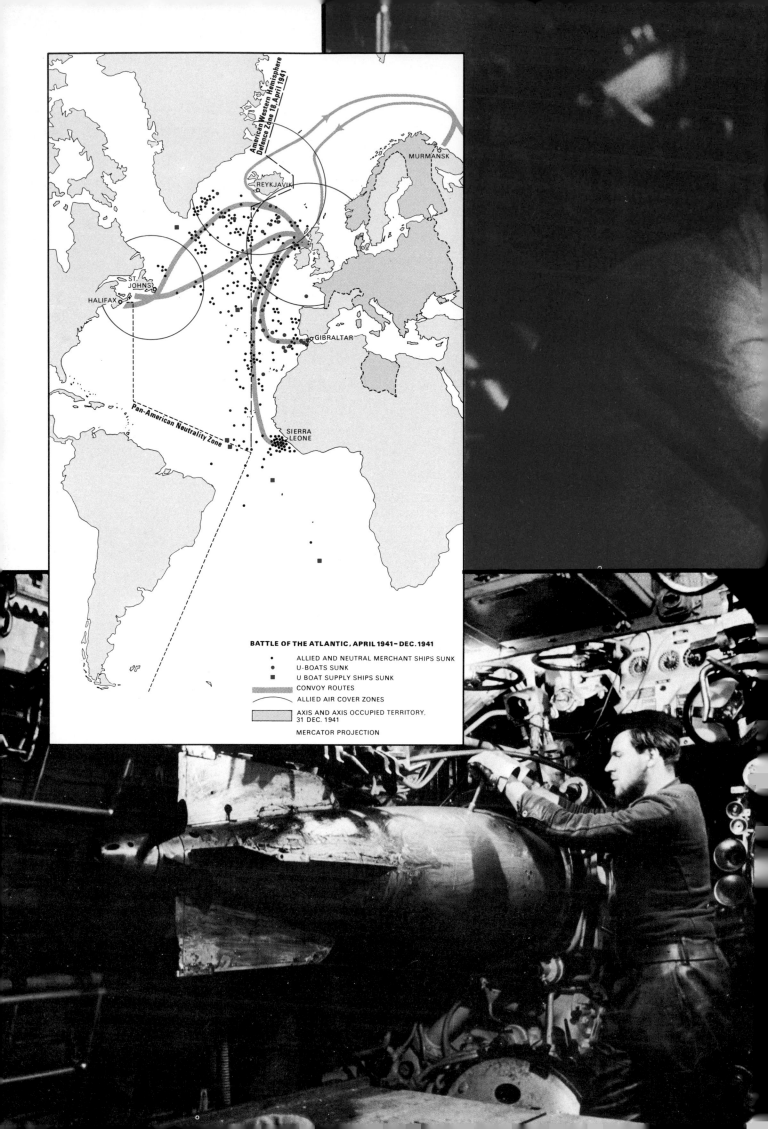

BATTLE OF THE ATLANTIC, APRIL 1941–DEC. 1941

- · ALLIED AND NEUTRAL MERCHANT SHIPS SUNK
- ● U-BOATS SUNK
- ■ U BOAT SUPPLY SHIPS SUNK
- ━━ CONVOY ROUTES
- ━━ ALLIED AIR COVER ZONES
- AXIS AND AXIS OCCUPIED TERRITORY, 31 DEC. 1941

MERCATOR PROJECTION

MURMANSK

REYKJAVIK

American Western Hemisphere Defence Zone 18 April 1941

ST. JOHNS

HALIFAX

GIBRALTAR

Pan-American Neutrality Zone

SIERRA LEONE

The race was still on, however, and by March 1941 new U-Boats were coming into service at the rate of 13 per month. Even so, the pressing need for training meant that only 27 out of the 98 already completed were operational. In the summer the U-Boats began to change their patrol areas to avoid the increasing number of air patrols, and some crossed the Atlantic to operate off Newfoundland. Others began to attack the convoys bound for Gibraltar, and here the pickings were found to be good. The long-range Focke-Wulf 200 aircraft operating from airfields on the Biscay coast were much more effective in co-operating with the U-Boats than before, and losses were heavy. But the U-Boats reported an ominous stiffening of the convoy's resistance. More and more ships were

getting radar, HF/DF, and a range of new weapons, and an airborne radar set was now available. On 27 August the U-Boat Arm suffered its only loss by outright surrender when K/Lt Hans Rahmlow surrendered *U.570* to an RAF Coastal Command Hudson bomber off Iceland.

U.570 was completed at Hamburg on 15 May 1941, two months after being launched. She was sent to Horten, near Oslo to complete her trials and training, and eventually she left Trondheim on 23 August for a patrol in the North Atlantic after which she was to continue to her new base at La Pallice outside Rochefort in Brittany. Evidently the training had not eradicated certain weaknesses in the morale of the crew, for there were reports of outbursts of bad temper. To make matters worse the boat encountered

Working on torpedoes was doubly difficult in the cramped conditions. The electric G7e torpedo also needed to be run at a specific temperature to avoid reducing its range.

rough weather, and many crewmen were sea-sick; *U.570* was in fairly poor shape. Rahmlow had taken her down to 60 metres to avoid the violent motion of the waves, but at about 1100 hours on the morning of 27 August he decided to come to the surface. After a quick look at the surface revealed no ships, he gave the order to blow tanks and surface.

Unfortunately for Rahmlow, his quick search had not revealed a Hudson bomber almost directly above, and the pilot and his lookouts were only momentarily surprised to see *U.570* come to the surface so obligingly. Seconds later depth-charges were exploding around the U-Boat, and she was being lashed by 20mm cannon-fire. As the smoke and spray subsided a white flag appeared on the conning tower; Rahmlow had decided to avoid further loss of life, not least because his sick and demoralised crew would probably not have obeyed his orders to dive or to man the 20mm anti-aircraft guns. The slightly nonplussed Hudson could do nothing

but circle the U-Boat while sending out urgent appeals for assistance to any warships in the area. Finally a trawler arrived about 12 hours after the original incident, but the weather was too rough to launch a boat, and so the wretched crew of *U.570* had to wait in their wallowing hulk until the next day before they could be rescued. To their credit it must be pointed out that they used the opportunity to destroy all traces of the Enigma machine and cipher-books, and no information fell into enemy hands.

The British kept the news quiet for some months, but made the most of their capture. The U-Boat was found to be in good condition, and was soon refitted for trials and evaluation.

She proved invaluable in determining the maximum diving depth and the turning circle of a Type VIIC U-Boat, as well as a score of minor points. For example, scientists from the Operational Research team who visited her after she was brought into a British port noticed that the 20mm cannon-fire from the Hudson had penetrated the pressure hull and had smashed the control panel. As this had been the principal reason why Rahmlow had been unable to dive to safety it was correctly deduced that aircraft should in future rake a surfaced U-Boat with cannon-fire if not in an ideal position to drop depth-charges; this would in all probability inflict sufficient damage to stop the U-Boat from diving, and give the aircraft time to make a more accurate bombing run. To flaunt their capture the British put U.570 back into service as HMS Graph, and even used her operationally for a short while, but she ended her unusual career by being wrecked on the Island of Islay in Scotland.

Rahmlow was now a prisoner-of-war, and when he joined his fellow-officers in a POW camp he was tried for cowardice by a secret court-martial convened by Otto Kretschmer. The unfortunate man was found to be innocent, but his First Lieutenant was judged to have been in dereliction of his duty in not avoiding surrender or scuttling the boat, and the court held that he should, if necessary, have arrested Rahmlow. How all this was to have been achieved on the tiny conning tower platform of U.570 is hard to imagine, but the military code of honour had to be satisfied somehow. During the rest of the war no other U-Boat was captured in this way, although an American task force did manage to board U.505 in 1944. However her circumstances were more like those of U.110, and the U.570 case remains an isolated example of the lone case where an entire U-Boat crew simply decided not to continue the fight. Her capture came at the end of the second phase of the U-Boat war; in the last quarter of 1941 new factors were about to be brought into play, and they would alter the entire course of the war.

The arrival of U.570 in a British port after her capture. Although no cipher material was captured the possession of a Type VIIC complete with her G7e torpedoes gave the British invaluable information about their foes.

WITHIN SIGHT OF VICTORY

A rupture with the United States was bound to occur and U-Boats would be the cause, whatever their intentions. The Americans had, as already stated, shown their preference by promcting a policy of helping Great Britain with 'all aid short of war', and to ensure that the cargoes of munitions, raw materials and food reached their destination the US Navy extended its Neutrality Patrol zones. In March 1941 the Lend-Lease Bill was enacted to allow war-material to be 'lent' to the British for the duration of the war and a month later the Defence Zone, in which US warships protected their own merchantmen, was extended to 26° W. Then US troops were sent to garrison Iceland as a guarantee of its neutrality, although British and Canadian convoy escorts continued to refuel in Icelandic harbours.

The position for the U-Boats was a tricky one, for the distinctive four-funnelled silhouette of the older American destroyers was now common to the US Navy, the Royal Navy and the Royal Canadian Navy. Nor was this similarity confined to the old escorts; the newest American destroyers of the *Benson* and *Bristol* Classes looked like the numerous destroyers of the

A minesweeper or *raumboot* escorts *U.37* into Lorient. As the war progressed the enemy's aerial minelaying increased the hazards faced by U-Boats in transit.

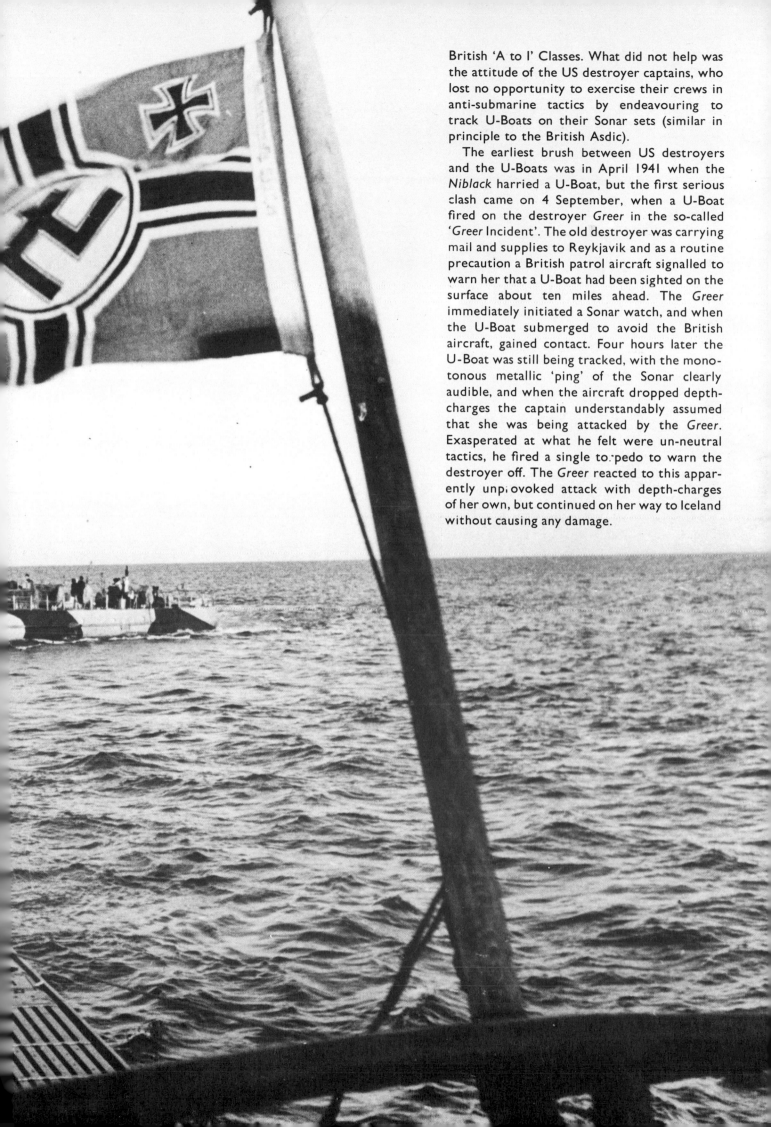

British 'A to I' Classes. What did not help was the attitude of the US destroyer captains, who lost no opportunity to exercise their crews in anti-submarine tactics by endeavouring to track U-Boats on their Sonar sets (similar in principle to the British Asdic).

The earliest brush between US destroyers and the U-Boats was in April 1941 when the *Niblack* harried a U-Boat, but the first serious clash came on 4 September, when a U-Boat fired on the destroyer *Greer* in the so-called '*Greer* Incident'. The old destroyer was carrying mail and supplies to Reykjavik and as a routine precaution a British patrol aircraft signalled to warn her that a U-Boat had been sighted on the surface about ten miles ahead. The *Greer* immediately initiated a Sonar watch, and when the U-Boat submerged to avoid the British aircraft, gained contact. Four hours later the U-Boat was still being tracked, with the monotonous metallic 'ping' of the Sonar clearly audible, and when the aircraft dropped depth-charges the captain understandably assumed that she was being attacked by the *Greer*. Exasperated at what he felt were un-neutral tactics, he fired a single torpedo to warn the destroyer off. The *Greer* reacted to this apparently unprovoked attack with depth-charges of her own, but continued on her way to Iceland without causing any damage.

US warships were now permitted to shoot on sight at hostile submarines, but it was more than a month before another incident occurred. This was on 17 October when *U.568* accidentally torpedoed the destroyer USS *Kearny* during a confused convoy action. The US ships were hopelessly mixed up with British, Canadian and Free French warships, in a disordered action in defence of a hard-pressed Canadian convoy. At about 0200 hours the *Kearny* had dropped depth-charges in accordance with orders which permitted the 'embarrassment' of U-Boats, and in the fitful glare from a blazing oil tanker the commander of *U.568* fired a salvo of three torpedoes at what he assumed was a hostile escort. Only one of the spread hit the *Kearny*, full in her forward fire-room, but it was enough to tear an enormous hole in her and bring her to a shuddering halt in a cloud of smoke and steam.

The destroyer survived and was repaired in Icelandic anchorage, but the death of 11 sailors and the wounding of another 24 caused a wave of public indignation in the United States. Not enough, however, to cause a significant change in the political climate. Exactly two weeks later the old destroyer *Reuben James* was nearing the Mid-Ocean Meeting Point (MOMP), the 'chop-line' at which US warships handed over care of their merchantmen to British and Canadian escorts, when she was hit by a torpedo from *U.562*. This time the ship sank with the loss of two-thirds of her crew, but even this was not enough of an affront to American dignity, although the President sought powers from Congress to put the Coast Guard under naval control. The U-Boat commanders chafed under the restrictions, as they felt that they were running the risk of being sunk without being able to hit back, but Hitler still refused to allow them a free hand. Only when the Japanese attacked Pearl Harbor on 7 December did he finally declare war on the USA. It was a brave gesture, but it gave President Roosevelt the excuse he was looking for to support the war in Europe. Although some of his military advisers felt that America should deal with Japan first, Roosevelt was adamant that Germany was the most dangerous enemy and should be defeated first.

The riposte by Dönitz was characteristically swift and decisive. By Christmas Day, only 18 days after Pearl Harbor, six Type IX U-Boats were on their way across the Atlantic to attack shipping off the east coast. Another six boats were diverted to reinforce them and with this force Dönitz hoped to strike a paralysing blow before the Americans could organise themselves. This operation, codenamed 'Paukenschlag' or drum-roll, produced undreamed-of results.

To the U-Boat crews it was the second 'Happy Time'. To their surprise and delight the Americans were not merely inexperienced but totally

One of *U.558*'s victims off the coast of Brazil, possibly the *Triton*.

U.557 **at Danzig in the Spring of 1941. She was lost in collision eight months later.**

The crew of *U.557* on her return from patrol.

The *Troisdoc*, another of *U.558*'s victims.

unprepared for a campaign against their shipping. There was no blackout and navigation lights burned brightly; shipping was unescorted and even the naval patrols were obligingly punctual in their movements. Not since 1915 had there been such easy pickings for U-Boats, and they reaped their grim harvest with astonishing ease. Even the limited countermeasures were largely ineffective because the merchant ships broadcast messages in clear, giving their course, speed and position frequently. For example *U.123* was able to sink eight ships in 24 hours; it is no wonder that 58 ships were sunk in January, a total of more than 300,000 tons.

The US Navy was very short of aircraft, and even when Army Air Force planes were put under Navy control the pilots proved to be badly trained in navigation and could do little to co-operate with ships. There were no specialised anti-submarine escorts, and an apparent absence of any coherent doctrine. The US Navy had been sceptical of the value of the British convoy system, and hoped to control the U-Boats by means of 'offensive patrolling'. This was the very doctrine which had nearly brought the British to their knees in 1917, and its hold on the minds of senior US Navy admirals is all the harder to understand in the light of the important part played by American escorts in the defeat of the U-Boats in 1917–18.

The situation had not been fully anticipated by the British, and the horrific toll in American waters made further inroads into their precious supply of shipping. The losses in the Caribbean, for example, where U-Boats even found it possible to use guns instead of torpedoes, were particularly heavy among oil tankers, the most precious merchant ships of all. Anti-submarine escorts had to be transferred to the United States under 'Reverse Lend-Lease' to form the nucleus of a special escort force until such time as the shipyards could build new warships. It must not be forgotten that the US Navy was also heavily committed in the Pacific, and had sustained heavy losses; it was not possible to devote all resources to the Atlantic.

By June 1942 the balance was tipping back, with convoys and better anti-submarine measures in force, but the U-Boats were still highly dangerous. It had been found that even the smaller VIIC boats could reach New York, and in April the first of a new type of U-Boat appeared, the Type XIV 'milch cow' or U-tanker. Basically a Type VII with large fuel capacity and stowage for reload-torpedoes and essential stores, the 'milch cow' was intended to rendezvous with ordinary U-Boats in mid-Atlantic, to refuel them and replenish torpedoes, enabling them to spend longer on patrol. It was found, just as in the latter part of World War I, that the number of torpedoes was the governing factor in determining how long a U-Boat

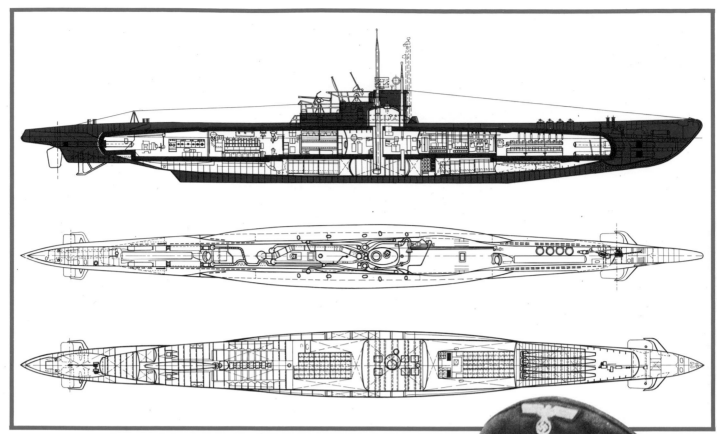

Left: *U.557* at the time of her commissioning in February 1941. The ice on the guard rails and jumping wires was not dangerous, but in the Arctic extreme cold could freeze the vents.

Above: An officer of *U.557*, possibly Paulshen, her CO.

Top: Side elevation, top deck plan (centre) and bottom deck plan of a type VIIC U-Boat.

should stay on patrol. Provided she had enough fuel to get to and from her patrol area, she could stay until she ran out of torpedoes, and so the new variants of the standard Type IX and Type VII boats incorporated increased stowage for torpedoes. For example the Type VIIC, the most numerous type of U-Boat built throughout the war, carried 14 torpedoes, as against 11 in the original VIIA; the IXA and IXB carried 22 torpedoes and the IXD_2 carried 24, a total of three reloads for each tube.

By July the total number of U-Boats in commission rose to 331, the total which Dönitz had wanted for so long, with 140 operational and 191 on trials and training. Even so, only 29 extra boats could be maintained on station in the Atlantic. Trials in the Baltic had been delayed by the severe winter, and in addition there were calls to divert U-Boats to the Mediterranean and the Arctic. Against this, the first results of the enormous shipbuilding programmes of the Allies were beginning to be seen, with large numbers of merchant ships as well as escorts coming forward. Events were moving to a climax, and nobody knew better than Dönitz that victory would finally go to whichever side could replace its losses faster. Anti-submarine tactics had become refined, with each scientific advance being matched by a corresponding advance on the other side, and the longer the confrontation was postponed the stronger the Allies would become.

The decision was made in August, when Dönitz decided to reduce the effort against American shipping in the Caribbean and off the east coast. He reasoned that it was possible to keep three times as many U-Boats on station in the Western Approaches as on the western side of the Atlantic, and so the U-Boats would be put to better use on the eastern side. The wolf-packs continued to operate much as they had in 1941, but now the increasing effectiveness of shore-based aircraft led them to operate beyond the outer limit of these aircraft. This was the dreaded 'Black Gap' in mid-Atlantic and once a convoy entered the zone, the losses could become unbearable. In August 1942 convoy *SC.94* was attacked by 18 U-Boats; 11 ships were lost for only two U-Boats. In October *SC.104* lost eight ships for three U-Boats, and in November *HX.217* lost 15 ships for three attackers. There were occasional reverses too, such as *HX.217* at the end of the year, whose escorts sank two U-Boats out of a pack of 22 but lost only two merchantmen. During the period August–December 1942 the monthly sinkings averaged about 100 ships (500,000 tons) for approximately ten U-Boats per month.

The problem for the Allies was that they were not merely fighting to get ships through to the British Isles. It was essential to use the British and American armies in an offensive role with the eventual aim of liberating Europe and defeat-

ing Germany. The first move was to make a large-scale amphibious landing in French North Africa, cutting off Rommel's Afrika Korps and the Italian Armies in Cyrenaica and freeing the Middle East oilfields from the threat of capture. This was the 'Torch' landing of November 1942, and if in retrospect the Allied High Command seems to have been over-eager to go over to the offensive, it must be remembered that the war had been going for over two years, and it was politically desirable to show the Allied nations that their Armed Forces were capable of defeating those of the Axis. But the decision to run large troop convoys from the United States and Britain meant that the escort forces needed to protect them had to be withdrawn from the Atlantic. As the U-Boats and the Allied escorts

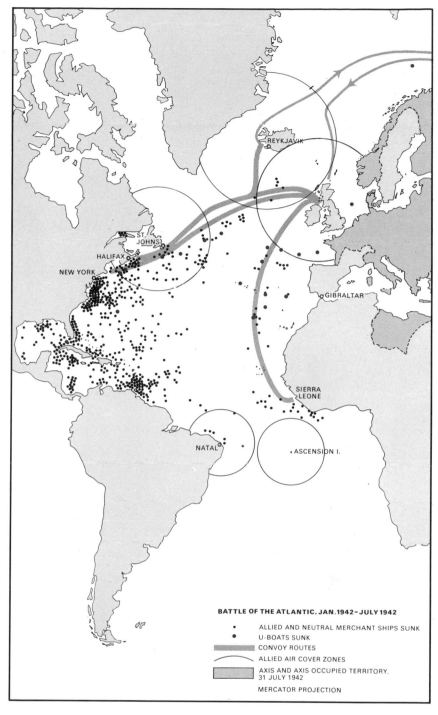

BATTLE OF THE ATLANTIC, JAN.1942–JULY 1942

- ·   ALLIED AND NEUTRAL MERCHANT SHIPS SUNK
- ●   U-BOATS SUNK
- ▬▬   CONVOY ROUTES
- ◠   ALLIED AIR COVER ZONES
- ▨   AXIS AND AXIS OCCUPIED TERRITORY, 31 JULY 1942

MERCATOR PROJECTION

The inboard profile and deck plans of a Type VIIC. The heavy black line on the profile indicates the pressure hull.

were fairly evenly matched this automatically reduced the pressure on the U-Boats, and they were able to take advantage of this. In the month of the 'Torch' landings they sank 119 ships totalling 729,000 tons.

Dönitz estimated that a monthly total of 800,000 tons of shipping sunk would defeat the Allies, even allowing for the vast resources of the United States. But, as in 1917, the magic figure was apparently passed and still the Allies were able to carry on. In fact the average during this period was only 650,000 tons, thanks to the tendency for U-Boat commanders to exaggerate the tonnage of their victims; the Allies were

Left: *U.156* at Lorient in July 1942. The conning tower has been fitted for the FuMO-29 radar array: the top row is for reception, the bottom for sending.

Top: A tramp steamer sinks after being torpedoed by *U.558* in the Caribbean.

Above: Two Type VIICs rest in Norwegian waters near Narvik.

further from collapse than they seemed.

Two significant improvements in the U-Boats' weapons were introduced in the second half of 1942. The first was not really a weapon but rather a countermeasure. It was the Metox radar-detector which enabled U-Boats to avoid being surprised on the surface at night by aircraft fitted with radar and the Leigh searchlight. The second was the acoustic homing torpedo, which promised a much higher hit-probability. The first homing torpedo was the T4 *Falke* (Falcon) and it finally became operational in January 1943. Only 30 were used out of the 100 issued, and it was soon replaced by the

improved T5 *Zaunkönig* (Wren), which was given the acronym GNAT (German Naval Acoustic Torpedo) by the Allies, an altogether more appropriate name. The *Zaunkönig* was chiefly used against escorts because the noise-pattern of fast-running propellers was easier to home onto, and the only defences against it were to proceed very fast or very slow, or to use noisemakers ('foxers'). However in the long run it did not achieve the effects hoped for simply because sinking escorts did little to harm the convoy system; the only way in which U-Boats could exert decisive pressure on the Allies was by sinking merchantmen, and every warship torpedoed meant one less torpedo to fire at merchantmen. The Germans had high hopes for the *Zaunkönig*, and believed that it hit 53 per cent of its targets. Thanks to a clerical

error in post-war analysis it was also believed
that some 6000 of them were fired, but in fact
the figure is only 640, and the hit-rate was only
six per cent. In comparison, a total of more than
2500 *Zaunkönigs* were expended during the
development and trials period.

In January 1943 the U-Boat strength stood at
400 boats with over 200 available for operations,
and Dönitz was convinced that the moment of
victory was at hand. He had been successful in
getting U-Boats withdrawn from Norway to
reinforce the Atlantic flotillas, and with the
new torpedoes it would be possible to inflict
heavy losses on the convoy-escorts. All that was
needed was to destroy two or three big convoys and the Admiralty would then be forced
to abandon the system giving the U-Boats their
long-awaited chance to strangle the Atlantic
lifeline. The United States would remain hostile
but she could do little to redress the balance in
Europe, and the losses inflicted on her shipping
would be of incalculable value to the Japanese.
For the moment, however, the weather was so
atrocious that both convoys and U-Boats were
fully occupied in surviving. Even so, the small
convoy *TM.1* lost seven out of nine tankers, a
victory on a scale which had not happened since
1940. The disaster was directly caused by a series
of technical failures which left the four escorts
without a functioning radar set between them,
and by the lack of air cover.

Bottom: *U.558* takes on diesel oil from a *milchküh* **U-tanker**.

Below: *U.557* in February 1941.

136

In February Dönitz managed to get over 100 U-Boats to sea for the first time, and two big convoy battles were fought. Against *ON.116* the U-Boats managed to sink 14 ships for the loss of only one attacker, but *ONS.165* lost only two ships, and its escorts sank two U-Boats. During the whole month, however, only 34 ships were sunk in convoys and 13 U-Boats were sunk. In March Dönitz laid a trap for a slow convoy, *SC.122* (52 ships) and the fast *HX.229* (25 ships) with a long patrol line of 29 U-Boats. The fast convoy was located first, and in eight hours eight ships went down. Against *SC.122* one U-Boat, *U.338*, was able to sink four merchantmen with only five torpedoes. In a desperate attempt to fight the convoys through the encircling wolf-pack the two senior escort commanders decided to join the convoys together to strengthen the escort, but this did not prevent the U-Boats from sinking another nine ships over the next three days.

It was the biggest convoy battle of the war, and it cost 140,000 tons of shipping on one side, and three U-Boats on the other. Every conceivable weapon and tactic had been available to the escorts and still the U-Boats had defeated them. The Admiralty seriously began to consider abandoning the convoy system, reasoning that independent sailings might be better than nothing, and would give time to allow new countermeasures to be devised. During the whole month the U-Boats sank 108 ships totalling 672,000 tons, but what was remarkable was that 72 of them were in convoys. The Allies could muster 500 escorts and 1100 aircraft in the Atlantic, and it seemed to older officers like 1917 all over again.

Below centre: The gun-crew of *U.558* is engulfed in spray as a wave breaks over the deck. Judging by the fact that the man on the left is wearing only shorts and a Mae West, it must be in the Caribbean.

Below: *U.557* (foreground) and a sister U-Boat are frozen in during training in the Baltic early in 1941.

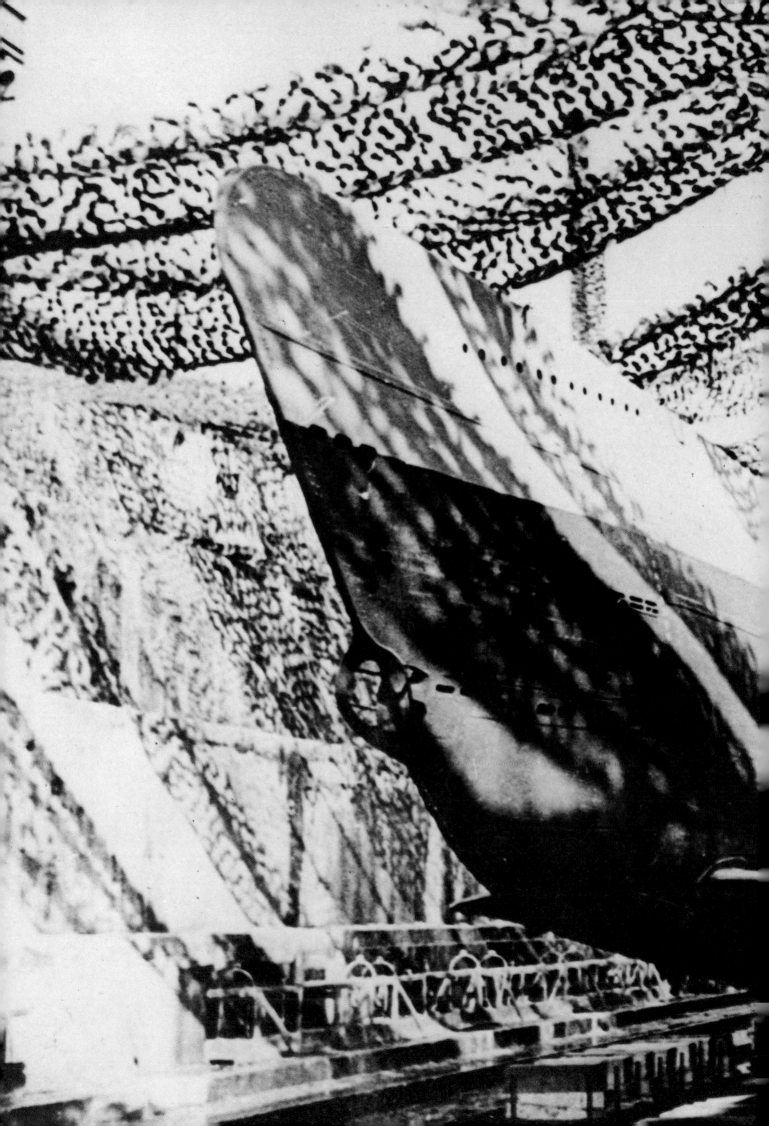

Below: *U.561*, with some Army guests on board, passing through the Kiel Canal.

Left: *U.558* lies under the illusory shelter of camouflage nets in a French dry dock.

Below: A *milchküh* supply U-Boat comes alongside *U.558*. These U-tankers suffered heavy losses as they were made top priority for enemy anti-submarine forces.

And then, sudden
for the U-Boats. In A
to half the March f
shot up to 15 bringir
to four ships per U
interrelated reason
escort groups and t
had been withdraw
cover Operation Tc
Western Approache
equipped support
several hard-pressed
escort carriers mear
had air cover all the v
the 'Black Gap' was r
was also helped by tl
range bombers for ar
the silent work don
deciphering the U-I
with great rapidity.
factor of all was a su
between the Allies' s
man countermeasure
been noted that the M
enabled U-Boats re
under cover of darkn
equipped aircraft cam
the Allies introduce
(ASVIII) to their aircr
up the pulses. Thanks
scientific teams, the
the conclusion that t
betraying the positic
Another error was m
interceptions to some
radar, despite the fac
analysts had found m
in deciphering convoy

When the villain wa
radar the damage was c
to produce a new se
thought. The U-Boats
Metox and this hind
Doubts about the equ
countermeasures did
moment. Two succes
traps by large convoys
cious Dönitz to demar
service should run a che
to see if they were be
seems hard to credit,
it was impossible to b
and the evasions must

In May the U-Boats
they had sown. When co
by every available U-Bo
escorts exacted a toll of
use of aircraft from sm
hard for the U-Boats e
convoys, and it was fou
to pick up a convoy wa
merge by aircraft as soo
mit the information

Although in the final analysis the operations of U-Boats away from the decisive Atlantic Theatre of operations did little to influence the course of the War, they are nonetheless interesting. Apart from the deliberate onslaught on American shipping in January 1942 which was an extension of the battle raging in the Western Approaches, they formed no part of the central U-Boat strategy formulated by Admiral Dönitz and were usually forced on him.

The first diversion was to the Mediterranean in October 1941 when British surface ships and submarines were raiding the lines of communication between Italy and North Africa and threatening the successful operations of Rommel and the Afrika Korps. The decision was made by *Oberkommando der Wehrmacht* (OKW), the Supreme Command, over the head of Dönitz, who knew only too well how dangerous the Mediterranean could be to U-Boats. The Straits of Gibraltar can be entered with relative safety from the Atlantic inwards because the current runs in that direction, but getting out is extremely hazardous. The other disadvantage is that the clear waters of the Mediterranean give the advantage to patrolling aircraft, which can spot a submarine 50 feet below the surface. Any U-Boats sent to the Mediterranean, argued Dönitz, would never get out again, and would be hunted down sooner or later. He was right, but that did not stop the six boats sent from giving a good account of themselves. In the first three months they sank the carrier *Ark Royal*, the battleship *Barham* and the cruiser *Galatea*, and completely altered the balance of power in the eastern Mediterranean. The British found that their anti-submarine tactics had grown rusty, as they had only been practising on the Italians, and the skill of the U-Boats came as an unpleasant shock.

The *Ark Royal* was hit by a single torpedo from *U.81*, commanded by K/Lt Guggenberger, and although destroyers tried to tow her back to Gibraltar the flooding got out of control, and this fine, modern aircraft carrier capsized within 30 miles of safety. The loss of HMS *Barham* was more tragic. She and other battleships were exercising in the Gulf of Sollum near Alexandria when *U.331* under Freiherr von Tiesenhausen slipped past the destroyer-screen unnoticed. Suddenly the old ship (she had fought at Jutland 25 years before) reeled as three torpedoes struck her aft. She heeled over rapidly to port, and when she was on her beam ends, her after-magazines suddenly detonated in a shattering explosion. When the smoke cleared the ship had disappeared, taking with her 962 officers and men. She was the only British battleship to

be sunk at sea by a U-Boat during World War II.

Nearly a year later *U.73* sank the elderly carrier HMS *Eagle* during the great 'Pedestal' convoy to relieve Malta, and during the same operation the Italian submarine *Axum* sank the anti-aircraft cruiser *Cairo*. Other British warships accounted for include the destroyers *Partridge* (by *U.565*), *Porcupine* (by *U.602*), *Martin* (by *U.431*), *Laforey* (by *U.223*), *Gurkha* (by *U.133*) and *Jaguar* (by *U.652*).

The Type VIIC *U.443* and a sister in dock in La Spezia in December 1942.

The somewhat prickly relationship between the *Kriegsmarine* and the *Regia Navale* meant that the U-Boats used Italian bases but were not allowed to operate under Italian command. The poor showing of the Italian submarines in the Atlantic still rankled, and the Germans resented the fact that they had to reinforce a navy which had such a convincing superiority in numbers. Italian training and tactics were regarded as highly suspect, and Dönitz refrained from asking for operational control over the Italian boats at Bordeaux in order to be able to refuse to allow reciprocal control over the Mediterranean U-Boats. The Mediterranean was not as popular as might be expected, for the U-Boats were not designed to operate in a warm climate and their ventilation was not adequate for the job. In the Atlantic up to 1943, it was possible to spend some time on the surface and the men were encouraged to relax to save their energy for later; in the Mediterranean the heat made everyone lethargic and the constant threat of air attack called for a special degree of alertness.

The collapse of Italy in 1943 did not mean the surrender of the U-Boats in Italian ports for the Germans turned on their recent ally with an eagerness which showed how shallow their partnership had been. In fact things turned out the other way – several Italian submarines were taken over by the Germans. They were given

UIT-numbers, but none of them was commissioned before the end of the War. Nine VIIC types were transferred to the Italian Navy under an agreement signed in April 1943 under which the Italians would provide nine large boats to transport rubber and other strategic raw materials from the Far East, in exchange for an equal number of U-Boats. They had just been delivered by the German shipbuilders and were being used to train the Italian crews when the Armistice was signed in Italy, whereupon they were seized and reincorporated into the German Navy.

The larger Type IX boats proved to be too slow in diving for the North Atlantic, and suffered very heavy casualties. As a result the *Seekriegsleitung* (SKL) ordered Dönitz to use them away from the main convoy routes. Although, as noted, Dönitz disliked the idea intensely, he had no choice, and so the big U-Boats began to operate further south. They were active off the west coast of Africa, and as many more independently routed ships were encountered they did well. In fact the Type IXB boats did better than any other class of U-Boats in terms of ton-

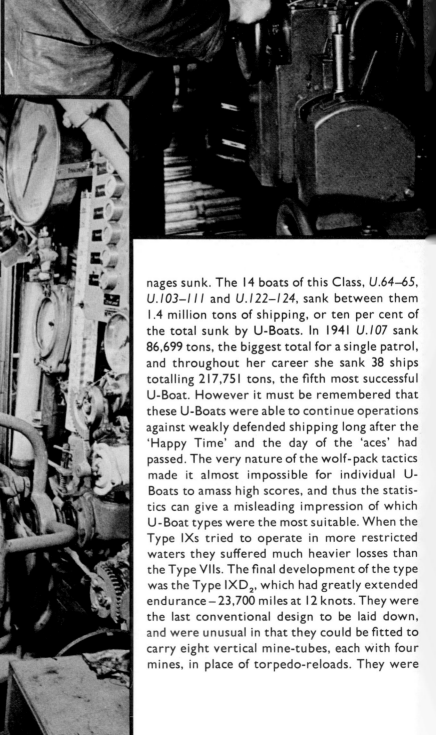

nages sunk. The 14 boats of this Class, *U.64–65, U.103–111* and *U.122–124*, sank between them 1.4 million tons of shipping, or ten per cent of the total sunk by U-Boats. In 1941 *U.107* sank 86,699 tons, the biggest total for a single patrol, and throughout her career she sank 38 ships totalling 217,751 tons, the fifth most successful U-Boat. However it must be remembered that these U-Boats were able to continue operations against weakly defended shipping long after the 'Happy Time' and the day of the 'aces' had passed. The very nature of the wolf-pack tactics made it almost impossible for individual U-Boats to amass high scores, and thus the statistics can give a misleading impression of which U-Boat types were the most suitable. When the Type IXs tried to operate in more restricted waters they suffered much heavier losses than the Type VIIs. The final development of the type was the Type IXD$_2$, which had greatly extended endurance – 23,700 miles at 12 knots. They were the last conventional design to be laid down, and were unusual in that they could be fitted to carry eight vertical mine-tubes, each with four mines, in place of torpedo-reloads. They were big boats – 287 feet long with a surface displacement of 1600 tons – and they proved capable of reaching the Indian Ocean. Several operated in the Mozambique Channel and off Mauritius where they proved a great danger to the shipping which was routed around the Cape of Good Hope to avoid the Mediterranean.

One of the most unusual adventures befell *U.126* which had a rendezvous with the disguised raider *Atlantis* in November 1941 near Ascension Island. While the raider refuelled the U-Boat the captain, K/Lt Bauer, and his No 1 went aboard the host-ship as guests. Suddenly the alarm was sounded, and a British heavy cruiser appeared on the horizon; the raider attempted to bluff her way out of the trap by pretending to be an American ship, but the cruiser, HMS *Devonshire* stayed well clear while she radioed the Admiralty for confirmation. An hour later, when London confirmed that the ship was not a genuine merchantman, the cruiser opened a brisk fire with her eight-inch guns at a range of 11 miles. The *Atlantis* was abandoned and scuttled, and *U.126* dived early on during the action, but without her captain

and No 1. This meant that the executive 'brain' of the boat was missing, making it impossible for her to even try to scare off the *Devonshire*.

After dark *U.126* surfaced again and hunted for the survivors in the boats, but as there were over 200 they could not all be accommodated. Bauer, relieved to be back on board his U-Boat, radioed for help, and U-Boat HQ directed several to the scene with the supply ship *Python*. The supply ship took the survivors on board and proceeded to refuel some of the U-Boats, only to be interrupted by another British cruiser, HMS *Dorsetshire*. The *Python* gallantly put herself between the cruiser and the U-Boats to give them time to dive, and was soon set on fire by eight-inch shells. The U-Boats had just taken on large quantities of stores, and were so badly out of condition that they could not attack the *Dorsetshire*; one of them later reported that she was bobbing up and down like a yo-yo because the stores had not been properly stowed. But K/Lt Merten of *U.68* felt that he ought to try one last trick, and so he blew tanks, surfaced and headed for the *Dorsetshire*. It worked; the cruiser turned away to

Top left: The port diesel control room in the Type IXB U.65, operating out of Brest in September 1940.

Bottom left: U.65's hydroplane operators watch the depth-gauges.

Below: The cylinder head of one of U.65's diesels.

avoid a possible torpedo-attack. The U-Boats were able to divide the survivors of the *Atlantis* and the *Python* between them and make their way back to France.

Norway was probably the least popular posting for U-Boats. The weather was as big an enemy as the British escorts and aircraft, with freezing fog, black ice forming dangerous top-weight, and the risk of vents freezing in the sub-zero waters of the Arctic. Even in harbour there was the prospect of long hours of darkness during the winter. Summer was better, but the never-ending daylight meant that recharging batteries had to be done under the most dangerous conditions. The only advantage of operating in the Arctic was the fact that the varying salinity of the water helped to create 'thermal layers', which deflected Asdic beams. If a U-Boat could locate one of these she was relatively safe underneath it. The results against Arctic convoys did not compare with the scores in the Atlantic partly because the weather made it so hard to locate them, but also because there were so few convoys. The main success of the northern U-Boats was against convoy *PQ.17* in 1942, when ten ships were successfully torpedoed after the convoy had scattered.

Below: *U.107* heads into the setting sun. Because the Type IXBs operated away from the well-defended Western Approaches, they scored bigger successes as a class than the Type VIICs.

Bottom left: *U.107* and her victim. This Type IXB boat sank 20 ships totalling 115,040 tons under one captain.

The invasion of Russia had persuaded the British to run convoys to north Russia, but it also led the Germans to send U-Boats to the Black Sea. The purpose was partly political for the land-locked Black Sea had little strategic significance; one reason was to bolster the morale of the Romanians and another was to help to persuade Turkey to join Germany. Just as the UB-Boats had been transferred to Pola, it proved possible to send the small Type II U-Boats to the Black Sea without going through the Mediterranean. But this time there was a difference: six were sent from Hamburg down the River Elbe to Dresden, and from there taken on giant road-transporters along the *autobahn* to Regensburg and refloated on the River Danube. From here it was a straight run down to the sea, and all six reached Constanza by the spring of 1943.

The flotilla, comprising *U.9*, *U.18–20* and *U.23–24*, operated out of Constanza and Feodosia, and during some 50 patrols they accounted for about 45,000 tons of shipping. The only casualty was *U.9*, which was hit by a Russian boat in harbour. The others were cut off by the advancing Russian armies at the end of the War and had to be scuttled, but their crews chose to be interned in Turkey, their former ally of 1914–18.

Above: The Type IXC *U.154* (right) transfers a spare torpedo to the Type VIIC *U.564* in the Western Antilles in July 1942.

Hitler's attitude to his Japanese partners in the Berlin-Rome-Tokyo Axis was ambivalent, to say the least. On the one hand he stressed the importance of helping the Japanese because they would tie down the British in the Far East, but on the other hand the practical help, apart from his declaration of war on the United States after Pearl Harbor, was very limited. For one thing the distance between Japan and Germany was so immense that until the very long-range IXD$_2$ Type U-Boats and others were available it was scarcely feasible to try to get there. The insularity of the Japanese and the condescending racial attitude inspired by Nazi doctrine did not bode well for smooth co-operation, if experience with the Italians was anything to go by, and as a third problem there was Dönitz who objected strongly to any further siphoning off of U-Boats from the Atlantic battle.

What clinched the decision was the mopping up of the surface raiders and blockade-running merchantmen towards the end of 1942, as British forces got to grips with the problem. They had brought valuable cargoes of rubber, tin, opium, wolfram and rare commodities desperately needed by German industry, and it was felt that U-Boats might be able to emulate the feats of the *Deutschland* in 1916 by taking over the task. The drawback was that even the

biggest ocean-going U-Boats were designed primarily as fighting vehicles, not cargo-carriers, and could only carry some 120 tons of zinc, 80 tons of raw rubber and 15 to 20 tons of other commodities – a tiny yield for so much effort. Still, even small quantities were better than nothing, and 11 U-Boats were earmarked for the 'Monsoon Group'.

The first group left France in July 1943, but only six boats reached the Far East; five were sunk. The second group fared worse, only one boat survived in the Far East. They encountered severe problems, what with bad diet, malaria and difficulties with the Japanese. Maintenance was a perpetual headache, for a complicated craft such as a U-Boat needs a lot of maintenance after a voyage of thousands of miles. Unskilled labour could not cope with the problems and the Japanese either could not or would not help, and so the weakened and malaria-ridden crewmen had to carry out their own repairs. Spares would have had to come from Germany, and even the tools provided were of poor quality.

Great consideration was given to carrying maximum cargo. The reload torpedoes were omitted to make more room. Pure zinc tins were used for food, so that they could be flattened and saved. External containers in the deck-casing were also used for the non-perishable materials.

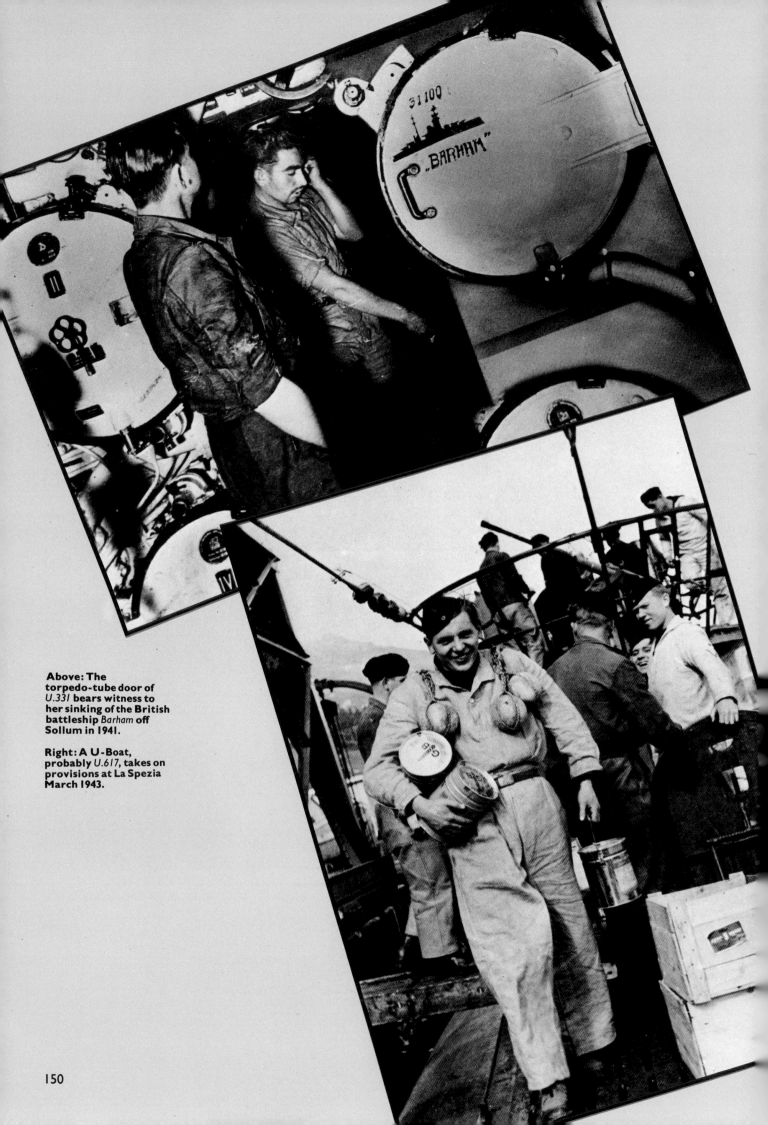

Above: The torpedo-tube door of *U.331* **bears witness to her sinking of the British battleship** *Barham* **off Sollum in 1941.**

Right: A U-Boat, probably *U.617*, **takes on provisions at La Spezia March 1943.**

150

In July 1943 *U.511*, a Type IXC boat, was handed over to the Japanese on Hitler's orders, as part-payment for the raw materials supplied. She was renumbered *RO.500* and used for trials of various items of German equipment. Similarly the Type IXC$_{40}$ boat *U.1224* was handed over in February 1944 and became *RO.501*. At the time of Italy's surrender in September 1943 *Commandante Alfredo Cappelini* and *Luigi Torelli* were in the Far East, and they were immediately seized by the Japanese, handed over to the Germans and renumbered *UIT.24* and *UIT.25*. The swapping game finally came to an end when Germany surrendered in May 1945; the Japanese seized the six U-Boats lying in their harbours and called them *I.501–506*

Eventually the Japanese gained some benefit from their allies. At the end of the war they began to use such innovations as the *schnorchel* (nostril), and their design for a fast underwater boat, the *I.201* Class, had many features of the German Type XXI. It made use of a German MAN lightweight diesel to allow maximum power on a small displacement, but in other respects it was a development of previous ideas of wholly Japanese origin.

The Far Eastern operations of the U-Boats must go on record as the most expensive misuse of valuable submarines in World War II. The efforts seem so prodigious in relation to the risks, the privations of the officers and men, and the meagre results. The other peripheral operations of the U-Boats could at least be justified in terms of diverting enemy resources and shipping sunk, but this could not be said of the Japanese venture.

THE FINAL PHASE

On 31 May 1943, only a week after Dönitz gave the order to his U-Boats to withdraw from the Battle of the Atlantic, he met the *Führer* to discuss the future. Dönitz was now Commander-in-Chief of the Navy following the resignation of Admiral Raeder, and although he never carried out his earlier threats to scrap the surface fleet and devote all resources to U-Boat warfare, he now had much greater influence over planning.

There was only one way, said Dönitz, to reverse the 'trend' (he might have used the word 'defeat', but the crushing reverses of April and May 1943 were always referred to as a temporary setback) and that was by introducing advanced technology to make U-Boats much more effective. There were, however, three tactical ideas which could be tried as interim measures. The first was the *Zaunkönig* homing torpedo, which was being produced in sufficient numbers to make a difference to encounters between U-Boats and Allied escorts. The second was the 2cm '*Flak vierling*', a four-barrelled anti-aircraft gun with a high rate of fire. Many of the recent losses had been inflicted by Coastal Command Liberator bombers and Sunderland flying boats, and it was reckoned that a well-armed U-Boat had a fair chance of shooting down one of these comparatively clumsy four-engined aircraft. This had already happened in the Bay of Biscay, where long-range aircraft hunted for U-Boats in transit to their patrol areas in the Bay of Biscay.

Above: The captain inspects the *tauchretter*, the breathing apparatus used to escape from a sunken U-Boat. It was similar to the Davis Submarine Escape Apparatus (DSEA) used by the British.

Left: A lookout aboard *U.132* scans the horizon for hostile aircraft or fresh victims.

Right: The conning tower of *U.333* riddled by cannon shells and machine gun bullets after an air attack. She was lucky to escape and may have already closed down for diving. Also, the aircraft may have used all its depth-charges.

The third idea was, in fact, a development of a Dutch idea which in turn may even have originated in the fertile brains of the *Ingenieurs Scheepsbouwkantoor* before the war. The Royal Netherlands Navy had designed an airmast or *schnorkel* (nostril), a tubular mast fitted with a valve at the head; its main purpose was to provide ventilation when the boat was running 'trimmed down' in rough weather, but it also allowed the diesel motors to be run while the boat was submerged at periscope depth. When Dutch submarines fitted with the device fell into German hands in 1940 it was examined by technical experts and dismissed as a curiosity, as they felt that the ventilation system in U-

Below: The German propagandists were proud of the U-Boats, and as a result there are some outstanding colour photographs of U-Boats at sea.

Boats did not need improvement. But in 1943, when the dramatic increase in the effectiveness of Allied airborne anti-submarine measures made it very difficult to recharge batteries even under cover of darkness, the *schnorkel*, or to give it its correct German spelling, the *schnorchel*, was re-examined.

Some imperfections in the original Dutch devices were ironed out, and the first *schnorchel* was tested in *U.58* off Neustadt in the summer of 1943. The main problem was the valve, which had to function much like the ball-cock in a lavatory cistern, shutting as soon as a wave lapped over it or the boat increased her depth inadvertently, and the air-induction pipe had to

Left: In a desperate attempt to counter the growing threat from Allied anti-submarine aircraft Admiral Dönitz armed U-Boats with more AA guns to use them as 'flak-traps'. Although this outfit of quadruple and twin 2cm guns looks impressive, U-Boats were hopelessly outmatched in this contest and losses to air attack continued to rise.

Right: A briefing for U-Boat personnel before a patrol.

be modified to reduce the wake as much as possible. The *schnorchel*-head was considerably larger than a normal periscope, and would appear on radar, but only to a ship or aircraft in the vicinity, and so it was a great help in reducing the risk of detection. However, it was only a defensive measure, for a U-Boat could not attack using the *schnorchel* in case the noise of the diesels gave away her position, and the engine noise would prevent the hydrophones from being used to track the target. The maximum speed while *schnorchelling* was reduced to six knots, because one diesel was needed to run the generator to recharge the battery, and because of the 'feather' of spray caused by the head.

Below: Although U-Boats were bigger and better equipped than 20 years before, rough weather inflicted the same misery on bridge personnel.

The long-term outlook was more promising. First there was Dr Walter's revolutionary hydrogen-peroxide turbine, which used an oxygen-rich fuel (Perhydrol) burnt with oil to produce a mixture of gas and steam to drive a turbine. The oxygen sustained combustion, making it a 'closed cycle' system independent of the outside air, and the turbine produced speeds as high as 20 to 25 knots. This, if it could be adapted to drive U-Boats, would transform the whole nature of undersea warfare. The average convoy escort, with its speed of 16–19 knots, could be outrun and outmanoeuvred, and U-Boats would become 'true submarines' instead of torpedo-craft capable of submerging

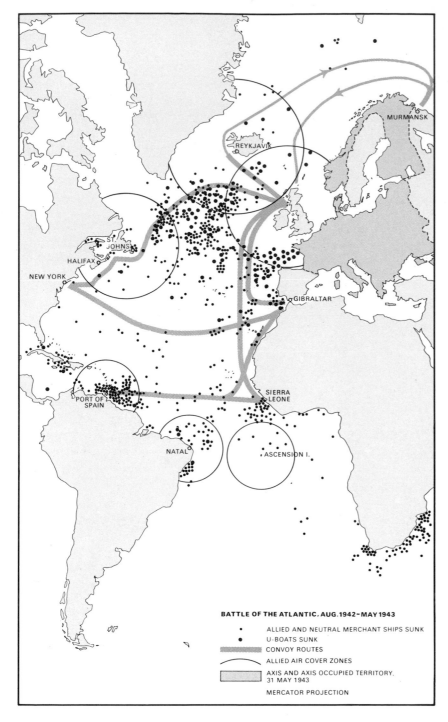

BATTLE OF THE ATLANTIC, AUG. 1942 – MAY 1943

· ALLIED AND NEUTRAL MERCHANT SHIPS SUNK
● U-BOATS SUNK
▬ CONVOY ROUTES
◠ ALLIED AIR COVER ZONES
▣ AXIS AND AXIS OCCUPIED TERRITORY, 31 MAY 1943

MERCATOR PROJECTION

U-Boat crews were rested and retrained. At the end of August the first of the new forces were ready to renew the struggle, and in all 28 U-Boats and a 'milch cow', known as the *Leuthen* Group, were ready to go to sea. They now had armoured conning towers which had been extended to provide platforms for the *flak vierling*, and in their torpedo-tubes they carried the new *Zaunkönig* torpedoes. Still under the delusion that the Metox radar-receiver had caused their discomfiture, the U-Boat Command had insisted that the boats be re-equipped with the *W.Anz* receiver in place of the old 'Biscay Cross', and it was noted with delight that the enemy did not appear to have located any of the U-Boats. But on 4 September a U-Boat reported that a British aircraft had attacked her at night, and the *W.Anz* receiver had given no warning of radar. This was believed to be a coincidence, and when Dönitz learned that his U-Boats had evaded the Allied patrols and were in position across the convoy routes he exhorted them in a personal message, 'The *Führer* is watching every phase of your struggle. Attack. Follow up. Sink.'

Two convoys were attacked, the slow *ONS.18* and the fast *ON.202*, and when the enemy learned of the concentration of U-Boats the two formations joined together, making a total of 66 ships guarded by 15 escorts. The frigate *Lagan* took a *Zaunkönig* in the engine-room and lost her stern, and in the confusion *U.238* slipped through the screen and sank two merchant ships. But the long-range Liberator bombers covering the convoy had the American equivalent of the *Zaunkönig*, a homing torpedo called the Mark 24 Mine (for security reasons) designed to home onto the noise of a diving U-Boat's propellers, and this weapon was used to sink *U.338*. The U-Boats hit back, and during the night of 20 September another two escorts were sunk. Thick fog hampered the U-Boats, but they were doing better than they had for many months, and two nights later they sank another escort and four merchantmen.

To Dönitz the battle appeared to vindicate his new tactics handsomely, but there were several things which he did not know. Although his U-Boat commanders had reported the sinking of 12 escorts and nine merchant ships, they had only accounted for three escorts and six merchant ships, in exchange for three U-Boats. The *Zaunkönigs* had tended to explode prematurely or on hitting the wake of a fast-moving ship. The *Leuthen* Group had evaded Allied air patrols not because the *W.Anz* receiver was protecting them but because they had hugged the Spanish coast, making them hard to detect on radar. The relative lack of success of the aircraft at night had occurred because the aircraft operating over the two convoys had not been equipped with searchlights or illuminating rockets.

temporarily to escape detection. The ability to close in on a convoy rapidly or to approach stealthily and then escape at high speed would give U-Boats the initiative, and even give them a chance of reversing the course of the War. By early 1943 it was clear that Germany's chances of winning against the growing might of the Allies were diminishing rapidly, and although a U-Boat victory would not by itself beat the Russian armies, the destruction of Anglo-American shipping would free German resources for a war on only one front once more. Without imported fuel the British would no longer be able to bomb German industry, and the might of America would be neutralised.

The first of the new measures were put into operation in the summer while the battered

The result was that the *Leuthen* Group was very roughly handled when it tried to repeat its performance against *SC.143* in October; three U-Boats were sunk in return for one escort and one merchantman. A week later the *Schlieffen* Group fared even worse, losing six U-Boats and sinking only one ship in the convoy *ON.206*. The idea of using U-Boats as 'flak-traps' did not work either, even when a group stayed in a tight formation to increase its firepower. Although some successes were scored the pilots soon learned to use new tactics, and even modified the 'wolf-pack' idea to suit their needs, with co-ordinated attacks from different bearings. Support groups of warships were sent into the Bay of Biscay, and if a U-Boat managed to fight off a single aircraft she ran the risk of being sighted by one of the famous hunting groups under such renowned U-Boat killers as Captain F W Walker RN.

Fitting the *schnorchel* was expedited to try to cut the losses, but it did nothing to put the U-Boats back into the battle. It was an extremely unpleasant device to use in any sort of choppy sea. As the waves washed over the *schnorchel* head the valve kept snapping shut, but the diesels continued to draw in massive quantities of air (two or three revolutions of the diesels would exhaust the air contained in a Type VIIC's

Above: The lookout climbs to the crow's nest on its light collapsible mast. In the safer waters of the South Atlantic the extra height proved useful in scouting for targets.

Right: Marking up victory pennants showing the tonnage of ships sunk. One of Dönitz's problems was the inevitable tendency of U-Boat captains to exaggerate the size of their victims. This led to a serious over-estimate of the Allies' shipping resources in 1942-43.

hull), causing a partial vacuum. The result was popping ears and bulging eyes (permanent damage to ear-drums was not uncommon), and if the weather was particularly rough the diesels would have to be shut down repeatedly, making the process even more tedious. The result was to make the U-Boat commanders even more defensive, and although they continued to be dangerous opponents the Allied escort commanders, all commented on the falling off of their willingness to push an attack home.

It was also evident to the U-Boat commanders that the old workhorse Type VIIC design could not be developed much further. It was cramped and small for operating in mid-Atlantic, and of course, had never been intended to operate so far away; the lack of room meant that supplies

Above: In 1940-41 aircraft co-operated with U-Boats to find ships. The enemy countered by providing small aircraft carriers to accompany the convoys.

Left: Tankers were a prime target for U-Boats as their cargo was vital to the enemy's survival. One torpedo was enough to set the whole ship ablaze, and few survived. The crew's chances were just as slender, with burning oil covering the water faster than they could swim.

of fuel and spare torpedoes were restricted, and placed severe limitations on crew-comfort. This is hardly surprising, for the design had been 'stretched' several times to meet the changing requirements of the Atlantic battle and it was, in any case, an adaptation of a much older design.

What was needed was a new type of U-Boat, specially tailored for the new conditions, and by mid-1943 several designs had taken shape to fill this need. On the one side there was the Walter turbine, which promised ultra-high speed, but a lot of development still needed to be done

before it could become operational. On the other hand it would be possible to build a boat with a streamlined hull and much greater battery-capacity, so that she could have a good underwater speed in short bursts. All the previous improvements could be built in, a better *schnorchel* allowing 10–12 knots, extra torpedoes and even an efficient anti-aircraft armament. This was the 'Electro U-Boat', so-called to distinguish her from the Walter types on the drawing boards, and she would be about twice the size of a Type VIIC. An important

internal improvement would be the provision of mechanical reloading gear for the torpedoes. Normally a U-Boat had to withdraw from the attack-zone to reload her tubes, and each torpedo took half an hour to reload using chain tackles; with mechanised reloading the U-Boat would be able to remain in the attack-zone and fire a second salvo, thereby doubling her effectiveness.

The new U-Boat project was designated Type XXI, and the detailed design work was put in the hands of a special team under Krupp's chief naval architect, Dr Cords. When it was calculated that the first Type XXI boat would not be ready until early 1946 it was clear that some way of shortening the time taken for design and construction must be found. *Reichsminister*

Right: A victim seen against an idyllic background.

heavy equipment such as motors could be installed in the sections. From here they would be trans-shipped again to three assembly yards at Bremen, Danzig and Hamburg. The movement of the sections had to be done by canal barge, as each section was far too big to be moved by road or rail; a No 3 section, containing the diesel motors, was 27 feet long and 25 feet high, and weighed 150 tons. It was estimated that assembly would take 12 weeks, during which time the eight sections would be welded together and the various air, oil and water piping and electrical wiring would be connected.

Dönitz obtained Hitler's permission for the Type XXI programme in July 1943, but the *Führer* pointed out caustically that the U-Boat

Top left: *U.124* and an escort vessel or minesweeper putting to sea.

Centre left: This sort of photo could only be taken during training, in the seclusion of the Baltic. The 'shelf' below the insignia on the conning tower is a spray deflector.

Below: A relaxed moment on the conning tower of *U.706*. The ring is the direction-finding 'loop' aerial, which retracted when diving. It enabled enemy radio-signals to be tracked, but could not pick up radar transmissions.

Albert Speer chose Otto Merker, an expert on mass-production of heavy trucks, to run the *Hauptausschuss Schiffbau* or Chief Shipbuilding Committee. Although knowing next to nothing about shipbuilding, Merker quickly saw that the worst holdup was the time each U-Boat hull had to remain on the slipway; this meant that a Type VII, for example, occupied precious space for a period varying from 36 to 50 weeks. He proposed to cut this time drastically by reducing the Type XXI hull to eight prefabricated sections, which would be built by factories away from the shipyards. These could then be shipped to 60 assembly yards, where the

Left: *U.552* docks at St Nazaire on 27 April 1942. She escaped the holocaust of 1943 and was scuttled in the last days of the Third Reich in May 1945.

Arm had previously demanded unlimited building of Type VIICs; why was it now so important to build a new type of U-Boat? The Third Reich was achieving miracles of production in the face of massive bombing and shortages in every field. The existing programme of U-Boat building was consuming 6000 tons of steel per month and the torpedo-factories were using a further 1500 tons. Still, Hitler could see that the only hope for the U-Boat Arm was to be re-equipped with more effective boats. He endorsed the scheme enthusiastically, but ordered Speer to cut building times even further, and to introduce three-shift working if necessary, to produce 40 Type XXI U-Boats per month before the anticipated earliest date of November 1944.

This only complicated the problem further, and Dönitz had to explain that 40 U-Boats a month could not be manned. The increased manpower allotted to the *Kriegsmarine* was to be about 103,000 men, but its estimated requirements were already 335,000 men below the required figure. Given the 1943 rate of U-Boat construction the Navy was still short of 200,000 men, and a 25 per cent increase in U-Boat construction would exacerbate matters. The officer-candidates who had entered the U-Boat Arm just before the outbreak of war had all become U-Boat commanders by mid-1943, and Dönitz was forced to ask for officers to be transferred

Above: The camouflage nets give a curious appearance to the men of *U.100* alongside the pier at Lorient. Her loss, with that of *U.99* and the 'aces' Schepke and Kretschmer, marked the end of the 'happy time' for the U-Boats in the Western Approaches.

labour. But by some strange process of logic, these energetic measures were not matched by a similar ruthlessness about the conventional boats still building. The Type VIIC continued to be built in the shipyards and to compound the error, the work was done by skilled labour, whereas work on the novel and complex Type XXI boats was left in the hands of 'diluted' labour, a Third Reich euphemism for a mixture of a small number of skilled men padded out with slave-labour, women, old men and boys.

Above: The *Seehund* midgets were built to defend coastal waters against invasion. Known also as Type XXVIIB U-Boats, they were the most successful of the K-Craft or *kleine kampfmittel*.

Right: A *Biber* midget, another of the K-Craft which harassed Allied shipping after D-Day

Far right inset: U-Boat training as seen by *Signal*, the German propaganda magazine. Here crews learn to use the tauchretter in a special tank.

Far right: U-Boats under construction. More and more resources were devoted to building U-Boats, but the conflicting needs of the *Wehrmacht* and *Luftwaffe*, as well as a lack of manpower meant that the race could never be won.

from the Army and Air Force. These expatriate' U-Boat captains did very well in their new environment, but it goes to show how over-stretched the U-Boat Arm was by 1943, and how difficult it was going to be to try to produce any startling new developments in 1944–45.

Not content with producing the master-plan to boost Type XXI construction the Cords team designed a 'utility' version of the design. Known as the Type XXIII, it was for use in coastal waters, in the Mediterranean and in the Black Sea, and carried only two torpedoes. Its range was only 1300 miles and its 14-man crew lived in extremely cramped conditions, but it was capable of 12½ knots submerged. It was to be fabricated, but in only four sections, and did not make such heavy demands on steel and

The choice of the Type XXI for mass-produc-tion did not mean the end of the Walter boat. On the contrary, work continued and a large number of Type XVII boats were laid down. If the continuation of the Type VIIC programme was a mistake, this was a bigger one. For one thing the technical problems with the Walter turbine had not been solved; the fuel was a corrosive and explosive liquid which had to be housed in tanks open to the air. The smallest impurity such as dust or rust could cause the release of oxygen, followed by spontaneous combustion, but the fire could not be put out by sand or a foam blanket, and so the liquid had to be cooled rapidly by drenching it with water. It had other undesirable properties, such as being able to burn through metal, cloth and skin,

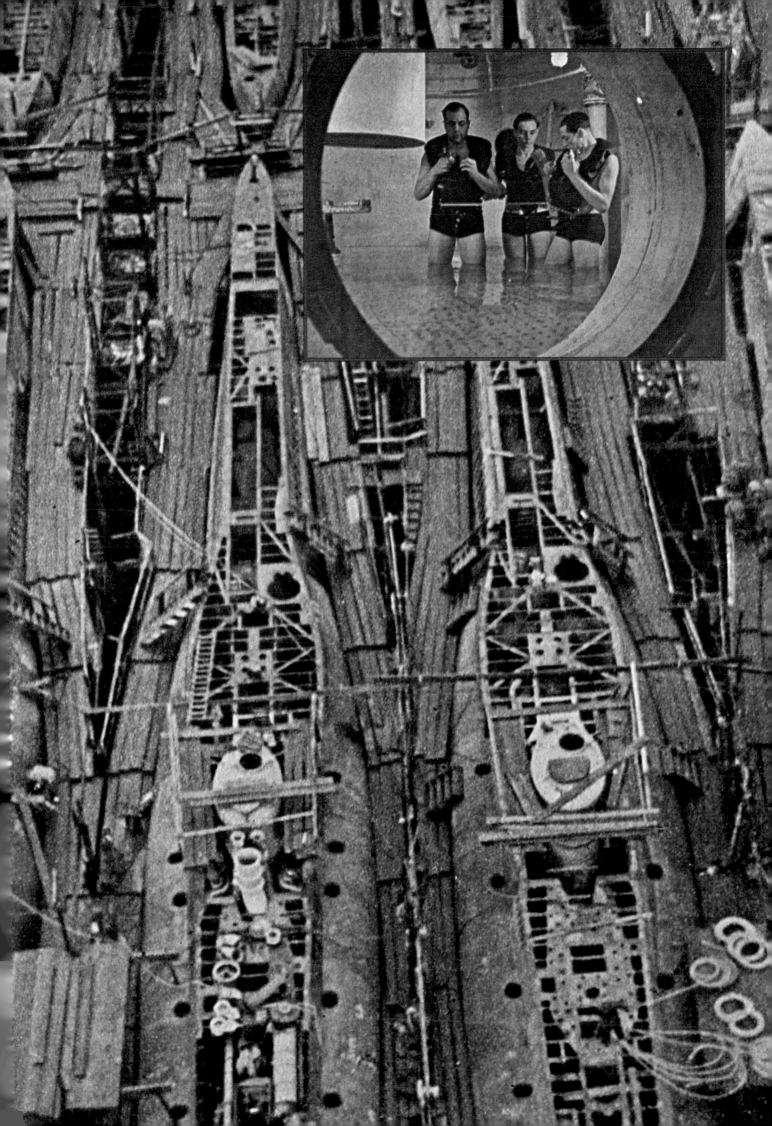

and it was sensitive to sudden shock. The manufacture was fraught with danger and highly expensive. The Type XVII boats could make 25 knots underwater, but the 40 tons of Perhydrol carried gave an endurance of only 80 miles, more appropriate to a U-Boat of 1906 than 1943. Only two torpedo-tubes and four torpedoes were carried, as against the 23 carried by the Type XXI. Seen in this light the Walter U-Boats must rank with Hitler's ideas for 100-ton tanks as a time-wasting and resource-wasting exercise in the pursuit of higher technology for its own sake. As it was, the XVIIA and XVIIB designs were started before any of the operating problems were fully understood, and so they tied up shipyards, men and materials which could have been devoted to the Type XXI Programme.

Another diversion of resources, but one much easier to justify, was the building of *Kleine Kampfmittel* or small battle units. These were an extraordinary variety of midget submarines and 'human torpedoes' for use against invasion forces. Most of these were assault weapons which could not be described as submarines, but the Types XXVIIA and XXVIIB were true miniature U-Boats. The Type XXVIIA was known as the *Hecht* (Pike), and was intended to be a seven-ton minelayer, capable of carrying a two-man crew and one limpet mine a distance of 90 miles. It proved of limited use, mainly because it proved hard to produce a suitable mine; they were all used for training, some of them converted to carry a torpedo under the keel and others with a 'wet and dry' compartment for a frogman. The XXVIIB, known as *Seehund* (seal) was altogether more successful. Displacing 15 tons, it carried two 21-inch torpedoes slung under the hull, and was driven by a conventional diesel/electric combination. Unlike the smaller midgets they were allocated U-Boat numbers: *U.2111–2200* and *U.2205–2300* were *Hechts* and *U.5001–6351* were *Seehunds*. The Naval Staff was rightly sceptical of their value, and in action most of them achieved little of value. However they did have one unexpected virtue: they were so light that a depth-charge explosion did not sink them, as the blast merely threw the boat aside. One can only guess at what it must have been like to be a member of the crew when this happened.

While the Type XXI and Type XVII U-Boats were being built the existing U-Boats had somehow to continue fighting the battle. Very late in the day Dönitz acted to remedy the poor liaison between the U-Boat Arm and the scientists. Late in 1943 he ordered the formation of the *Wissenschaftlicher Ruhrungsstab* or Scientific Operations Staff, to study the interaction between scientific research and operational experience – something which the Allies had done throughout the War with devastating results. In his own words addressed to his officers and men, the Commander-in-Chief

Below: This was not the result of an air attack but the effect of a tanker ramming *U.333*. There was always a risk that a U-Boat could be rammed by a ship in convoy while she was stalking another victim. The propeller noise blanketed sounds from astern, and the narrow field of vision from the periscope made it hard to get an all-round view.

Top left: A Type VIIC sinks by the stern while the crew get ready to abandon ship.

Bottom left: The conning tower of a U-Boat seen from an attacking aircraft.

admitted that the enemy's scientific superiority had made the U-Boats impotent. He appointed Professor Küpfmüller as its head, and made him responsible directly to the Commander-in-Chief. The new arrangements were successful in eliminating some of the worst areas of muddle, particularly in producing an effective radar-research receiver, which was so desperately needed by the U-Boats. Even so, the myth about the Allied aircraft using the much-maligned Metox receiver to home onto U-Boats was not exposed for the nonsense that it was; the new organisation reported that centimetric radar had been introduced after the Metox receiver had been withdrawn.

An important advance in the second half of the year was the introduction of a new search radar for the U-Boats themselves. Known as the *Hohentwiel*, it would allow the U-Boats to detect enemy aircraft on radar using antenna mounted on the conning tower. But the long months of uncertainty, and the fear of some counter-measure which could detect the radar-pulses meant that many commanders did not trust the *Hohentwiel*, and in many U-Boats it was left switched off.

A less objectionable device was the *Aphrodite* anti-radar balloon. This was a three-foot balloon filled with hydrogen trailing three lengths of aluminium foil, and moored to a sea-anchor to allow it to drift. The idea was to release numbers of these in the Bay of Biscay, in the hope that

enemy aircraft would track them by radar, but in practice the aluminium foil streamers failed to give sufficient cross-section to stand out on a cathode ray tube as a radar contact. Nor were they easy to launch. There was a danger of the whole contraption getting snagged in the railings and projections of the conning tower and on occasion the balloons exploded while being filled. No U-Boat commander would be happy at having a radar target moored overhead, even for a few minutes.

There was also a decoy developed to use against Asdic. This was the *pillenwerfer* which could be fired from inside the U-Boat. It functioned like a huge Alka-Seltzer, releasing large bubbles which dissipated slowly and gave a realistic echo to an Asdic beam. However their existence was known to the enemy, who called them Submarine Bubble Targets (SBTs), and only an inexperienced operator was likely to mistake them for a real contact.

The U-Boats continued to receive heavier anti-aircraft guns long after the slaughter of 1943 had shown how ineffective they were as flak-batteries. The 3.7cm Flak 43 was similar to the Swedish Bofors gun, and it could fire about 100 one-pound shells a minute at an aircraft. To provide some protection for the gunlayer and loaders, the conning tower was altered to include an armoured shelter on either side, known as *kohlenkasten* (coal scuttles). In a blinding glimpse of the obvious the U-Boat Command

**Left, right and below:
Three more** *Signal*
**photographs taken in
the early period of the
U-Boat war.**

advised bridge personnel to take cover by kneeling behind the armour plating, as remaining in the open had already cost many lives which might otherwise have been saved. The extra weight of the armour made the Type VII boats top-heavy, and in rough weather they could roll as much as 30° each way, putting a great strain on the crew.

Official orders were also explicit about the frightening effect of rocket-attacks by aircraft. The red glow, the smoke trail and the whistling roar of a salvo fired at a distance of only 150 yards could terrify inexperienced crewmen, and the instructions reminded U-Boat commanders that any sort of retaliation by the U-Boat tended to unsettle the aircraft's aim, and would make it very difficult to get a hit with these inherently inaccurate weapons. Only 'rigorous discipline' could overcome the panic likely to ensue.

Unless the commander elected to man his anti-aircraft guns and fight it out, the normal routine was to make as rapid a descent as possible, and to achieve this U-Boat crews developed a drill which became known as the 'Battle

Left below: US Navy Liberators sank *U.231* on 13 January 1944 when she attempted to get near a convoy within reach of the American coast.

Bottom left: The slim, black hull of the U-Boat is almost hidden by the explosions of the depth-charges.

Below: The smoking conning tower of *U.175* under the guns of the US Coast Guard cutter *Spencer*, 17 April 1943.

Right: Depth-charges away! An American aircraft drops a 'stick' over the position of a U-Boat which has just submerged.

Far right: The presence of aircraft with the convoy made it more and more difficult to work the wolf-pack system. Even an unsuccessful attack on the shadower broke his contact with U-Boat HQ and the pack.

Right centre: A distant view of a U-Boat under attack from an American aircraft.

ONI-(Op-16-P-5) No. 001 - 914

ONI-(Op-16-P-5) No. 601 - 969

of the Seconds'. Regardless of the risk of a broken ankle or of landing on another man, the bridge personnel shot below as fast as they could. When it was found that the broad, flat desk-casing tended to make a U-Boat 'stick' on the surface, scientists suggested that boats should be modified to reduce the width of the casing. Several U-Boats were given 'wasp-waists' by cutting away the casing forward and aft of the conning tower, and this reduction in deck-area reduced the diving time from 55 seconds to 35, greatly increasing the boat's chance of survival.

Navigation in mid-Atlantic was a problem for the U-Boats, and in 1943 a big radio transmitter was built at Quimper on the North Brittany coast near Brest which was capable of sending accurate bearings a distance of about 1000 miles. Known as *Sonne*, it was a great improvement in fixing the position of a U-Boat, and had it been available earlier it might have made a difference to the wolf-packs in 1942–43. It was very simple to use, as the U-Boat's radio operator tuned into the *Sonne* frequency and related the bearings received to a grid map. The Allies were angry to discover that one of the *Sonne* stations was in neutral Spain, but on the advice of Dr R V Jones, Head of the Scientific Intelligence Department at the British Air Ministry, no diplomatic protest was made as the *Sonne* transmissions were proving even more useful to Allied aircraft operating against the U-Boats! The British name for the system reflected the humour of the situation; as *Sonne* meant 'sun' the codename chosen was derived from the Spanish for words meaning 'with sun', *con sol* or Consol. Four of these stations are still being used for civil aviation.

The small submarines had been produced to try to defeat the Allies' amphibious landings which everyone knew must come soon, and they received their baptism of fire at the Anzio landings in Italy, but their main purpose was to hamper the assault in Europe. Admiral Krancke, who was designated *Marinegruppenkommando West*, or Commander of Naval Forces West, bore the main responsibility for naval defences against the expected landings in the Pas de Calais. In addition to his small battle units he had the U-Boats in their bases on the Britanny and Biscay coasts. Here they were safe from the bombing raids with which the British and American Air Forces vainly tried to stop the U-Boats. These 'pens' had massive roofs of reinforced concrete and had been built by the Todt Organisation from 1942 onwards. They remain one of the wonders of modern military fortifications. They were inspired by the original bomb-proof shelters built at Bruges in World War I, but were built on an altogether more massive scale.

Although far from beautiful, the pens had a certain grim functional symmetry. The roof

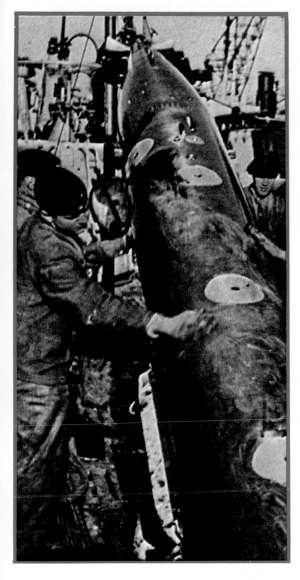

varied from 20 feet to 24 feet in thickness, and even though the original proofs had defeated armour-piercing bombs, the designers incorporated an additional safeguard in the form of an air-space between an upper and lower layer of concrete, to give a delayed action fuze time to act before penetrating the lower layer. In fact no RAF or USAAF bomb had inflicted the slightest damage on a U-Boat pen so far, and as a result work on the U-Boats could continue while death and destruction rained down on the surrounding dockyard. The pens contained fuel bunkers, torpedo-workshops and all the support facilities needed to overhaul U-Boats. By early 1944, therefore, the U-Boat Arm possessed secure bases for its U-Boats from Trondheim in Norway down to St Nazaire on the Bay of Biscay, and nothing the massed four-engine bombers could drop was likely to harm the U-Boats. In fact an enormous amount of effort, to say nothing of the aircrews shot down and killed, was wasted in futile efforts to hit the U-Boats in harbour.

Krancke's plan, therefore, was to leave the U-Boats in their pens until there was definite news of an Allied landing across the Channel.

As soon as the location and destination of the invasion fleet were known, the U-Boats were to head for the area, risking heavy losses to push past the Allied defenders and get at the vulnerable invasion convoys. The distance from Brest to Calais was 300 miles, about a day's run for a U-Boat. The Allies had a good idea of what Krancke would do; indeed, he had little choice for his surface forces were negligible. Therefore they planned a massive 'bottling' operation at either end of the Channel, which would exclude the U-Boats from the invasion routes, using the best anti-submarine groups from Western Approaches Command and some 350 aircraft. Not unnaturally the operation was codenamed 'Cork', and the intensive training even went to the lengths of ordering British submarines to try to run the gauntlet.

True to his unceasing attention to the leadership of the U-Boats, Dönitz drafted battle orders for the invasion. Every enemy vessel involved in the landing, even if it had only one tank or a handful of soldiers on board, was a target of the utmost importance, and was to be attacked regardless of risk. Minefields and shoals were to be disregarded if it meant closing the invasion

Left: The shark-nose shape of a U-Boat in dock.

Centre: Torpedoes are loaded on board.

Above: The flag flies above this surfaced U-Boat, pictured here in *Signal*.

Above: Two U-Boats in a 'pen' at St Nazaire. These bomb-proof bunkers contained all the light, power and workshops needed to repair a U-Boat. Only special weapons developed at the end of the war could make any impression on their massive construction.

Right: Unfinished Type XXI boats on the slipways of the Blohm & Voss shipyard in war-torn Hamburg.

fleet, and every boat which inflicted loss would have fulfilled its purpose, even if it was sunk in the process. As he succinctly put it, every man and every weapon destroyed *before* reaching the beaches reduced the enemy's chances of establishing a bridgehead.

At 0513 hours on the morning of 6 June 1944 all boats of the Landwirt Group stood by, and the Atlantic coast U-Boats started their last pitched battle in a doomed attempt to stop the D-Day Invasion. That night a group of eight boats from Brest were attacked, and *U.415* was so badly damaged that she had to turn back. A total of 22 sightings were made by aircraft that night, and of the seven U-Boats attacked two were badly damaged and two were sunk. Seven of the group of 15 which had left Brest were fitted with the *schnorchel*, which gave them some measure of protection, but even this was not enough to save *U.212* from a savage mauling, and she had to limp back to La Pallice. Still, there were 42 U-Boats left, six with *schnorchels*, and they were still heading east towards the D-Day beaches.

On the following night the U-Boats ran into the dense 'Cork' air patrols. Within a short while a Liberator bomber sank *U.629* and *U.373* in the space of half an hour. Next morning *U.413* fought a Halifax bomber to a standstill, but was so shaken up that she had to return to Brest, and in the next two days *U.740* and *U.821* were sunk. Only *U.441* managed to get clear, but on 12 June she received orders to break off the attempt and to return to Brest. However she was sunk only 50 miles from the safety afforded by the concrete pens of Brest.

None of the U-Boats without *schnorchels* had been able to get as far as the Channel Islands, and five more of the surviving 22 boats were to be damaged by air attacks. Admiral Krancke admitted defeat by calling off the attack on 12 June and decided to hold the survivors in reserve in case a further amphibious landing occurred on the Biscay coast.

The eight *schnorchel*-fitted boats did better initially, but two of them depleted their batteries and had to put into Guernsey leaving only six boats creeping slowly up the Channel. They scored a rare success by torpedoing two British frigates, but at the cost of losing one U-Boat. Only on 15 June, nine days after the first Allied soldiers had waded ashore on the Normandy beaches, did *U.621* reach the main shipping route. She managed to sink a tank landing ship, but failed in attacks on two American battleships, and was then driven off by the escorts. The *schnorchel* had been a major factor in these boats' immunity from detection for it was very difficult to pick up on radar unless the weather was calm; sometimes the exhaust fumes condensed to form 'smoke'. The fact that only eight boats had been fitted with the device can be chalked up as the only tangible contribution made by the ceaseless bombing of land targets before the Invasion; most of the components and the conversion kits sent from Germany were lying in railway wagons in French goods yards, trapped there by the remorseless Allied aerial bombardment of the rail network.

The first air attack on a *schnorchel*-fitted U-Boat took place on 18 June, but she was only slightly damaged; *U.1222* was not so lucky on 11 July when she was the first to be sunk. The crew seemed to be inexperienced, for the aircrew of the Sunderland noted that in his haste to dive, the commander took his boat down at too steep an angle. Her stern shot out of the water, exposing a perfect target for a 'stick' of four depth-charges.

The U-Boats based in Germany and Norway were trying just as hard to penetrate the eastern end of the invasion area, and they were encountering equally fierce opposition. In June five U-Boats were sunk and four more damaged; in the following month four were sunk and six damaged. The net result of the protracted series of sea and air engagements at both ends of the Channel was the virtual immunity of the invasion fleet to U-Boat attack. The midgets sank a handful of ships; E-Boats and torpedo boats sank a few more, but the losses were negligible and had no effect on the Allies' successful establishment of a foothold in Europe.

The U-Boat Arm's long tenure of the French Atlantic coast came to an end in August as the Allied armies advanced south from Normandy. The 9th Flotilla was disbanded, and the crews of the U-Boats which had returned too damaged to be repaired were sent back to Germany. As the bases were abandoned or cut off one by one, the crews were issued with small arms and used as infantry. U-Boat crews fought heroically in the defence of Brest until the fortress fell, and on 3 September *U.256* took the commander of the 9th Flotilla, *Fregattenkapitän* Lehmann-Willenbrock to Norway.

The brunt now fell on the U-Boats in Norway and Germany. The number of boats fitted with *schnorchels* was now large enough to permit patrols to be started in the coastal waters around the British Isles for the first time since

1940. The pickings were good – 14 merchant ships in the last four months of 1944 – but hardly an impressive percentage of the 12,000 merchantmen convoyed through these waters at the same time. On the other hand only seven U-Boats were sunk, and large numbers of British warships were tied down defending these convoys. It was a stalemate which could only be broken by the arrival of the new Type XXI and Type XXIII U-Boats or the collapse of Germany.

Orders for no fewer than 290 Type XXI boats had been placed back in 1943 and despite all Hitler's imperatives, the delivery date for the first was the end of February 1945. The 140

Type XXIII boats ordered at the same time were to be ready from February 1944 onwards. The Allies were well aware of the progress on these boats, witnessed by aerial reconnaissance, and the vital role of the German canal-system was not overlooked. In the autumn of 1944 the Dortmund-Ems and Mittelland Canals were repeatedly attacked, and damage to them inflicted serious delays to Otto Merker's carefully tailored schedules. On 10 January 1945 he complained to Albert Speer that disruption of canal transport meant that the railways would have to be used to move the U-Boat sections to the assembly yards. But this meant breaking down the 150-ton sections into smaller sections

Below: The U-Boat war as the German public believed it still was.

light enough to be carried on rail wagons. This cancelled out most of the advantages of pre-fabrication, but there was no alternative.

Germany was staggering under the hammer-blows of round-the-clock bombing, and many other factors began to affect the U-Boat con-struction programme. The Type XXIs and Type XXIIIs relied on large batteries, but three out of the four factories producing lead-acid accu-mulators had been forced to cut or even stop production due to bomb-damage and the fourth happened to be the smallest factory. The diluted labour used in the shipyards was hardly the best-motivated workforce in the world, and its semi-skilled, ill-fed and conscript labourers found the complexities of assembly too much for them. But in spite of all this 90 Type XXI boats and 31 Type XXIIIs were launched by December 1944, and in theory 60 of the former and 23 of the latter had been completed. The phrase 'in theory' is used because new and sophisticated machines could not be sent out with untrained crews, and in the absence of experience with fast-running U-Boats it was necessary to test and evaluate the boats to enable their crews to get the best out of them. And to add to the insuperable problems of the U-Boat Arm, RAF Bomber Command now directed its efforts to intensive minelaying in the Baltic training areas.

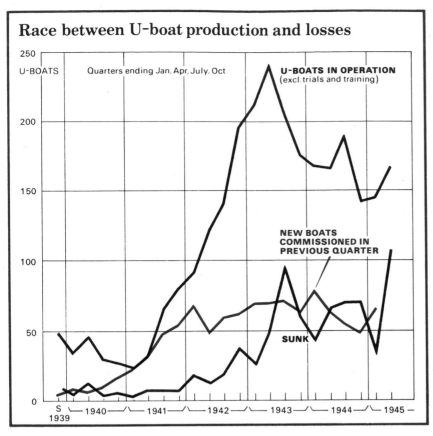

Race between U-boat production and losses

250
U-BOATS

Quarters ending Jan, Apr, July, Oct

U-BOATS IN OPERATION
(excl. trials and training)

200

150

**NEW BOATS
COMMISSIONED IN
PREVIOUS QUARTER**

100

50

SUNK

0

S 1939 — 1940 — 1941 — 1942 — 1943 — 1944 — 1945 —

The mining campaign sank very few U-Boats, but it disrupted the training programme severely. Channels had to be swept repeatedly, and when they were blocked the U-Boats' training programme had to be stopped; to stray out of the swept channel was to invite certain disaster. The freezing of the Baltic in the winter months imposed further restrictions and with the advance of the Russians from the east, there was in any case very little of the Baltic left for the uninterrupted period of training so necessary for a U-Boat trying to achieve efficiency. In January 1945 the training areas were even attacked by anti-submarine aircraft in an attempt to catch the U-Boats unawares. Liberators attacked U-Boats in three daring night raids in February, and although they achieved no sinkings they showed that no corner of the Baltic was now safe.

The first Type XXIII to become operational was *U.2324* under *Oberleutnant* Hass in January 1945. On 29 January she left Bergen, and on 18 February she sank a merchantman off Sunderland. Five more sisters came into action in February and March and managed to sink six victims. These small boats were hard to detect, whereas a Type VIIC at this time was almost

certain to be sunk in coastal waters by massive counterattacks. The philosophy of the Electro U-Boat had been proved to be right, and when it is remembered that a Type XXIII boat carried only two torpedoes, the potential of the Type XXI boats was immense. Now the muddle and the waste of resources in 1943 made itself felt. No one can doubt that 50 Type XXIs in mid-1944 would have been better than 200 Walter boats in mid-1945. However, only *U.2511* under *Korvettenkapitän* Schnee managed to leave Bergen on an operational cruise, on 30 April. He encountered a British anti-submarine group in the North Sea but evaded them easily by retracting his *schnorchel* and running at 16 knots.

At 1514 hours on 4 May Dönitz, now the Chancellor and supreme ruler of Nazi Germany under the terms of the will of Adolf Hitler, ordered his U-Boats to cease hostilities. The 45 U-Boats at sea were to return to base; 33 were on passage and 12 were in British coastal waters. Only eight received the signal and responded, and one of these was Schnee's *U.2511*. On his way home he decided to test the capabilities of his Type XXI boat by carrying out a dummy attack on a British cruiser sighted north of the Faeroes. To his delight he was not detected by the escorting screen, and having reached a firing position, withdrew without being detected. Germany's unconditional surrender was signed on 7 May by which time only two U-Boats had obeyed the order to cease hostil-ities. Dönitz drafted an order to take effect from midnight that night, instructing the U-Boats to surface, report their positions and proceed to ports designated by the Allies. That night six more U-Boats turned for home, and next day the first formal surrenders took place. Another 13 surrendered, leaving four missing. Two of these, *U.963* and *U.1277* scuttled them-selves off Lisbon some days later; *U.979* ran aground on the Dutch coast; and *U.977* made a dramatic trip to seek asylum in Argentina.

The last act was an echo of 1918. An order from the British Admiralty on the morning after Dönitz had broadcast his surrender orders, confirmed that all U-Boats were to proceed on the surface, flying a black flag, to Loch Eriboll, Beaumaris Bay and Weymouth. From there they were sent to Loch Alsh and then across the Irish Sea to Lishally, or to Loch Ryan. In all 156 U-Boats surrendered in this way, but a further 221 were scuttled by their crews in defiance.

The balance sheet was a terrible one. Between 1939 and 1945, 1162 U-Boats were built and 784 were lost from all causes; by far the greatest number (632) were sunk at sea. With their Japanese and Italian allies the U-Boats had sunk 14,687,231 tons of Allied and neutral shipping, and most of this was done by U-Boats. They sank 175 Allied warships, and can be credited with a very large proportion of the 30,248 British merchant seamen and the 73,642 men

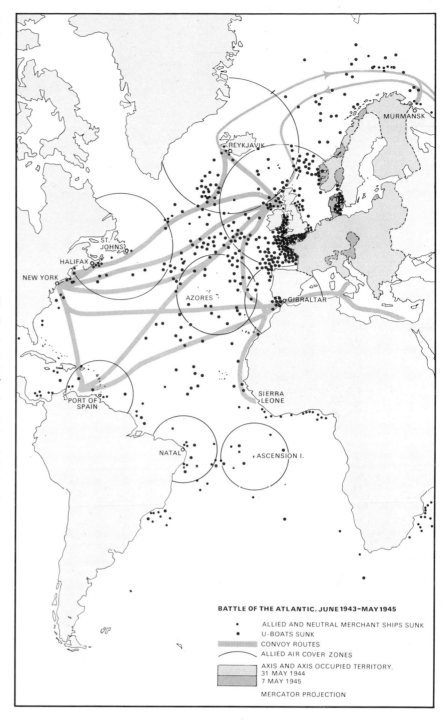

BATTLE OF THE ATLANTIC, JUNE 1943–MAY 1945

· ALLIED AND NEUTRAL MERCHANT SHIPS SUNK
● U-BOATS SUNK
— CONVOY ROUTES
— ALLIED AIR COVER ZONES
AXIS AND AXIS OCCUPIED TERRITORY,
31 MAY 1944
7 MAY 1945
MERCATOR PROJECTION

of the Royal Navy who died in World War II. Once again Germany had risked all on her U-Boats, and once again she had suffered a crushing defeat. Out of the 40,000 persons who served in U-Boats 28,000 were killed and only 5000 fell into enemy hands. By the end of 1944 nobody believed in final victory, although there was always hope that Dönitz and his scientists might somehow turn the tables. Yet they followed the Admiral and returned his paternal interest in their day-to-day operations with a dogged devotion which far outshone the indoc-trinated loyalty of such elite units as the Waffen SS. Few military leaders in modern times have commanded so potent a force as the U-Boat Arm, and few have had the fortune to be so well served by their men.

Left: Only three Type XXI boats were commissioned by May 1945. Bombing of canals and plants making parts held up many more.

177

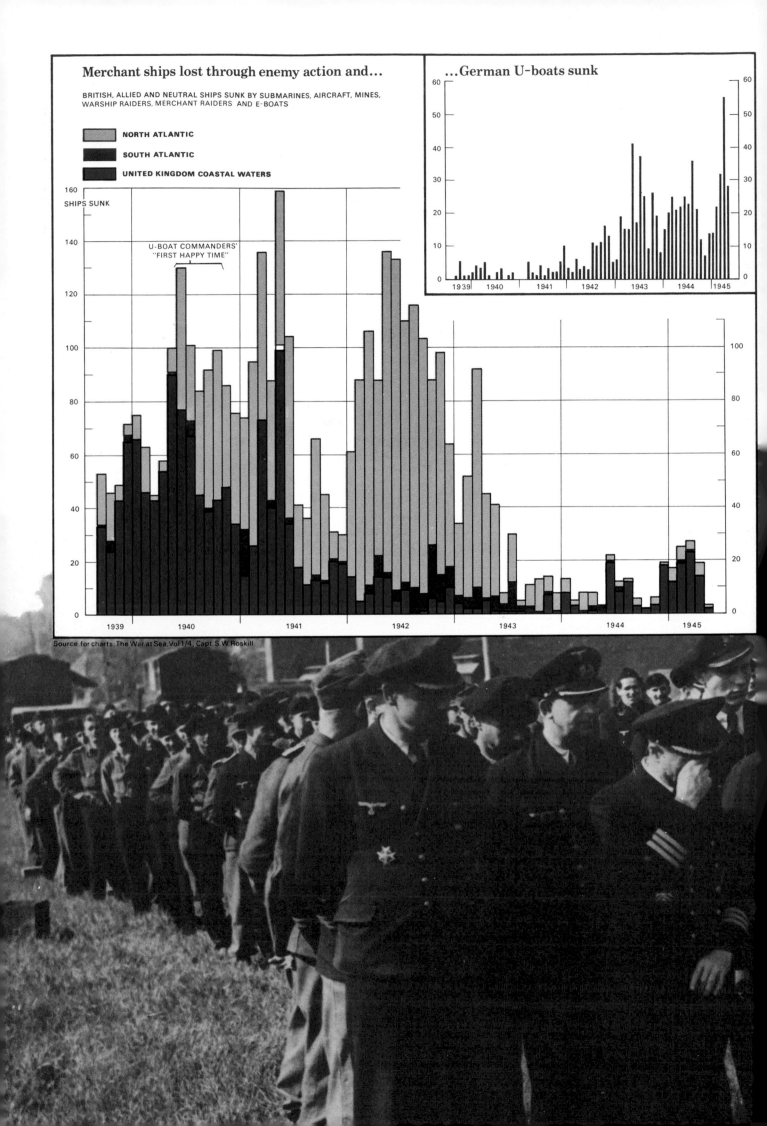

Merchant ships lost through enemy action and...

BRITISH, ALLIED AND NEUTRAL SHIPS SUNK BY SUBMARINES, AIRCRAFT, MINES,
WARSHIP RAIDERS, MERCHANT RAIDERS AND E-BOATS

- ◻ NORTH ATLANTIC
- ◼ SOUTH ATLANTIC
- ◼ UNITED KINGDOM COASTAL WATERS

SHIPS SUNK

U-BOAT COMMANDERS'
"FIRST HAPPY TIME"

160
140
120
100
80
60
40
20
0

1939   1940   1941   1942   1943   1944   1945

...German U-boats sunk

60
50
40
30
20
10
0

1939   1940   1941   1942   1943   1944   1945

Source for charts: The War at Sea, Vol 1/4 ; Capt. S.W. Roskill

Scharnhorst sunk,
26 Dec 1943

from
1941

Arctic Circle

MURMANSK

REYKJAVIK

ARCHANGEL

TRONDHEIM

Supplies to Russia

MOSCOW

LIVERPOOL

KIEL

WILHELMSHAVEN

Battle of the Atlantic
(Peak 1941-43)

ST. JOHNS

LORIENT

HALIFAX

Bismarck sunk,
27 May 1941

GIBRALTAR

Supplies
Russia

Below: The final muster
of U-Boat personnel at
Kiel after the surrender.

A THIRD GENERATION OF U-BOATS

The sounds of war had barely died away as teams of Allied investigators worked frantically to discover as much as they could about the new U-Boats which had so nearly started a second Battle of the Atlantic. The reason for the haste was the knowledge that the Russians were also hunting for information and nobody believed that they would share what they found with anyone else.

One visible product of this search is a three-volume history of U-Boats compiled by the late Sir Alfred Sims, then a constructor in the department of the Director of Naval Construction, the Royal Navy's design department. Sims and his investigators carried out one of the most thorough searches imaginable, and even investigated all the family connections between people like Dr Walter and Admiral Dönitz. Several interesting points emerged about differences between German and British practice for example, but of course its main value was to record all that was known about the latest developments. The *schnorchel* was immediately tested, and within three months the British submarine *Truant* was at sea evaluating it. Vast quantities of torpedoes, equipment and drawings were shipped back to Britain for examination, and British and American salvage teams worked on two Walter boats which had been scuttled off Cuxhaven.

The British and Americans were luckier than the Russians, for their armies had overrun Hamburg, Kiel and Wilhelmshaven, where most of the important technical material was to be found; the Russians captured Stettin and Danzig, which meant that they captured a lot of incomplete hulls and rather less technical information. To their delight, the Americans and British found that the Type XVIIB Walter boats, *U.1406* and *U.1407*, were in working order, and they were soon removed for further examination. Work was proceeding on the U-Boats at Lishally too, and many interesting items of equipment came to light. For example the *schnorchel* heads of some of the boats had a sponge rubber coating intended to 'absorb' radar pulses and so reduce the strength of the return echo. It was made of corrugated rubber, coated in aluminium paint. Another device was a rubber covering over the entire hull which deadened Asdic pulses in a similar manner; the boat *U.1105* was known as the 'Black Panther'.

Many of the latest U-Boats were fitted with automatic depth-keeping. This device used a pendulum to correct trim with the after-hydroplanes, and a hydrostatic valve to control the bow planes. It helped to reduce the strain on the operators of the diving planes, particularly when the boat was running at periscope depth

or using the *schnorchel*. The automatic torpedo-loading gear was of particular interest to the inspecting teams; it comprised pairs of arms on either side of the torpedo-room, each carrying two torpedoes. The torpedoes were brought into position on bogies, and then lifted up in line with the open door of the tube.

Early in 1946 the three former Allies involved in the disposal of U-Boats, the United States, Great Britain and the USSR, announced a Three-Power Agreement, under which the three navies were allocated ten U-Boats each; all others were to be scrapped or destroyed. Specific exceptions to this were *U.505*, which

On 4 June 1944 a US Navy hunter-killer group was able to board and capture *U.505*. Only three U-Boats were captured in World War II, and only two were brought into port.

Above: Stores and miscellaneous loot from *U.505* in the hangar of the escort carrier *Guadalcanal*, flagship of the task force.

Right: After being tested by the US Navy, *U.505* was given to the Chicago Museum of Science and Industry and is the only surviving Type IXC U-Boat in the world.

had been boarded and captured by a US Navy hunter-killer group off the Azores in 1944, and the ex-Dutch *UD.5*, which was returned to the Royal Netherlands Navy and given her original number *O.27*. The distribution was as follows:

Royal Navy: *U.190, U.712, U.953, U.1108,*
             U.1171, U.1407, U.2326, U.2348,
             U.2518 and *U.3017*
US Navy: *U.234, U.530, U.858, U.873,*
             U.889, U.977, U.1105, U.1406,
             U.2513 and *U.3008*
Soviet Navy: *U.1057, U.1058, U.1064, U.1231,*
             U.1305, U.2353, U.2529, U.3035,
             U.3041 and *U.3515*

In addition Great Britain transferred *U.926, U.1202, U.4706* and *U.995* to the Norwegian Navy, and out of its share *U.190* went to the Canadians and *U.2518* and *U.2326* to the French. The remaining seven were run for two or three years under N-numbers, while the hydrogen-peroxide driven *U.1407* became HMS *Meteorite*. The US Navy christened *U.505*, the USS *Nemo*,

a reference to the captain of the *Nautilus* in *Twenty Thousand Leagues under the Sea*, and she was run for trials and experiments until 1953. A year later she was given to the Chicago Museum of Science and Industry where she can be seen to this day as a permanent exhibit. The others were all used experimentally; the Walter boat *U.1406* did not prove very successful, but the Type XXI *U.3008* was modified and ran for three years. The two surplus boats, *U.805* and *U.1228*, were sunk as targets in February 1946.

After the Armistice the scrapping of U-Boats had proceeded slowly and had provided work for ship-breaking firms for years, but as most of the work was done in Germany it had enabled a great deal of material to be saved for research. This time the Allies were determined that the U-Boat Fleet would be of no use to anyone but themselves, and so the Royal Navy was given the task of sinking the boats left in its hands. Under the codename 'Operation Deadlight', a dreary procession of U-Boats was towed out and sunk by detonating scuttling charges off Malin Head, Northern Ireland. Between

November 1945 and 20 January 1946 a total of 116 rusting U-Boats went to the bottom in deep water. On the other side of the world the U-Boats which had been taken over by the Japanese in May 1945 had in turn been handed over to the victors in August, and were similarly disposed of; four surrendered in the East Indies and were scuttled by the British and three were scuttled in Japanese waters by the French Navy.

The Russians were not content with their ten U-Boats, and a large number of Type XVII and XXI hulls were taken back to Leningrad in various ways. The hull of the incomplete carrier *Graf Zeppelin* was repaired at Stettin, and her 750-foot long hangar was filled with miscellaneous bits of U-Boats as well as some more luxurious items of loot. Unfortunately for the Russians the exercise did little for either their submarine specialists or their aircraft carrier designers, for on 15 August 1947 the wallowing hulk hit a mine 15 miles north of Rügen, and the great weight of U-Boat material in the upper part of the ship made her heel over rapidly and capsize.

The state of post-war tension led to a much more rapid use of the knowledge gained from studying U-Boats. The knowledge of how close Admiral Dönitz and his U-Boats had come to winning the War made all the leading navies

look closely at the information coming out of Germany, and the fact that this information was in the hands of the Soviet Union did nothing to allay the fears of the Western navies in the NATO alliance. Furthermore Stalin sanctioned an immediate start on building a large force of submarines on the assumption that he could reap the same benefits as the Germans in the event of a war with the West. The so-called 'Type XXI technology' was noticeable in all submarines from about 1948 onwards: streamlined hulls, simple uncluttered conning towers, enlarged batteries and mechanical loading of torpedoes.

The US Navy was the first to take the plunge, with its GUPPY Program, an acronym derived from Greater Underwater Propulsive Power. Large numbers of the big *Gato* and *Balao* Class boats, built for the great submarine campaign which had helped to strangle Japan's sea power, were taken in hand for varying degrees of modernisation. The full treatment involved not only 'cleaning up' the hull by removing deck guns and enclosing the periscopes, *schnorchel* (now Americanised to snorkel, or Anglicised to 'snort') and radar masts in a smoothly faired 'fin', but also remodelling the hull-lines at the bow and stern to make the boat more manoeuvrable under water. However the main legacy

from the Type XXI was a double battery capacity, and to achieve this the 'Guppies' had to be cut in half to allow an extra section to be added. These submarines could then achieve as much as 15 knots under water although they suffered from the same limitation as the Type XXI and all other 'submersibles', a relatively short endurance while running at full speed. Sooner or later an electrically driven boat must snorkel to recharge her batteries.

Naval Museum there is a magnificent model of a 'W', cutaway on one side and full hull on the other; the peculiar formation of the rudder, faired into the stern, is an exact copy of the Type XXI, and it has been observed on much later submarines, even the big nuclear boats. The French Navy, which had lost so many submarines during the War, was forced to keep a Type IXB, Type IXC, two Type VIICs and a Type XXI running for nearly 15 years, in order to

The other important legacy of the U-Boat war was the Walter principle. The Russians certainly experimented with a captured Type XVII boat and are believed to have built more to their own design, but it is generally accepted that they were failures. In December 1949 the British HMS Meteorite (ex-U.1407) was handed over for scrap after three action-packed years for her crew who regarded her as only 75 per cent safe. Design studies were already in hand for two improved submarines running on a form of Perhydrol, and they were ordered shortly after the scrapping of the Meteorite. Known as HMS Explorer and HMS Excalibur, they were completed in 1956–58. They were somewhat safer than the prototype, but to her crew the Explorer was always known as 'HMS Exploder'; history does not relate what nickname was dreamed up for her sister, but there are many tales of how the entire crew mustered on the casing to escape the dense clouds of smoke pouring up through the hatches. They were credited with a speed of 25 knots and provided useful experience of fast underwater manoeuvring, but the advent of nuclear power made the whole explosive concept hopelessly uncompetitive. After serving as fast targets for training anti-submarine forces they were sold in the mid-1960s.

The Soviet Navy ran a number of Type XXI boats for many years, and their numerous 'W' or 'Whiskey' type (in NATO parlance) drew heavily on the German design. In the Central

provide training and experience for her new designs. The Blaison (ex-U.123), Bouan (ex-U.510), Millé (ex-U.471), Laubie (ex-U.766) and Roland Morillot (ex-U.2518) all bore the names of distinguished French submariners, and provided invaluable experience for the later Narval and Daphne Classes before being scrapped.

Other U-Boats survived: the Type VIIC U.573 had been interned in Spain in 1942 and she spent many years under the Spanish flag as the G.7. The Norwegians soon scrapped the Knerter but the other three remained in service under the names Kya, Kaura and Kinn, and more will be heard of them subsequently. By the mid-1950s most of these old U-Boats were no longer recognisable, having lost guns and having their conning towers modified, but a few retained the characteristic look of the wartime U-Boat. Submarines do not last forever, and it must have seemed to most people that, apart from U.505 in the heart of Chicago, there would be no U-Boats left within a decade or so but they were wrong.

In 1954 the growing fear of Russian expansion led the NATO Alliance to reconsider the status of West Germany. This time there was no Versailles Treaty, for Germany had surrendered unconditionally in 1945, and there were now two Germanies, one under American, British and French occupation, and the other under a very pro-Russian Communist regime. With large armies on the other side of the Iron Curtain it was felt that the only way to bolster the

defences of Western Europe was to allow the re-emergence of German land, sea and air forces, and out of this was born the new *Bundesmarine* or Federal German Navy.

Immediately after the accession of the Federal Republic to NATO in 1955 the first steps were taken to create a balanced naval force. Its role was laid down by NATO and was seen to be principally the defence of the exit to the Baltic, the Kattegat. For this the *Bundesmarine* would require light surface forces and small submarines. The Western European Union (WEU) Treaty stipulated a limit of 350 tons on the standard displacement of any submarine built, and also ruled out any unconventional form of propulsion such as a nuclear reactor or a hydrogen peroxide turbine; it was to be diesel-electric or nothing.

To recreate a submarine service after a break of 11 years was a difficult task. This time there

was no team of experts working in another country and no hoodwinking of foreign officials; the final catastrophe of May 1945 had annihilated any such scheme, and in any case the Western Allies and the Russians between them had taken every scrap of paper and in some cases the technicians as well, to put German expertise to work on their own submarines. The easiest and cheapest solution was to recover some U-Boats from the bottom of the Baltic and restore them to working order. Two Type XXIIIs were found; *U.2365* had been bombed by an aircraft of RAF 311 Czech Squadron on 5 May 1945 and then scuttled in the Skagerrak three days later, while her sister *U.2367* had sunk on 5 May after colliding with another U-Boat during an air attack in the Great Belt. In 1956 the two boats were raised and surveyed and were found to be in sufficiently good repair to warrant rebuilding. Both boats were towed to Kiel where they were refurbished in the Howaldt shipyard. It was a strange quirk of fate which brought these U-Boats back to the yard which had built the Nordenfelt submarine way back in 1891, the first modern submarine to be built in Germany.

The two submarines were recommissioned on 17 August and 1 October 1957 and were given the names *Hai* (shark) and *Hecht* (pike) respectively (for a time they had been known as *UW.20* and *UW.21*).

Although much larger than the permitted limit of 350 tons, a Type XXI was also salved for use in testing electronics and sonar. She was *U.2540* which had been scuttled off Flensburg on 4 May 1945 after being damaged by an aircraft of the RAD 2nd Tactical Air Force in the Great Belt. She was raised in 1957 and repaired by Howaldt in 1958–59; to honour the great Bavarian pioneer and to stress her experimental status she was renamed *Wilhelm Bauer* and recommissioned in September 1960. She later served with the *Erprobungstelle für Marinewaffen* or Experimental Station for Naval Weaponry. As a further link with the past, the first officer appointed to command the new U-Boat force was *Kapitän zur See* Otto Kretschmer, the greatest ace of World War II. Kretschmer was appointed head of the *Kommando der UBoote* in November 1958 and was succeeded by another famous World War II captain, *Kapitän zur See* Topp. In 1967 the name of the command was changed to *UBootflottille*, but throughout the time it has been divided into the training section or *Lehrgruppe* and the operational squadron or *Geschwader*.

The little *Hai* and *Hecht* served humbly but usefully, but on 14 September 1966 the *Hai* was lost accidentally off the Dogger Bank, and although subsequently raised, she was now well beyond her age limit. She was not repaired, and in September 1968 her sister *Hecht* followed her to the scrap-yard. They were only stopgaps, and while they were being refitted in 1957 orders had been placed for three of a totally new design. They were known as the Type 201, and were the brain-child of Professor Ulrich Gabler, a wartime U-Boat constructor who had formed a design firm, *Ingenieurkontor Lübeck* (IKL). No one with a sense of history could have missed the significance that the launch of *U.1* on 21 October 1961 marked the third time that a series of U-Boats had been started; it was just over 55 years since the launch of the first, and only 26 years since the launch of the second *U.1*.

There were many unusual features about the new *U.1*. For one thing she was built of a new non-magnetic steel to reduce the risk of loss from magnetic mines and of detection by aircraft equipped with magnetic sensors; this requirement is dictated by the shallowness of the Baltic. Being so short (less than 143 feet) and having a hull diameter of no more than 15 feet there was no room for reload-torpedoes, and so the entire outfit of eight torpedoes had to be accommodated in the bow. To do this it was necessary to dispose the torpedo-tubes in a semi-circle in the top half of the bow, and horizontally, as in the letter 'D' lying on its side. The hull form was also unusual, with a short, fat centre section, a square, bluff bow and a tapering after-section with a single five-bladed propeller.

Unfortunately severe corrosion was encountered with the *Ubootstahl 52*, the special anti-magnetic steel developed for *U.1–3*, and so it was necessary to stop work on the slightly larger Type 205 boats, *U.4–8*. These five boats had been ordered shortly after the first three to take advantage of a relaxation of the WEU Treaty, allowing submarines of 450 tons to be built. After a great deal of trouble two new steels were developed, A3CY and AMCR1 (later known as AM10 and AM20), and *U.1* and *U.2* were taken in hand once more to have their hulls entirely replated. *U.4–8* were given a slightly different treatment with a zinc coating to their hull-plating, but the net result was an alarming rise in cost of what were intended to be small and economical boats. The two rebuilt boats recommissioned in 1966–67 but *U.3* was not considered worth the expense, and she was subsequently paid off and scrapped. The rebuilding enabled *U.1* and *U.2* to be brought up to the standard of the Type 205 boats and they were then regarded as being units of that class.

After a further four boats were built, work started on the Type 206 design to take advantage of a further concession under the WEU Treaty allowing the building of six 1000-ton U-Boats. They are simply scaled-up versions of the original design, still using the single compartment, retractable hydroplanes of a patent IKL design and eight bow torpedo-tubes firing 538mm homing torpedoes.

One of the peculiarities of these new U-Boats is the very small crew, dictated by the small

Right: A Sea King helicopter hovering over the new *U.18*.

Below: In 1961 the first of a new series of U-Boats was launched. To play its role in NATO the new Federal German Navy was given permission to design and build its own submarines.

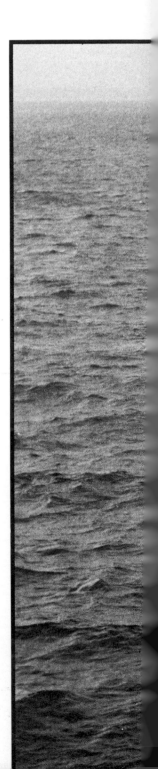

186

dimensions. Every man is a specialist, and therefore all 22 are either commissioned or non-commissioned officers. The space is so limited that there is no question of living on board and the crew embarks for each mission, more like an aircraft than the traditional U-Boat putting to sea for a lengthy patrol. The propulsion is by electric motor, taking current from accumulator batteries, just as in the very earliest submarines, but small diesel generators of 1200bhp allow recharging by using the *schnorchel* mast. The extra tonnage has been used mainly to

Norwegian Navy to order 15 submarines of the *Kobben* Class of the slightly modified Type 207. This is another example of history repeating itself, for the first *Kobben* was delivered by Krupp's Germania Yard in 1914. Another pair were built in the Royal Dockyard, Copenhagen to Type 205 plans.

After 1973 the WEU Treaty permitted the construction of submarines up to 1800 tons, but nothing was done about this for a while as Germany's overseas customers were more interested in the 1000-ton Type 209 design. To

The after end of U.995's **control room.**

provide bigger battery capacity and greatly improved sensors. In addition to their torpedo armament they carry mines disposed in a unique circular stowage outside the pressure hull. This allows the mines to be laid with the simplest arrangement for taking in seawater ballast as compensating weight, and at the same time it entails no sacrifice in torpedo-armament.

These are not the only U-Boats to be built in Germany in recent years. In 1965 two small research submarines, known as *versuchs-Uboote VUB I–II* were ordered from Krupp's Atlas shipyard in Bremen; they were commissioned in 1965–66 under the names *Hans Techel* and *Friedrich Schührer*, and they were little more than submersible test-beds for weapons and sensors. The growing reputation of the IKL Type 205 submarines and the desire of NATO to produce standard designs, led the Royal

date, a total of 23 submarines have been ordered to this design: Argentina (2), Colombia (2), Ecuador (2), Greece (7), Indonesia (2), Peru (2), Turkey (4) and Venezuela (2). In addition three boats were ordered by Israel in 1972 but to get around the political embarrassment of upsetting Germany's Arab customers a licence was given to the British submarine-builders, Vickers Ltd. The design is based on the German 500-ton Type 206, not the larger export design.

The latest development is for a 750-tonner called the Type 210, and like the Type 207, it is being designed in conjunction with the Norwegians whose problems in defending the exit to the Baltic are very similar to those of the Federal German Navy. The Type 210 is intended to come into service in the 1980s by which time the current Types 205 and 207 will need replacement.

The last chapter in the U-Boat story is much less prosaic. As we have seen, *U.995* was given to Norway by the British in 1945 and was renamed *Kaura*. Although stripped of her deck gun and altered in minor ways she remained basically unchanged until the time came in 1953 to scrap her. The hull was towed to Germany for scrapping by a commercial ship-breaking firm in January 1963 and might have gone the way of her two sisters had it not been for the efforts of a group of German ship lovers. It was felt that whatever the risk of the outside world seeing it as a resurgence of Nazi militarism, the achievements of the U-Boat Arm were worthy of commemoration, and funds were raised to preserve *U.995* as a memorial to the U-Boats, their crews and their designers.

It was a struggle, for the Federal government was well aware of what offence might be given to people outside Germany, and for some time the old U-Boat lay at her moorings. When a party of people visited her to examine the state of the hull, one ex-constructor confessed that he felt a twinge of uneasiness as he smelt the old familiar whiff of chlorine gas. He could not make himself enter the U-Boat, for as he later admitted, he had not risked his neck in testing new U-Boats for five years to end up dying in one 20 years later. Plans were made to put *U.995* to rest on dry land next to the starkly simple memorial to the World War I U-Boat crews erected at Laboe outside Kiel in the 1920s.

Today it is possible to examine *U.995*, just a bus-ride outside Kiel. She has been beautifully restored to wartime condition, with deck gun, AA guns, Hohentwiel radar aerial and all the between-deck fittings. Access doors have been cut in the starboard side of the hull forward and aft, so it is possible with only minimum discomfort to walk through the boat. Nothing written can convey the exact feeling of authenticity gained from seeing how small a Type VIIC U-Boat was. Not that *U.995* with her bright paintwork and antiseptic cleanliness can recapture the smell and the dampness which is what U-Boatmen remember. Even *U.505*, which is preserved at Chicago and can also be examined in detail by visitors, is one of the bigger Type IXC boats, and so has rather more internal space.

The only other U-Boat to be preserved is *U.1*, the founder of the dynasty. She was rescued from the scrap-heap by Krupp's in 1919 for preservation as a memorial to the work done by the firm. Bomb damage wrecked her in World War II, but she has been rescued and restored by the *Deutschesmuseum* in Munich, and there she can be seen. The hull has been cut into sections to show the method of construction and the machinery. Although hardly typical of the U-Boats, UB- or UC-Boats which made up the underwater fleet of Germany in 1914–18, she is a fascinating relic and a link with the modern boats. Looking at her it is hard to believe that the extraordinary change in submarine technology has taken place in less than 60 years.

Two generations of U-Boats have come and gone leaving a terrifying toll of devastation behind them and transforming the very nature of sea warfare. Now a third generation has appeared, and one can only hope that they are never called on to emulate the achievements of their forebears.

The bow torpedo-tubes in *U.995*. Even the hygienic cleanliness of a museum exhibit conveys the idea of how small a Type VIIC really was.

INDEX